Lamps and Lighting

Lamps and Lighting

A manual of lamps and electric lighting prepared by members of the Research and Engineering Staff of British Lighting Industries Ltd., and the technical staffs of the associated companies:

Atlas Lighting Limited
A.E.I. Lamp and Lighting Co. Ltd.
Ekco Ensign Electric Limited

General Editors:

H. HEWITT, C.Eng. M.I.E.E., F.I.E.S.
A. S. VAUSE, M.Inst.B.E.

AMERICAN ELSEVIER PUBLISHING COMPANY, INC.
NEW YORK
1966

© British Lighting Industries Ltd. 1966

AMERICAN ELSEVIER PUBLISHING COMPANY, INC.
52 Vanderbilt Avenue,
New York 10017, New York

LIBRARY OF CONGRESS CATALOG CARD NUMBER 66–29475

Printed in Great Britain

Preface

This book is a successor to the Atlas Lighting Manual, which was first published in 1961. The present volume, however, contains a good deal of additional material and is written primarily as a textbook. It is hoped that it will be of value to students of lighting and electrical engineering, applied physics, building technology and architecture, as well as to those who are concerned with the design of lamps and fittings and the installation of lighting systems.

One of the editors of the Atlas Lighting Manual was the late Mr. H. C. Weston, whose death in 1963 was a loss to all who are interested in lighting and vision. We consider it a privilege to be able to include in this volume the two opening chapters which Mr. Weston prepared for the earlier book.

The editors and authors wish to acknowledge the assistance of many other colleagues who have helped in preparing material for the book.

August 1966
H. HEWITT
A. S. VAUSE

Contents

1*

CHAPTER 1

Light and Sight

The nature of light. What is called 'light' or 'visible radiation' is electromagnetic energy radiated at very short wavelengths and therefore at very high frequencies. It forms only a small part of the whole gamut of electromagnetic radiation, which extends from invisible cosmic rays of the shortest known wavelengths to invisible radiation of longer wavelengths than any used for 'broadcasting' (Fig. 1.1). In fact, the visible spectrum, from its violet to its red ends, is due to radiation which varies in wavelength from about 16 to about 30 millionths of an inch (roughly, 400 to 750 nanometres*) and whose corresponding frequencies range from about 750 to about 400 billion cycles per second.

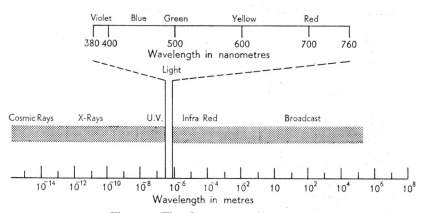

Fig. 1.1   The electromagnetic spectrum

The human eye is not equally sensitive to these different wavelengths and their corresponding frequencies of light. The visual sensations they are capable of exciting have two fundamental characteristics, namely, colour

* One nanometre (nm) = 10 Angstrom units.

and brightness. But a stronger sensation of brightness (or *luminosity*) is produced by a given energy of medium wavelength (yellow-green) light than by an equal energy of visible radiation of short (blue) or of long (red) wavelength. In other words, the visual efficacy, or luminous efficiency, of visible radiation is proportional to the wavelength of the radiation in the manner shown by Fig. 1.2.

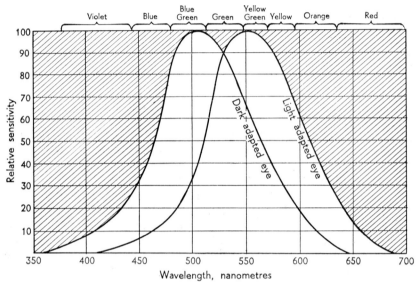

Fig. 1.2   The relative sensitivity of the average eye to different wavelengths

Account is taken of this fact in measuring light (photometry). Actually, instead of indicating directly the physical energy of light, photometers are designed to indicate the corresponding *luminous flux* or visually effective value of the radiation. The unit of luminous flux is the *lumen* and, very roughly, a total flux of 12 lumens is emitted by an ordinary candle. If all these 12 lumens could be directed on to a surface 1 square foot in area the illumination or 'strength of light' on the surface would be 12 lumens per square foot, or 12 British units of illumination. This unit of illumination—the *lumen per square foot*—is still sometimes called the 'foot-candle'. The metric unit of illumination is the lumen per square metre, which has the commendably short name *lux*. One lumen per square foot (abbrev.: lm/ft²) is equal, approximately, to 10 lux.

The difference in luminous efficiency of light of different wavelengths may be exemplified by the lumen output of coloured fluorescent tubes. An efficiency of 80 lumens per watt is obtained for green light but only 3 and 15 lumens per watt for red and blue lights respectively. Although these efficiencies are influenced by technical factors, they differ proportionately to much the same extent as do the visual efficiencies of equal radiant energies of low (red), medium and high (blue) frequency.

The eye and vision. The eye contains a very large number of light receptors of two kinds. These are *rods*, which are capable in certain conditions of responding to extremely weak light, and *cones*, which are relatively insensitive and respond only to more intense stimulation (Fig. 1.3). In natural or artificial 'twilight' both kinds of receptors are operative.

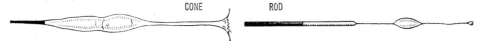

CONE ROD

Fig. 1.3 Elements of the retina (enlarged approx. 300 times)

Adequate stimulation of the cones excites sensations of colour as well as of luminosity or brightness, but when the rods alone are in operation vision is achromatic, that is, only brightness is appreciated.

The receptors are distributed over the whole interior of the back hemisphere of the eyeball (see Fig. 1.4). They form the outermost layer of a thin transparent nervous lining—the *retina*—which is, in fact, an outgrowth of the brain reaching towards the surface of the body to sense the light. In one small area of the retina, close to the optical axis of the eye, the receptor population is particularly dense and consists only of cones. This area is called the *fovea* (the pit). At all levels of illumination which are sufficient for cone or *photopic* vision it is the foveal cones that are used for scrutinising the scene. They give to vision its greatest acuity because each of them has its own 'private line' to the 'seeing part' of the brain cortex which thus receives the most minutely detailed information about the luminous scenes scanned by the fovea.

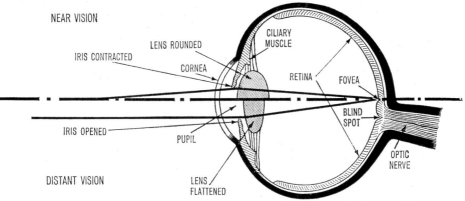

NEAR VISION

CILIARY MUSCLE

LENS ROUNDED

IRIS CONTRACTED

CORNEA

RETINA

FOVEA

BLIND SPOT

IRIS OPENED

PUPIL

OPTIC NERVE

DISTANT VISION

LENS FLATTENED

Fig. 1.4 Sectional diagram of the eye, adjusted for near and distant vision

The remainder of the retina which surrounds the fovea contains both cones and rods, but the proportion of cones diminishes and the proportion of rods increases as the retina extends from its centre to its periphery. Moreover, the capacity for discriminating detail, i.e. *visual acuity*, is greatly reduced at all parts of the retina beyond the fovea because, in these regions, groups of receptors 'club together' and share a common line or optic nerve fibre to the visual cortex. In this way the 'grain' of the eye's light-receiving tissue is made coarser and this is advantageous in several ways.

Firstly, if the discrimination of the retina was uniformly fine over its whole area it would be impossible to pay attention to any particular part of the field of view. Attention is essentially an act of selection and one that is quite indispensable for all purposeful seeing. It is made possible by the existence of the small focal area of the retina which is superlatively discriminative. Moreover, the focusing mechanism of the eyes is designed for sharpening the foveal image and the system of muscles provided for turning the eyes is adapted for directing the fovea towards whatever parts of a view are most relevant to the observer's purpose from time to time. A further advantage of the organisation of 'suburban' (*parafoveal*) receptors into groups connected to a common nerve fibre is that the group as a unit becomes more sensitive than its individual members. When these individual receptors are too weakly stimulated to be effective the collective effect on the receptor group may prove adequate. This result is characteristic of rod, i.e. nocturnal or *scotopic*, vision in which it is more important that the eyes should be sensitive to very weak light than that they should be able to detect fine detail. A strict analogy to the grouping of rod receptors for this purpose is afforded by the paralleling of photocells for the measurement of very low levels of illumination.

Before leaving the retina, it may be mentioned that on the nasal side of the fovea there is another small area in which all the nerve fibres associated with the individual and collective light receptors are bunched together before leaving the eye as the *optic nerve*. Since there are no receptors in this part of the retina, see Fig. 1.4, and the fibres of the optic nerve are not directly stimulated by light, this retinal area is blind. The existence of this small *blind spot* is ordinarily of no consequence because, in binocular vision, that small part of the field of view which one eye does not see at any particular moment is seen by the other eye.

In any case, even in monocular vision, incessant small movements of the eye shift the image of a scene on the retina so that the whole of it is seen. The retinal receptors rapidly become adapted to a constant light stimulus. For this reason, if it were possible—which it is not—to keep the eyes absolutely still for a short time, seeing would fail temporarily. Frequent change of stimulation of receptor units is essential for vision and this is ensured with ordinary non-uniform fields of view by the normal restlessness of the eyes. Another kind of adaptation by which the instantaneous range of visual sensibility is adjusted to the prevailing average *luminance* (photometric brightness) of the environment is referred to later.

Although in scotopic vision the eye can respond to very weak light, its *contrast sensitivity* is considerably poorer than that of the light-adapted eye. At ordinary levels of illumination it is possible to detect a very slight difference of brightness between two adjacent 'patches' of the field of view if these are not very small. In fact, under the most favourable conditions, this *differential threshold*, as it is called, may be as small as 1%, although the minimum

s. In the case of the eye this adjustment is called *adaptation*. It is not ed by changes in pupil area but by a photochemical and nervous process. process is not so rapid as the pupilliary response whose purpose is to ent—as far as possible—the overwhelming of the eye with light such as ld otherwise occur temporarily when it is suddenly exposed to some tively high brightness. On the other hand, it prevents 'light starvation' en the eye is suddenly exposed to some relatively very low brightness. us, the eye uses large changes of pupil aperture partly to 'play for time' ile the process of adaptation is being accomplished, after which the pupil nds to return to a moderate size. Sudden extreme constriction of the pupil accompanied by discomfort and this is what is experienced when the gaze ncounters very bright light sources. Prolonged extreme constriction is also ncomfortable and this occurs when the whole field of view is so bright that he process of adaptation cannot cope adequately with the situation.

The eye is said to be *dark-adapted* when it has become conditioned to such dim lights that only the rod receptors in the retina will respond to them: this is the condition of *scotopic* vision. The eye is *light-adapted* when the ambient light is bright enough for the retinal cone receptors to be responsive: this is the condition of *photopic* vision. Full dark-adaptation after exposure to bright light requires about an hour to become established. Full light-adaptation after exposure to darkness is established much more quickly. The degree of dark- or of light-adaptation present at any given time depends chiefly on the average prevailing field luminance, and if this changes slowly there is a gradual change in the eye's state of adaptation without any discontinuity during the transition from photopic to scotopic vision. This transition takes place naturally in the course of twilight, during which both cone and rod receptors are responsive, although the former play a progressively smaller and the latter a progressively larger part in vision.

Adaptation has a marked effect upon the apparent brightness of the visible environment. Hence, on entering an interior after becoming adapted to the prevailing luminance outdoors on a bright day the interior appears to be dimly lighted: when adaptation to the lower level of luminance is established the interior appears brighter and may well be considered as quite satisfactorily bright. This aspect of adaptation is one that the lighting designer must always bear in mind. It should be noted, too, that vision is most comfortable, and on the whole most serviceable, at levels of luminance which are not very close to either the upper or the lower limit of the photopic range. Further, the state of adaptation of the eyes affects their sensitivity to flicker. At high levels of field luminance the flicker fusion frequency comes to its maximum although, even then, a frequency of 100 per second is imperceptible to most persons.

Binocular vision and the mobility of the eyes. Although the image formed in each eye of anything that is looked at is a two-dimensional one, the possession of two eyes working in perfect collaboration makes three-dimensional vision or *stereopsis* possible. The eyes are set sufficiently far apart for each of them to look at any object from a slightly different angle. Thus,

difference that can be detected between very small areas is considerably greater. When, however, the illumination is reduced to twilight level colour vision begins to become ineffective and small degrees of brightness difference or contrast are not discernible. This is another reason why vision at very low levels of illumination is far less detailed than it is at moderate and high levels.

As the absorption of light is necessary to initiate the visual process, certain pigments are provided in the retina for this purpose. The best known of these is 'visual purple' (or rhodopsin) which is associated with rod vision. Other visual pigments exist and are associated with cone, and therefore with colour, vision. Various theories of colour vision have been advanced but the most widely held is the trichromatic theory. According to this, the perception of all colours arises from the stimulation of one or more of three fundamental sensation systems involving three types of cones or three kinds of cone pigments having overlapping absorption spectra, although each is most effective at different wavelengths corresponding, respectively, to red, green and blue. Whatever the exact nature of the mechanism may be, it seems certain that the first step in the transition from visual stimulant, i.e. light, to visual sensation is photochemical. Light is absorbed by retinal pigments which are thereby bleached and subsequently regenerated for further use. The immediate outcome of this activity is the excitation of electrical impulses which are propagated from the retinal receptors along the optic pathways to the visual cortex of the brain where they arouse visual perceptions. The rate of propagation is about 4 miles per minute, i.e. about 16 times faster than the speed of a champion distance runner, and the actual time for the course between the eye and the perceiving brain is less than 2 milliseconds. It is important to note, however, that there is a latent period between stimulation of the eye and the rise of the resultant sensation, and this period varies with the strength of the stimulus. At ordinary levels of luminance the latent period is very brief, but at low levels it is one of the factors that slow down the speed of vision.

The fact that vision is the product of a highly complex and extensive anatomical and psychophysiological system cannot be over emphasised. The eyes themselves—marvellous as they are in intricacy of structure and delicacy of function—are but the superficial organs of sight. But the information they collect for transmission to the central, 'out of sight' parts of the visual system is vital. If it is grossly insufficient because the lighting of the scene before the eyes does not reveal enough detail, or if the scene is inherently chaotic then seeing, in the practical sense of recognition, does not occur. But the perceptual part of the visual system usually *strives* to achieve recognition and often succeeds only by supplying from memory some of the information that the eyes fail to gather because the external scene is either too dim or is exposed to view too briefly. 'Ease of seeing' means visual perception that can be accomplished confidently, without mental striving and without visuomuscular stress, about which something is said later.

The optical system of the eye. The function of the retina is to take 'impressions' of external scenes 'point for point'. To make this possible the eye is provided with an optical system able to image the external luminous field on the retinal receptor-mosaic. This system consists of the *cornea*, which is the transparent window of the eye, and the *lens* inside the eye, whose refractive power can be varied by muscular action. The cornea is the principal refractor of the eye; it provides about 70% of the eye's total refractive power. But the focusing power of the cornea is fixed, while that of the lens has to be variable so as to enable near or distant objects to be sharply focused. In cameras this adjustment of focus is done by varying the distance between the lens and the sensitive film. In the eye, however, it is done by varying the curvature, and therefore the power, of the lens. The act of focusing the eye— which is called *accommodation*—is effected by the *ciliary muscle*. This ring-like muscle inside the eyeball encircles the rim of the lens from which it is separated by an annular space. Within this space are the radial ligaments which attach the transparent envelope or capsule containing the lens to the muscle. When a change of accommodation becomes necessary to maintain distinct vision, the ciliary muscle contracts or relaxes as required and thus alters its pull upon the 'equator' of the lens capsule. In this way the plastic lens is either flattened temporarily or allowed to assume a more nearly spherical shape (see Fig. 1.4).

It is very important to appreciate that the accommodation of the eye involves muscular work. Provided this work is kept within normal bounds all is well, but if excessive accommodation is demanded of the eye frequently, or for fairly long periods, then the ciliary muscle will be temporarily 'strained'. This is what happens if work is protracted in bad lighting such that the eyes have to be brought very close to the work to make out the important details. No muscular system of the body can long be kept working very near to its maximum capacity without undue fatigue.

Throughout life, the lens of the eye progressively becomes less plastic and so unable to alter its curvature so much as it can in early life, in spite of the fact that the ciliary muscle continues to be capable of trying to accommodate the eye for near vision. Thus, the shortest distance at which distinct vision is possible becomes insidiously greater as the years pass and, in consequence, the apparent size of critical details gets smaller. By middle age the shortest distance for which the eye can be focused becomes inconveniently long for people who have to do 'fine' work, and supplementary artificial accommodation, i.e. 'reading' glasses, becomes necessary. At this stage the eyes are said to be *presbyopic*, but it should be clearly understood that presbyopia is not a disease but is simply one of the irreversible biological changes that are inevitable. But, while the direct compensation for it is the use of proper glasses for close work, it is also particularly important at this period in the life of the eyes that they should have the benefit of abundant light. Given this, the eyes can operate at a high level of acuity—since acuteness of vision is directly proportional to retinal illumination—and so be best equipped to cope with somewhat smaller retinal images.

The dioptric system of the eye undergoes two other changes with time which restrict the passage of light through it to the sensitive retina. One of these changes is a progressive discolouration of the lens. This results in a

selective absorption of light, so that what actual only reduced quantitatively but is also changed in especially in its shorter wavelength (blue) compo lens is not usually of much consequence before late can be countered only by providing sufficient illumi an illuminant which emphasises blues if the ap particularly necessary.

The pupil and its roles. The other ocular change the illumination of the retina is the reduction in size of This, also, is chiefly significant late in working life and necessity for good lighting, not only for elderly (and often workers but also in domestic dwellings occupied by elder the 'amount' of light which reaches the sensitive film in a ca the setting of the aperture so, too, does the amount of light w retina in the eye; the smaller the aperture the 'stronger' mu for a good 'picture'.

The diaphragm that regulates the aperture of the eye is call is a ring of muscular tissue situated immediately in front of the the camera diaphragm, it operates automatically in response to retinal illumination due to external fluctuations of light. It does t some of the nerve fibres from the retina, together with some of th nerve fibres that activate the muscular iris, form a 'feed-back' 'reflex arc'.

The iris is a restless organ, incessantly making small variations diameter of the pupil as well as making larger variations whenever t of view becomes very dim or very bright and when the eye is sub suddenly to large changes of illumination. But when the ambient lumi is moderate, and also when it changes very gradually within the mod range, the pupil tends to assume an average or 'physiological' size wi diameter of 3 to 4 millimetres. It then serves not only to admit sufficient li to the eye but also to limit favourably the spherical aberration of the ey optical system while allowing suitable depth of focus. When the field of vie is very dim the pupil can dilate to about twice its normal diameter and so admit about four times as much light to the eye. On the other hand, when the field is very bright, the pupil constricts to a minimum diameter of about 2 millimetres. Thus, the control of light admission by means of the pupil is limited to a range of 16 to 1 and this adjustment is quite insufficient to allow the eye to function usefully throughout the enormous range of illumination levels from that on a moonless night to that of summer noon. These extremes are in the ratio of more than 10,000 million to 1.

Adaptation of the eye. The light sense can respond effectively only to a very much narrower range of luminance at any one time so its sensitivity has to be suitably adjusted when it is called upon to function within different ranges—just as the sensitivity of an ammeter has to be adjusted by means of shunts to make it suitable for measuring electrical currents within limited

the two monocular images are not identical but differ in a way that informs the seeing brain that they represent a single scene having depth. The separation of the eyes is not sufficient to make distance vision stereoscopic in the same way but, of course, there are various visual clues which, even to one-eyed persons, are sufficient to indicate depth in a distant scene, although visual judgment of depth is far less accurate than it can be in near stereoscopic vision.

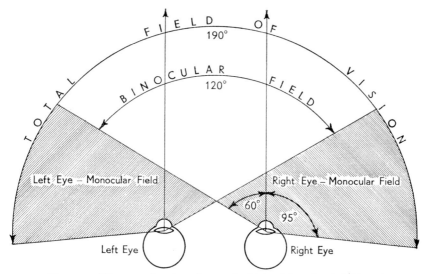

Fig. 1.5   Diagram showing the total width of the visual field and binocular portion of the field

Apart from the stereoscopic sense, which is very valuable in many forms of close work, the possession of two eyes also provides a very wide visual field (rather more than 180 degrees) although binocular vision is characteristic only within the overlapping areas of the two monocular fields (see Fig. 1.5). Binocular single vision depends upon each eye's line of sight (*visual axis*) meeting that of the other eye at a common point of regard. No matter where the eyes look, whether near or far, straight ahead or in some other direction, their visual axes must converge, i.e. the two eyes must turn towards each other, just sufficiently to direct the two *foveae* to the same object. If the correct angular adjustment of the eyes, each to the other, is not maintained, double vision (*diplopia*) results. This happens temporarily in states of fatigue or intoxication. It would be habitual in cases of squint but for the fact that the squinter learns to suppress or ignore one of the double images.

To bring about the necessary amount of *convergence* according to the viewing distance for which the eyes are *accommodated* at any time, and also to turn the eyes to look at any part of the environment, each eye is provided with six external (*extra-ocular*) muscles (see Fig. 1.6). The muscles of each eye work as a team and the two teams must always act in a manner complementary to each other. The automatic co-ordination of the activity of all these motors of the eyes is not the least of the wonders of the human visual system. But, in a fair proportion of persons the balance of power is precarious in near vision and is only maintained at the cost of unusual nervous control. Such

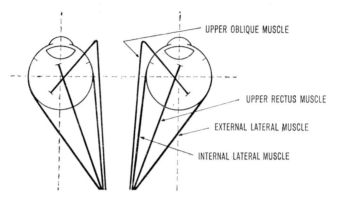

Fig. 1.6   Plan diagram of the two eyes showing most of the extra-ocular muscles provided for the purpose of executing all possible eye movements

persons have a latent imbalance of the extra-ocular muscles (called *hetero-phoria*) which increases their liability to suffer strain on doing close work. This is one of the reasons why the aim in lighting for 'fine' work should always be to render the detail visible, if possible, without any need for very near viewing.

Fixation of the gaze; reflex and voluntary.   The presence, or the abrupt appearance, of a moving or a specially bright object in the periphery of the field of view tends to set the motor of the eyes into motion in such manner as to aim the gaze at the intrusive object. The shift of the gaze is involuntary and is effected by the *fixation reflex* which—in a more primitive form— underlies the biological phenomenon of phototropism, as exemplified by the flight of the moth to the candle. Things that *attract* attention visually or *distract* the eyes from things to which their attention has been given voluntarily, do so by triggering the fixation reflex. Normally, however, movements of regard are made in response to impulses from the frontal lobe of the brain which are initiated voluntarily. These impulses can, and very frequently do, override those of the fixation reflex, otherwise purposeful seeing would be impossible. Nevertheless, competition between the voluntary and the involuntary mechanisms of visual attention is sometimes strong enough to engender unwelcome feelings of effort. For example, a sense of considerable effort is experienced in resisting the attractive power of a glaring headlight on a dark night and in keeping the eyes on the darker but more relevant part of the road ahead. The 'discomfort' occasioned by the presence of any excitingly bright objects or lights which are near the focal field of view at any time is partly due to resisting the fixation reflex.

CHAPTER 2

Looking and Lighting

Visual tasks. Every visual task involves the solution of a visual problem and the problem is always one of identity. It would be fatuous to attempt to look for anything without knowing what we are looking for; indeed, it is impossible to do so. A mental 'picture' of the object of our search is more than a mere aid to our looking, it is the indispensable prerequisite for any and every act of scrutiny undertaken to discover whether this or that is present in the scene surveyed. We may of course not be looking for one particular thing but for every particular characteristic of a thing and, in this case, we are undertaking an exploration with the object of getting to know all about the field that presents itself, usually so that thereafter we shall *recognise* it when we see it again and, perhaps, be able to discern selectively some particular part of its make-up.

Suppose we have an inspection job: we can only pass or reject an article if we know what it should look like if it is faulty and how it should look if correct. The job may be to reject the article if it appears to be in *any* way dissimilar to the pattern exhibited by the reference standard we are given, or it may be to reject the article if it looks dissimilar in one or more specific details. In the first case we have no need to bother with the precise nature of the dissimilarity but only to become aware that the appearance of the article is not exactly like that of our standard or sample. In the second case, we have to ignore some features of dissimilarity if we see them and reject the article only if we see other features which are the prescribed unwanteds; we have, in this case, to be more discriminating than in the first case and, if the appearance of the unwanted feature differs very little from features which can be tolerated, then our visual examination may have to be very critical indeed. Many examples will come readily to mind which illustrate how little may be the difference between two objects of the same sort one of which is acceptable while the other is not. Thus, the proof-reader who may be expecting to see the word 'shook' must be sure that what is offered to him is not 'shock'; yet there is only one small detail that differentiates one word from the other.

When we have seen a thing many times, or scrutinised it very thoroughly, our mental image of it becomes so complete that we are adept at spotting this thing when we look for it, even under somewhat adverse conditions of visibility. People to whom it is much less familiar may look for it in vain or be long in finding it, even under favourable conditions. The acquisition of preperceptions gives us *visual skill* and the possession of specialised pre-perceptions gives us specialist visual skill. This visual skill is not necessarily highly correlated with native visual capacities; some people with subnormal vision become very skilled at some visual tasks that better but unpractised eyes cannot do so well.

The performance of visual tasks generally involves preoccupation with some relatively small part of the prevailing general field of view or *panorama*. In many habitual occupations vision is focused most frequently upon one such local or 'focal' area the contents of which make up what has been termed the *ergorama*—that is, the work-scene or view.

Although the extraction of necessary information from an ergorama is greatly facilitated by the visual skill already mentioned, clearly it also makes demands upon the native or inherent visual capacities of the worker or observer. But the extent to which the native visual capacities of any person are actually usable at any particular time depends upon the prevailing conditions of lighting. So, if these conditions are to be made as favourable as possible for the performance of particular visual tasks, it is necessary to know what characteristic elements of each work-view are crucial and what levels of capacity should be made available for their ready perception. These critical or identifying details are visually nothing but areas which differ more or less noticeably in brightness and/or colour from adjacent parts of the field of view, and whose apparent size may be anything from large to minute. Their discovery and description should be included in any systematic job analysis and their measurement or estimation in appropriate numerical terms enables visual tasks to be graded, ranked or 'evaluated' in order of severity and of lighting requirements in the most scientific way. Modern lighting codes contain many examples of practical tasks assessed as to the level of illumination desirable for them, but so immense is the variety of visual tasks that they can never be listed exhaustively in this way.

The act of extracting information from a visual scene—that is, the per-formance of a visual task—involves ocular muscular work in scanning the ergorama and keeping its parts in focus. This part of the visual task, the mechanism for which has been described in Chapter 1, can be facilitated by lighting the whole of the field to be scrutinised in such a way as to reveal its crucial elements, so far as possible, without the eyes having to grope about with many fruitless movements before 'sighting' them.

The more refined design of lighting for particular visual tasks calls for fairly comprehensive knowledge of the nature of the ergorama. This includes, (a) the form of the crucial items, (b) how they are likely to be distributed, (c) how big or small and how distant from the eyes they are, (d) how much and in what way they differ in reflectivity from their immediate surroundings and (e) whether they are stationary or in motion. Given this information, a suitable level of illumination can be deduced from available basic data and it can be understood how other conditions of lighting, such as the direction and spectral quality of the light, should be designed to make the critical details readily visible. Unplanned lighting may well camouflage or mask important details instead of revealing them.

Most fields of view contain details which are irrelevant to the purpose of the moment and, while their discrimination is not necessary, their presence sometimes increases the difficulty of seeing relevant items. Many examples of this will come to mind readily; a proverbial one is the 'needle in a pottle of hay' and a more homely one is the 'lost' collar stud that lies amidst the diverting pattern on the carpet! Lighting can overcome this sort of difficulty only when it can be arranged to brighten the wanted item preferentially—to highlight it or give it saliency so that it catches the eye. As a rule it is not so much wealth of detail but conspicuity of certain crucial details that is needed in performing visual tasks.

Many visual tasks involve the perception of transient or fugitive detail, that is to say, detail that is not an entity itself but appears briefly when the spatial relation between two or more actual objects changes. It may be difficult to describe the nature of such detail and to measure it. Here, however, exposure time is limited and perception must be accomplished quickly or not at all. In another class of visual tasks the critical detail is virtually imperceptible. This apparently paradoxical statement means that the visual task consists in perceiving diminishing detail down to the vanishing point, as in setting the divisions of vernier scales to coincidence, in reading pointer and dial instruments with precision, in threading a needle, and so on. Fortunately, the normal acuity of sight for this kind of task is extraordinarily good: nevertheless it demands good lighting.

Marginal visual information. The detailed information we get from an ergorama by foveal vision is always accompanied by some information derived from other parts of the total field of view and this is sometimes very important. For example, in driving a road vehicle the 'marginal awareness' we have of what is passing by in the peripheral parts of the field of view— parts, that is, to which our gaze is not directed—is very helpful even though we do not—and usually do not need to—see the contents of these parts of the visual field distinctly. The same is true of industrial and, indeed, of all environments in which relative movement occurs between ourselves and other objects. This is one of the reasons why it is generally necessary for the whole environment to be adequately illuminated.

Looking as a pleasant 'task'. Although it is true that in all purposeful seeing we are performing visual tasks, it is not usual to think of looking at things about us when we are not 'at work' as a task. On the contrary, we often do it for pleasure; a pleasant 'sight' is positively enjoyable. But we are fortunate indeed if 'every prospect pleases'. However, the fact that our 'feelings' may be affected—often very subtly—by the appearance of the visible environments in which much of our time has to be spent should always be borne in mind with reference to lighting. Whether an environment appears agreeable or disagreeable often depends in no small measure upon how it is lighted.

Basic requirements for good lighting. The principal characteristics of good lighting are implicit in the foregoing account of vision and visual tasks. However, they are summarised briefly here, although the techniques by which they can be provided require the fuller consideration which is to be found in other chapters.

Firstly, and most obviously, the level of illumination should be high enough to allow the eyes to function as efficiently as may be adequate for any particular purpose of leisure or labour. A low level of illumination may not only be sufficient but be actually most desirable for certain purposes while, for others, moderate or even very high levels are desirable. For working environments it is generally desirable to provide a moderately high general level of illumination even if no exacting visual tasks have to be done. This is because alertness and activity tend to be stimulated by generous ambient brightness which has a tonic effect conducing to feelings of well being and *joie de vivre*. This 'amenity' level of illumination should not, as a rule, be less than about 15 lm/ft² and could well be much higher. Levels of illumination for a large number of interiors are given in the I.E.S. Code.

The very high levels of illumination necessary for the most exacting visual tasks are usually required only over relatively small areas. They can, therefore, be obtained by supplementary local or localised lighting, and it may be only in this way that the actual work-view can be made somewhat brighter—as it should be—than the less relevant surrounding scene.

A given level of illumination, whether obtained by general or by general plus local lighting, will only be fully effective if it is not accompanied by glare. Generally, glare is not due to excessive apparent brightness of the total field of view (popularly called 'too much light') but to the presence in this field of local areas whose luminance is much higher than the average ambient luminance. Therefore, the luminance of sky-lit windows and of artificial lighting equipment must be kept down within ordinary angles of view so that it does not unduly exceed the luminance of surrounding areas of the panorama. Glare, in fact, is almost always a matter of excessive luminance contrast and this is true whether the bright 'core' of this contrast is one of the installed light sources or whether it is an excessive highlight seen by reflection from some shiny or highly polished surface.

Glare has two effects upon those exposed to it. If it is slight it may cause only a vague and indefinable disagreeable feeling. When it is more intense it may be distracting and cause annoyance, irritation and a definite feeling of discomfort. Probably at this stage it also depresses visual sensitivity to some extent and, of course, when it is dazzling vision is temporarily impaired quite seriously.

While excessive luminance contrast must be avoided, too little is also undesirable, as tending to make an illuminated environment appear flat, uninteresting and monotonous. Extreme diffusion of the light may have this effect. Most distributions of light should be planned to have certain directional characteristics sufficient for casting helpful shadows, such as are necessary for revealing the details of textured materials and modelling solid objects. A little light suitably directed may be more revealing than a high level of illumination produced by so-called 'shadowless' lighting.

The spectral quality of the light may be particularly important in some circumstances, as where the visual tasks involve critical colour matching and colour discrimination. In other situations the creation of satisfying cosmetic effects, or the most pleasing colour rendering of an environment, involves the use of a particular variant of the 'white' illuminants now available from fluorescent sources, or the use of a combination of different light sources.

Lighting and the environment. From what has already been said it will be clear that lighting is not only required to facilitate visual tasks, but also to reveal—and even enhance—the whole environment. In fact, as the cost of artificial light has been reduced over the years and the lighting needs for visual tasks have been more easily met, developments in lighting have been concerned more with its quality than with its quantity. This has been reflected in the I.E.S. Code, which now includes the Limiting Glare Index System, designed to eliminate the excesses of direct glare in general lighting installations. The Code also makes some tentative suggestions about the brightness ratios which may be found to be acceptable in the environment, and on the degree of modelling which might be sought. But these elements in the scene, while they can be separately identified, are not independent of each other. Moreover, the standards by which we judge these elements are not measurable standards, but subjective judgments. For these reasons, therefore, new methods of study have been necessary, to explore ideas in lighting which reach out beyond the accepted techniques of lighting planning.

The search for new standards of acceptability has emphasised the need for subjective studies to try to discover how the eye responds to brightness ratios, brightness patterns and colour pattern. For any particular situation the response to all these things is governed to some extent by the state of adaptation of the eye, which we discussed in the previous chapter. Luminances, which can be measured, need to be converted into 'apparent brightnesses', before any design methods can proceed and 'scales of apparent brightness', as devised by Hopkinson and used by Waldram, are a subject of further study at the present time.

The increases in levels of artificial lighting have met a real need for better visual conditions in working interiors, and much lighting equipment is now used in daytime hours in those areas which do not receive adequate light from windows. The concept of 'permanent supplementary artificial lighting' aims not only to provide adequate illumination in areas distant from windows but also to create acceptable brightness gradients and offset the effects of sky glare.

It will be seen from this that lighting design for many interiors will in future be concerned with both natural and artificial lighting and their integration into a comprehensive scheme. In this process window design will be an important element; but window design is also important to the thermal character of a building, and it is logical, therefore, that visual and thermal factors should be considered together.

Again, with the increased levels of artificial light has come a realisation that the heat inevitably created by any electric lighting installation can be an important component in the thermal environment, and this is a further justification for considering lighting requirements as part of a whole environmental system, including thermal, visual and other factors.

CHAPTER 3

The Language of Light

In this chapter, the labels given to the different ways of 'packing light' will be defined and discussed. Also some of the basic laws relating these labels (or photometric terms) to each other will be explained. There is often difficulty in visualising the concepts used in photometric terms and it is hoped that the following introductory remarks will be helpful.

Everyone has an intuitive idea of the meaning of *illumination*: it is the degree of concentration of light falling on a surface. However, what is important to the observer is not so much the concentration of light falling *on* a surface as the concentration of the light reflected *from* a surface, because it is this light that affects the eye and makes an object visible. This light gives a surface the property of brightness. However, it is necessary to distinguish between apparent and physical brightness; between what is seen and what is measured. An example will serve to make the distinction clear. The headlights of on-coming motor cars appear extremely bright at night, but are barely visible on a sunlit day. Their physical brightness (or brightness measured by a meter) is obviously the same in both cases, but their subjective or apparent brightness is much greater when the eye is adapted to seeing conditions at night. This difference arises because physical brightness depends solely on the concentration of light that an object emits in the direction of interest, but apparent brightness also depends on the way in which the surroundings affect the adaptation of the eye and the way in which the brain interprets the messages sent by the retina. Physical brightness is known as *luminance*, and apparent brightness as *luminosity*.

Another term needing some preliminary explanation is *luminous intensity*. This can be translated as *candle-power*; a term originating from the fact that it used to be measured by comparing the illumination given by an unknown source in a particular direction against the illumination given by a standard candle. The candle is not now used as a standard, but the new standard, the *candela*, is used in the same way.

Before plunging into the definitions, some justification is needed for the order that has been chosen for defining the various terms. Luminous flux will be defined first, followed by definitions of illumination, point source of light, luminous intensity and the remainder of the terms. This is the most logical treatment; *luminous flux* is the rate of flow of light energy, and terms such as illumination and intensity are measures of the closeness of the 'packing together' of the flux, that is the flux density.

Luminous flux. This is the rate of flow of light. Since in any medium light travels at a constant velocity, its rate of flow can only be altered by increasing or decreasing the flux density.

The symbol for luminous flux is F. The unit in which it is measured is the lumen, abbreviated to lm.

Illumination. This is a measure of the concentration of flux falling on a surface. It is measured in lumens per unit area. If F is the luminous flux, in lumens, falling on an area, A, then the illumination, E, is given by

$$E = \frac{F}{A} \text{ lumens per unit area}$$

The two most commonly used units of area are the square metre and the square foot. Lumens per square metre are called *lux*; a term used in continental countries. *Lumens per square foot* (Abbrev.: lm/ft^2) were formerly known as foot-candles, but the use of this term is now deprecated.

Point source of light. The point source of light is a mathematical concept that is used in the definition of intensity; it is simply a source that is infinitely small. It cannot be realised in practice; the nearest approach to it is a fixed star as seen from the earth.

Luminous intensity and the inverse square law of illumination. The illumination on a surface decreases as the square of its distance, d, from a point source, if its direction with regard to the source is kept constant. This is the inverse square law of illumination. If the rays of light are perpendicular to the surface (Fig. 3.1), the constant of proportionality is equal to the luminous intensity, I (or candle-power).

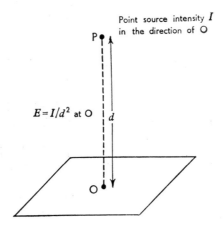

Fig. 3.1   Inverse square law of illumination

Hence, the illumination, E, for rays perpendicular to the surface is given by

$$E = I/d^2$$

The intensity I may, therefore, be regarded as the illuminating power of a point source of light in a particular direction. If E is measured in lumens per square foot and d in feet (or any other unit of length, provided that the same unit is used in E) then the intensity I will be in candelas, the unit of intensity. The abbreviation is cd.

The candela is defined as 1/60th of the intensity of a square centimetre of a black body at the temperature of solidification of platinum. A black body (or full radiator) is used because its spectrum at any given temperature can be worked out theoretically.

The truth of the inverse square law may be shown in the following way:

Consider a point source of light at the centre of a sphere of radius d. Let the intensity of the light source be the same in every direction. By symmetry, the direct illumination, E, on the surface of the sphere will be uniform over its surface. Since the area of the sphere is equal to $4\pi d^2$, E will be equal to $F/4\pi d^2$. Hence $E \propto 1/d^2$, since F is constant.

Cosine law of illumination. In the previous section, it was stated that $E = I/d^2$ for rays perpendicular to a surface. If the plane is inclined so that the normal is at an angle θ to the rays (Fig. 3.2), then the illumination E is given by

$$E = (I/d^2) \cos \theta$$

This is known as the cosine law of illumination.

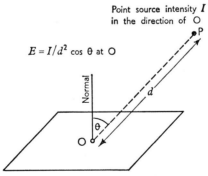

Fig. 3.2   Cosine law of illumination

Uniform diffuser. A surface that reflects or transmits light so that the intensity varies according to the cosine of the angle between any direction of view and the normal to the surface (Fig. 3.3), is known as a uniform diffuser. In practice no surface obeys this law exactly but some surfaces approximate to it. Magnesium carbonate and white blotting paper are two examples of surfaces which reflect light according to this law to a good approximation.

It is shown in Chapter 9 that a uniform diffuser having an intensity I normal to its surface emits πI lumens. This fact is used in the section in which units of luminance are discussed.

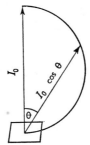

Fig. 3.3   Light distribution from a uniform diffuser

Reflection factor, ρ.   This is the flux reflected by a surface divided by the flux incident upon it.

Transmission factor, τ.   This is the flux transmitted by a medium divided by the flux incident upon it.

Luminous Emittance, H.   This is the flux emitted by a small area of a surface, divided by the area considered.

It is measured in lumens per unit area, but is distinguished from illumination by being a measure of the flux emitted from a surface and not a measure of the flux received. However, the two are related by reflection factor in the following equation:

$$H = \rho E$$

where H is luminous emittance.

It should be noted that luminous emittance takes no account of the way in which the reflected flux is distributed. The distribution of the reflected flux is of importance in the concept of luminance.

Orthogonally projected area.   Before luminance can be defined, the

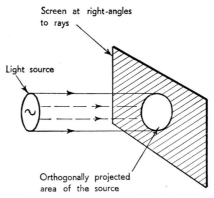

Fig. 3.4   Orthogonal projection

concept of orthogonally projected area must be introduced. This can be explained as follows. Consider a beam of parallel light coming from a surface in the direction of view. If a screen is held at right angles to the beam, as shown in Fig. 3.4, the area enclosed by the boundary of the beam is the orthogonally projected area of the source in that direction. For a source having a plane surface, the projected area is equal to the surface area multiplied by the cosine of the angle between the direction of view and the normal to the surface.

Luminance. As stated in the introduction to this chapter, luminance is physical brightness. It is the intensity of a source in a given direction divided by its orthogonally projected area in that direction. If the luminance varies across the source, then the luminance of any point on that surface is found by considering an infinitely small area at the point in question.

The most common units are candelas per square foot or inch, stilbs (cd/cm^2) and nits (cd/m^2). The symbol is L.

There is another system of luminance units. In this the luminance of a surface is expressed as the luminous emittance of a uniform diffuser of the same luminance. As an example, consider a surface having a luminance of one cd/ft^2. A uniform diffuser of luminous emittance π lm/ft^2 would have the same luminance. Now a uniform diffuser emitting 1 lm/ft^2 is said to have a luminance of 1 footlambert, so the surface has a luminance of π footlamberts (ft-L).

The advantage of this system is that if the illumination on a uniformly diffusing surface is known, it is necessary only to multiply by its reflection factor to find its luminance. For example, if the illumination is 60 lm/ft^2 and the reflection factor is 50%, then the luminance of the surface is 30 ft-L. Units in the two systems are compared in Table 3.1.

TABLE 3.1

Units of Luminance Compared

Units of area	Emittance of uniform diffuser	Equivalent luminance in terms of emittance of uniform diffuser	Equivalent luminance in candelas per unit area
Square metre	1 lm/m^2	1 apostilb	$\frac{1}{\pi}$ cd/m^2
Square foot	1 lm/ft^2	1 footlambert (ft-L)	$\frac{1}{\pi}$ cd/ft^2
Square centimetre	1 lm/cm^2	1 lambert (L)	$\frac{1}{\pi}$ cd/cm^2 or stilbs

Luminance of uniform diffuser. The luminance of a uniform diffuser remains constant no matter what the direction of view. This may be shown to be true by considering a small area, δA, of a source. Let this be small enough to be considered as being flat. The intensity (Fig. 3.3) at an angle θ to the normal is $I_0 \cos \theta$. Its projected area in this direction is $\delta A \cos \theta$. Hence, its luminance is equal to

$$\frac{\text{Intensity}}{\text{Projected area}} = \frac{I_0 \cos \theta}{\delta A \cos \theta}$$

$$= \frac{I_0}{\delta A}$$

This result is independent of θ, so the luminance remains constant.

Solid angle. In the calculation of flux from a source it is necessary to make use of the concept of solid angle. A useful stepping stone to understanding this is to consider how plane angles are measured in radians. Suppose in Fig. 3.5a it is required to find the angle that AB subtends at C. Join BC and

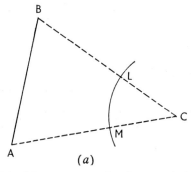

Fig. 3.5(a)   Measurement of a plane angle in radians

AC and draw an arc of unit radius with its centre at C, so that it cuts BC and AC at L and M. The required angle in radian measure is equal to the length of the arc LM. If the arc were not of unit radius, the angle would be found by dividing the arc LM by its radius.

Similarly, if in Fig. 3.5b the solid angle that A subtends at C is required, draw a sphere centre C and find where the cone from A cuts it. Let the area of that part of the surface of the sphere enclosed by the cone be A'. Then the

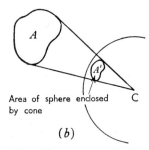

Area of sphere enclosed
by cone

(b)

Fig. 3.5(b)   The concept of solid angle

solid angle subtended by A is equal to A' divided by the square of the radius of the sphere. As with radian measure, it is equal to A' if the sphere has unit radius. Solid angles are measured in steradians. The symbol is ω.

The solid angle subtended at its centre by a hemisphere is 2π steradians, and by a sphere is 4π steradians. An infinitely large flat plane will subtend a solid angle of 2π steradians at any point below it.

Flux from a point source. In Fig. 3.6 let P be a point source illuminating an area A of a sphere. Let P be at the centre of the sphere, which has a radius r. Also, let the intensity of the source in the direction of A be constant and be equal to I.

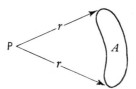

Fig. 3.6   Flux from a point source

Because all points on A are equidistant from P, the illumination over its surface will be constant and equal to I/r^2. If I is measured in candelas, the illumination will be in lumens per unit area. Therefore, the total flux falling on A is equal to IA/r^2.

Now the solid angle, ω, subtended by A at P is A/r^2.

Hence the flux F falling on A is given by $F = I\omega$.

This relationship leads to a second definition of the lumen, which, however, depends on the candela; this states that the lumen is the flux emitted in unit solid angle by a uniform point source of one candela.

It also shows that intensity may be regarded as flux per steradian. That is, it is the concentration of flux (or flux density) in a cone subtended by a source. In general the intensity of a point source will vary with direction within the cone, so that it is more strictly correct to say that intensity is the flux per steradian in an infinitesimal cone, the axis of which is in the direction of view.

This relation can be used for finding the luminous flux from lighting fittings, and the method of using it is explained in Chapter 8.

CHAPTER 4

The Production of Light

Daylight. This chapter is concerned with artificially produced light but a brief reference should first be made to a far more plentiful source, namely natural sunlight and the diffused daylight resulting from it. The sun emits a very wide spectrum of radiation with numerous narrow absorption bands (the Fraunhofer lines). After absorption in several narrow regions of wavelength by components of the atmosphere, particularly water, ozone and oxygen, this radiation reaches the earth's surface but meanwhile it is partially scattered by gas atoms and molecules, also by dust. It is also reflected by the earth's surface and by clouds, hence a rather complicated spectrum results both in direct sunlight and in the light from the sky and the clouds. There are great variations in intensity, spectrum and colour with climate, time of day and season but regular patterns of change have recently been established. From these, representative spectral distributions can be selected for standards, by reference to which artificial daylight sources are made for use in colour matching and similar tasks. Further references are made to this in Chapter 5 where an example of the spectral distribution is shown (Fig. 5.6).

In the following a survey of the known methods of generating light will be made, with special attention to gas discharges in view of their practical importance. Luminescence is also considered at length for the same reason.

Combustion. The artificial production of light began with the discovery of fire, which was usually the combustion of solid vegetable matter, particularly wood. Much nearer to our own times the use of vegetable and animal oils and waxes became general, passing over to mineral oils and coal gas comparatively recently. The light came largely from the flames of the combustion process, with more or less light according to the completeness of burning. In general a smoky flame produced more light than a clear one. Explaining this in modern terms we should say that the rapid oxidation of the combustible materials produced a great deal of energy, mostly as heat, but with a very small fraction appearing as visible light. Luminosity of the flames was mostly due to suspended carbon particles raised to red or white heat.

Flash bulbs. Photographers use a controlled form of combustion in expendable bulbs containing aluminium or zirconium wire. This burns rapidly in oxygen when ignited by a primer on an electrically heated filament in the bulb. The emitting material is mainly the white-hot particles of oxide produced by the combustion.

Heating refractory solids. Any alternative to combustion requires the continuous input of energy to a material capable of emitting light, preferably without being itself melted or evaporated in the process. This had to await the discovery of the electric current. The first modern artificial light source was in fact the arc between carbon rods demonstrated by Davy in 1802, the electrical energy being used up in raising the electrode ends to incandescence. The arc lamp had a considerable success and is still with us. A recent American version (the 'concentrated arc lamp') made in small wattages provides a very small source of extremely high intensity by an arc, operating in argon between a tantalum tube packed with zirconium oxide and a molybdenum plate.

Filament lamps: black bodies: flames. Further developments by electrical heating followed with the carbon filament lamp (1879) and later with osmium, tantalum and tungsten wires operating in vacuum, or an inert atmosphere. The complete unifying principle which explains their operation was given by Planck in 1901. This allows the calculation of the power radiated by a solid body at any wavelength of the spectrum when the body is held at a known temperature. This is called *thermal radiation*. A condition is that the body must be 'black', that is, it must absorb all radiation, infrared, light, ultraviolet, etc.) falling on it. This is not the case for any real material, but tungsten filaments behave approximately as black bodies (or 'full radiators') except that they radiate much less at any wavelength than the equivalent

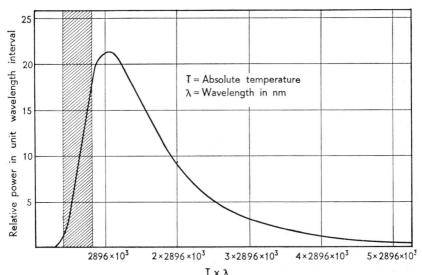

Fig. 4.1   Black body power distribution (generalised)

black body would; however, the spectrum of the light they emit can be computed fairly accurately if their temperature is known. Fig. 4.1 shows a generalised form of the black body emission curve for any absolute temperature as given by Planck's formula, according to which the power per unit wavelength emitted at wavelength λ, is

$$C_1 \lambda^{-5}/(\exp C_2/\lambda T - 1).$$

Here C_1 and C_2 are constants related to atomic constants and the velocity of light. The curve is of the same shape for any temperature, but its location on the wavelength scale depends on the temperature.

The maximum emission (per unit wavelength interval) is seen to be in the infrared ($\lambda_{max} = 1000$ nm) if $T = 2896$ °K, or in the green ($\lambda_{max} = 500$ nm) if $T = 5792$ °K. The shaded section is the approximate location of the visible spectrum when the emitter is at 2896 °K, for example a 1000 W tungsten lamp. In Fig. 3.1 the height of the peak is on an arbitrary scale. It is proportional to T^5, while the total emission (ultraviolet, visible and infrared) is proportional to T^4; of this total about three-quarters is emitted on the long wavelength side of the peak, wherever this peak may be located on the scale of wavelengths.

The carbon particles in flame sources also behave like the theoretical 'black body', but generally reach a lower temperature than the filament in a lamp, hence the light appears redder. As the temperature rises the colour of the light emitted by an incandescent body is first red, then yellow, then more white; for reasons of efficiency it is desirable to have the temperature as high as possible. Tungsten cannot be operated much above 3000 °C unless evaporation is controlled and the bulb kept free of dark deposits. This can be achieved by the introduction of iodine into the bulb, which since it must be kept above 250 °C, is made of silica (see Chapter 15).

An attempt to use still more refractory materials is seen in a radiofrequency lamp from U.S.A., where the light emitter is a small block of tantalum carbide heated by radio waves to about 3500 °C. Filaments of the same and related materials have also been considered as a replacement for tungsten, but at present their use is limited by brittleness. For the production of visible light it would be most efficient to maintain an incandescent body at about 6600 °C, a temperature unattainable except momentarily; this would give a luminous efficiency of 95 lm/W compared with the present maximum of about 30 lm/W for incandescent lamps. These values of efficiency and others quoted in this chapter refer to the initial output of a newly made lamp and take no account of the decline which occurs in all light sources during their continued operation. Flames, which are composed of hot gases, are often transparent, in other words they absorb only a little of the radiation falling on them; therefore they do not themselves radiate nearly as well as black bodies in spite of their high temperature. A mass of hot gas can, however, become a black body if it is sufficiently thick to absorb outward streaming radiation completely as in the sun, which behaves rather like a black body at about 6000 °K. The black body condition can also be approached by a mass of gas at a sufficiently high pressure.

GAS DISCHARGES

Low pressure. Apart from his work on the arc, Davy was one of the pioneers in the investigation of the conduction of electricity in gases. His work and Faraday's led to the well known Geissler tubes (1856) followed much later by tubes made by Moore for lighting purposes. These contained air, nitrogen or carbon dioxide, were operated at high voltages and emitted spectra composed of lines and bands. In 1907 Claude made his first tubes filled with low-pressure neon, and from this and other rare gases a wide range of coloured tubular lighting has developed, mostly applicable to signs and decoration. Light-producing current flow in low-pressure mercury vapour was also known as early as the time of Geissler, but again a long period elapsed before practical light sources were made. The low-pressure discharge in mercury vapour is itself of low luminous efficiency (about 5 lm/W) and unsatisfactory colour. It has little or no application in this primitive form. Its great value in the now common tubular fluorescent lamp will appear later.

To obtain a clear idea of how an electrical discharge through a low-pressure gas or vapour generates light it is necessary to consider mechanisms of electrical conduction. In a solid conductor the current is carried by the movement of free electrons through a tightly bound lattice of atoms, which apart from thermal vibrations are immobile. Metallic conductors contain about as many free electrons as fixed atoms, which accounts for their high electrical conductivity. The only direct effects of the passage of an electric current are the heating of the conductor and the appearance of a magnetic field around it. The emission of light is a secondary effect and occurs only if the solid is heated sufficiently to become incandescent. In gaseous conductors, by contrast, the current is carried both by electrons and by positive *ions*, which are gas atoms deficient in one or more electrons normally resident in one of the outer electrons shells surrounding the atomic nucleus. Heating and magnetic effects are observed but in addition light is emitted even when the gas is quite cold. The light is generated by an atomic excitation process, described in detail later, which does not occur in solids except a rather special group of materials which exhibit the property of electroluminescence.

Gases normally contain neither free electrons nor positive ions and are therefore electrical insulators. A gas may be made to conduct electricity only by the process of ionisation, which is the separation of electrons from atoms, resulting in the presence of free electrons and a proportion of positive ions. Electrons freed by an ionising process can move under the influence of an electric field, just as in a metal, but in addition a positive ion movement occurs in the opposite direction to the electron movement. Thus an electrical discharge through gas or vapour consists of two counter streams of electrons and ions.

Fig. 4.2 illustrates an electrical discharge through a tube of ionised gas. Negatively charged electrons move towards the positive electrode or anode, and positive ions move towards the cathode; the total current is therefore the sum of the ion and electron currents. Although the numbers of ions and electrons in unit volume of the gas are almost equal, the ions contribute very little, usually about 0·1 % to the total current. This is because ions have much greater mass than electrons and consequently move more slowly under the same electric force. However, the presence of positive ions in a gas discharge greatly reduces the voltage required to pass large electron currents, an effect known as neutralisation of space charge.

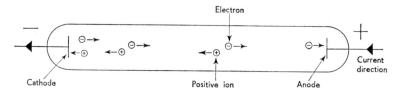

Fig. 4.2 Electric discharge through a tube of ionised gas

Conduction through a gas is very dependent on the efficiency of the ionising process. At any instant the conductivity depends not only on the rate of ionisation at that instant but also on the previous rates of ionisation. The electrical characteristics of a conducting gas are therefore very complicated and no simple law, such as Ohm's law, is obeyed. Before considering the details of the electrical characteristics it is necessary to examine the mechanism of the most important ionising process, namely ionisation by electron impact.

Ionisation by electron impact. When a free electron collides with a neutral gas atom one of three things may happen:
  (1) The electron may rebound with very little loss of energy: an elastic collision.
  (2) The atom may be 'excited', and the electron loses most of its energy.
  (3) The atom may be ionised, releasing one of its electrons.
The probability of any one of these processes depends on the energy of the electron involved in the collision, ionisation requiring the highest energy. Electron energies are generally expressed in electron volts (eV), the unit being the energy gained by an electron in moving between two points one volt different in potential. The ionising energy for mercury is 10·42 eV, and for argon 15·7 eV, which means that in a mixture of mercury vapour and argon, the mercury is preferentially ionised. Thus an electrical discharge in mercury cannot take place unless at least 10·4 V is applied across the electrodes and in practice a much greater voltage than this is necessary to maintain the discharge, because of energy losses in the gas and at the electrodes. Even when sufficient voltage is available to maintain a discharge through a gas, no ionisation will occur unless a number of free electrons are present initially.

Initial ionisation. Several sources of electrons are available for this.
  (1) Residual ionisation from a previous discharge.
  (2) Thermionic emission from a hot cathode.
  (3) Photoelectric emission from electrode surfaces.

(4) Field emission from electrodes.

(5) Ionisation by radioactive materials present in the gas or on the surfaces of the tube.

Residual ionisation does not last more than a few seconds after a discharge ceases so that this source is only important in discharge lamps if immediate restarting is required. In the hot cathode fluorescent lamp the main source of electrons is thermionic emission from the cathodes, while in the cold cathode fluorescent lamp, the high-pressure mercury vapour lamp, and other discharge devices, one or more of the other three sources of initial electrons is present.

Cumulative ionisation. At each ionising collision of an electron with a neutral atom, two free electrons are produced in place of one. Successive ionising collisions therefore result in a rapid build up in numbers of free electrons and ions, provided that losses due to recombination and diffusion to the walls of the tubes are not excessive. Cumulative ionisation of this kind, sometimes referred to as an electron avalanche, occurs whenever a discharge lamp starts, and occupies a time measured by a few thousandths of a second.

Electrical characteristics of a discharge. The conductivity of a discharge is proportional to the ion concentration which increases with the discharge current. The resultant increase in conductivity is usually so great that the voltage required to maintain the current falls as the current rises; the volt–ampere characteristic has a negative slope. One important consequence is that most discharges are not inherently current-limiting and for stable operation from a constant voltage supply the circuit must include a current-limiting device such as a resistor. For a.c. operation the resistor may be replaced by an inductor, a capacitor, or combinations of these with the advantage of minimising power losses. Voltage and current waveforms in a.c. circuits may be very distorted and it is not possible to perform any simple calculations to obtain an accurate relationship between r.m.s. values of voltage and current.

The production of light by a gas discharge. The use of a gas discharge as a light source is made possible by the existence of an energy storage process by atoms, known as *excitation*. Atoms may be excited by electron impact when the electron energies are insufficient to cause ionisation. Excitation energies are series of discrete levels shown by energy level diagrams, an example of which is illustrated by Fig. 4.3. An energy level may be regarded as a possible orbit for one of the outer electrons of the atom; the highest energy level is equal to the ionisation energy when the electron escapes from the atom. An electron in an atom which is raised from the ground state, the lowest energy level, by collision with a free electron, remains in the higher level for a short period of time, usually less than one microsecond. On returning to the ground state the stored energy of the excited atom is radiated as light. Every energy change has a definite wavelength of light associated with it and the energy levels of the atoms are made evident by the line spectrum of light emitted by excited atoms. Not all of the excited states are capable of losing energy by radiation, for example the lowest excited state of mercury at 4·6 V has no spectral line associated with it. The lowest excited state that can radiate produces what is often referred to as 'resonance radiation', which is important in low pressure discharge lamps because it is very efficiently generated. In the case of mercury at low pressure the resonance radiation is at 253·7 nm in the short wave

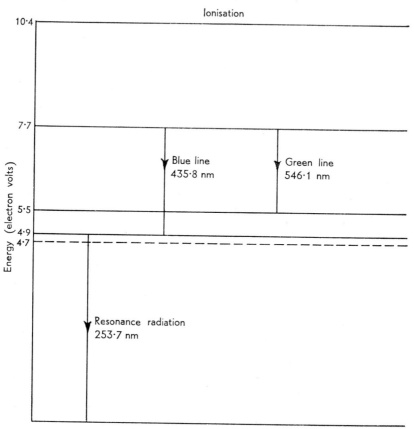

Fig. 4.3   Simplified energy level diagram for mercury

ultraviolet region, but sodium has resonance radiation in the yellow region of the spectrum at a wavelength of 589·3 nm. Under favourable conditions of low pressure and low current density the resonance radiation can be produced by a discharge tube with an efficiency of 50% or more; i.e. half of the electrical power input emerges as radiation covering a very narrow band of the spectrum. A tubular lamp can be operated close to the ideal conditions but as the mercury resonance radiation is invisible a fluorescent material must be used to convert it to visible light, and the overall efficiency of light production is then much lower than 50% because of losses occurring in the fluorescence conversion process, discussed later in this chapter. The power loading of a fluorescent lamp operating at maximum efficiency is rather low, being about 10 W/ft for $1\frac{1}{2}$ in. diameter tubes. If the loading is increased in order to obtain greater light output, the efficiency declines. A similar behaviour is displayed by the low-pressure sodium lamp.

In a practical vapour discharge lamp it is found necessary to include one or more of the inert gases neon, argon or krypton in addition to the vaporisable metal. There are two main reasons for this:

(1) To give easier starting and more efficient operation by reducing the rate of loss of ions and electrons to the wall of the tube.

(2) To prolong the life of the electrodes by reducing sputtering and evaporation rates.

The inert gases have relatively high-energy levels and so are not appreciably ionised or excited in the discharge, except perhaps immediately after starting when the vapour pressure may be too low to be significant. The sodium lamp, for example, shows the red colour of a neon discharge at first but gradually changes to the yellow colour of sodium as the tube temperature rises.

The choice of inert gas pressure is a compromise between the requirements of easy starting, high efficiency and long lamp life; typical values of gas and vapour pressures in some types of lamps are as follows:

Low-pressure tubular fluorescent:	mercury	0·01 torr
	argon	3·0 torr
High-pressure mercury:	mercury	2000 torr (when hot)
	argon	30 torr
Sodium vapour:	sodium	0·004 torr (when hot)
	neon + $\frac{1}{2}$% argon	10 torr

High pressure. Pressures greater than about one atmosphere (760 torr) are considered to be high for gas discharge purposes, and although the electrical conduction process involving ionisation by electron collision occurs just as in a discharge at low pressure, the light emission process is modified as the pressure increases. Resonance radiation is readily re-absorbed by the gas which generates it and very little escapes from the discharge tube at high pressures; for example the mercury resonance radiation at 253·7 nm is almost entirely suppressed in lamps operating at several atmospheres pressure, hence their efficiency cannot be increased by using phosphors excited by this wavelength of ultraviolet radiation. Other wavelengths of radiation can be emitted with very great intensity and owing to the mutual interference of closely packed atoms the spectral lines are broadened into bands. At very high pressures the radiation approximates to a continuous spectrum, similar to that produced by an incandescent solid.

The intensity of radiation in any part of the spectrum is limited to that which a black body at the same temperature as the gas would emit. However, the gas temperature at the central core of a high-pressure discharge can far exceed the melting point of any solid so that the luminance of this type of light source can be much greater than that of any other. The efficiency

2*

obtainable is about 50 lm/W for mercury vapour. It can be made even greater than for a black body radiator by choosing vapours which have reduced emission in the infrared or ultraviolet parts of the spectrum. As an example of this, high-pressure lamps with fused silica envelopes containing metal iodide vapours have been made with efficiencies in the region of 85 lm/W to 90 lm/W and wide spectral distribution imitating the effects of the daylight spectrum. This recent development uses the more volatile iodides to achieve metal vapour concentrations greater than are possible with the metals alone. Such materials as sodium, thallium, indium, scandium and thorium have so far been used.

Another type of lamp employs a relatively high pressure of sodium vapour in an envelope of polycrystalline alumina and has an efficiency greater than 100 lm/W. The spectrum of this high-temperature sodium lamp shows the sodium resonance lines broadened to cover most of the visible region, but in the 589 nm region there is darkness because of strong re-absorption.

The high-pressure discharge in xenon gas is particularly useful because it provides a source with a very close resemblance to daylight in colour rendering properties. The spectrum of xenon consists of very many lines forming what is virtually a continuum at high pressure when line broadening takes place. There is, however, considerable emission in the infrared and ultraviolet regions resulting in a relatively low lamp efficiency of 30 lm/W to 50 lm/W. Compact-source versions of the lamp have found considerable application in film projectors and studio lighting equipment. Long arc types of flood lighting, having lower gas pressures than usual, have been designed with power ratings as high as 65 kW. The last mentioned types may, in principle, be operated directly from a constant voltage supply without the need for a current-limiting device in the circuit, since they have a positive volt–ampere characteristic. The xenon discharge is also the basis of a photographic lamp, the 'flashtube', producing very short duration, high intensity flashes by condenser discharges.

LUMINESCENCE

This term is used to denote the emission of light by conversion of some of the energy absorbed by a material, when the emission is greater than the thermal radiation expected from the same body at the same temperature. This condition normally applies to a restricted band of the spectrum. An alternative term is *fluorescence*, formerly considered to be the *instantaneous* rise or decay of light output in contrast to the visibly slow decay of *phosphorescence* occurring after the excitation process. In general luminescent materials are near room temperature when operating, consequently their visible black body radiation is entirely negligible and their luminance is aptly described as 'cold light'. The following treatment will commence with methods by which the absorbed energy is supplied and continue with a survey of available materials and their applications.

Chemical reactions. Some chemical reactions, mostly slow oxidation of organic substances in living animals, give rise to feeble light emission (fireflies, glowworms, oceanic plankton). Non-biological reactions between chemical substances are known which produce similar effects. The oxidation of phosphorus in air was a very early observation in this field.

Excitation by charged particles. High-energy protons or α particles (charged hydrogen or helium atoms respectively) can be detected in nuclear work by the luminescence they evoke in plastic or crystal scintillators. In luminous paints a luminescent powder is mixed with a radium or mesothorium compound providing α particles by radioactive fission which continues over long periods of time without appreciable decay of output, though the powder may deteriorate under the bombardment. The radioactive strontium 90 decays with the emission of high speed electrons or β rays, and may also be used to make long-lived luminous paint. There are types of radioactive gas, namely tritium (isotopic hydrogen) and krypton 85, which emit β rays and have been used in sealed glass containers with suitable fluorescent screens as long-lived, though feeble, light sources.

Electrons of lower speed are the exciting agent in cathode-ray tubes, used as indicators of all kinds and for television picture reception. In contrast to the radioactive sources, where energy of the particles is extremely high but unalterable and the incident density of radiation is normally very small, cathode-ray sources transfer more useful energy to a luminescent material by far more particles of smaller individual energy, so that from them we may obtain a reasonable light yield with less deterioration of the luminescent material under bombardment. Though the cathode-ray tube is primarily an indicating device, its use as a light source has been seriously considered.

Some semi-conductors have the property of emitting light when recombination of charge carriers (electrons and holes) occurs at a *p-n* junction. Gallium arsenide and similar materials have been excited in this way by direct currents, showing high efficiency of light production. At present the constructions are very small and expensive, and no general use in lighting appears to be in sight. The phenomenon has long been known to occur in silicon carbide, though at very low efficiency.

Excitation by electric field. Electroluminescence is a form of light production developed since 1950 to useful levels for indicators and signs, though scarcely to levels for general lighting. The luminescent material is used in a thin layer between plane electrodes, one being transparent to allow the light to emerge. In this device, similar to a capacitor, the special phosphors appear to be capable of locally enhancing the alternating field applied to them. The increased field strength can then excite electrons in the phosphor crystal to levels of energy from which they can make transitions with light emission. The mechanics of light emission does not differ at all from that following excitation of a phosphor by ultraviolet; only the way of producing the free electrons is different. Efficiency is in the region of 5 lm/W to 10 lm/W.

There is no reason why a direct rather than an alternating voltage could not be used for producing electroluminescence, except that the internal charges produced by freed electrons oppose the field and the highly insulating phosphor material becomes polarised. Phosphors of higher conductivity do show some luminescence under d.c. and there is an ill-defined boundary between this intrinsic electroluminescence and the 'carrier injection luminescence' provoked by d.c. in such materials as silicon carbide and gallium arsenide, discussed in the preceding section.

Excitation by electromagnetic radiation. This is by far the most important method of exciting luminescence. Electromagnetic radiation includes radio waves, infrared, visible light, ultraviolet, X rays and γ rays. When absorbed by certain materials (phosphors) a part, but not all of the energy may be re-emitted as visible light, and nearly always the wavelength of this emission is longer than that of the radiation absorbed (Stokes' law). Consequently the most convenient way of exciting phosphors is by the use of the ultraviolet radiation which is produced in gas discharges besides the visible lines of longer wavelength. In special cases it is useful to have infrared or ultraviolet luminescence, but our main concern is with the visible spectrum and with inorganic solids which convert the absorbed radiation into light. Liquids and gases can also be excited to luminescence, but with low efficiency and little utility.

The low-pressure mercury arc in argon is the basis of the fluorescent lamp. This owes its efficiency to the initial conversion of 50% or more of the electrical energy in the discharge to ultraviolet radiation at wavelengths of 253·7 nm and 185 nm. With appropriate phosphors this gives high efficiency of white light production, rising in the past 25 years to about 80 lm/W, a value which cannot be challenged by any source depending on emission from hot solids.

High-pressure arcs in mercury produce other ultraviolet wavelengths near 365 nm, and different types of luminescent material are necessary to take advantage of this emission. Usually they are of red fluorescence to compensate for the lack of red wavelengths in the line spectrum of mercury. Phosphors have also been used with some iodide arcs, which already have more extensive line spectra than mercury alone, in order to use the ultraviolet emission of mercury and other metals in the discharge.

X rays or γ rays from radioactive materials are very short wavelength radiation, and they excite many materials to luminescence. However, their great penetrating power reduces the amount of energy which can be absorbed by a screen of reasonable thickness, so that light outputs are small and useful only for indicating purposes (radiology, testing of materials, nuclear work).

Under very high excitation and precisely controlled optical conditions, some crystalline phosphors having line emissions under normal conditions emit the same wavelengths in very powerful narrow beams of coherent light rather than their usual random, diffuse emission. This is laser action, present applications for which depend on the output power concentration rather than on luminous efficiency. Suitable organic phosphors in solution also show the effect. Gas lasers are low-pressure discharges excited by high frequency electric currents to emit in some of the normal atomic frequencies of the gaseous atoms and again in narrow coherent beams; this type of light emission from gases is not normally considered as fluorescence though this is largely a question of definition.

Materials. Although only solid luminescent materials are of practical value for lighting purposes, there are many interesting cases of luminescence in gases and liquids. Numerous procedures in analytical chemistry use liquids excited by ultraviolet radiation for detection of specific substances and their quantitative determination.

The first solid luminescent materials known were, on account of limited means of experiment, those showing light emission after exposure to natural daylight or sunlight. This afterglow is still known as phosphorescence, and the term *phosphor* was used as long as 300 years ago to denote such materials. It is now used in a general way to denote all solid luminescent materials. When the term was introduced the artificial production of these materials was naturally very primitive and not until suitable ultraviolet sources and methods of experiment were available could any rational advances be made. It was then realised that many natural minerals are fluorescent, and that by synthesis in a purer chemical state, though in the original crystallographic form, they can be made more efficient as phosphors. Later a multitude of phosphors in various crystal forms were synthesised, often having no known mineral counterpart or perhaps only a non-fluorescent one.

High-energy particles and γ rays are often detected by large transparent single crystals of sodium iodide and similar salts. Luminous paints are mostly based on zinc sulphides of hexagonal structure. Cathode-ray tube screens may be made from zinc and zinc cadmium sulphides or from fluorides, silicates, phosphates, borates, tungstates, aluminates and other compounds of the alkaline earth metals (Be, Mg, Ca, Sr, Ba, Zn, Cd.). Following new cheaper methods of separating rare earths, their application in phosphors has greatly developed, in particular for improved red phosphors for colour television viewing tubes. Tubular fluorescent lamps use the same materials as cathode-ray tubes (with the exception of the sulphides) and also some phosphors poorly excited by cathode rays, particularly the so-called halophosphates based on the apatite crystal lattice. The short ultraviolet radiation causing luminescence is not transmitted by glass, consequently the phosphor must be inside the arc tube.

High-pressure mercury lamps were formerly provided with sulphide phosphors which have now been superseded by more robust materials of silicate, germanate or arsenate type. These are excited by ultraviolet of wavelength 365 nm and thus make good the deficiency of red light. Since this wavelength of ultraviolet is transmitted by the quartz arc tube, the phosphor can be placed on the outer bulb in a reasonably cool location.

X rays were originally made visible in diagnostic work by screens of barium platinocyanide, but at present zinc cadmium sulphide screens are widely employed. The photographic action of X rays may be increased by blue-fluorescent calcium tungstate screens in contact with the film. In electroluminescence the zinc sulphides of cubic structure are all-important: their detailed composition differs from that of other sulphide phosphors and they respond less efficiently to ultraviolet or cathode rays.

The conclusion from experience is that each phosphor needs to be adapted in composition or structure to the particular type of excitation in view: few if any phosphors are equally efficient under a number of different types of excitation.

Phosphor preparation. The two main classes of inorganic phosphors in which we are interested are those of sulphide type, and the oxide based phosphors. The former includes selenides, tellurides and mixed crystals of combinations of these very similar components. The sulphides are generally prepared by chemical precipitation methods from solutions. They are best adapted to excitation by cathode rays, long wavelength ultraviolet or electrostatic fields. Phosphors in the second class are nearly all made by heating together solid components in powder mixtures, and they have a crystal lattice or matrix based on tetrahedral groups of oxygen atoms instead of similar arrangements of sulphur atoms in the sulphides. These 'oxygen-dominated' phosphors are useful for cathode-ray excitation but much more so under short wavelength ultraviolet.

The sulphides have to be heated after synthesis to about 800 °C or higher to develop a well-marked crystalline structure in place of the very fine grain of the precipitated sulphide; otherwise no appreciable luminescence occurs. On the other hand, the oxygen-dominated materials are normally exposed during their synthesis to temperatures of the order of 1000 °C, which is sufficient to develop the necessary crystal structure. Again, whereas any wet precipitated phosphors are very close to the composition agreeing with an exact chemical formula, say ZnS, those synthesised dry are usually made to formulations well away from exact chemical equivalence because experience has shown that only in this way can many of them reach their maximum luminescence efficiency. Probably the slow and incomplete reaction between solid powders is one underlying reason for this.

Another chemical feature of the great majority of phosphors is that a small amount of some foreign atom or atoms must be incorporated into the matrix to produce luminescence. In sulphides this activator need be only 1 part in 10,000 of the whole, but its chemical nature has a profound effect on the colour of luminescence. The kind of atomic structures produced by these foreign atoms have been interpreted in many different ways, none of which is universally accepted and none of which is capable of direct experimental proof.

In oxygen-based phosphors the amounts of activator are of a higher order and the one used most is manganese. One of the earliest and best known phosphors in this class is zinc silicate, similar to the mineral willemite, which is still useful as an oscilloscope tube screen material and in certain fluorescent lamps, where its bright green emission colour is an advantage. Pairs of activators are often used in phosphors especially when one is manganese, by virtue of the process called *sensitisation*. A matrix with manganese may be inefficiently excited by short wavelength ultraviolet; the same matrix with another activator, often lead, bismuth or antimony, called the sensitiser, may be efficiently excited but to an unwanted colour of luminescence. With both activators, part of the energy absorbed by the sensitiser is passed on internally to the manganese, which emits its characteristic luminescence in addition to that due to the sensitiser. The best known example is that of halophosphates which are activated by antimony and manganese.

Organic luminescent materials are familiar in 'Dayglo' paints. Some consist of pure organic dyestuffs like rhodamine deposited on synthetic plastics in suitably fine grain size for making a paint. They operate by virtue of the blue and ultraviolet radiation present in natural daylight. Colourless organic dyes with blue fluorescence under ultraviolet are used as 'fluorescent brighteners' in synthetic detergents and white textiles. Their faint violet or blue fluorescence offsets the slightly yellowish fabric colour to produce a 'brighter white'.

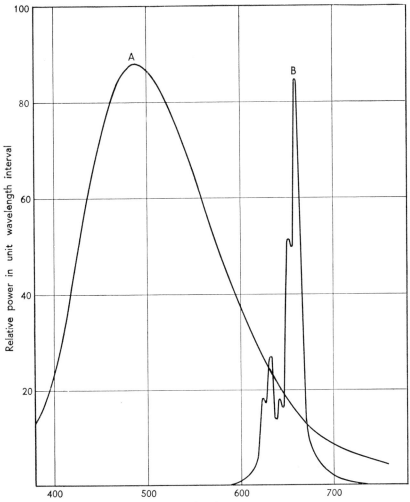

Fig. 4.4 Emission spectra of two phosphors (A, barium titanium phosphate and B, magnesium fluorogermanate)

Emission spectra. Whereas the fluorescence of unrestricted atoms (in gases) consists of sharp lines, the mutual interference which occurs in liquids, and still more in crystalline solids, causes a widening of what are fundamentally lines into bands. Some of these are evidently broadened lines, others are so wide that they cover the whole of the visible spectrum. See Fig. 4.4 in which the two curves are not on the same vertical scale. Almost all these spectra, if measured as energy or power and plotted on a frequency or wave number scale, agree closely with one or more bands in the form of Gaussian error functions. Figs. 4.4 and 4.5 show one such band on wavelength and wave number scales respectively; with the latter the close agreement between a theoretical Gaussian curve and the observed curve is evident.

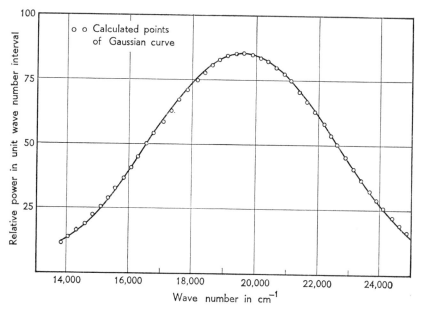

Fig. 4.5   Emission spectrum of a phosphor (barium titanium phosphate)

In the sulphide phosphor series, where the activator may be copper, silver, gold or a halogen, the Gaussian band analysis has allowed several independent bands to be isolated for each material. There are well known mutual relations and regular shifts through the visible spectrum with changes of composition, particularly with the substitution of zinc by cadmium. Fig. 4.6 gives the analysis for a zinc sulphide activated by copper. Less regularity is found in the oxygen-dominated materials, though if sensitisation occurs it is easy to observe the decrease of the sensitiser band and the increase of the manganese band as the relative proportions of the two activators are varied. This often gives a useful range of different colours of emission, especially with the halo-phosphates in which a further range of colour shift is available by changes in the electronegative part of the compound (ratio of fluoride to chloride).

The widest bands arise from those phosphors with no apparent chemical impurity to provide an activator. There are only a few such phosphors, notably the tungstates. The most efficient phosphor in this class appears to be that with least foreign additions. The widest known band is probably that

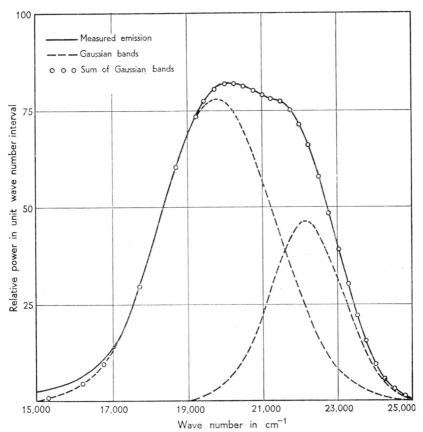

Fig. 4.6 Analysis of phosphor emission curve into Gaussian bands

of barium titanium phosphate, extending from ultraviolet to infrared with a peak in the blue-green as shown in Figs. 4.4, 4.5. Titanium is here not an activator but a major component acting as a modifier of the lattice structure.

Emission bands may appear in the ultraviolet or the infrared regions of the spectrum. Naturally visible emission is most useful and most widely studied. Little use has been found for infrared luminescence, though ultraviolet is valuable for special purposes ('black light' from fluorescent tubes or mercury lamps for display, theatrical effects, and in artificial daylight sources).

Luminous efficiency from phosphors. Apart from its value in providing light in an immense variety of colours, luminescence has another main advantage in the high efficiency at which this light can be obtained from electrical power, by comparison with incandescent sources which necessarily emit over 90% of the power input as invisible infrared. Generally speaking, high efficiencies are not reached with excitation of luminescence by high-energy particles or radiation, or by the low-energy fields of electroluminescence, but are best seen with moderate energy cathode rays, or ultraviolet radiation not far outside the visible region of the spectrum. Carrier injection luminescence in semiconductors is apparently highly efficient, but the optical conditions make it difficult for more than a small portion of the generated light to emerge.

The quantitative relations are best explained in the case of ultraviolet excitation. If a phosphor absorbs a beam of ultraviolet completely, and every quantum gives rise to a light quantum, the quantum efficiency is 1 or 100% and this state is nearly attained in suitable circumstances. Since by Stokes' law (put in modern terms) the absorbed ultraviolet quantum is greater than the emitted visible quantum, some energy is lost as heat and less than 100% reappears as useful light; though the quantum efficiency may be 100%, the energy efficiency must be less and cannot exceed the wavelength ratio. In a fluorescent tube the main exciting agent is ultraviolet of wavelength 253·7 nm. If the emitted light is at twice this wavelength (i.e. in the blue-green) no more than half the energy in the ultraviolet line can be emitted as light. An example is seen in an early application, that of green emitting zinc silicate phosphor on the walls of a neon tube. Even if the quantum efficiency is 100%, the conversion of energy from ultraviolet to visible light cannot be greater than the wavelength ratio, say 73·8 nm to 525 nm, or one-seventh, and the luminous efficiency is therefore low.

Efficiencies of light sources are given in lumens per watt of electrical power applied. The highest possible value is 680 lm/W, in which case the emission would be monochromatic green light of wavelength 555 nm. For a reasonable white, requiring a wide spectral distribution, no more than about 250 lm/W could be obtained. In practice moderate sized incandescent lamps give 12 lm/W and the fluorescent process in a tubular lamp with a near white emission yields up to 80 lm/W. It must be observed that in the latter case the current-limiting control, not required in an incandescent lamp, dissipates appreciable power and lowers the overall efficiency to about 65 lm/W. Nearly all discharge lamp circuits have the same disadvantage. In high-pressure mercury lamps with phosphors for colour correction the fluorescence is a minor adjunct to the discharge instead of being the main light-emitting process as in a fluorescent tube.

The earlier distinction between fluorescence and phosphorescence has given way to a classification of the processes by which light output increases on excitation, or decays after it. If the light-emitting process depends on transitions of electrons within the ions of the activator atoms in the phosphor, without the intervention of free or 'conductivity' electrons, the process of rise and fall of light are exponential and nearly independent of the temperature. If free electrons are involved, the processes resemble chemical reactions of the second order and are greatly accelerated by rise of temperature or by more powerful excitation. To the first class belong most oxygen-dominated lamp and cathode-ray tube phosphors, with decay times varying from less than a millionth of a second to a few hundredths; cerium and manganese are typical activators in these respective speed groups. Sulphides are typical of the second class and their decays may last for hours, or days, especially with copper activator. On the other hand, in zinc sulphide activated by manganese the behaviour is dependent on the manganese rather than on the sulphide. It is quite usual to find several independent decays of different period in the same phosphor. Fast decays are necessary for such purposes as indicators of nuclear particles (scintillators) or for transmission of film by television. In radar displays, some persistence is desirable to allow lengthy inspection of cathode-ray tube traces; and in discharge lamps a longer decay assists the suppression of flicker caused by the pulsed nature of the light output.

Temperature effects in phosphors. The effects of temperature on decay processes, discussed in the preceding paragraph, are accompanied by a more general action on the efficiency of luminescence. For a given excitation most phosphors have a maximum output of light at a particular temperature which is often near room temperature. As the temperature rises the efficiency falls to zero, with the increasing atomic vibrations in the crystal absorbing more and more of the power put in. This temperature quenching varies greatly in detail. Calcium tungstate loses all its luminescence at about 150 °C; whereas certain aluminates activated by chromium are still increasing in brightness up to 500 °C. Temperature resistance is necessary in phosphors used with high-pressure mercury lamps to give extra red emission, since they may be operating in the region of 300 °C. When a phosphorescing material (that is, one with decaying light output after being excited) is suddenly heated a burst of light will occur, followed by a fall to lower brightness. Part of the stored energy, due to be given out as light in normal phosphorescence, is prematurely released by the heating, but the total light output is likely to be less than it would have been if heating had not been applied to accelerate the process. Similar behaviour is observed if infrared radiation is used instead of heating; this often acts as described by *stimulation*; sometimes, however, it may decrease the total amount of phosphorescence by *quenching*. A similar kind of light emission occurs if there is stored energy but no visible phosphorescence, when *thermoluminescence* is produced on heating. Minerals subject to radioactivity in past ages frequently show the effect, and some synthetic phosphors do so after excitation by ultraviolet or ionising radiation.

Luminescence at high temperatures. This section will be concluded by a discussion of the case where the emitting solid is so hot that it is already emitting visible radiation, and it becomes difficult to separate any luminescence which may occur. One example, an obsolete light source, is the 'limelight' produced when a hydrogen or coal gas flame impinges on a block of lime. The white emission corresponds to a higher black body temperature than the real temperature of the lime, but perhaps not that of the flame. Part of the chemical energy released in the combustion is probably transformed into light at the solid surface. Another case is that of the gas mantle, in which a thorium oxide-cerium oxide mixture is held in a coal gas or other flame. There may be selective absorption of some parts of the spectrum and selective emission of others for the spectral distribution is a smooth curve very different from a black body distribution, with a peak near 660 nm. The colour appearance of the light may be described as similar to that of a tungsten filament lamp but more greenish. The efficiency calculated for the thermal energy of combustion under suitable experimental conditions reaches only 5 lm/W, therefore this light source has no future except in regions where gaseous or liquid fuels are more accessible than electricity, and here it is well established. Other oxides have been considered as possible selective emitters of visible radiation without the large infrared component from black bodies. Even with electrical heating of such oxides it is unlikely that light could be generated much more efficiently than by tungsten filaments and certainly not as efficiently as by gas discharges and luminescence.

Saturation in phosphors. Saturation implies a light output falling short of proportionality to the amount of excitation and it depends on rates of excitation and decay. It is evident only in cathode-ray tubes where an exceedingly concentrated stream of energy is applied to each spot of the screen (though for an extremely brief time). The effect is made visible if a mixture of phosphors of different colours and composition is used on a television screen, say a sulphide mixed with a silicate; the more rapid saturation of the former will cause a colour difference between shadows and highlights. When a phosphor has two emission bands they will usually saturate at different levels, while with a phosphor having one emission band only, saturation appears as a lowering of contrast in the picture.

Lumen maintenance with phosphors. This section is included because of its great importance in practical devices for producing light with luminescence, particularly the tubular fluorescent lamp. Although the power dissipated at a point in the phosphor layer is less than on a television screen by a factor of 10,000 or more, exposure goes on for thousands of hours in an atmosphere which is not inert chemically. The gradual loss of brightness which occurs in the lamp is an appreciable drawback. Methods of phosphor manufacture leading to more complete chemical combination, and methods of lamp manufacture leading to tubes less contaminated by traces of air, water and other foreign materials, have greatly improved the position, though the chemical and physical reactions responsible for phosphor deterioration are not yet fully under control or even understood. Reactions or physical absorption of the mercury on the surface layer of the phosphor grains is believed to play a large part, and different compositions of glass are also significant, because of the migration of sodium from the glass into the phosphor. Improvements in lamp performance can fairly be said to have resulted from empirical changes rather than planning based on a known mechanism of deterioration. There is still plenty of scope for research to improve the performance of these valuable materials, especially for lamps with power loadings above the normal ratings, when phosphor deterioration is accelerated.

CHAPTER 5

Colour Measurement

Colour measurement. In Chapter 4 the production of light is discussed in terms of power distribution in the visible spectrum. The colour appearance of a light source depends on this distribution, and so does the colour appearance of objects illuminated by the source. Since the eye appears to have a very limited number of different colour receptors, some lights having different spectral distributions look much the same and yet give noticeably different renderings of coloured objects. These facts are important in lighting, and to deal with them it is necessary to have a system of colour measurement.

The most widely used method of measuring colour is that laid down by the C.I.E. (Commission Internationale de l'Éclairage) in 1931. It ignores the varied responses of the eye caused by adaptation and assumes a standardised average observer. The method depends on the propositions (1) that most eyes have nearly the same colour responses; (2) that any colour of light can be exactly imitated (or 'matched') by a combination of not more than three pure spectral wavelengths of light, though not always the same three wavelengths; and (3) that if lights of two different colours are each matched in this way their sum will be matched by the sum of the two separate matching combinations, regardless of the spectral composition of the light. From the amounts so mixed the colour, or more precisely the hue, of the light can be identified by a point on a plane triangular diagram. The geometrical derivation, which will not be described here, is such that on the resulting colour chart, points representing new hues formed by mixtures of any two hues A and B lie on the straight line joining the points representing A and B, and the position of the new lines can be determined from the amounts of A and B on a simple centre of gravity principle.

In Fig. 5.1 the method of mixing three primaries is shown graphically, with different sets of primaries at the corners of the triangles. These primaries can be three real light sources, for example, a blue fluorescent tube A, a yellow sodium lamp B and an incandescent lamp with a red glass filter C; or they can be three spectrum wavelengths, DEF. The spectral composition of the primaries is unimportant, but the location of their hues is important. As shown in Fig. 5.1 the areas covered by the triangles ABC and DEF include only part of all the possible real hues, which are those contained within the locus of the spectrum hues PQR and the chord PR where purples are located. The C.I.E. system uses a triangle outside ABC or PQR, with imaginary primaries X, Y and Z, related mathematically to real ones. In the resulting chart only a fraction of the triangle is occupied by real hues, but conversely none of these are outside the triangle XYZ.

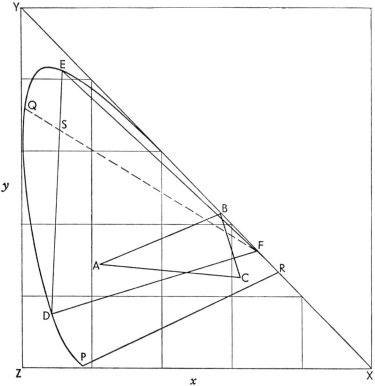

Fig. 5.1   C.I.E. chromaticity chart illustrating different sets of primaries

Hues are expressed in numbers by three co-ordinates whose sum is made equal to unity, hence only two need be written down, usually x and y, which form a chromaticity specification (Fig. 5.2). Very roughly x, which is the fractional amount of the X primary, is associated with redness, y with greenness and z with blueness. For all real colours x, y and z are always positive, and this is one main advantage of the mathematical fictions X, Y and Z. For example, the blue–green spectrum hue Q in Fig. 5.1 cannot be matched by any combination of positive amounts of D, E and F; but the hue S can be matched by certain amounts of D and E, or by other amounts of Q and F. Therefore, a combination of D and E matches another combination of Q and F, hence algebraically Q is matched by certain amounts of D and E *minus* another amount of F. This formulation of real colour in terms of negative amounts of other real colours is evidently unsatisfactory. On the other hand, Q can be specified as a mixture of positive amounts of X, Y and Z.

X, Y, Z and x, y, z are related by a set of linear equations to the corresponding quantities for a system based on red, green and blue spectral primaries similar to D, E and F.

The measurement in hue in terms of x, y and z may be performed (1) by visual colorimetry, which is matching the test light by a mixture of three lights of known hue but arbitrary spectral composition; a practical refinement is that more than three lights may be used to make matching easier, but this does not affect the general principle; (2) by colorimetry in which photocells are used to measure several selected parts of the test light isolated by colour filters; or (3) by measurement of the complete spectrum of the light in energy (or power) units. Method (3) is regarded as the fundamental, though not the easiest method to operate. In all three cases, subsequent calculation or prior calibration is necessary, taking into account the colour functions of the eye of the standard observer, given by the C.I.E. in 1931. The chart in Fig. 5.2 shows hue; it also shows saturation, or depth of colour, which is considered to reach a maximum at any pure spectrum hue. It does not show luminance, or (colloquially) brightness level, which requires a third dimension perpendicular to the plane of the XYZ triangle (see also frontispiece).

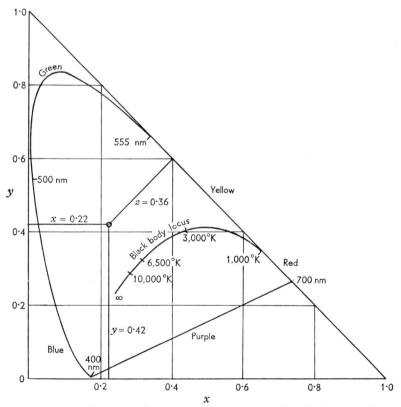

Fig. 5.2   C.I.E. chromaticity chart illustrating specification by co-ordinates

A few wavelengths are marked on the spectrum locus in Fig. 5.2, and some temperatures on the inner curved line which shows the chromaticities of black bodies at different temperatures (cf. Chapter 4).

A major limitation of the 1931 system is that equal spacings at different parts of the chart do not correspond to equal colour differences perceived by

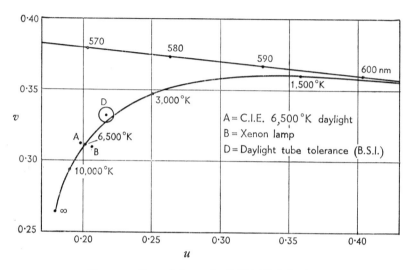

Fig. 5.3   Part of the 1960 C.I.E. U.C.S. chart

the eye. Since practical colour tolerances depend on perceptual differences, many attempts have been made to modify the C.I.E. chart to produce more nearly uniform spacing of hues, but there is no perfect solution. In 1960 the C.I.E. adopted one fairly good system based on work by MacAdam. In this U, V, W replace X, Y, Z with simple transformation equations between the two sets of quantities. For plotting the chromaticity co-ordinates, u and v are calculated from X, Y, Z or from x, y, z. Part of the resulting chart is shown in Fig. 5.3.

The discussion has so far been confined to the mixture of lights. The system is also applicable to measurement of the colours of illuminated objects, i.e. those not self-luminous, but the linear additive relations for lights do not apply to mixtures of surface colours. Yellow and blue lights mixed in suitable proportions give white; yellow and blue pigments do not, because their mixture is 'subtractive', a different process which will not be discussed further except for a brief reference to one important use for surface colours.

Colour atlases.   Though pigments are difficult to reproduce and cover a limited range of lightness and saturation, and though their appearance varies according to the light source, they can provide very useful reference standards of colour. With light sources it is impracticable to supply such standards conveniently or in considerable numbers. Many atlases covering wide ranges of hue and other attributes of colour are available and mostly they attempt equal perceptual spacing of the samples. The best known is the American Munsell system having upwards of 1000 samples of measured spectral reflectance, from which their colour appearance under any given light source can be calculated. They are more commonly used for direct comparison with other objects, preferably under daylight.

Colour appearance of light sources

Incandescent lamps. There is a small range of colour appearance between the low wattage lamp with somewhat yellowish light and the 'whiter' projector or photoflash lamps. Apart from widespread alterations of the colour by shades and reflectors, no attempt is made to control or alter colour of incandescent lights, which is determined by power input, filament design and gas filling if any. To be more precise, the colour is a function of the filament temperature, which determines the spectral distribution of the emission, as discussed in Chapter 4. To that discussion may be added some further details concerning non-black bodies. If we consider a tungsten filament at 2527 °C, its emissivity ϵ is nearly uniform throughout the visible spectrum, but it emits only about 43% as much light at any wavelength as a black body would. If ϵ were exactly constant, the emission curve would be of the same shape as that of the black body at 2527 °C (Fig. 5.4, curve A), but on a smaller vertical scale (curve B). The colour appearance of the real filament (a 'grey body') and the (imaginary) black body would then be the same. The emissivity of the tungsten is, however, about 10% higher at the blue end of the spectrum than at the red. Hence the emission curve is slightly tilted from the 2527 °C black body shape, as in curve C, and in the visible spectrum it agrees fairly closely (in shape, not in level) with that of a black body at 2587 °C (curve D). Consequently, from its colour appearance the tungsten seems to be at 2587 °C which is called its *colour temperature*. In absolute temperatures therefore a real filament temperature of 2800 °K corresponds to a colour temperature of 2860 °K. The relation between these temperatures is not very exactly known, but the general principle is of importance in setting up standard light sources for colorimetry. It is of little practical significance in everyday incandescent lamps, though the efficiency of tungsten as a light emitter is less than half what it would be if filaments were really black bodies. In other words more power could be put into a black filament and emitted without rise of temperature.

The term colour temperature should be applied only to spectral distributions close to the Planckian or black body distributions. In commercial practice this is not the case, and the colour temperatures quoted for light sources, especially fluorescent tubes, are often merely indications of the location of the chromaticity. For example, a Warm White tube said to be at '3000 °K' has a spectral distribution very far from that of a black body at 3000 °K, though its colour appearance may be the same.

A further step in naming colour temperatures of light sources from their chromaticity point is introduced when the point is not on the black body locus. The *correlated colour temperature* is the black body temperature of that

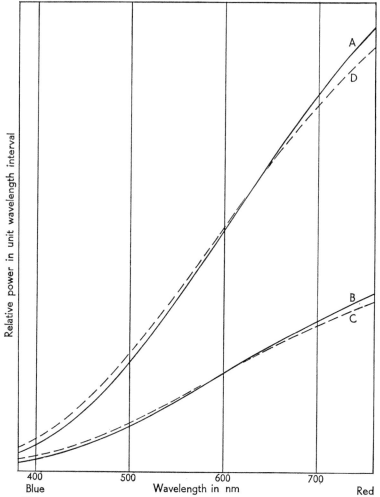

Fig. 5.4 Spectral emission of black bodies and tungsten filament

point on the locus which lies nearest (on a uniform chromaticity chart) to the chromaticity point of the source, for example, 6500 °K for the standard C.I.E. daylight distribution (see Fig. 5.3). The use of correlated colour temperature is perhaps justifiable for daylight distributions, but it has been much abused in the case of non-incandescent sources with chromaticities well away from the black body locus.

Many types of coloured incandescent bulbs are made for decorative purposes, where the colour filter layer may be applied externally or internally. There is little standardisation of these colours. In signal lights the position is much more orderly. Here the filter is normally separate from the incandescent source, and colour limits are well defined (see a later section in this chapter).

Low-pressure gas discharges. With a few exceptions these are used for advertising signs and decorative purposes and the colour is determined by the line spectra of the rare gases in the 'sign tubing'. In the case of mercury the power loading affects the discharge colour as discussed later.

Utility applications include neon tubes for airfield and hazard warning beacons, with their characteristic orange-red colour of light; and most important of all, the sodium lamp used in street lighting. After its initial warming-up period during which the red neon emission is seen, this source emits almost exclusively the sodium lines at 589 nm and 589·6 nm and no colour control or modification is possible.

High-pressure gas discharges. Mercury vapour is the main source to be considered under this heading. As pressure increases (by rise of temperature consequent on increased power input) the sharp line spectrum of the lower pressure tube changes into wider lines and a continuous spectrum appears as well, increasing in amount with the pressure. By far the greatest amount of power is still emitted in the broadened lines, but the colour tends to become slightly whiter.

The recent development of high-pressure arcs containing metal iodides allows an emission spectrum comprising the lines of several metals simultaneously and, according to composition, of very varied colour appearance and colour rendering.

The other well-established high-pressure source is the xenon arc, where a very good white light is produced with extension on both ultraviolet and infrared sides. This emission is claimed to be stable enough for use as a standard light source in colour measurement and matching, but it is difficult to ensure a constant output from high-pressure arcs, whether vapour (mercury) or gas (xenon).

Fluorescence, plus low-pressure arc. 'Sign tubing' mentioned before may be coated with phosphors to give a variety of colours for display. Cold cathodes are used, and tubes of standard lengths are available as alternatives to the usual hot cathode fluorescent tube, but the colours produced are not equivalent, even with the same phosphor, since loading and rare gas pressure are different.

Hot cathode tubular fluorescent tubes exhibit the most highly organised collection of coloured light sources, using the term coloured to include a variety of near white colours. There are two main classes: one consisting of tubes of the highest attainable light efficiency for a 'white' emission and the other ('de luxe') where some efficiency is sacrificed to provide a wider spectrum with better colour rendering.

It is evident that the fluorescent tube maker will be required to exercise greater control over colour than is required for the other light sources mentioned. One perennial difficulty may be emphasised. Fluorescent tubes are made in a variety of loadings (watts per unit of glass wall area) and their operating temperatures therefore differ. This affects the vapour pressure of the mercury and the colour of the light it emits, and to a small extent the efficiency of ultraviolet production. As a result there is a distinct difference in colour appearance, as well as in luminance, between say 5 ft 80 W and 4 ft 40 W tubes coated with the same phosphor. In installations with mixed tube sizes this is noticeable, especially for warmer colours, but the method of mass production of tubes makes it impracticable to use slightly different phosphor coatings to remove this colour difference.

The 'whites' so far discussed lie near the black body locus between 7000 °K and 2500 °K with some appreciably below the locus and therefore of slightly purplish colour. The greenish colours above the locus are unacceptable for general lighting in most cases, as are low-illumination levels of the colder colours. Small differences between the lamps of the same nominal colour are also objectionable when the conditions are favourable for colour discrimination; for example, in long lines of tubes in factories or offices, or in fittings with two or more unshielded tubes close together. This will be considered again under 'Specifications'.

Fluorescent tubes in the more saturated colours are useful for decorative purposes. The red and gold colours employ internal filter coat layers between glass tube and phosphor; blue, green and pink can be made with existing phosphors. If necessary external plastic sleeves can be added to modify the colour in the direction of greater saturation. A special use for this technique has been found in so-called 'white minus amber' lighting where a combination of tubes with pale blue and deep red emission respectively, each provided with an appropriate external colour filter, combine to give a near white light very deficient in yellow wavelengths. This is used to illuminate rooms where long afterglow yellow radar screens are viewed. Loss of contrast resulting from the ambient lighting can be greatly diminished by this means.

Fluorescence, plus high-pressure arc.   The problem here is to correct the colour rendering of the mercury arc rather than its colour appearance, which on account of the high intensity of the source is not usually inspected critically when in use. The usual method of colour correction is by employing a coating of phosphor material on the inside surface of the outer bulb. Another way to provide better colour appearance and colour rendering is to coat the outer bulb with a transparent purple filter. This, however, causes greater loss of lumen output. These attempts to improve the mercury arc are likely to be superseded by the more versatile and efficient metal iodide arc containing mercury, sodium, thallium, etc.

Control and specification of colour appearance

Incandescent lamps.   Source colour is not of much interest except in special cases like photographic lamps, and in lamps for colorimeter standards where calibration gives the appropriate voltage or current for operating the lamps at a desired colour temperature, say 2854 °K (illuminant A). This is in effect a colour rendering control in both cases mentioned, since colour appearance controls spectral distribution of incandescent sources. For photoflood lamps, the main object is to obtain high output by means of high filament temperature, with acceptance of shorter lamp life. The tungsten-halogen lamps have the same advantages of high filament temperatures without necessarily shortened lives, and the colour temperatures of different types are a matter of interest, if not control.

Light signals. The colour of transport signals, usually operated by incandescent sources (though also by oil lamps) are defined by areas on the C.I.E. chromaticity diagram. The essential requirement is not so much to control colours as to avoid confusion between similar colours. The areas of the diagram will, therefore, vary according to the number of colours in the system; if it includes white and yellow as independent signals, for instance, it will have a smaller area for white than in the case when white need not be distinguished from yellow. There are also grades of red and green of different precision whose use varies with the type of transport concerned. The subject is codified in BS 1376: 1953, where much information on light sources, filters and chromaticity requirements may be found. An international simplification of the scheme has been put forward by the C.I.E. (publication No. 2, W3.3, 1959). This reduces the number of variants, but in general its proposals are similar to those of BS 1376.

This subject is not so simple as might appear at first sight. Difficulties arise in the recognition of signals due to atmospheric absorption, especially by haze or fog, also due to the reduced discrimination of the eye when the retinal image is extremely small. Practical control of signals is also complicated, for chromaticity and filter transmissions must both be maintained within specified limits.

Tubular fluorescent lamps. In BS 1853: 1960 the nominal chromaticities are specified for five of the most widely used 'white lamps'. In principle, a factory production could be kept on the correct colour objective by colorimetry of sample lamps. This is too lengthy and difficult a control for high-speed production. Instead trial lamps are first made with any new batch of phosphor suspension, and these are compared visually with existing standard lamps known to be of the correct colour. Alterations are made to the suspension until the colour differences are perceptible only to skilled observers, at which point the suspension is released for factory use.

A well-operated production can maintain the colour appearance of a lamp type within quite small tolerances over periods of years including many successive batches of phosphor. This is more difficult if several independent factories are concerned, except in the unusual event of their using common working standards. BS 1853 therefore includes tolerances adequate to cover an appreciable spread between different makers, but the extremes of the tolerance would be unacceptable if found in a single batch of lamps, or between successive batches from one maker. Lamps have been circulated internationally for tests on the reproducibility of colour measurement with surprising variations between the results obtained in different commercial laboratories, as well as in national standardising laboratories. This is an unsatisfactory situation, but it seems inevitable unless those concerned with colour measurement have equipment of much higher quality (and cost) than is generally used at present.

The tolerances in BS 1853: 1960 (amended 1962) are expressed as 5 minimum perceptible colour differences (m.p.c.d.) in any direction from the nominal chromaticity point (see Fig. 5.5). MacAdam 1942 data on the

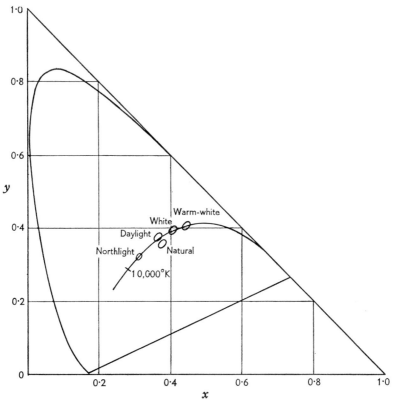

Fig. 5.5   C.I.E. chromaticity chart showing tolerance limits for
fluorescent tube colours

standard deviation of colour matching are used to determine the size and shape of the tolerance areas, which are nominally ellipses, with their major axes roughly parallel to the black body locus. For practical convenience the equivalent 12-sided figures are used. MacAdam's value of the standard deviation is taken as equal to the m.p.c.d. though this is perhaps theoretically unjustifiable. The tolerances have nevertheless proved to be of some practical value in revealing the difficulties of achieving greater general uniformity in lamp colours. Though appearing very small in Fig. 5.5 each ellipse includes large differences of colour appearance. Four are centred approximately on the chromaticity of the black bodies at 6500 °K, 4300 °K, 3500 °K and 3000 °K while the fifth (Natural) is an example of a 'de-luxe' colour not on the locus. Compare Fig. 5.3 in which the Daylight tolerance area becomes nearly circular as would be expected on a uniform scale of colour differences.

International agreements exist on similar lines but of limited scope. With the greater emphasis on colour rendering, the 'de-luxe' types of lamp with better colour rendering are likely to increase in number, and their colours have shown a tendency to move into hitherto unused areas of the chromaticity chart. Perhaps the inherent versatility of the fluorescent lamp is now being restricted by production problems which result from a multiplicity of different lamp colours.

High-pressure mercury lamps. No colour control is used on lamps with plain glass outer bulbs. When phosphor-coatings are added to increase red emission, the control is on the percentage of red emission, measured through a standard filter.

Measurement of colour appearance and colour rendering of iodide arcs offers considerable difficulties because of the complexity of the emission spectrum, also because the source is rather unstable for the purpose of precision measurement. Some kind of standardisation will be needed because of the immense variety possible in this type of light source.

Colour rendering. The colour appearance or chromaticity of light emitted by a source is not directly related to its colour rendering properties, which depend primarily on the details of the spectrum emitted. Colour rendering may be defined as the effect on the appearance of objects which is produced by a given illuminant, in comparison with the appearance under a standard source. The standard may be a real source or a theoretical spectral distribution; or the mental image of the 'correct' appearance of objects may be sufficient.

Surface colours. The principle which determines colour rendering effects is that the amount of light, of any given wavelength, received by the eye from a surface is proportional to the product of (1) the amount of light at that wavelength emitted by the source, and (2) the reflection factor of the surface at the same wavelength. A dark-blue cloth for example, will have a smooth spectral reflection curve rising to a peak in the blue and falling to zero in the yellow and red. Under a sodium lamp which emits two very close wavelengths in the yellow, the yellow light received by the eye is almost nil because the reflection factor of the cloth is near zero; in the blue region the reflection factor is not zero, but the emission of the lamp is. So once more no light reaches the eye, and the cloth appears black. In most cases the normal smooth reflection curves of coloured objects overlap the emission curves of the source, and their product, wavelength by wavelength, gives the spectrum entering the eye, where it is integrated to a colour sensation without conscious perception of the spectral distribution. The eye is not an invariable receptor like a perfect physical instrument for its responses depend on its recent exposure to light, the conditions of viewing, and other disturbing factors. At present it is too difficult to make satisfactory allowances for this adaptation of the eye in estimates of colour rendering, whether qualitative or quantitative.

Owing to the eye's insensitivity to spectral distribution as such, two sources may look exactly alike but have very different spectral emission curves, e.g. a sodium lamp, and an incandescent with a yellow glass or plastic filter. In the latter case the emission will rise steeply from zero in the green to a level value perhaps near 90% in the yellow, orange and red. A coloured surface will nearly always look different under such a pair of lamps and the same may happen with apparently similar sources of white or any coloured light.

There is another effect not generally appreciated. Consider a piece of white paper on the floor of a room with pink walls and ceiling and a near white lamp. The paper is directly illuminated by the lamp, but in part by light reflected once from the walls which, being pink, have absorbed some of the green wavelengths of light falling on them from the source. The paper therefore, appears more pink than if the walls were black (neglecting eye adaptation). However, some light is also reflected repeatedly from wall to wall before reaching the paper, and at each reflection a little more green light is absorbed. This increases the pinkness of the ambient light in the room, and the walls themselves appear more strongly coloured than if the light source illuminated merely a small sample of wall in an otherwise uncoloured room (white or black). These considerations are important in decorating interiors.

Standard sources. Colour rendering is largely a subjective matter to which it is difficult to attach numerical measurements. The idea of comparison with some acceptable appearance of the objects considered is, however, fundamental. The best known and most widely used light source is natural daylight, and variable though this is in intensity and spectral composition, it is a readily accepted standard for showing how objects 'ought' to look. A refinement in some industries is to use north daylight, which is erroneously assumed to be more constant, especially for the task of matching one coloured sample with another. Constant and reproducible sources including tungsten and/or fluorescent lamps are being used more and more to replace daylight, and in 1965 the C.I.E.* recommended a daylight type of spectral distribution at 6500 °K as a primary standard. This is shown in Fig. 5.6, together with the curve for a fluorescent tube which gives an acceptable imitation of this daylight distribution, and the Planckian black body curve for 6500 °K. The relative heights of these curves are arbitrary.

Incandescent lighting is so familiar that it is accepted as giving reasonable colour rendering, in spite of the large differences between its effects and those of daylight. The spectrum of daylight resembles a black body distribution and it may vary over a wide range of colour temperature, mostly between 5000 °K and 25,000 °K. Incandescent tungsten also conforms closely to the black body distribution (see Fig. 5.4), consequently near-black body spectra have been considered to give ideal colour rendering, and dissatisfaction with fluorescent lighting has been attributed to the spectral distribution of smooth bands combined with powerful narrow lines. It seems more likely

---

* Committee E.1.3.1., Colorimetry; final C.I.E. approval expected in 1966.

that the real reasons for dissatisfaction are the marked deficiency in red wavelengths, or the excess of blue in some types of fluorescent tube.

Fig. 5.3 shows that the standard daylight distribution has a slightly greenish chromaticity compared with the neighbouring black body colours. This makes it desirable to alter the slightly purple colour of the xenon arc (also shown in Fig. 5.3), an otherwise excellent light source for colour

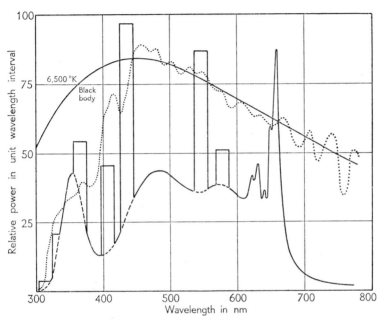

Fig. 5.6   Spectral distribution of daylight (dotted curve) and Artificial Daylight tube

rendering, by addition of green light or filtering with a pale green filter if daylight effects are to be imitated exactly. Such artificial daylight lamps have been made in U.S.A.

If measurements of colour rendering are to be attempted, it is necessary to have a closely defined standard, even if it is an imaginary one. For sources whose chromaticity lies near the black body locus it has been the custom to adopt the black body at the nearest point for comparison. Above 3000 °K the standard cannot be realised, but it is well defined mathematically, and of course its colour appearance can be reproduced by other means such as colour filters with incandescent sources. More recently spectrum distributions of average daylight at various colour temperatures have been introduced to replace the black body distribution over the range covered by daylight (5000 °K upwards).

Fluorescent lamps.   For long the emphasis in this form of lighting was on its efficiency. Tubes mostly emit plenty of blue light in the form of mercury

3+

lines, but little red, and since the eye is photometrically insensitive to both blue and red, there is a loss of lumen output if a red-emitting phosphor replaces part of some other. Thus little effort was formerly made to add to the red emission and the unbalanced colour rendering was accepted almost as an essential feature of fluorescent lighting. The loss of one effective red-contributing phosphor, zinc beryllium silicate, because of its poisonous properties, was a check to progress about 1948, and even now the best phosphors with red emission all have some disadvantage in difficulty of manufacture, or in poisonous character, or in excessive cost. With the reduced efficiency in lumens per watt incurred by providing a wide emission spectrum, fluorescent lighting still remains much more efficient than incandescent. It is now suitable for all kinds of application, the possibilities of good colour rendering having been demonstrated not only in working interiors but also in shops and in the home.

Fluorescent lighting is most criticised with regard to its effects on the appearance of foodstuffs, whether in the shop or the restaurant, and on skin colours. Certainly for the latter and often for the former, a deficiency of red in the light is unsatisfactory, but there are cases where it is desirable to remove part of the normal blue content of fluorescent tubes (for example if the light is of 'warm' appearance). In other circumstances it has been found useful to add an excess of red, for example in the 'De-Luxe Natural' tube which provides a type of distribution acceptable or even preferable in certain situations. It is important to remember that, except in laboratory experiments, there is rarely any opportunity to compare a collection of objects under a given lighting and simultaneously under a standard such as daylight. Memory is almost always invoked, unconsciously, to suggest the 'correct' appearance of objects seen. To provide light of a theoretically perfect spectral distribution for some purpose may be less rewarding than to arrive at the composition of an acceptable light by trial and error. This empirical approach is even more necessary if the disturbing effects of eye adaptation are to be included.

Colour-corrected high-pressure mercury lamps. In general the colour rendering of these lamps is no better than that of White fluorescent tubes unless metal-iodide discharge lamps are considered. Their high bulb temperature makes the selection of adequate red-emitting phosphors difficult since most of them show large falls of efficiency above 300 °C. Others are known with greater temperature resistance, but very long wavelength emission, consequently their contribution in terms of lumens is rather low. For adequate red rendering the emission should be between about 620 nm and 680 nm if undue expenditure of power input is to be avoided.

Photoflash lamps. Colour photography requires a properly balanced spectrum of light to give results which are acceptable even though they are often very far from exact reproductions of the scene photographed. The uncoated bulb emits a continuous spectrum and has a colour appearance similar to the 4000 °K black body. It can be used with colour film intended for incandescent lighting. When film designed for use in natural daylight is exposed with flash illumination the output of the bulbs must be modified to avoid excessive colour distortion in the pictures. A bulb coated with a thin blue lacquer, giving light equivalent to 5500 °K or higher, is required in this case. Electronic flash tubes in which a momentary arc is produced in xenon gas are also suitable for photography on daylight film, though the light is slightly more purple than natural daylight at about 6000 °K (see Fig. 5.3).

Specification of colour rendering. Only for fluorescent tubes has any detailed attempt been made so far to control colour rendering, and this by a rough specification of the spectral power distribution of the light. In BS 1853:

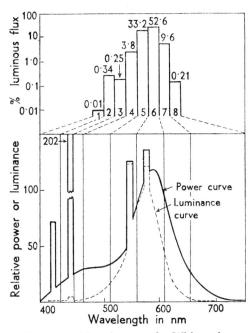

Fig. 5.7 8-band system for White tube

1960 the spectrum is divided into eight bands, with limits at 380, 400, 420, 440, 460, 510, 560, 610, 660 and 760 nm, and by multiplying the spectral emission curve by the visibility curve of the eye, point by point, each band is evaluated in terms of relative luminous flux (or luminance). Fig. 5.7 shows the method. The band divisions were chosen long ago when colour rendering was not so well understood, and these divisions have been found far from satisfactory. The method is now used mainly for control of spectral distribution without any real meaning in terms of colour rendering. The correct numerical values of tolerances on the bands, or their limits in terms of maximum or minimum, still provide an unsolved theoretical problem. The known variations of the product (the lamp) are at present allowed to control the specification, or in other words the nominal lamp itself is the standard of comparison, and not some independent light source or spectral distribution.

A better division into bands, giving less extreme variations of luminance between the centre and end bands, and with a sounder experimental basis, has resulted from work at the N.P.L. from about 1955 onwards. The limits of the bands are at 400, 445, 510, 540, 590, 620 and 760 nm, which have been determined by direct measurements of observer tolerance to changes in the amount of light in each band, with adjustments in the limits until the eye appeared to be equally sensitive to a certain percentage change in each band. A method of assessing quality of colour rendering of a light source is based on these six bands, using for comparison a reference standard, normally a black body of similar colour temperature. Tolerances have been determined statistically from the experimental observations used to establish the band divisions.

Various schemes have been devised for combining arithmetically the values of energy or luminance in bands to arrive at an assessment of colour rendering properties in a single figure. The N.P.L. method does this and also attempts to take account of interactions between bands since, for example, colour rendering is less affected by simultaneous reduction in two bands of complementary colour than by a reduction in only one of them. Interest in these figures of merit is largely at the higher ratings, to distinguish between lamps with good colour rendering. At the lower level there is the sodium lamp with (by measurement) the worst possible colour rendering properties. An uncorrected mercury lamp emits at several wavelengths and therefore allows more object colours to be distinguished than is the case with the nearly monochromatic sodium lamp. It thus gives a more accurate appearance. However, in acceptability many would rate it lower than sodium because of the more unpleasant appearance of complexions. This psychological factor in colour rendering suggests the danger of purely objective ratings.

It is doubtful if band methods will differentiate subtle changes in the spectra of light sources which may have perceptible effects in colour rendering. The more concise the system of rating, the less information it gives, and it seems likely that the lamp designer will always feel a need to examine the full spectrum of a light source, even though a small number of bands may be convenient for rough comparisons, or for quality control of a spectral distribution without regard to its colour rendering properties.

Another colour rendering measurement based on rather different principles and where the whole emission spectrum is used instead of integrated bands, is the Test Colour method recommended by the C.I.E. in 1965. The underlying idea is that the shifts in colour of samples, when their illumination is changed from a standard light source to a source under test, give a measure of the similarity of the sources and hence a measurement of colour rendering is possible. The vector shifts of a selection of coloured Munsell samples are calculated on a uniform chromaticity system (the 1960 C.I.E. U.C.S. chart, Fig. 5.3) and a single colour rendering index derived from the arithmetic mean of the vector lengths. Daylight spectrum distributions are used for the reference standard over part of the range of existing lamp colours, and black body distributions for the warmer colours. The selection of test colour samples is somewhat arbitrary, while the measurements involved are difficult and the computations extensive. Other drawbacks of the method are the fact that no use is made of the vector shift directions, the lack of adequate provision for eye adaptation effects, and the lack of information on suitable tolerances for the index specifications. Some of these limitations also apply, of course, to other types of colour rendering measurements. No doubt further work on the C.I.E. method will solve some of these problems, and the procedure may eventually become standard in lamp testing. This method is fully described in C.I.E. Publication No. 13, E.1.3. 2., 1965.

CHAPTER 6

The Control of Light

Optical design in the present context is the means by which the light distribution from a source is modified to an acceptable approximation to that required. It includes obtaining an acceptable appearance, unlit and lit, and choosing materials and processes which will give consistent results in production at an appropriate cost. The final product should be capable of maintained performance in service or be cheap enough to be thrown away when it has deteriorated.

Methods of light control. Light control is effected by reflection, refraction, diffusion and partial or complete obscuration.

Reflection. Specular reflection at any point on a surface (see Fig. 6.1) follows two laws:

    (1) An incident ray and its reflection lie in the same plane as the normal to the surface at the point considered.
    (2) The angles from the normal to the incident ray and the reflected ray are equal.

Surface characteristics may change somewhat with angle of incidence, spectral distribution or polarisation of light, but such effects are usually negligible and the simplicity of these laws makes it possible to design specular reflectors with a high degree of confidence.

If a surface is fully diffusing its luminance is the same for all directions of view and depends on the product of illumination on the surface and luminance factor, or reflectivity, of the surface. The projected intensity in any direction is that product multiplied by the projected area in that direction.

Practical surfaces are rarely fully diffusing and reflection characteristics change considerably for small changes in surface finish and vary with angle of incidence for the one surface. If an image of the source can be seen in a glossy surface such as vitreous enamel, there is a specular and a diffuse component, the proportions varying with the angle of incidence. If a brighter patch can be seen in the region where a specular image would be expected, there is a strong preferential or spread reflection at angles close to the direction of specular reflection, with rapid decrease as the angle increases. Little confidence can be placed in calculated light distributions from such surfaces until they have been proved in practice.

A wide range of finishes is obtainable in metal from specular, through satin matt to a heavy matt. With anodised aluminium it is not practicable to control characteristics to an intermediate state as small changes in processing result in changes in the final product which cannot be assessed until processing is complete. Super-purity metal is used for highly specular finishes. Control of spreading effects is possible by forming a shallow pattern on a specular surface.

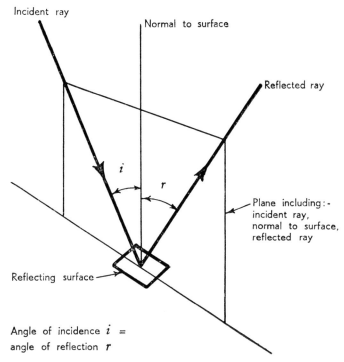

Fig. 6.1 Specular reflection at a surface

Specular and diffuse reflectors are most suitable for deflecting light through a large angle, say through from 45° to 180° from its initial direction. If the angle of deflection is less than 45° an unduly large area of reflector is required to intercept any quantity of light flux.

The characteristics of some reflector surfaces are summarised in Table 6.1.

Refraction. Simple refraction is used for deflecting light through a small angle, efficiently by up to about 30° and less efficiently to about 40°. At each surface between refracting medium and air (see Fig. 6.2) the basic laws are simple:

1. The incident and refracted ray, and the normal to the surface lie in one plane.
2. The angles from the normal to the ray in air and the ray in the medium

TABLE 6.1

Characteristics of Reflector Surfaces

Material	Type	Reflectivity	Notes
Aluminised glass (front surface)	Specular	·90 to ·94	Aluminised plastic also available; may be sealed to rigid surface. Must be protected, as will withstand light cleaning only.
Silvered glass (back surface)	Specular	·80 to ·90	Rigid, but needs careful mounting; can be exposed to weather or moderate heat. Patterned surfaces give spread of light if required.
Super purity aluminium (electro-brightened and anodised)	Specular / Semi-matt	·75 to ·85 / ·72 to ·80	Soft, easily formed but easily distorted. Not suitable for exposure to weather; where high specularity not required commercial purity material holds its shape better. Where reflector surface not worked by spinning, etc., reflector quality finish may be desirable.
Chrome plate	Specular / Satin matt	·62 to ·67 / ·50 to ·56	On nickel-copper base; better weather resistance than anodised aluminium.
Magnesium aluminium alloy	Slightly diffusing	·73 to ·77	Hard, but can be deep drawn and formed.
Stainless steel	Specular but can be semi-matt or matt	·55 to ·65 / ·52 to ·56	Hard and retains shape though difficult to form.
Opal Perspex	White, diffusing with gloss	·17 to ·83	Can be formed under heat; fair degree of weather resistance if cleaned regularly; some grades transmit, hence lower reflectivity value. Diffusion increases with reflectivity. Temperature limited to 70 °C.
Vitreous enamel (porcelain enamel)	Matt white with specular component	·60 to ·80	Good weather resistance unless chipped.
Stove enamel white	White matt with slight gloss	·60 to ·85	Formerly not weather resistant but modern materials and processes much improved.
Rigid PVC	White	·80 to ·85	Temperature limited to 55 °C.
White paint	White with gloss	·75 to ·88	Some modern paints have a high degree of weather resistance.

are related in that their sines are in constant ratio. The ratio of the sine of the angle in air* to that in the medium is the refractive index of the medium.

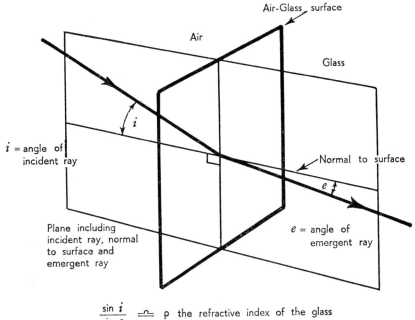

$$\frac{\sin i}{\sin e} = \rho \text{ the refractive index of the glass}$$

Fig. 6.2   Simple refraction at an air–glass surface

This ratio usually varies with the wavelength of the light; although this is a major problem in visual optical systems, it rarely worries the designer of lighting fittings.

The refractive index and other characteristics of some glasses and plastics are given in Table 6.2.

Calculation of a ray path or the inclination of the surfaces of a refracting medium to achieve a given deflection of the light can be quite lengthy. The process is considerably simplified if the normals to both surfaces of the medium are in the same plane as the incident and refracted rays. Then design can be facilitated by a chart similar to that in Fig. 6.3 which shows the relation of the angle of incidence i, the angle of the emergent ray e and the prism angle A. If two of these are known the third can be read off. If the prisms are formed on the side facing the light source, i and e are transposed. Usually light arrives at a point on the refractor over a band of angles. Such a chart enables the designer to concentrate on building up the required light distribution and to appreciate whether the element under consideration will be effective.

The effectiveness of a prism in a given direction is dependent on the

* Strictly in vacuum, but the difference is small.

3*

TABLE 6.2

Characteristics of some Glasses and Plastics

Material	Refractive index for sodium light	Annealing or softening temperature	Thermal expansion coefficient per °C	Notes
Commercial soda-lime glass	1·5 to 1·53	500 °C	9 to 12×10^{-6}	Used for lighting equipment where its temperature would not exceed 450 °C and it is not subject to thermal shock. Most easily worked.
Lead glass	1·639	430 °C	9×10^{-6}	Used for decorative glass rather than lighting fittings.
Borosilicate glass	1·47	730 °C	4×10^{-6}	Most suitable for lantern glassware where temperatures are high or thermal shock due to icy rain may be experienced. More difficult to work, but can be pressed or blown into mould with figuring if required.
Fused silica	1·46	1140 °C	$0·5 \times 10^{-6}$	Too expensive for ordinary lighting fittings.
Alumino-silicate	1·53	750 °C	$4·5 \times 10^{-6}$	High resistance to thermal shock and mechanically strong. Too expensive.
Polymethylmethacrylate (Perspex, Diakon, etc.)	1·49	80 °C	80 to 100×10^{-6}	Perspex can be shaped and machined. Diakon can be moulded or extruded. Should not be subjected to temperatures exceeding 70 °C or excessive concentration of infrared or ultra-violet. Certain organic solvents may attack or cause crazing.

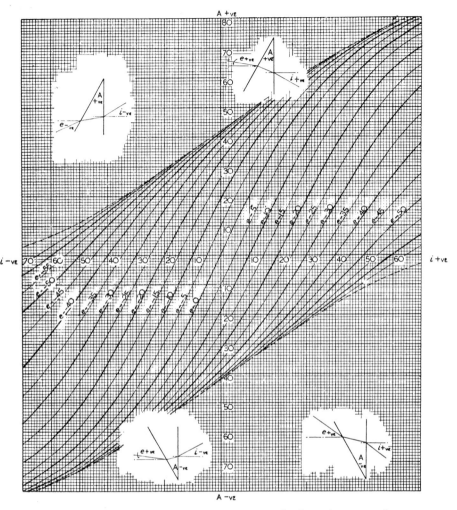

Fig. 6.3   Chart for determining prism angle given the range of
angle of incidence and required angle of emergent light
Refractive index $\mu = 1\cdot490$

fraction of the projected area which is flashed and the brightness at which it is flashed, or $f_1 \times f_2$, where f_1 is the working width of a prism as a fraction of the total width, including return face and radiused edges as indicated in Fig. 6.4(a) and f_2 is the transmitted brightness as a fraction of the incident brightness. Usually the thickness of material and light absorbed are small. The main losses are 4% by reflection at the first surface and a further 4% at the second, provided the light path is nearly normal to the surfaces and these are smooth and clean. Usually the light is more oblique and losses increase slowly to about 20% at 60° and rapidly after 80°.

As the angle of incidence on the second surface increases the proportion of light reflected goes up rapidly and the effectiveness of the prism becomes quite small. When the angle reaches $\operatorname{cosec}^{-1}\mu$ (where μ is the refractive index of the material) all of the light is reflected. Use is made of this in the total internal reflection prism, which can deflect light between 40° and 90° as shown in Fig. 6·4(b). Such prisms are usually much less effective than simple refracting prisms; the surfaces must be clean and smooth and more width is taken up by radiused edges. A retro-reflector, deflecting light by 180° can be made by arranging for total internal reflection at two surfaces (Fig. 6.4(c)); formerly used for glass reflectors, the commonest use today is probably the corner-cube variant for red reflectors on the rear of motor vehicles.

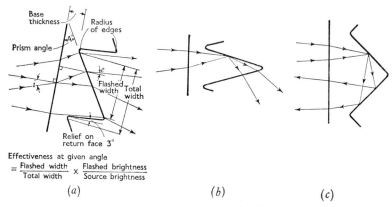

$$\text{Effectiveness at given angle} = \frac{\text{Flashed width}}{\text{Total width}} \times \frac{\text{Flashed brightness}}{\text{Source brightness}}$$

(a)   (b)   (c)

Fig. 6.4   Types of prism (a) Refracting prism indicating effectiveness for one angle of view, (b) Total internal reflection prism, (c) Reflecting prism using total internal reflection at two faces

If the prism angle varies over the depth of the prism, possibly forming a concave (fluted) or convex (reeded) cylindrical surface, the different parts deflect the light rays by different amounts and a spreading of light in one plane results. This can be used, with or without prisms, to reduce the intensity in a given direction or to spread the bright pattern or flashing of a refractor plate or cover glass and hence improve its lit appearance. A wide range of fluted and reeded glasses is available, together with beaded (strong spreading effect) and hammered (slight spreading effect) patterns. Patterns can be designed to give a stronger spreading in one direction than the other, and in a blown or pressed glass bowl varied spreading effects can be produced on different areas as required.

Diffusion. Diffusing media may consist of microscopically small clear spheroidal particles in a clear matrix of a different refractive index. Light intercepted by one of the small spheroids mostly enters and escapes at quite a large angle from its original direction after one or more total internal reflections. Looking at a light source placed behind a thin layer of such material, the source is seen at a brightness reduced by the amount of light so dispersed, and surrounded by a haze the brightness of which depends on the source and the diffuser. The haze is usually somewhat brighter closer to the source. If thicker layers of material are used, a larger proportion of the light is intercepted by the particles; the brightness of the observed source is reduced and the veiling haze increases. Finally the source contrast with the haze becomes so small that it is obscured. With the thin layer a small proportion of the light is heavily diffused and the remainder is virtually unaffected. As the thickness is increased the proportion which is diffused increases and when the source is obscured the emergent light is heavily diffused. In practice such surfaces are likely to be viewed obliquely rather than at right angles; the thickness of material then traversed by the light depends on the cosine of the angle of view and a much thinner layer of material may give adequate diffusion. Materials also vary according to the particle size; as this is increased more light tends to be spread in a forward direction and the fraction reflected back decreases. Data on some plastics diffusers are given in Table 6.3.

TABLE 6.3

Data on some Plastics Diffusers

Perspex ⅛ in. thick	Transmission factor	Reflection factor	Diffusion factor
OPAL 030	·78	·17	·41
OPAL 043	·58	·37	·81
OPAL 040	·55	·41	·87
OPAL 050	·40	·56	·89
OPAL 028	·28	·67	·89
OPAL 038	·80	·83	·89
ISORA (PVC Film) daylight blue	·78	·17	·40

Note: Diffusion Factor is arbitrarily defined as $\left(\dfrac{B_{20°} + B_{70°}}{2B_{5°}}\right)$ where B is the luminance when viewed at the angle indicated from the normal. Light incident on other surface.

Light sources. Optical systems comprise refracting, reflecting, diffusing, clear and obscuring elements, depending on requirements and on the characteristics of the light source. It is useful to project an image of the source in one or more directions to explore its luminance distribution. The patterns of a variety of sources are shown in Fig. 6.5.

General Lighting Service Lamps. If the lamp bulb is clear, the light source is the incandescent filament. As seen in Fig. 6.5(a), this occupies a certain space but does not fill it. As far as coils of the filament are concerned the designer may use an average value of luminance, approximately the total light output divided by a factor equal to 9·25 times the projected area of the filament straightened but not stretched. This may be over 4000 cd/in². The path of the filament in what may be called the source space varies from one lamp to another and changes even when the lamp is replaced in its holder. The size and design of the optical system is determined by the source space size and the average luminance, which is the directional intensity from the source divided by the projected area in that direction. The flashing of a specular reflector will not be uniform but will be an irregular skein of brightness covering, say, 15% of the area in the case of large wattage GLS lamps or 30% in the case of type B2 projector lamps, for which the source may appear as in Fig. 6.5(b). The optical design problem is complicated by the manufacturing tolerances on the position of the centre of the source space relative

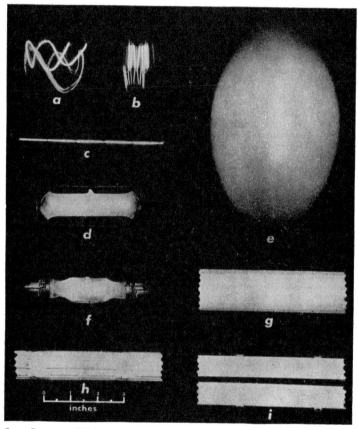

Fig. 6.5   Images of light sources

(a) 1500 W GLS lamp filament
(b) 1500 W type B2 projector lamp filament
(c) Section of 1500 W tubular-quartz tungsten-halogen lamp filament
(d) Arc of 400 W uncorrected mercury vapour lamp
(e) 400 W colour-corrected mercury lamp
(f) Arc of 400 W metal iodide lamp
(g) Section of 80 W tubular fluorescent reflector lamp
(h) Section of 200 W linear sodium lamp
(i) Section of 150 W sodium U-tube

to the lamp cap, and by variations in the way in which the lamp is held by, for instance, a GES lampholder. It may be necessary to provide means of adjusting the position of the source space centre to the optical centre in the case of a narrow beam projector. Some of these lamps can be operated universally, i.e. in any attitude, but better life is obtained when they are in their preferred position.

With a pearl bulb the lamp represents a dual source, i.e. a low-brightness source the size of the bulb with a brighter source superimposed at the filament position.

Line filament lamps (tungsten-halogen). Projectors for photographic transparencies, small cine projectors and car headlamps may use a small precisely located filament in a fused silica bulb including iodine: design is straightforward. For the floodlighting of areas or buildings and lighting in buildings such as churches, the 500/750/1000/1500 W range of line filament lamps may be used. The source is a single coil some $\frac{1}{16}$ in. diameter (as shown in Fig. 6.5(c)) which occupies a position somewhere in a source space of say $\frac{1}{8}$ in. diameter, by between $4\frac{1}{2}$ in. and 10 in. long depending on the wattage. Most of these lamps must be operated within $4°$ of the horizontal, the exceptions being some lamps enclosed in an outer jacket.

With line sources such as these and tubular fluorescent lamps, linear sodium lamps, uncorrected mercury lamps and the new metal iodide discharge lamps, it can be shown that the intensity normal to the long axis of the source is approximately equal to the lumen output divided by a factor of 9.25.

Discharge lamps without colour correction. Most of these are high-pressure arcs some few inches long and about $\frac{1}{4}$ in. diameter (Fig. 6.5(d) and (f)). The source space may be a little greater: in the uncorrected mercury lamp, for instance, the arc axis may vary by $\pm\frac{1}{4}$ in. Metal iodide lamps and high-pressure sodium lamps, although of good colour, come within this category, but are new and developing: up-to-date data should be sought when required for design purposes. Sodium lamps too are passing through a period of rapid development. A section of the arc of a linear sodium lamp is shown in Fig. 6.5(h). With these lamps the intensity may be greater in some directions than others and this may have to be allowed for in design: that much of the light emanates from the sheath of the arc can usually be neglected. In the U-tube type, shown in Fig. 6.5(i), intensity normal to the long axis and source space dimension vary by nearly $2:1$ for different directions of view. This, together with variation in arc tube location, must be taken into account where light distribution is critical.

Colour corrected discharge lamps. These employ a high-pressure mercury arc in an outer bulb coated internally with a fluorescent powder. The powder diffuses much of the light from the arc, depending on the characteristics of the coating; it also fluoresces red and makes up for this deficiency in the light from the mercury arc. Because diffusion of the light from the arc is incomplete, as shown in Fig. 6.5(e), the source may have to be considered as a dual source for design purposes.

Reflector type lamps use specially shaped bulbs and reflecting coatings as well as fluorescent powder; a window is left for light to emerge in the required directions. These lamps do not usually require an external optical system.

Discharge lamps with an integral filament ballast may be treated as dual sources.

Tubular fluorescent lamps. These may be regarded as uniformly bright in all directions when great concentration of light is not required: the source space is the same as the lamp size. As explained in an earlier section, the intensity in a direction normal to the long axis is approximately equal to the lamp light output divided by the factor 9·25. The average luminance is this intensity divided by the projected area, viz. lit length × diameter. Apart from the small increase due to light reflected back on to the source and diffused, no system of reflectors or refractors can increase the effective brightness of such a source which does not transmit its own light; only losses are incurred. The maximum intensity obtainable is that from the lamp direct plus the reflector area multiplied by say 75% of the lamp brightness.

Where a higher intensity is required, reflector or aperture type lamps may be used. In these a reflecting coating reduces the brightness over most of the circumference and enhances that of the gap where it is left off. In optical design such lamps may be dealt with by means of a drawing, say 4 × full size, on which the angles subtended by the brighter and less bright areas of the lamp at a point on a reflector or refractor can be measured. A section of such a lamp is shown in Fig. 6.5(g).

Optical design methods. Optical design can be based on calculation of intensities as the product of brightness and area of 'flash' in a given direction, or by light flux calculation. The former is suitable for the lower brightness, more extensive sources and the latter for compact high-brightness sources. Some filament lamps present a special problem in that both aspects must be considered. Methods can conveniently be discussed by analysing or describing a variety of systems.

Parabolic specular trough reflectors. The considerations are the same for any line source. Control in the plane normal to the long axis would usually be dealt with first; consideration would then be given to the practicability and usefulness of control in planes including the long axis.

The trough may be parabolic in section with the lamp in focus as shown in Fig. 6.6(a). The variables are:

d — the diameter of the source (in.)
f — the focal length of the parabola (in.)
a — the aperture of the reflector (in.)
ρ — specular reflection factor of the reflector material
L — the luminance of the lamp (cd/in^2)

The direct intensity from the lamp $= L.d$ per inch length over angles up to θ_1 from the axis of the paraboloid.

The reflector flanks begin to obscure the lamp and the direct intensity falls off uniformly to $\frac{1}{2}L.d$ at θ_2 and zero at θ_3. The parabola is defined as a curve any point on which is equidistant from a line, the directrix, and a point, the focal point or focus. From an origin midway between the line and the focus the parabola follows an equation $y^2 = 4fx$. Its characteristic is that any ray from the focal point is reflected parallel to the axis. Thus the reflector will be fully flashed when viewed from a distance along the axis of the parabola and intensity in that direction will be:

$$I_{max} = \rho L(a - d) \text{ per unit length of reflector}$$

The term d is omitted if the lamp is transparent to its own radiation; it is often negligible when d is small compared with a.

The reflector will be flashed to an angle θ_4 off axis, depending on the size of the source:

$$\theta_4 = \tan^{-1} d/2S$$

where S is the distance from the focus to the reflector flank.

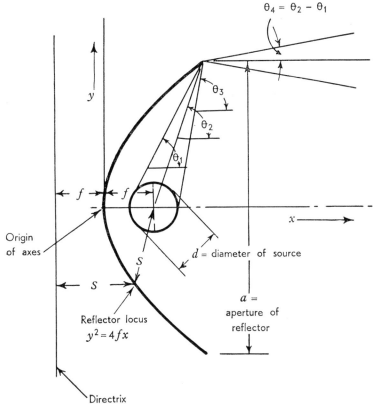

Fig. 6.6 (a)   Specular trough reflectors   Parabolic profile

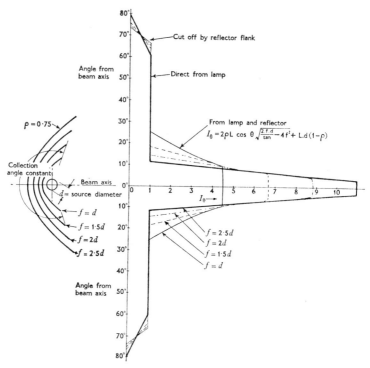

Fig. 6.6 (b) Specular trough reflectors   Polar curves of light distribution for
various apertures and focal lengths, with constant collection angle

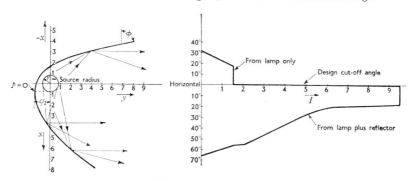

Fig. 6.6 (c) Specular trough reflectors   Profile and polar curve for cut-off at
given angle

From the definition of the parabola S is also the distance from the directrix, i.e.

$$S = x + f$$

and
$$\theta_4 = \tan^{-1}\left(\frac{8fd}{a^2 + 16f^2}\right)$$

For values of θ from o to θ_4 the intensity from the reflector is:

$$I_\theta = I_{max} \cdot \cos \theta$$
$$= \rho L(a) \cos \theta \text{ per unit length}$$

Beyond this the reflector will be flashed only to a width

$$2y = \sqrt{\frac{2fd}{\tan \theta} - 4f^2}$$

At angle θ,

$$\text{Intensity} = I_{max} \cos \theta . 2y$$

$$= 2\rho L \cos \theta \sqrt{\frac{2fd}{\tan \theta} - 4f^2}$$

This falls to zero at

$$\frac{2fd}{\tan \theta} = 4f^2 \quad \text{or} \quad \tan \theta = d/2f$$

The intensities may thus be calculated to give the polar curve. In practice the source space diameter is known, and the focal length and aperture can be varied independently, giving rise to a wide range of distributions. As focal length f is increased with constant collection angle, the aperture a and intensity I_{max} increase but beam angle is reduced, the polar curves varying as shown in Fig. 6.6(b).

Specular trough reflectors of special profile. Where a sharp cut-off is required above or below the beam, the reflector profile is modified so that the upper or lower reflected ray at any position across the reflector emerges at a given angle. Calculation of the profile is preferable to a graphical construction if the source is cylindrical, as cumulative errors may spoil the sharpness of the cut-off. If the source space is irregular the data for the calculation would need to be scaled from a drawing.

The calculation is made as follows. Referring to Fig. 6.6(c), the source is cylindrical of radius r and the cut-off is to be complete at angles above the y axis, which runs horizontally in the figure. The slope of the profile,

$$\phi \text{ (radians from the vertical)} = \tan^{-1} dy/dx$$

and is zero level with the bottom of the source; the distance between the profile at this point and the centre of the lamp, in the y direction, is $c/2$. The co-ordinates of points on the profile are calculated by substituting values for the slope p ($= dy/dx$) in the following equation:

$$x = p(c - 2r\phi) - r$$
$$y = \tfrac{1}{2}[x(p - 1/p) - r(p + 1/p)]$$

If a cut-off is required at an angle other than at the y direction, say α from this direction, it is easier to calculate for a horizontal cut-off and then swing the reflector round, transposing to x' and y' where

$$x' = x \cos \alpha - y \sin \alpha$$
and
$$y' = y \cos \alpha + x \sin \alpha$$

A light distribution may be required such as to give a uniform illumination across an area. This design is considered in detail, as although each designer would have his own variations the basic procedure is typical. Here it is explained once, but in practice the designer is lucky who does not have to start again and again to reach the best reflector contour.

The required light distribution is calculated from the formula $I_\theta = E \cos^3 \theta / H^2$, where I_θ is the intensity at an angle θ to the downward vertical, E the required illumination and H the mounting height. If 1 lm/ft^2 is required, from 60 ft mounting height, the polar curve required is as shown in Fig. 6.7(a). This is plotted in rectangular co-ordinates which are convenient because, with a linear source, areas under the curve are proportional to light flux and it is easier to appreciate what quantities are concerned.

It is assumed that the lamp is horizontal: light flux intercepted by a parallel strip subtending 1° at the lamp axis, i.e. a 1° sector, is equal to $(9{\cdot}25/360) \times I$. Assuming that the beam extends to 60° from the downward vertical, then

$$\text{the beam flux required} = \int_{\theta = 0°}^{\theta = 60°} \frac{9{\cdot}25}{360} \times \frac{E \cos^3 \theta}{H^2} \cdot \mathrm{d}\theta$$

Actually the beam extends beyond 0° and 60° to allow the intensities to 'run back', and the flux would be determined from the polar curve.

A light output of rather more than twice this amount would be required, to allow for losses in collection, reflection and transmission. A 24,000 lm lamp might be chosen, with a distribution of light as superimposed on Fig. 6.7(a). The light may emanate from a source space of 0·2 in. diameter.

The first stage in design might well be to draw up a balance sheet to check that the flux available suffices, as follows:

(1) Proceed in steps along the required polar curve and increase intensities by a factor of 1·1 to allow for losses at the front glass, and plot curve.
(2) Subtract the intensity direct from the lamp to give as remainder that required from the reflector.
(3) Assuming the reflector is of ·75 reflectivity, increase these intensities by a factor of 1·33 to give that needed on to the reflector: make a further allowance if the angle over which the reflector collects light is limited in the plane including the lamp axis.
(4) Sum this to compare with that available for collection from the lamp.

Starting the reflector at (180° + 40°) at a point say 1 in. clear of the outer of the lamp bulb, and considering the element extending to (180° + 38°) the flux intercepted is best reflected to provide the intensity required just above the 40° direction in the beam; building up the beam in this way gives the smallest profile. If the intensity required from the reflector is I_r, and that from the lamp is I_s, this reflector element, with a specular reflectivity of ρ, would provide the necessary flux over a range of θ of $X° = (40 - 38) \times \rho \times I_s/I_r$.

The mean angle of the reflected flux is $(40 + X/2)°$.

The average slope of the reflector element from the vertical is $\frac{1}{2}$(mean angle of direct ray + mean angle of reflected ray).

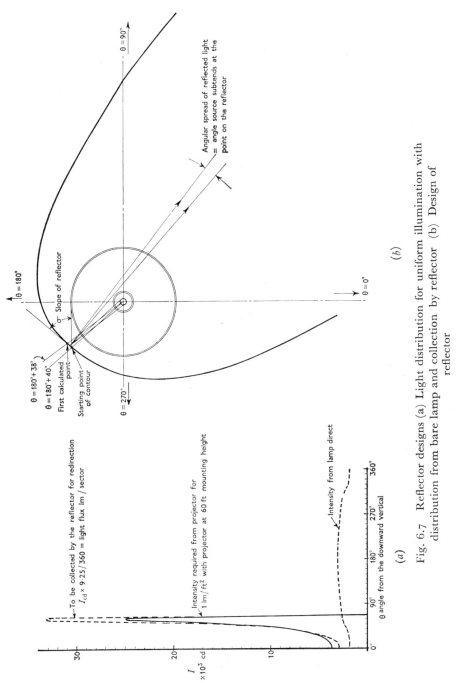

Fig. 6.7 Reflector designs (a) Light distribution for uniform illumination with distribution from bare lamp and collection by reflector (b) Design of reflector

A line from the starting point at this angle intersects the ($180°$ + $38°$) direction to give a point on the reflector contour. Continuing the process gradually builds up the contour. Nowadays precise calculation is practicable and obviates cumulative drafting errors. A calculated profile, following a planned light flux redistribution, is shown in Fig. 6.7(b).

If the distance from reflector to source space is such that the latter subtends an angle equal to or less than $X°$ the design can be proceeded with on this basis. If the angle subtended is greater than $X°$, the reflected flux must be allocated to build up intensity over this greater angle. The intensity produced will be less, pro-rata with the increase in angle, and will need to be built up further by flux from the next zone. Provided this is done methodically it introduces no real difficulty unless the angle is considerably greater. It then becomes necessary to check the design on flashed area because the reflector is too small relative to the source space. It is not possible then to achieve the same control over light distribution. If the peak intensity is important the mouth width or aperture is determined as the flashed width necessary to produce that intensity with the reflector brightness obtainable. This problem arises with fluorescent tubes and possibly colour-corrected mercury lamps where the source space is larger. With these sources a full-size scale drawing can be used to enable the angles of the extreme rays from the source at the reflector element to be measured. Allowance can be made for the extra brightness in the region of the arc in the mercury lamp and of 'window' brightness in the case of the reflector type of fluorescent tube.

Reflector system for cut-off street lighting lantern using sodium lamp. The requirement is specified in BS 1788: 1964, 'Street Lanterns'. Briefly a beam is required up and down the road. The beam is defined as the solid angle including directions at which the intensity is not less than 90% of the peak. This should include the direction at $65°$ to the downward vertical. The peak should be of an intensity between 2 and 4 times the mean lower hemispherical intensity (MHI) and the run-back above the beam should be such that an intensity ratio of 1·2 is reached between $72°$ and $78°$ to the downward vertical, and the intensity ratio at the horizontal should not exceed 0·15. There are further restrictions on downward intensities.

The lamp is arranged transversely across the road. The problem is to design a reflector of the smallest mouth width which will give the required distribution, or better still one which lies midway in the permitted range. The reflectors, as shown in Fig. 6.8, are designed in cross section in a similar way to that discussed in the previous section. First the source space is drawn in; in the case of the 200 W linear sodium lamp it will be circular, of 1 in. diameter.

In designing the reflector it is logical to start from the outer edge. This should obscure the lamp at the horizontal but not in the direction of the beam or some $2°$ above $65°$. This construction initially determines the mouth width, but this may need adjusting later. The reflector zone which can be seen from $67°$ to the downward vertical will be designed to be flashed in this direction and the zones above at gradually lower angles at which the light

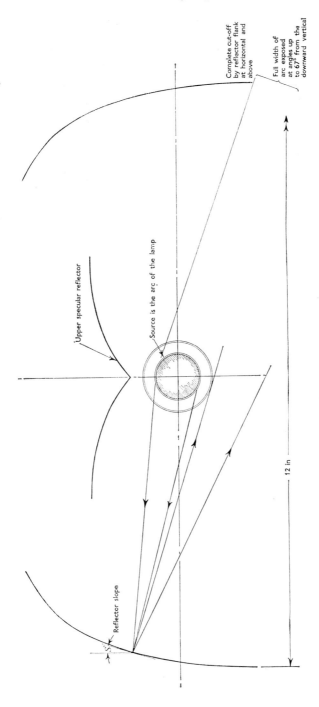

Fig. 6.8 Reflector design for street lantern with cut-off light distribution, using the 200 W linear sodium lamp

can escape without obstruction. There is always a tendency for the available flux to be less than required at angles below the beam but with an excess directly below the lantern. The mouth of the reflector would have to be widened somewhat and the design started again.

Matt trough reflectors. Probably the most reliable and speedy method of design is by making models; for a long lamp it is only necessary to make up a section a few inches long, using a filament lamp in a diffusing cylinder to simulate a fluorescent tube. Alternatively a 2 ft section might be tested using a smaller lamp or a larger lamp with the ends masked. The degree of light concentration with large sources and matt reflectors is small.

Spun reflectors for GLS lamps and other symmetrical sources. Similar considerations apply as for specular trough reflectors, but the calculation is a little more complex because the luminous flux associated with a given intensity varies with the angle to the downward vertical (see Fig. 6.9). A zone factor is

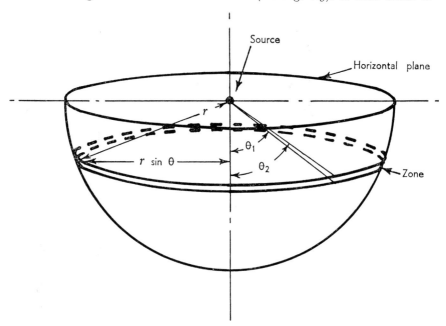

Fig. 6.9   Zone factors used in design of a spun reflector

involved equal to the solid angle of the zone. The whole of the lower hemisphere from the downward vertical to the horizontal is 2π steradians; that from θ_1 to θ_2 is $2\pi(\sin \theta_2 - \sin \theta_1)$.

A balance sheet must again be prepared, with light flux available from the source on one side and that required, stepped up to allow for reflection and transmission losses, on the other. Design starts from the part of the reflector near the axis and, for the smallest reflector, using this part to reflect light near and on the opposite side of the axis. This scheme is suitable for compact high-brightness sources but may need to be changed if the source is large and obstructs the reflected light.

Refractor design for sodium street lantern. Design procedure is the same whether the linear or U-shaped arc tube lamp is used. Both are operated nearly horizontally transverse to the road, the U-lamp with one limb of the arc tube above the other. The polar curve required is specified in BS 1788: 1964, 'Street Lanterns'. As a first step, this is plotted in terms of candle-power together with that of the lamp.

In the case of the linear lamp the intensity in the plane normal to the lamp axis varies in a ratio 4:3. It gives adequate downward intensities and hence it is desirable to reflect the upward flux from the lamp sideways into the beam and at angles just below. A specular V-section upper reflector is used. The U-tube lamp has a sideways intensity about twice that of the downward and upward intensities and empirically it has been found that a flat diffuse upper reflector is best.

The design of the refractor plate is similar in both cases. The prisms are formed to be flashed from a few degrees above the peak and downwards. The refractors start at a point on the direction at 75° to the downward vertical from the centre of the arc, as shown in Fig. 6.10. It will be found that a suitable concentration of light can be obtained if the distance of the refractor from the lamp is such that the arc subtends about 15° at the reflector.

The prisms may be formed on the inside of the bowl or may be formed on a separate plate sealed on to the inside of the bowl. Choosing the latter and assuming the side of the bowl slopes out 15° from the vertical for convenience

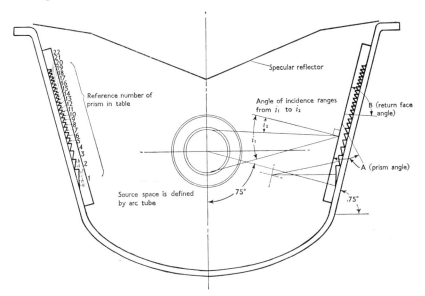

Fig. 6.10   Refractor plate for street lantern of semi-cut-off distribution with 200 W linear sodium lamp

TABLE 6.4

Prism Design Data—Semi-cut-off Sodium Refractor Plate

Prism Reference Fig. 6.10	Range of angle of incidence (degrees)	Prism angle (degrees)	Angles to downward vertical at which prism is flashed	Flashed depth of prisms as viewed at angle to the downward vertical indicated (inches)								
				61°	62·5°	65°	70°	75°	80°	82°	84°	85°
1a	11·2 to −8·4	8·5	82·0 to 62·2	—	·1	·1	·11	·11	·11	·11	—	—
b	13·5 to −6·1	13	82·1 to 62·0	—	·1	·1	·1	·11	·11	·11	—	—
c	15·7 to −3·7	17	82·2 to 62·2	—	·09	·09	·1	·1	·1	·1	—	—
d	17·7 to −1·7	21	82·2 to 61·8	—	·09	·1	·1	·11	·11	·11	—	—
2a	19·5 to −0·1	23·5	82·7 to 61·9	·08	·09	·08	·1	·11	·11	·11	—	—
b	21·8 to 2·6	29·5	81·7 to 60·6	·1	·08	·08	·09	·09	·1	—	—	—
3	24·7 to 5·7	33·5	82·3 to 61·0		·1	·11	·12	·13	·13	·14	—	—
4	27·7 to 9·1	36	83·9 to 63·0			·1	·1	·11	·12	·12	—	—
5	30·3 to 11·9	41·5	83·1 to 61·1		·07	·08	·09	·09	·09	·1	—	—
6	32·4 to 14·4	44·5	83·2 to 61·0	·06	·06	·08	·09	·08	·09	·09	—	—
7	34·3 to 16·5	47·5	83·0 to 60·1	·05	·06	·07	·08	·08	·08	·09	—	—
8	36·3 to 18·5	49	83·9 to 61·1		·05	·06	·06	·07	·08	·08	—	—
9	37·8 to 20·4	51	84·0 to 61·0	·04	·05	·06	·06	·07	·07	·08	·08	—
10	39·1 to 22·1	53	83·7 to 60·3	·04	·05	·05	·06	·06	·07	·07	—	—
11	40·4 to 23·8	54	84·2 to 61·6		·04	·04	·05	·06	·07	·07	·07	—
12	41·6 to 25·4	55·5	84·2 to 61·6	·03	·04	·04	·05	·06	·06	·07	·07	—
13	42·8 to 26·8	57	84·1 to 61·0		·04	·04	·05	·06	·06	·07	·07	—
14	43·9 to 28·1	58	84·3 to 61·3		·03	·04	·04	·05	·06	·06	·07	—
15	44·9 to 29·3	59	84·4 to 61·4		·03	·04	·04	·05	·06	·06	·06	—
16	45·9 to 30·5	60	84·5 to 61·4		·03	·03	·04	·05	·06	·06	·06	—
17	46·8 to 31·6	60·5	85·0 to 62·6			·03	·04	·05	·06	·06	·06	—
18	47·7 to 32·7	61·5	84·9 to 62·2		·03	·03	·04	·05	·05	·06	·06	·06
19	48·5 to 33·7	62	85·2 to 63·2			·03	·04	·05	·05	·06	·06	·06
20	49·4 to 44·8	63	85·1 to 79·8				·04	·04	·05	·06	·06	·06
21	50·2 to 45·8	63·5	85·4 to 80·4							·05	·05	·06
22	50·9 to 46·6	64	85·6 to 80·7							·05	·05	·05
			Total	0·41	1·23	1·46	1·62	1·77	1·95	2·01	·81	·28

in manufacture, the procedure might be to mark off $\frac{1}{4}$ in. steps upwards from point A and measure for each the range of incidence angle. Alternatively lines at 2° intervals may be drawn from the source centre to intersect on the surface of the refractor plate and these points used. The required angle of prism at each point is determined from the chart in Fig. 6.3.

The series of prism angles would be determined and the graph of prism angle against distance along the plate would be drawn and the plate designed on this basis. Possibly a base thickness of $\frac{3}{32}$ in. would be allowed, return face angle of 87° (i.e. a 3° relief) and 0·02 in. radius at the prism edges. Narrow prisms would have flat faces but where the angle is small it may improve control if the prism angle changes progressively across the greater width. Table 6.4 shows the basis of the design of the plate of Fig. 6.10.

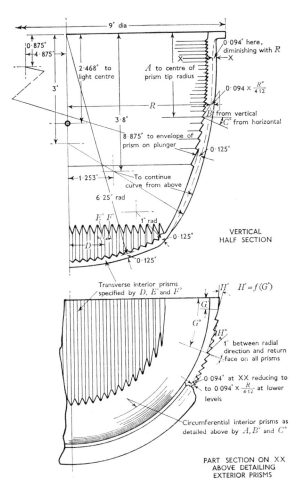

Fig. 6.11   Refractor bowl for Group B street lantern

It will be seen that as the angle of incidence increases and the prisms become steeper, they become less effective. The space they occupy can then be more efficiently flashed by means of a reflector. It is better to make this change rather than attempt to continue the refractor plate using total internal reflection prisms.

This is an extensive source and it is advisable to check the design on the basis of flashed area, as shown in the table. Flashed depth for each of the angles of view indicated is listed in the columns at the right of the table and the totals at the bottom are proportional to the intensity from the refractor plate.

Refractor bowl for side street lantern.   Discharge lamps are used increasingly for side street lighting in place of filament lamps and the design of a bowl of the same size to control the light of the larger source is not easy. The pearl filament lamp may be taken as a 1 in. diameter sphere while the colour-corrected mercury lamp, if the coating is thick, would approximate to 3 in. diameter. Fig. 6.11 shows the horizontal prisms on the inside of a vertical section through the bowl and external vertical prisms on a part horizontal section. Such an arrangement complicates design of the plunger of the mould and is an aspect to be cleared before designing on this basis.

Table 6.5 shows for a few prisms the angles chosen and the angles at which they are flashed, for both sources.

TABLE 6.5

Prism Design Data for Group B Street Lantern

(a) *Inner Circumferential Prisms*

These give control in the vertical plane.

With the pearl filament lamp the source space subtends $\pm 7°$ at the prismatic surface while with the colour-corrected mercury lamp this angle is $\pm 21°$.

Angle to light centre from horizontal (degrees)	Slope of bowl from vertical (degrees)	Chosen prism angle (degrees)	Angle to downward vertical over which prism appears flashed (degrees)	
			Pearl lamp	Colour-corrected mercury lamp
-20	19	4	74 to 61	89 to 46
-18	$18\frac{1}{2}$	6	$74\frac{1}{2}$ to $62\frac{1}{2}$	$89\frac{1}{2}$ to $47\frac{1}{2}$
-16	18	10	75 to 62	90 to 48
-14	17	12	76 to 63	89 to 49
etc.	etc.	etc.	etc.	etc.

(*Table* 6.5 *cont.*)

(b) *Vertical Exterior Prisms*

Angle from beam centre in azimuth (degrees)	Prism angle (degrees)	Flashing in azimuth (degrees)	
		Pearl lamp	Colour-corrected mercury lamp
0	0	−7 to +7	−21 to +21
5	10	−7 to +7	−22 to +21
10	19	−8 to +8	−25 to +21
15	26	−7 to +8	−29 to +23
20	30	−8 to +10	−40 to +26
etc.	etc.	etc.	etc.
etc.	etc.	etc.	etc.
90	30	+62 to +80	+30 to +96

Narrow beam floodlight. The basis of design is the same whether the GLS lamp or type B2 projector lamp is used. A higher intensity narrower beam results from the closer bunched filament of the projector lamp. In both cases means of focusing is desirable. Two schemes are used, as shown in Fig. 6.12; they give surprisingly similar results.

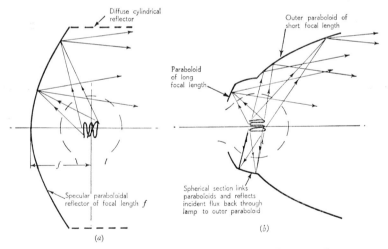

Fig. 6.12   Reflector systems for a symmetrical narrow beam

1. A relatively long focal length paraboloid provides the beam and a spreading cylindrical section screens sideways light. The lamp can conveniently be operated in a near upright position.

2. The reflector may consist of two parabolic sections joined by a spherical section. The lamp may again be near vertical but this means cutting into the reflector and often axial mounting is preferred.

Considering the second reflector in more detail, the parabolic section near the axis is made of longer focal length to clear the lamp envelope and the outer section of shorter focal length to get the maximum collection angle for a given diameter. Because the distance from source centre to reflector surface does not vary so much, the beam spread remains fairly constant for the different regions. The spherical section joins the two parabolic zones and if properly contrived reflects the light collected back through the lamp bulb on to the outer paraboloid.

The flux collected by each of these sections can be estimated from the polar curve of the lamp; for a 1 kW lamp the distribution might be:

(a)	Direct light into the beam	492 lm
(b)	Stray light	3398 lm
(c)	Direct to parabolic reflector	8060 lm
(d)	To parabolic reflector via spherical reflector	3440 lm
(e)	Stray via spherical reflector	—
(f)	Direct on to housing and diffusely reflected	2810 lm
(g)	Direct on to rear reflector	700 lm
	Total	18,900 lm

Assuming 92% transmission by front glass and 75% reflectivity,

$$\text{Estimated beam flux} = \cdot 92 \,[(a) + \cdot 75 \,(c) + \cdot 75^2 \,(d) + \cdot 75 \,(g)]$$
$$= 453 + 5561 + 1780 + 483$$
$$= 8277$$

or about 44% in a $\pm 20°$ beam

A third possibility is more often used for studio lighting. This consists of a spherical reflector behind the source reflecting the light it collects back near to the source and on to a front lens which focuses it. A large lens of requisite focal length would be too thick and a stepped or Fresnel lens is used.

Shaped spotlight. A beam tailored to the area to be lit may be required for stage lighting and for purposes such as dramatically lighting a picture. This may be obtained by projecting the image of a flashed condenser or field lens by a projection or objective lens as shown in Fig. 6.13.

A diaphragm in front of the field lens controls the shape of the beam. If the area to be lit to E lm/ft^2 is a square of side W_1 and is distance l_1 from the projector, then the diaphragm at the field lens needs to have dimension $W_2 = (W_1/l_1) \times$ distance from the projection lens (l_2). The focal length f_p, of the projection lens is given by

$$\frac{1}{l_1} + \frac{1}{l_2} = \frac{1}{f_p}$$

where l_1 and l_2 are of opposite sign.

The field lens diameter needs to be a little longer than $1.5 \times W_2$. Suppose 10% of the illumination is lost at each lens, the illumination required on the field lens is

$$\frac{E \times (W_1)^2}{(W_2)^2} \times \left(\frac{1}{0.9}\right)^2$$

The size W_2 depends on what source and reflector are available to produce this light flux density; if the density is high, a high-brightness source is needed. If a spot of the required illumination density can be produced over a specific area this determines W_2 and hence l_2 and f_p. The uniformity of the spot at the field lens diaphragm determines the uniformity in the area to be lit.

The focal length of the field lens depends on l_2 and its distance (l_3) from the reflector edge, i.e. $1/l_2 + 1/l_3 = 1/f_f$. The only advantage of such a lens is that it reduces the necessary size of the projection lens.

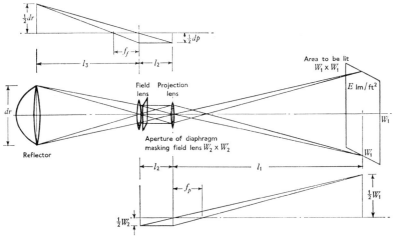

Fig. 6.13   Optical system for a beam covering a defined area

The latter needs to be of diameter $d_p \geq (l_2/l_3) \times$ diameter of the reflector d_r. Without a field lens it may need to be of greater diameter by $2 \times \sqrt{2} \times W_2 (l_2 + l_3)/l_3$.

This application is one of the few where colour fringing may be objectionable. It may be necessary to use a chromatically corrected projection lens.

CHAPTER 7

Lamp Measurements

Introduction. A wide variety of techniques are involved in the measurements associated with the development, production and use of lamps. Details of many of these measurements are incorporated in the numerous national and international specifications concerned with the quality and performance of lamps. Whilst such specifications cover the general requirements, there are some applications where environment necessitates special types of tests being employed before the suitability of a particular design of lamp can be verified.

Light-output characteristics

Standards. All light quantities are related to the primary standard of light, and in order to obtain accurate and repeatable measurements National and International Authorities will provide lamps calibrated to a high degree of accuracy for use as sub-standards by photometric laboratories. The responsible authority in Britain is the National Physical Laboratory, whose Light Division provide appropriate lamps measured to a stated degree of accuracy. The degree of accuracy of measurement is governed by the type of lamp and the calibration is strictly correct only at the time of measurement. Such sub-standard lamps are used to calibrate a number of working standards, which are subject to periodic checks. In this way the sub-standards are used infrequently, and will hold their calibration for a considerable time.

A photometric laboratory should have a range of lamps calibrated for luminous flux, covering the range over which it is desired to measure, and of the different types, i.e. tungsten filament, fluorescent tube, sodium discharge, etc. For measurements of luminous intensity it is usually sufficient to have calibrated a range of plane filament tungsten lamps of known colour temperatures in the range 2600 °K to 2854 °K. Such lamps should be selected for stability, and in the case of tungsten filament types, the filaments should be mounted rigidly and be in large bulbs to militate against the effects of blackening by tungsten deposition on the surface.

Radiation Detectors. Two types of cell are in general use for the measurement of light, the *photoemissive* type and the *photovoltaic* type. In the former electrons are emitted from a metallic surface by the action of radiation, and are transferred to an anode which is maintained at a positive potential by an external voltage. Thus a current dependent on the radiation will flow and produce a voltage drop across a resistor placed in series with the cell. In the latter type, radiation causes a transfer of electrons across a rectifying boundary, usually of selenium and iron or aluminium, and this current can be measured by a suitable meter. Unlike the photoemissive cell, no external voltage is required.

There are three main types of photoemissive cell—vacuum, gasfilled and photomultiplier. Of these only the first and last are used for measurement, since despite the increased current obtained from gas filled cells the performance is greatly affected by small changes in pressure and applied voltage.

Vacuum types have many advantages since they are stable over a long period and the current for a given quantity of radiation is practically independent of the applied voltage. A well made cell can have a high degree of linearity of response over a very wide range in the order of 50,000 to 1, with an accuracy of 0·1%, and is little affected by ambient temperature changes. Such types require an amplifier, and there are many circuits suitable. The spectral response is dependent on the materials used for the surface, and the cell should be selected with the most suitable response for the type of measurement required. The measurement of spectral power requires a response covering the region of the spectrum to be investigated, and cells are available which are sensitive to the ultraviolet and infrared regions as well as the visible part of the spectrum. The basic requirement is that there shall be adequate response in the bandwidth required.

For photometric purposes there is a different need; that the spectral response shall approximate closely to the Visibility Function of the Standard Observer for Photopic Vision—the $V\lambda$ function. This function was adopted by the C.I.P.M. in 1933, from data proposed by the C.I.E. No existing surface meets this requirement so it is necessary to correct as closely as possible by means of filters. A suitable surface is the Bi–O–Ag–Cs type, and a high degree of correction is possible by means of liquid filters.

The photomultiplier cell uses intermediate electrodes, dynodes, each at a fixed potential above the other and gives a high degree of amplification which is usually sufficient to dispense with the need for an amplifier and allow the use of a galvanometer only. A wide variety of such cells are available, some of which are particularly suitable for the measurement of light and radiation having wide spectral bandwidths, very high sensitivities and low noise.

Where the highest degree of accuracy is not required, as in routine measurements, photovoltaic cells are convenient to use, requiring only the connection of a micro-ammeter, or galvanometer. The spectral response of selenium departs from that of the Standard Observer, having a higher response in the blue and red regions of the spectrum, and some response in the ultraviolet region. Suitable correction filters can be obtained, and certain

4+

cells are supplied already corrected. These cells have a linear relationship between illumination and current over a restricted range, and this is dependent primarily on the value of the load resistance. It is therefore recommended that before a cell is used, this relationship should be determined for the loading of the meter with which it is to be used. This can conveniently be done on a photometric bench and the technique is described in a later section. The Campbell–Freeth circuit can be used where a high degree of sensitivity is required, with the further advantage of operating the cell as though it were connected to a circuit of zero resistance.

The advent of digital instruments of high orders of accuracy and convenience of use offers advantages in replacing delicate analogue instruments. In general the output of a cell is too low to give a reading of sufficient accuracy and some form of amplification is necessary. A stable transistorised-circuit having a gain of 30 has been developed and it would seem that future developments will be along these lines.

Photoconductive cells are of particular use for the detection of infrared radiation since their response is mainly in this part of the spectrum. Perhaps those most useful for this purpose are the lead sulphide, lead telluride and indium antimonide types, although many other materials are known with similar properties. There is, however, one cell which has a response in the visible region and this is the cadmium sulphide type which is used in some designs of photographic light meter.

Silicon and germanium semi-conductor photocells have maximum response in the infrared region, but are also sensitive to visible radiation and they can give some 10 to 20 times greater current for a given illumination than a vacuum photoemissive cell. They are similar in design and construction to other semi-conductor devices, i.e. transistors, and have similar temperature characteristics.

A *thermopile* is essentially a device for converting radiation into heat and using this heat to produce an electric current by means of thermocouples. A blackened surface is used giving a close approximation to a full receiver and it is therefore nearly independent of the spectral composition of the incident power. The error due to selectivity is in general between 2% and 3%. Because it is a temperature sensitive device the effects of ambient must be considered, especially when measuring lamps of low output. They are most suitable for measurements in the infrared region and it is possible to obtain vacuum thermopiles with stable characteristics and high sensitivity. The use of a low-frequency radiation chopping system has many advantages, one of which is that high gain a.c. amplifiers can be used.

Because of the limitations of space it is not possible to give more than very general remarks on photocells, and for further information the references should be consulted and manufacturers approached. One general point must be made; it is of the highest importance to ensure that all detectors be fully exposed to the radiation to be measured. Failure to do this will lead to substantial inaccuracies in measurements.

The Photometer Bench.　　Where measurements involving direction and distance are concerned a photometric bench is required. Such a bench gives a facility for mounting lamps such that distance between the photometer head and lamps may be adjusted and accurately measured (Fig. 7.1). The photometer

Fig. 7.1   A photometer bench

head may consist of either a photocell or a visual device such as the Lummer–Brodhun Contrast Head. A photocell is more commonly used, but the visual head is fundamental in operation and has the merit of enabling luminous intensity and colour-temperature measurements to be combined, as described later. In the Lummer–Brodhun Contrast Head the observer compares two adjacent fields, each having a trapezoidal patch in the centre. At the point of balance, equal contrast is perceived on both sides of the field, with a difference in luminance of some 8% between each trapezoid and background.

Because a bench makes use of the inverse square law it is necessary that distances shall be measured to a high order of accuracy.

The bench should be set up in a darkroom, though if this is impossible it can be enclosed with curtains. The darkroom should have its walls painted with matt black paint, and the bench should be set up in the centre of the room to minimise the effects of reflections from the walls, and for convenience of use. Screens should be placed between the lamps and photometer head to ensure that no stray light reaches it. They can be of aluminium painted matt black with apertures of various sizes in the centre. It is of the highest importance to ensure that there is adequate screening and failure to observe this will cause large errors.

The measurement of luminous intensity. Two methods will be described, the first using a Lummer–Brodhun Contrast Head, and the second using a photocell as detector.

An appropriate calibrated lamp is selected and mounted on the photometer bench together with the test lamp, ensuring a correct alignment. If the distance between the standard lamp and the photometer head is kept constant the calculations are simplified if I_s/d_s^2 is made equal to a round figure, so that

$$I = kd^2 \quad \text{in which} \quad k = I_s/d_s^2$$

where I_s = luminous intensity of the standard lamp

I = luminous intensity of the test lamp

d_s = distance from photometer head of standard lamp

d = distance from photometer head of test lamp

The standard lamp should have the correct voltage applied to it and be allowed to stabilise, and test lamp should also have a voltage applied somewhere near its rated value and also be allowed to stabilise. If a measurement is required at a given colour temperature a series of readings should be taken by at least three observers in which they adjust the voltage on the test lamp, obtain a luminance balance of the head by adjusting the distance between the test lamp and the head and noting the colour difference; this will be seen as a contrast between blue and red. If the test lamp appears too blue on the appropriate sections of the head then its temperature is too high and the voltage should be reduced; conversely if it appears too red then the voltage should be increased. This procedure should be repeated until no colour difference is observed and equality of luminance is seen in the head. The distance and the test lamp voltage should then be noted. It is good practice for a second observer to note the voltage and distance readings so that the first observer is not influenced by his previous results. Each observer's readings should then be averaged and a mean result obtained for the complete set of readings.

If the colour temperature is not required and the lamp is to be measured at some specified voltage, the observer simply obtains the best luminance match ignoring any slight colour difference.

Where lamps of different colour appearance have to be measured, such as mercury vapour against a tungsten filament standard it is difficult to assess the point of equality accurately, and it is necessary to reduce the colour difference as far as possible by means of a coloured filter. Such filters must be of a known transmission and this taken into account in the calculations.

A more accurate technique, especially suitable for standardisation, is to use a substitution method. In this a comparison lamp is used whose sole function is to maintain a constant illumination on one side of the head. The bench is set up as before except that the comparison lamp is used instead of the test lamp, and runs at a fixed voltage throughout. After readings are taken with the standard lamp it is removed and the test lamp substituted. Readings are again taken and the results calculated. This is quite simple since

$$I_s/d_s^2 = I_c/d_c^2 = I_t/d_t^2$$

where I_s = luminous intensity of standard lamp

I_c = luminous intensity of comparison lamp

I_t = luminous intensity of test lamp

d_s = distance from photometer head of standard lamp

d_c = distance from photometer head of comparison lamp

d_t = distance from photometer head of test lamp

When a photocell is used, it should be corrected to the $V\lambda$ response, and can conveniently be mounted in a box containing baffles and painted matt black. This will restrict the field to a narrow angle and help to minimise stray light. The photocell should be mounted at the end of the bench and the standard lamp set up as before. Two methods can be used. In the first the photocell is maintained at a fixed distance from the lamp to be measured and two readings taken of the photocurrent; the first being that of the standard lamp and the second of the test lamp. The ratio of the photocurrents is then equal to the ratio of the luminous intensities.

In the second method the respective distances of the lamps are adjusted until a convenient identical photocurrent is obtained in each case. The luminous intensities are then in the ratio of the distances squared. This technique is convenient when the test lamp differs in luminous intensity from the standard, and also has the advantage of eliminating error due to any non-linearity of the photocell-galvanometer combination.

A mixture of the two methods may sometimes be employed to advantage, but in this case both the ratio of the photocurrents and of the distances squared govern the calculation of intensity.

The measurement of luminance. For lamps of high luminance the luminous intensity can be measured as already described and dividing this value by the projected area of the surface. It is often convenient to place an aperture of accurately known area in front of the lamp, particularly if there is variation in luminance across the lamp. Where the luminance is below 650 cd/m^2 a mirror can be placed over one side of the plaster screen in a Lummer–Brodhun head such that the image fills one part of the comparison field. A balance is obtained against a luminous intensity standard, and if the luminance is equal to L then $L\rho = E\rho'/\pi$, where ρ and ρ' are the reflection factors of the mirror and plaster screen respectively and E the illumination due to the standard lamp.

There are no limitations of the value of luminance when a photocell is used as a detector, the luminous intensity of a given area can therefore be measured and the luminance calculated.

Measurement of small sources of light, or of the luminance distribution of a source, require different techniques. One method is to use a lens to form an image of the source, the illumination being measured at the desired part of the image. If s is the area of the lens aperture, τ its transmission, E the illumination of the photometer or photocell and d the distance between this and the second focal point of the lens, then the luminance $L = Ed^2/s\tau$.

The calibration of photocells and lightmeters. The photometric bench provides a convenient means of determining the relationship between illumination, the photocurrent of photocells with their associated instruments, and of calibrating lightmeters. The method is the same in both cases and consists of mounting the photocell on the bench and aligning it with the sub-standard lamp. The distance of the lamp is varied and noted for a given instrument reading. It may be necessary to use a series of standard lamps of different luminous intensities in order to cover the range. In the case of lightmeters, scaled in values of illumination, it is convenient to adjust the distances of the lamp such that the meter reads a series of convenient values.

When the photocells are not corrected for the $V\lambda$ function it must be noted that such measurements are only correct for illumination of similar spectral composition to that of the particular calibrating standard.

The measurement of luminous flux.   Lamps designed for general lighting purposes are rated in terms of their total output of luminous flux, so that this measurement is of the greatest importance. Fundamentally, luminous flux is measured by determining the average intensity of a lamp in all directions in space and multiplying this by 4π. Lamps so measured can be used as primary standards from which other lamps can be calibrated by means of a photometric integrator.

If a lamp is placed within a sphere, the inner surface of which is painted with a non-selective uniformly diffusing paint, the illumination on any one area is contributed to equally by the light reflected from all other equal areas. It can thus be seen that the luminance of any part of the sphere wall is a measure of the average intensity of the lamp in all directions, provided that part receives no direct light from the lamp. It is therefore necessary to provide a screen to prevent direct light falling upon the area in which measurements are to be made, and this area commonly takes the form of a small, non-selective diffusing window in the wall.

The practical form of such an integrator involves considerable departures from the theoretically ideal conditions and this prevents its application as an instrument for the direct measurement of absolute values. The integrator should therefore be regarded as a comparative device dependent upon correct calibration with lamps of known lumen values. To minimise these limitations the screen should be as small as possible and be positioned one third of the distance from the lamp to the window, and all the internal fittings be painted with integrator paint. The requirements for the paint conflict, in that the effect of the screen demands a high reflection factor, whereas the reduction of absorption errors requires a low value. A compromise is achieved by using a paint of 80% reflection factor.

Although the ideal integrator shape is spherical it is possible to use other forms, such as cubes, rectangular boxes, etc., where working standard and test lamp are geometrically similar.

Measurement is carried out by means of a colour corrected photocell mounted behind the integrator window. It is useful to have some means of controlling the illumination on the photocell, particularly when lamps of widely differing luminous flux are to be measured, and this can be done by means of a series of stops or an iris diaphragm. It is necessary that the photocell surface is fully flashed under all conditions. Another useful feature of an iris diaphragm is that the measuring instrument if suitably scaled, can be made to give a direct reading of luminous flux, without the need for factors.

The integrator should be as large as possible commensurate with acceptable sensitivity and convenience of handling (Fig. 7.2). Its dimensions should be

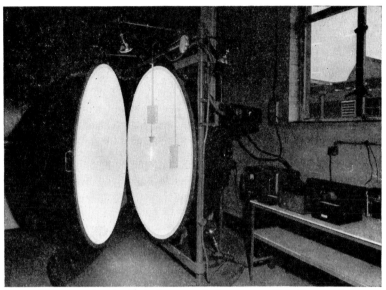

Fig. 7.2 A spherical photometric integrator (6 ft diameter)

at least six times the overall length of the lamp. This requirement offers problems in the case of long lamps such as fluorescent tubes, where the size becomes impracticable. However, smaller integrators can be used successfully providing direct substitution is employed (i.e. where the sub-standard lamp is identical in all respects to the lamps being measured), and the major dimension is not less than $1\frac{1}{2}$ times the length of the lamp. An alternative method to that of direct substitution is to have the standard and test lamps simultaneously in the integrator and to take measurements of each in turn.

For the measurement of tungsten filament lamps the power supply should be stabilised and can be either a.c. or d.c. Since the luminous flux varies as approximately four times the voltage it is necessary to measure the latter accurately, and the voltmeter should be a high-grade instrument. It is customary to measure the luminous flux for the rated voltage of the lamp, although current is sometimes used for some special types.

There are many types of discharge lamp, each type covering a range of power ratings and dimensions. With all discharge lamps some form of control gear (ballast) is necessary to limit the current to the designed value. The supply should be stabilised a.c., and measurements may be taken for the rated power, or as is now commonly specified, for the appropriate voltage of a reference ballast. A reference ballast is a control device giving characteristics closely approximating to the design value. Because of the reactive nature of the circuit the disturbances caused by the introduction of instruments must be taken into account. This can be done either by correcting for the known losses; or by removing all instruments after noting their readings with the exception of a meter reading the input voltage to the circuit before taking the photocell reading.

Adequate time must be allowed for the lamp fully to run up before measurements are taken. Special precautions must also be taken when measuring fluorescent tubes because of their temperature dependence. For this reason the temperature should be held constant during test, preferably at 25 °C and means for measuring this should be provided in the integrator.

The measurement of spectral distribution. This requires an instrument capable of separating the homogeneous light from a lamp into a spectrum, with provision for isolating discrete bands of known width. Such instruments are called monochromators and can be of great complexity. Space does not permit a detailed description of the various types, but a simple instrument will be described to show the basic principles.

The light passes via an entrance slit and a collimating system of mirrors or lenses. The parallel beam is then dispersed into a spectrum by means of a prism or diffraction grating which is rotatable by means of a control calibrated in wavelength. The angle of the dispersing element determines the wavelength of the light to be further transmitted onward through the optical system from which it emerges through an exit slit. The slits are adjustable and their settings determine the bandwidth on each side of the selected wavelength.

For lamps producing a continuous spectrum it is usual to adjust the slits to give a bandwidth of 5 nm or 10 nm and to take readings at these intervals. Where the lamp has a line spectrum or a mixture of line and continuum, it is necessary to reduce the slit width if a fully detailed exploration is required.

Calibration is carried out by measuring a lamp of known spectral distribution, usually a tungsten filament lamp, under the same conditions as the test lamp. For each point of measurement the ratio of the measured voltage from the detector due to the test lamp and that for the calibrating source, multiplied by the relative spectral distribution factor for the calibrating source, gives a relative spectral distribution term for the test lamp. Similar terms are found for each point of measurement throughout the desired spectrum. The results may conveniently be plotted as a relative spectral power distribution curve for the lamp.

When absolute values of power are required, further calculation must be undertaken. Normally this is based on some photometric property of the lamp, i.e. its total output of luminous flux or its luminous intensity in a given direction. The former will result in the total radiated power from the lamp, in watts per 5 nm band for example and should be used only when the radiation is spectrally homogeneous in all directions. Where the radiation is not homogeneous, or where lamps having directional properties are involved, then the calibration may be based on the value of luminous intensity. This will give corresponding units of watts per unit solid angle (steradian) per 5 nm band and should be coupled with the specified direction (i.e. that in which both the radiometric and photometric measurements were made).

In order to obtain the factor k by which the relative values are multiplied to give absolute values it is necessary to solve the equation

$$k \sum J_t \lambda V \lambda = \frac{\text{lm or } I}{680}$$

where $J_t \lambda$ = relative power readings

$V \lambda$ = the Standard Observer functions

lm or I = luminous flux or luminous intensity of the lamp

and 680 = the theoretical maximum conversion efficiency of electrical energy into light.

The use of computers can save much of the labour involved in these calculations.

The measurement of colour. The colour of the light emitted from a lamp is generally expressed by the chromaticity co-ordinates x, y and z of the C.I.E. system (see Chapter 5). These can be derived from the spectral power distribution data by multiplying the power at each wavelength interval by each of the distribution co-efficients, $\bar{x}$, $\bar{y}$ and $\bar{z}$, at the same interval, and adding the products, i.e. $\sum J\lambda\bar{x}\lambda$, $\sum J\lambda\bar{y}\lambda$ and $\sum J\lambda\bar{z}\lambda$. Reduction of these values to a unit equation will give the chromaticity co-ordinates for the lamp. It is customary to take the wavelength interval at 5 nm or 10 nm and if spectral lines are present the wavelengths at which they occur must be included. When a computer is used for calculation of spectral data it will save time if it is also programmed for the derivation of chromaticity co-ordinates.

Colorimeters provide a direct means of assessing colour by producing suitable stimuli. In one form employing colour filters, a visual colour match is made between the test lamp and a measurable mixture of the light transmitted through the filters from a standard lamp. Such designs show great ingenuity in ensuring that the light transmitted through the filters and seen by the observer is homogeneous. With knowledge of the chromaticity co-ordinates of the filters for the particular standard lamp used (usually a Standard Illuminant) and the proportions of each filter required to effect a match, it is possible to calculate the results in terms of the chromaticity co-ordinates for the test lamp. The number of filters used is generally three but there is a design using six which is capable of a high degree of accuracy. It is essential that users of visual colorimeters be tested for normality of colour vision and it is advisable that several matches be made by more than one observer if a high order of accuracy is desired.

A three-filter system may also be used in association with photocells, in which case the cell-filter spectral response must be a close approximation to that of the distribution coefficients. If the three photocurrents are in the

4*

correct proportions for some other standard, then the readings for a test lamp will give the chromaticity co-ordinates when unified. Instruments designed on this principle are not, in general, as accurate as the visual type but they have the advantage of speed and ease of operation. For the highest accuracy they should be calibrated with lamps of known chromaticity co-ordinates similar to the test lamp.

The mask and dispersion type of colorimeter has a lens and prism, or grating system, so arranged that the light passing through an entrance slit is dispersed into a spectrum, in the plane of which are masks cut to the shape of the distribution coefficients. These shapes also take into account the response of the photocell which measures the integrated light transmitted through the masks.

The measurement of ultraviolet and infrared radiation. Space does not permit a full discussion of these measurements so that only the general principles will be described. The ultraviolet region below 200 nm must be measured in a vacuum because of its strong absorption by air, the apparatus and detectors being chosen to suit these conditions. Usually the ultraviolet bandwidth of most interest is between 200 nm and 400 nm and this can be measured by spectroradiometric means using a suitable detector or, if only the total quantity of radiation is required, a simpler instrument comprising a detector, amplifier and meter can be used. The spectral characteristics of the detectors must be known, for their response often extends into the visible region of the spectrum and this can result in substantial errors if the detector receives the total radiation from the lamp. In such cases filters must be used to isolate the bandwidth required.

Infrared radiation can be measured in much the same way and with similar precautions except for the far infrared region which presents problems of measurement not appropriate for discussion in this book.

Electrical characteristics

Measurements. The electrical quantities most frequently required are the voltage drop across the lamp, its current and its power consumption. In all cases the voltage should be taken at the lamp terminals so that the voltage drop due to the supply leads and any instruments in the circuit is not included in the reading. This is best achieved by an additional pair of leads taken from the lampholder to the voltmeter or to the potential-coil of a wattmeter.

All instruments have a loading effect to a greater or lesser degree and this must be corrected for, particularly when more than one instrument is in circuit at the same time. Instrument loadings should be as small as possible and it is good practice to have the minimum of instruments in circuit, at any one time.

These measurements on filament lamps present little difficulty but discharge lamps require special consideration. The latter will require some means of limiting the arc current which for a.c. supplies is usually provided by a choke or high reactance transformer. The voltage waveform across the lamp is very distorted, which means that the instruments must be capable of measuring r.m.s. values of non-sinusoidal waveforms and must therefore have a frequency bandwidth covering high orders of harmonics.

For accurate results instruments should be of precision grade and provide unambiguous readings. They should be calibrated regularly against standard potentiometers and the necessary corrections applied to the readings.

It is often required to study the waveform of discharge lamps and this can best be done by means of an oscilloscope. If harmonic analysis is required it can be obtained by the use of an instrument from which components at selected harmonics can be read directly.

Humidity testing. Where lamps are required for use under conditions of high humidity which may affect the capping cement or cause arcing, it is necessary to test them under similar controlled conditions. A typical test requires that lamps shall be subjected to a temperature of 60 °C and 99% humidity for 16 hours, cooling to room temperature over a period of 8 hours and that this cycle shall be performed three times for each test quantity of lamps. At the end of the final cooling period the lamps are wiped dry, left in normal conditions for one hour and are tested for cap adhesion.

The apparatus consists of a lagged test chamber with a removable front panel to permit the insertion of lamps, loaded in wire baskets. This panel is secured with wing nuts and an asbestos gasket provides a seal. An observation window, which is covered with a hinged flap, is provided in the centre of the panel. A thermostat is incorporated within the chamber, as is also a fan which is belt driven from an external motor. A lagged water tank containing an immersion heater is attached to the chamber and a pipe conducts steam into it. A return pipe is provided from the concave base of the chamber back to the tank, and a time clock automatically controls the cycling.

Less severe tests are sometimes required, and these can use saturated chemical solutions at near ambient temperatures to provide the desired humidity. Lamps tested in this way are usually subjected to voltages applied between terminals and cap immediately after the prescribed period in the chamber.

Thermal characteristics

Measurements. The importance of the operating temperature of filaments, cathodes and gases within incandescent and discharge lamps is fundamental to their design and operation. Other thermal characteristics have also to be considered in relating the suitability of any particular lamp to particular environments in service. These include cap and cement temperatures when in the holder, temperature of the cables connected to a holder and in the case of certain discharge lamps, the temperature of the air in the vicinity of the lamp envelope.

Bulb temperatures may also be of vital importance where environmental fire or explosion hazards exist in the atmosphere; for example, some types of dust and gases, or where there is some risk of thermal shock from liquids or draughts.

A comprehensive investigation into the operating thermal characteristics of some widely used incandescent lamp fittings was made by the Electrical Research Association, during the period 1930 to 1934, in collaboration with numerous manufacturers and the methods of measurement, now widely adopted internationally, have been developed from this early exercise. During the last ten years close collaboration between many countries, through relevant international standardisation committees, has enabled practical and relatively simple test methods to be devised and accepted as being suitable for both the lamp and lighting-fittings industries.

The general requirements for such test methods are:
(a) A suitable test enclosure, which will eliminate draughts but will permit free circulation of air.
(b) A method of measuring the temperature of a small area or spot at any point on the lamp surface, without disturbance to the overall temperature distribution of the surrounding parts.

The draught free enclosure now generally accepted as standard (Fig. 7.3), has the top and at least three sides of double-walled construction, the base being solid. The walls are made of perforated metal sheet and are separated to form a gap of approximately 150 mm. The perforations are prescribed as being 2 mm (maximum) diameter, the areas of the apertures taking up approximately 40% of the total area. An important requirement is that the size of the cabinet must be such that the ambient temperature within the test enclosure will not exceed 40 °C during a test. The lamp under test is posi-

Fig. 7.3   A temperature measurement cabinet

tioned approximately in the centre, the mounting arrangements being such as to permit free circulation of convection currents around the lamp. Ambient temperature within the cabinet is usually measured by means of a mercury thermometer, screened from radiation by concentric, open-ended cylinders of polished metal, and placed level with the lamp about half-way between lamp and wall of the enclosure.

Temperature measurements on the lamp are made by means of thermo-couples of fine gauge wire, of low thermal conductivity; those wires exposed to radiation from the lamp being bright and polished. In some specifications the materials recommended for the thermocouples are nickel/nickel-chromium, or iron/constantan but some laboratories prefer to use nickel-chromium/nickel-copper, nickel-chromium/nickel-aluminium, or iron/nickel-copper.

Other devices for surface temperature measurements are available, such as thermistors but these have not yet been adopted for specification purposes.

Considerable care must be exercised in ensuring that the thermal contact between the thermocouple and the part of the lamp being measured is adequate, without disturbing the thermal characteristics of the lamp. Methods found to be suitable, depending upon circumstances, include mechanical clamping, soldering with the minimum amount of solder, or by an adhesive; the latter requiring special care in ensuring contact without 'lagging' effect.

The emf developed by the thermocouple is preferably measured by an appropriate potentiometer circuit. Cold junctions are usually kept in a small, deep Dewar-vessel containing suitable liquid, e.g. glycerine, to prevent rapid changes in temperature. An ice/water mixture may be used, providing its temperature is kept under observation and is especially useful when measuring temperatures only a little above ambient temperature, if the sensitivity of the potentiometer is not sufficiently high. The cold junction temperature is usually measured by mercury thermometers.

Many national and international specifications relate temperature require-ments to an ambient of 25 °C and it is preferable that the temperature of the air in the test enclosure remains at 25 ±5 °C. If this temperature differs from 25 °C, the measured value of temperature rise can be converted to the value corresponding to an ambient temperature of 25 °C, by means of the following formula:

$$\Delta t_{25} = \Delta t_m + \tfrac{1}{3}(t_{amb} - 25)\sqrt{\frac{\Delta t_m}{100}}$$

where Δt_{25} = temperature rise at 25 °C ambient

Δt_m = temperature rise measured at t_{amb} (actual ambient)

This formula is valid for specification purposes over a range of ambient temperature from 15 °C to 40 °C.

Temperature measurements on incandescent lamps have always included that of the cap in the vicinity of the junction with the glass envelope and in recent years several specifications require compliance within maximum values. As the lampholders affect the cap temperature to an extent depending upon the holder design, some standardisation of test conditions is necessary. For this purpose the thermal effect of a lampholder is simulated by the use of a metal sleeve around the lamp cap. The design of this sleeve is specified in detail to assist unified conditions of testing. A thermocouple is soldered to the sleeve in a prescribed position and the two leads are attached to the sleeve, parallel to its edge, over a length of at least 20 mm. This is to minimise conduction losses by reducing the temperature gradient along the thermo-couple leads. Electrical supply connections are made with copper wire, of specified diameter and length, soldered directly to the two cap contacts in the case of the B.C. type, or the centre contact of the cap and the sleeve of the test lampholder for E.S. lamps. The adoption of the simulated lampholder has done much to improve the reproducibility of individual lamp measure-ments, by integrating the variations in temperature which normally exist around the lamp cap.

When thermal tests in lighting fittings are being made, thermocouples are usually soldered directly to the lamp cap shell at the point on the periphery 3 mm from the cap mouth and above the centre of the filament wreath. Cable insulation temperature measurements are obtained by inserting a thermocouple into a slit in the cable insulation and suitably securing.

In all tests of this nature it is important to ensure that when the thermo-couple is attached to any part which is connected to the electrical supply, that part must be at earth potential. The use of a double-wound isolating transformer with an independent earth, applied to one side of the secondary winding, is recommended.

As the light output of fluorescent tubes is dependent upon the temperature of the lamp envelope, occasions arise when this has to be measured. For several years after the introduction of these lamps, the average wall tempera-ture was determined by measuring the change in resistance of a wire spiral wound around the outer surface of the tube. The directions of winding were usually opposed, from the centre outwards, so as to minimise inductive effects from the arc but difficulties arose in using this method, due to the high tem-perature gradients in the vicinity of the electrodes. In later years it has become customary to adopt the temperature midway between the caps, and on the underside of the tube, as a reference for luminous flux/temperature characteristics.

Incandescent filament and discharge lamps can present problems when required to operate in abnormally low ambient temperatures, down to $-40\ ^{\circ}\mathrm{C}$, or so. Filament lamps must be capable of withstanding not only the shocks arising from infrared radiation when first switched on but also the sustained stresses caused by the high temperature gradients developed in the envelope, base and caps during continuous operation. Discharge lamps have to withstand similar thermal shocks and stresses but also require measurements of electrical characteristics and light output, under such conditions.

These requirements necessitate the use of special extra-low temperature refrigerator cabinets, in which uniformity of temperature is very important, especially for long lamps such as the 8 ft fluorescent tube. The shape, construction and interior finish of the cabinets must permit relative measurements of light output to be made.

Observation of convection currents. Temperature measurements provide most of the thermal information of interest to lamp usage but occasions arise when knowledge of the pattern formed by convection currents is desirable. The technique adopted for this purpose is the Schlieren (from the German meaning streak, or striation) which is used widely in aerodynamic and ballistic research. Much has been written about the many variations in applying the technique but the principle may be understood by the following brief description of a simple form of apparatus.

An optical system of mirrors and/or lenses, with a light source, is arranged so that a parallel beam of light illuminates the test object under observation. A second optical system produces an image of the light source at a focal plane beyond which a camera is suitably located, so as to give an image of the test object on a photosensitive surface. A sharp knife-edge is placed at the focal plane referred to above and adjusted so as to intersect part of the light rays directed towards the camera lens. In the absence of any disturbance of the air around the test object, its image on the camera screen will have a clear surround, reduced in brightness by the knife-edge. When the temperature of the test object rises above ambient, convection currents will be formed due to the changes in density of the air. The changes in density result in corresponding changes in refractive index of the air in the vicinity of the test object. Thus, the paths of the light rays passing through the air surrounding the object are deflected and some of these will impinge upon the opaque portion of the knife-edge and will not pass on to the camera screen. The resulting picture on the camera screen thus becomes a silhouette image of the test object, surrounded by bright and dark streaks, indicating the pattern and movement of the convection currents.

Many of the variations introduced by users of this technique relate to modified forms of knife-edge; wedge filters are also used. Colour filters may also be employed, so that colour photography can be applied. The study of the flow pattern of convection currents produced by lamps, has led to better understanding of the factors which contribute towards the operating temperature of lampholders, cables and lighting fittings.

Vibration characteristics. Automobiles, aircraft, ships and trains are typical examples of environments where lamps are subjected to vibration during normal use. When one, or more, of the components in a lamp are excited to resonance by a particular frequency in the vibration spectrum at the lampholder, the life of the lamp may be reduced. It is possible for two designs of a particular lamp, having the same external dimensions and electrical performance characteristics under static conditions, to have very different lives when subjected to certain vibration conditions. Hence, in such applications, knowledge of the environmental vibration characteristics is essential to achieving a satisfactory design. Furthermore, it is necessary to be able to test prototypes of the lamps under simulated conditions equivalent to those occurring in service.

Various types of test machines exist which are designed to produce particular vibration conditions and these can be a valuable aid to quality control, for testing the endurance of lamps under these specific circumstances. Such machines do not, however, permit a comprehensive examination of lamp characteristics in relation to other environments.

A modern form of integrated laboratory system for vibration measurement, analysis and endurance testing, is described below.

The vibration conditions at the point of installation of the lamp, for instance in a motor car, are measured and recorded with the aid of piezo-crystal accelerometers, or similar devices, plugged into the lampholders. The orientation of each accelerometer is so arranged that it is sensitive to the most severe mode of vibrations occurring at that position. The accelerometers are connected, through appropriate amplifiers, to a multi-track tape recorder installed in the vehicle. Test runs are then made at various speeds over typical road surfaces, the outputs of the accelerometers being recorded on the tape, together with a spoken commentary which supplies any extraneous relevant data.

Later, in the laboratory, the tapes are 'played back' into electronic analysers. Each channel of the tape record gives an output voltage proportional to the mechanical acceleration to which the accelerometer on the vehicle was subjected on the test run. This output voltage will, at an instant (t), be of the form:

$$V_t = V_1 \sin (2\pi f_1 t) + V_2 \sin (2\pi f_2 t + \theta_2) + V_3 \sin (2\pi f_3 t + \theta_3) + \cdots$$

where V_1, V_2, V_3, etc., are the voltages proportional to the accelerations at the component frequencies f_1, f_2, f_3, etc., with corresponding phase angles of zero, θ_2, θ_3, etc.

The electronic analyser may be a cathode-ray tube (panoramic type), which presents an instantaneous graph of frequency against voltage and provides an immediate analysis of the complex 'vibration voltage' wave form. A more advanced technique utilises a valve voltmeter, incorporating an elaborate selective filter network, and a pen-chart recorder. The output of the valve voltmeter is fed into the chart recorder, which is electromechanically coupled to the filter selector switch in such a way that the pen records, on a moving chart, a graph of the voltage (i.e. proportional to acceleration) against frequency, over the range of 10 c/s to 2500 c/s during continuous scanning of portions of the tape record. Thus, the significant frequencies, together with the associated magnitude of acceleration, can readily be determined.

The other major portion of the system consists of equipment for studying the behaviour of the lamp under controlled vibration conditions. An electrical oscillator unit generates sine-wave oscillations of controllable amplitude and frequency (10 c/s to 2500 c/s). These are fed through an amplifier to a vibration generator, which converts the electrical oscillations into mechanical sinusoidal vibrations, which are then applied directly to the lamp.

The electrical oscillator unit provides also a secondary sine-wave output, differing in frequency from the primary output by up to 2 c/s. This output is used to control a flash-tube, which functions as a light-source in an optical system, providing an enlarged silhouette image of the lamp under test. This stroboscopic viewer can be adjusted to provide a slow-motion picture of resonance effects in parts of the lamp; or, by alternative manual control, critical examination may be made of the movement of, for instance, the individual coils of a filament. Thus, the whole construction of a vibrating lamp can be studied in extremely slow motion, over the entire range of frequency. Such detailed examinations may be made with the lamp unlit, or lit. Endurance tests of prototypes can also be made with the same apparatus.

An important feature of such test equipment concerns calibration. The accelerometers are initially calibrated individually in millivolts output, per unit of acceleration (g). The accelerometers used for service tests are also used to monitor the wave-form and acceleration of the vibrations to which lamps are subjected throughout laboratory investigation. Calibration of the tape recorder and amplifier is achieved by utilising the vibration-generator with an accelerometer attached, the controlled output being fed into the tape-recording equipment and subsequently 'played back' to the chart recorder.

CHAPTER 8

Lighting Fittings—Performance Data and Photometry

In this chapter a description will be given of the ways in which performance data relating to lighting fittings can be presented for the use of the lighting engineer. This will be followed by an outline of the photometric measurements which have to be made to arrive at these data.

Some data are most conveniently presented in tabular form, other data are better in graphical form. Utilisation factors, British Zonal classifications, and light-output ratios are usually given in tables. Their use will be described in the next chapter. Graphs are used because they enable the performance of a lighting fitting to be assessed at a glance. Some of them enable short cuts to be taken in estimating the performance of a fitting in a particular situation.

Graphical representations

Polar curve. The polar curve, as its name implies, is drawn on polar co-ordinate paper. It shows how the luminous intensity of a fitting varies with direction in a cone with its apex at the centre of the fitting. For instance (Fig. 8.1), it would show how the intensity varies as a photocell, facing A, is

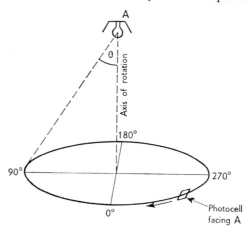

Fig. 8.1   Measurement of a conical polar curve

moved round the circle. θ, the apex angle of the cone, can be varied as desired and the axis of rotation can be inclined at any angle. Usually θ is made equal to a right angle and the axis of rotation is horizontal, so the polar curve shows how the intensity varies in a vertical plane. Two examples of *vertical polar curves* for symmetrical tungsten reflector fittings are shown in Fig. 8.2.

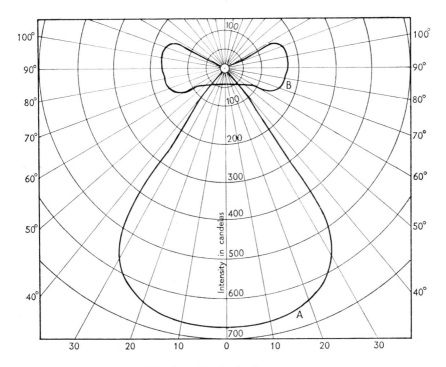

Fig. 8.2   Vertical polar curves

Intensities are measured along the radial lines. Thus curve A shows an intensity of 680 cd directly underneath and an intensity of 580 cd at 30° from the downward vertical and so on. With fluorescent fittings, the polar curve usually changes in shape as the vertical plane is rotated about the vertical axis through the centre of the fitting. Consequently its performance is usually represented by a curve in a plane through the long axis and a curve in a plane through the short axis of the fitting.

The polar curve of a uniformly diffusing flat surface of small area facing downwards is a circle tangential to the 90° axis of the graph, as shown in Fig. 8.3. This is sometimes called a *tangent sphere distribution* because if the polar curve were rotated about the downward vertical axis to show the distribution in a three dimensional form, a sphere would result which would be tangential to the 90° axis. Fluorescent fittings give an approximately semicircular polar curve in a plane through the long axis, unless there is some modification by louvers or prismatic diffusers.

There are two disadvantages of polar curves. Firstly, they can be deceptive because the area included by the curve is not proportional to the flux emitted by the fitting. Thus curve A in Fig. 8.2 which includes a larger area

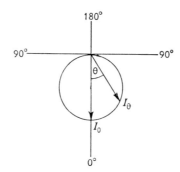

Fig. 8.3　The polar curve of a uniform diffuser is a circle, since $I_\theta = I_0 \cos \theta$

than curve B really represents less flux than B (provided the fitting is symmetrical about the vertical axis). However, for symmetrical fittings there is a construction called a Rousseau diagram (see p. 112) for finding from a polar curve the flux in any zone.

Secondly, if the rate of change of intensity with angle is great, the curve becomes nearly parallel to the radial lines and it is difficult to read off values. This is the case with concentrating fittings such as spotlights, for which rectangular co-ordinates are used (see p. 107).

Isocandela diagram.　This is a method of representing the performance of a fitting in all directions and not just in one plane as with a polar curve. Imagine the fitting to be suspended in the centre of a large transparent sphere. On this draw lines joining points of equal illumination. These correspond to lines of equal intensity, that is isocandela lines, since the surface of the sphere is equidistant from the fitting. This sphere can then be projected on to a flat surface in much the same way as a map of the earth, with lines of longitude and latitude as a reference grid, to give an *isocandela diagram*.

The projection chosen is such that an area in a given boundary on the diagram equals in value the corresponding area on the surface of the sphere. That most commonly used is the sinusoidal projection, in which the length of the lines of latitude are proportional to the sine of the angle of elevation or declination. It is also known as Sanson's net. Fig. 8.4 shows an isocandela diagram for a street lantern.

The advantage of this type of diagram is that it shows the complete distribution of the fitting; also, the flux in any zone can be calculated as described on page 113.

The main disadvantage of the isocandela diagram is that it is difficult to estimate the intensity between isocandela lines, and for street lighting fittings

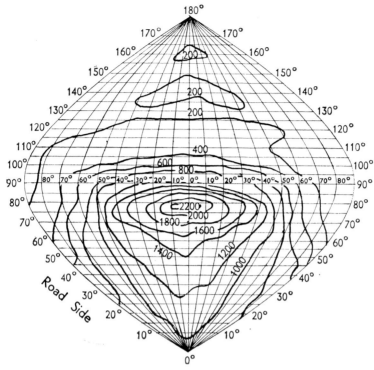

Fig. 8.4   Isocandela diagram of a sodium street lantern

separate vertical and conical polar curves through the main beam are asked for in BS 1788: 1964.

Cartesian or rectangular co-ordinates for concentrating beams.   Because of the second disadvantage of polar curves mentioned earlier, it is better to use *rectangular co-ordinates* for concentrating beams. This principle is shown, for a 14 in. diameter projector, in Fig. 8.5 where the intensity is plotted along the

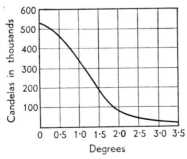

Fig. 8.5   Luminous intensity diagram for 14 in. diameter projector

ordinates and the angles along the abscissae. For such a distribution the polar curve would appear as a very narrow loop.

Road luminance diagrams for street lanterns. These show the luminance of the road surface by means of isoluminance lines drawn on a perspective diagram of the road. Two of these are shown in Figs. 8.6 and 8.7 for a uniform intensity source of 1000 cd and also for a sodium lantern. Both direct approximately the same number of lumens below the horizontal, but because the lantern directs more flux on to the road surface, it gives nearly twice the road luminance.

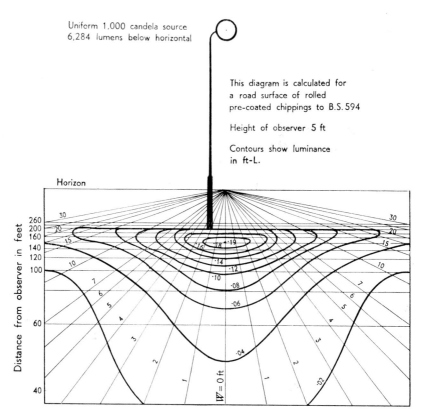

Fig. 8.6   Iso-luminance diagram of uniform 1000 cd source
(for correct perspective, view at 9 in.)

Illumination diagrams. These diagrams are used to show the illumination in horizontal and vertical planes, usually by means of equal illumination contours. A typical one is shown in Fig. 8.8 for a street lantern mounted at 25 ft, with conversion factors in Table 8.1 for other heights,

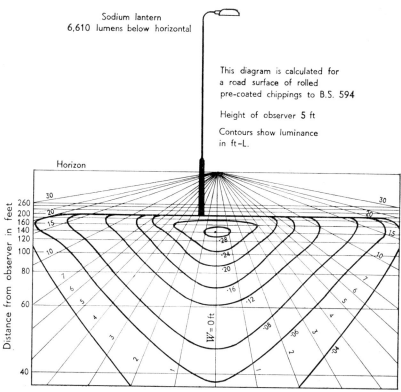

Fig. 8.7 Iso-luminance for a street lantern
(for correct perspective, view at 9 in.)

In interior lighting the illumination at a point often results from a number of fittings, and the illumination diagram has the disadvantage that a substantial amount of work is involved in superimposing the diagrams to find the total illumination from all the fittings. Moreover, no account is taken of inter-reflections, but an estimate of their contribution can be made by subtracting the utilisation factor for zero ceiling and wall reflection factor from

TABLE 8.1

Table of Correction Factors for Converting Illumination Values based on 25 ft Mounting Height to Values at Other Mounting Heights

MOUNTING HEIGHT—FT

15	16	17	18	19	20	21	22	23	24	25	26	27	28	29	30	31	32	33	34	35

CORRECTION FACTOR

15	16	17	18	19	20	21	22	23	24	25	26	27	28	29	30	31	32	33	34	35
2·78	2·44	2·16	1·93	1·73	1·56	1·42	1·29	1·18	1·08	1·00	0·923	0·855	0·797	0·742	0·695	0·650	0·610	0·574	0·540	0·510

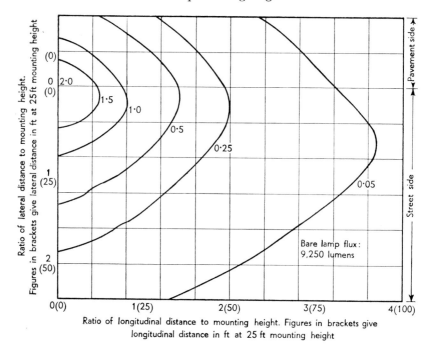

Fig. 8.8   Illumination on the horizontal plane in lm/ft² for a street
lantern at mounting height of 25 ft

the utilisation factor for the ceiling and wall reflection factors under consideration. This gives the fraction of bare lamp flux reaching the working
plane by inter-reflection only.

British Zonal Classification

The British Zonal Classification classifies lighting fittings according to the
degree of concentration of their light distribution in the lower hemisphere, a
British Zonal Classification of 1 (or BZ 1) being the most concentrated distribution and a BZ 10 being the least concentrated. The method of calculating
the classification is given in *I.E.S. Technical Report* No. 2, but the flux in
each 10° zone from the fitting has first of all to be determined by the *Zonal
method* described below.

The British Zonal Classification is used in the short method of calculating
utilisation factors, described in *I.E.S. Technical Report* No. 2, and in the
calculation of glare indices, described in the next chapter.

Calculation of luminous flux from fittings. Almost all methods of
calculating flux from a fitting depend on the fact that the flux in a zone is
equal to the average intensity in the zone multiplied by the solid angle
subtended by the zone at the centre of the fitting. If a fitting is imagined to be
surrounded by a sphere of unit radius the area on this sphere will be numerically equal to the solid angle subtended by the zone.

Zonal method. In this method the unit sphere is divided into horizontal zones which subtend known angles of elevation at the centre of the sphere as shown in Fig. 8.9.

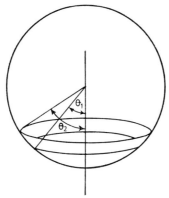

Fig. 8.9   Horizontal zone of sphere whose upper and lower boundaries subtend angles θ_2 and θ_1 with the downward vertical at the centre of the sphere

If the lower and upper boundaries of the zone subtends angles of θ_1 and θ_2 with the vertical axis then the solid angle it subtends is given by:

Solid angle subtended by zone (zonal constant)

$$= 2\pi(\cos \theta_1 - \cos \theta_2) \text{ steradians}$$

$$= 4\pi \sin \left(\frac{\theta_1 + \theta_2}{2}\right) \sin \left(\frac{\theta_2 - \theta_1}{2}\right) \text{ steradians}$$

TABLE 8.2

Values of Zonal Constants for 1, 2, 5 and 10 Degree Zones

1 Degree Zones		2 Degree Zones		5 Degree Zones			10 Degree Zones		
Zone limits (degrees)	Zonal constant	Zone limits (degrees)	Zonal constant	Zone limits (degrees)		Zonal constant	Zone limits (degrees)		Zonal constant
0–1	0·0009	0–2	0·0038	0–5	175–180	0·0239	0–10	170–180	0·095
1–2	0·0029	2–4	0·0115	5–10	170–175	0·0715	10–20	160–170	0·283
2–3	0·0048	4–6	0·0191	10–15	165–170	0·1186	20–30	150–160	0·463
3–4	0·0067	6–8	0·0267	15–20	160–165	0·1649	30–40	140–150	0·628
4–5	0·0086	8–10	0·0343	20–25	155–160	0·2097	40–50	130–140	0·774
5–6	0·0105	10–12	0·0418	25–30	150–155	0·2531	50–60	120–130	0·897
6–7	0·0124	12–14	0·0493	30–35	145–150	0·2946	60–70	110–120	0·993
7–8	0·0143	14–16	0·0568	35–40	140–145	0·3337	70–80	100–110	1·058
8–9	0·0162	16–18	0·0641	40–45	135–140	0·3703	80–90	90–100	1·091
9–10	0·0181	18–20	0·0714	45–50	130–135	0·4041			
				50–55	125–130	0·4349			
				55–60	120–125	0·4623			
				60–65	115–120	0·4862			
				65–70	110–115	0·5064			
				70–75	105–110	0·5228			
				75–80	100–105	0·5351			
				80–85	95–100	0·5434			
				85–90	90–95	0·5476			

Values of zonal constants are given in Table 8.2 for $1°$, $2°$, $5°$ and $10°$ zones. For most fittings it is sufficient to take the zones in equal steps of $10°$. To obtain the average intensity in any particular zone the candle-power at the midpoint of the zone is taken; thus for the $30°$ to $40°$ zone the candle-power at $35°$ is taken.

For linear (e.g. fluorescent) fittings the weighted average of the intensity at $35°$ would be taken. This is derived as follows:

$$\text{Average intensity} = \tfrac{1}{12}\{I_0 + I_{30} + I_{60} + I_{90} + \cdots + I_{270}\}$$

where the subscripts refer to the angles of azimuth.

Since the fitting is symmetrical about the transverse and longitudinal vertical planes,

$$I_0 = I_{180}$$
$$I_{30} = I_{150} = I_{210} = I_{330}$$
$$I_{60} = I_{120} = I_{240} = I_{300}$$
$$I_{90} = I_{270}$$

Hence

$$\text{Weighted average intensity} = \tfrac{1}{6}\{I_0 + 2I_{30} + 2I_{60} + I_{90}\}$$

Russell angles. In the zonal method each value of average candle-power for the various zones has to be multiplied by a different solid angle; a rather laborious procedure. In the *Russell angle method* each zone is chosen so that it subtends the same solid angle, and the average intensity is taken on the line which divides the zone into two equal areas. To find the total flux it is therefore only necessary to total the intensities, divide by the number of zones (to give the average intensity of the fitting), and finally multiply by 4π to find the total flux emitted by the fitting.

Russell angles for various numbers of zones are given in Table 8.3.

TABLE 8.3

Russell Angles for the Calculation of Luminous Flux

20 Angles (degrees)

18·2 31·8 41·4 49·5 56·6 63·3 69·5 75·5 81·4 87·1 92·9 98·6 104·5 110·5 116·7 123·4 130·5 138·6 148·2 161·8

10 Angles (degrees)

25·8 45·6 60·0 72·5 84·3 95·7 107·5 120·0 134·4 154·2

The disadvantage of this method is that the uneven spacing of the readings makes it difficult to draw the polar curve without taking additional readings, but it does save time by reducing the calculation involved.

Rousseau diagrams. The *Rousseau diagram* is a graphical construction shown in Fig. 8.10 for finding the luminous flux from the polar curve, but it can be readily applied only to axially symmetrical fittings.

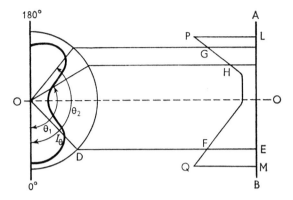

Fig. 8.10   A Rousseau diagram for finding the flux
represented by a polar curve

A semi-circle with centre O and of any convenient radius large enough to
enclose the polar curve is drawn. AB is drawn parallel to the 0°–180° axis
of the curve. Consider the intensity I_θ at any angle θ. Produce I_θ to meet the
semi-circle at D. Drop a perpendicular DE on AB and mark off the distance
EF equal to I_θ. This procedure is then repeated for a number of steps, say
at 10° intervals, and a complete curve PQ is drawn.
   The flux is given by:

$$F = 4\pi \left(\frac{\text{Area PLMQ}}{\text{LM}} \quad \text{in candelas} \right)$$

If the flux, F, in any zone from θ_1 to θ_2 is required it is given by:

$$F = 4\pi \left(\frac{\text{Area under GH}}{\text{LM}} \quad \text{in candelas} \right)$$

Isocandela diagram and planimeter. Consider the isocandela diagram in
Fig. 8.4 and suppose it is required to find the flux in the zone between the
1000 and 1200 isocandela lines. The area of this zone is measured with a
planimeter and multiplied by the average intensity, that is 1100 cd. The
units in which this area is measured should be such that the area of the
whole diagram is equal to 4π units. This is repeated for every zone and the
sum of the results gives the total flux from the source.

Sector method for fluorescent fittings. This is an approximate method and is
strictly applicable only if the intensity distribution in any plane through the
axis of the fitting is similar in shape to the intensity distribution of the
bare tube.
   The intensity distribution of the bare lamp in a plane through the short
axis is plotted in Cartesian co-ordinates as shown in Fig. 8.11, curve PQ,

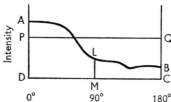

Fig. 8.11   Intensity distribution for fluorescent tube (PQ) and fitting (ALB) on Cartesian co-ordinates

and this is repeated for the fitting, curve AB. Then the light output ratio of the fitting is given by:

$$\text{L.O.R.} = \frac{\text{area ALBCD}}{\text{area PQCD}}$$

and

$$\text{L.O.R. for } 0°\text{--}90° \text{ zone} = \frac{\text{area ALMD}}{\text{area PQCD}}$$

$$\text{L.O.R. for } 90°\text{--}180° \text{ zone} = \frac{\text{area LBCM}}{\text{area PQCD}}$$

It should be noted that the flux in, say, the 0°–40° zone is not proportional to the area under the curve between the 0° and 40° ordinates. The method is only valid for the 0°–90° and 90°–180° zones.

Wohlauer's method.   In this method the flux from a fitting is obtained directly from the polar curve (Fig. 8.12). This is divided into a number of convenient equal zones having an angular width of $\theta°$. Horizontal lines L_1L_1, L_2L_2, L_3L_3, etc., are drawn joining the mid-zonal intensities to the 0°–180° line. These are summed in candela units and multiplied by $4\pi \sin(\theta/2)$ to give the total flux from the fitting. This method can only be applied to axially symmetrical fittings.

Illumination diagrams.   The flux falling on a surface can be calculated by using the following relationship:

Flux = average illumination (lumens per unit area) × area of surface.
This method is only readily applicable to fittings with concentrating beams where all the flux is concentrated in a reasonably small area. If equal illumination contours are drawn the flux can be found in a manner analogous to that for isocandela diagrams. The area (in appropriate units) between two contours is found by means of a planimeter, and this is multiplied by the average illumination to give the flux falling between the two contours. This procedure is repeated until the whole diagram is covered, and hence the total flux falling on the surface is found.

Laboratory measurements of flux and intensity

Integrators.   An integrator is an enclosure used for comparing the total light flux emitted from a fitting or source with that from a standard or known source. This type of measurement can also be made with a polar curve

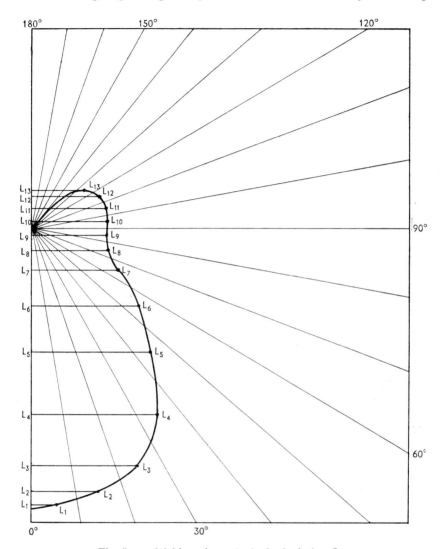

Fig. 8.12   Wohlauer's method of calculating flux

apparatus, which will be described in the next section, but the integrator has the advantage that the light output can be determined by taking very few readings, usually only four on a fitting with a single light source.

Its mode of working depends on the principle that the illumination received at any point on its wall from the remainder of the integrator (and not directly from the fitting) is proportional to the total luminous flux emitted by the fitting. Ideally the integrator should be spherical in shape as shown in Fig. 8.13, with a matt white finish inside. The fitting is centrally placed and if it is linear (like a fluorescent fitting) its axis should be at right angles to the photocell or window at W. A screen is positioned at S so that no direct light reaches the window from the fitting. The reading is taken at W with a photocell or alternatively, for greater accuracy, the luminance of an opal glass window at W is measured by means of a photometric bench. It is important that the photocell or window is flush with the wall of the integrator.

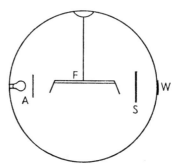

Fig. 8.13   A typical integrating sphere
A   auxiliary lamp
F   fitting
S   screen
W   window
Note that linear sources should be perpendicular to both
screen and window as shown

To find the light output ratio of a fitting, the bare lamp or tube used in the fitting is suspended in the integrator and allowed to stabilise. A reading L is taken. This is repeated with the bare lamp in the fitting and a reading M taken, then

$$\text{light output ratio} = \frac{M}{L} \times 100\%$$

If there is more than one lamp in the fitting L would be the total of the bare lamp readings.

Compensation has to be made for the fact that the fitting and the bare lamp absorb some of their own inter-reflected light when they are being tested. This compensation is effected by using an auxiliary lamp, as shown in Fig. 8.13, which illuminates the fitting by indirect light only. Separate readings Q and R are taken with the unlighted fitting and bare lamp in the integrator, using the auxiliary lamp, then,

$$\text{light output ratio} = \frac{M}{L} \times \frac{R}{Q} \times 100\%$$

Although not as accurate, non-spherical integrators are more economical to make, and are sufficiently accurate for most practical purposes. If the two sources of light to be compared have similar distributions then non-spherical integrators are quite satisfactory. The most commonly used type is a cube, but a cube with the corners cut off is an improvement, and the photograph shows a 20-sided type (Fig. 8.14).

Fig. 8.14   A 20-sided integrator which opens in two halves
(the control panel is seen in the foreground)

Light distribution photometers.   These are used for measuring the variation of intensity with angular position round a lighting fitting. In one of the simplest forms of apparatus, the photocell is moved in an arc round the fitting (either on a track or on the end of an arm) to obtain intensity readings at different angles of elevation, and the fitting is rotated about its own vertical axis to enable readings to be taken at any angle of azimuth. This type of apparatus is commonly used for obtaining data for polar curves, and is often called a polar curve photometer. Sometimes the photocell is fixed (as in the goniometer described later) and different angles of elevation are obtained by rotating the fitting about a horizontal axis.

Polar-curve photometers are used for measurements on general purpose fittings and street lanterns; fittings which do not project a very concentrating beam of light. Essentially the polar-curve photometer should fulfil two requirements. Firstly, the length of the optical path from the fitting to the light receptor should be at least five times the largest dimension of the fitting to be tested, in order that the inverse square law will operate with a reasonable degree of accuracy. Secondly, the apparatus should test the fitting in its working position. This is important with fluorescent fittings because the output of the tube depends on the temperature of the air surrounding it, which in turn depends on the orientation of the fitting. Also some lamps, e.g. certain types of mercury vapour lamp, can only be burnt in the vertical position.

The optical path can be lengthened by using mirrors as shown in Fig. 8.15.

Fig. 8.15   A polar curve photometer (the mirror in the top foreground reflects light from the fitting into the photocell box just visible to left of mirror. The arm on which the mirror and photocell are fixed rotates through 180°)

Readings are taken by stopping the arm at intervals and noting the deflection at the light recording instrument. The most important precaution to be observed is to make sure that no stray light enters the light receptor. Also draughts should be minimised when testing fluorescent fittings.

Spotlights and floodlights emitting a concentrating beam of light must be tested at a greater distance than non-concentrating fittings. These fittings usually depend on a parabolic reflector to control the light. A point source placed at the focus of such a reflector would emit a parallel beam. In practice, owing to the finite size of the filament, the light will be spread as shown in Fig. 8.16. From this it can be seen that the inner rays of the reflected cones of

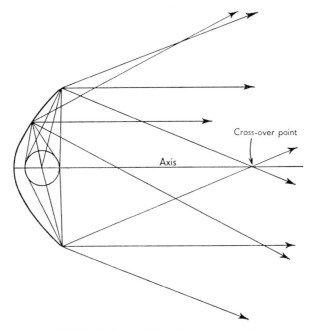

Fig. 8.16   Formation of cross-over point

light cross over the axis. The point at which the rays from the edge of reflector cut the axis is known as the cross-over point. If the reflector is viewed from beyond this point it will appear fully flashed (except in areas where there are inaccuracies in the contour). The inverse square law only applies to a reasonable degree of approximation beyond this point, which, therefore, determines the shortest test distance. An optical path of 100 ft is usually sufficient for projectors used for floodlighting applications. The fitting is mounted on a goniometer (Fig. 8.17) which allows it to be turned in elevation and azimuth. The most convenient arrangement is to have the light path horizontal. The size of light receptor should be sufficiently large to even out the effect of striations.

Photometric procedures.   Photometric test procedures are fully described in BS 3820: 1964. These apply to most types of lighting fittings, but BS 1788: 1964 should be consulted for street lighting lanterns. These documents detail how the effective light centre of the fitting is found, the appropriate heating-up periods of the bare lamp and fittings, and the number of readings to be taken round the bare lamp and fitting.

5+

Fig. 8.17   Model of a goniometer

Laboratory measurements of luminance.   Luminance measurements can be made in three ways:

(1) *From the polar curve.*   The projected area of the fitting in the direction of view is divided into the intensity in that direction. (The projected area can be found either by photographing the fitting from as great a distance as possible and finding the area by means of a planimeter, or by measurement from a drawing.)

(2) *By means of a reflex camera* in which a colour corrected photocell is fixed in the focal plane, as shown in Fig. 8.18. The area covered by the photocell is marked on the ground glass screen. The image of the object to be measured is registered in this marked area, and the mirror is then moved up out of the way, allowing the light to fall directly on to the photocell. The deflection given by the galvanometer will then be proportional to the luminance of the object. For fluorescent fittings the camera can be calibrated in terms of the nominal luminance of the bare tube, by focusing the bare tube on to the ground glass screen. It cannot be used for tungsten lamps because of the small size of the filament. The best way to overcome this restriction is to use the

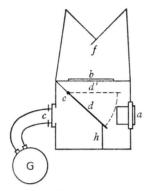

Fig. 8.18   Reflex camera adapted for luminance measurements

a	lens	*d'*	mirror in up position
b	ground-glass screen with equivalent position of photocell (*c*) marked on	*e*	hinge
		f	hood
c	photocell	G	galvanometer
d	mirror at 45°	*h*	rest for mirror

bare lamp to illuminate a plate of known reflection factor. If the intensity of the bare lamp in the appropriate direction is known, this can be used to calculate the luminance of the plate.

The focus of the camera must be kept fixed all the time unless a correction is made. For simplicity the camera can be replaced by a cylindrical tube with black baffles as shown in Fig. 8.19, but the disadvantage of this is that it is difficult to ascertain the field of view of the photocell.

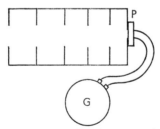

Fig. 8.19   Cylinder with baffles for measuring luminance
P   photocell   G   galvanometer

(3) *By visual method.* The visual type of instrument usually contains a standard luminance source which is compared in luminance with the field to be measured. The two are observed together in the eyepiece and the luminance of the standard source adjusted to match the unknown source by moving calibrated neutral wedges into the optical path. The S.E.I. meter is of this type, and because of its portability is also useful for field measurements.

Field measurements. Illumination calculations assume ideal conditions, such as uniformly diffusing reflecting surfaces, empty rooms, and walls of all the same reflection factor, which are rarely found in practice. There is, therefore, very often an element of uncertainty in the figures obtained, and it is advisable that the lighting engineer should take measurements in the completed installation to find if the levels of illumination and luminance agree with those planned. This check will enable him to learn from his measurements how to allow for departures from ideal conditions, and so supplement his future calculations with experience.

Illumination measurements should be taken with a meter which is known to be stable in its calibration. It is preferable that the photocell should be cosine-corrected, and corrected to the colour response of the eye, unless a correction factor is known for the colour of lighting being measured.

For checking the illumination on a horizontal working plane, the photocell should be held at the level of the working plane, with its surface horizontal, the operator being careful not to obstruct the light falling on the cell. If the average illumination is required, as many readings as possible should be taken at equally spaced intervals in the installation.

A check should be made on the voltage, especially with incandescent installations where a 1% variation in voltage gives a 4% variation in output. Fluorescent fittings should be given at least 20 minutes to warm up, preferably longer for totally enclosed diffuser fittings.

If possible a note should be made of the length of time the lamps have been operated so that a correction factor can be applied for ageing.

Luminance measurements are most easily made with an S.E.I. meter (mentioned earlier), but because of the difficulty of matching the spot with coloured surfaces the average of at least two readings (preferably from different observers) should be taken at each point.

An alternative method for finding the luminance of the room surfaces is to measure the illumination and multiply by the reflection factor of the surface. If the illumination is measured in lumens per square foot, the luminance will be in footlamberts, assuming uniform diffusion.

CHAPTER 9

Lighting Calculations

The planning of a lighting installation may be a simple operation in which the main objective is the provision of a recommended maintained general illumination required over a certain area, or it may involve the preparation and presentation of more detailed information regarding the illumination at specific points in a room, or the luminance of the main room surfaces and data from which the quality of the lighting may be judged.

The first operation referred to above allows the designer to determine the number and arrangement of lighting fittings of a particular type (chosen as suitable for the application under consideration) required to give the recommended illumination.

For more detailed planning, such as the determination of illumination at specific points, more advanced calculation techniques are often needed.

There is also a need for more precise data on luminance distribution in rooms and this of necessity requires the use of more advanced lighting design techniques.

PLANNING THE GENERAL LIGHTING INSTALLATION

For many interiors a general lighting scheme can be employed. In these general lighting schemes the lighting fittings are often arranged in a regular array where the spacing of the fittings along the rows is substantially the same as the spacing between the rows, and the spacing between the walls and outer rows of fittings is approximately half the spacing between the rows. In the case of long linear sources the spacing along the rows may be less than between the rows, or continuous runs of fittings may even be employed.

The appropriate spacing will be determined by the light distribution from the fitting, the level of illumination required, the height of the building and other practical considerations, e.g. the available roof structure members to which the fittings can be easily attached. Manufacturers of lighting fittings specify for any given fitting a maximum spacing-to-height ratio which is determined from a consideration of its light distribution and the spacing required to provide illumination in the horizontal plane such that the minimum value is not less than 0·7 of the maximum. In practice, spacing/height ratios may vary from 0·5 to 1·5 and a method of determining recommended maximum values for axially symmetrical distributions is given in BS 398: 1948.

The 'lumen' method of design. The most frequently used (though limited) method of lighting installation design depends upon a determination of the total flux required to provide a given value of working plane illumination and is generally known as the 'lumen' method.

Basically the procedure is to determine the quantity of light flux which the sources must emit to obtain the required value of task illumination extending over the whole of the working plane, plus that which is lost by absorption in the lighting fittings and by the room surfaces. It depends upon knowing or being able to calculate the ratio of the utilised flux to the total flux emitted by the light sources—the *utilisation factor* (*coefficient of utilisation*).

The 'lumen' method can be expressed using the formula:

$$F = \frac{E_{av} \times A}{U.F. \times M.F.}$$

where F = total flux required in lumens

E_{av} = average working plane illumination

U.F. = utilisation factor

A = the area of the working plane

and M.F. = maintenance factor.

Utilisation factor. The British Zonal Method for determining the U.F. (given in the I.E.S. Technical Report No. 2) considers separately the contributions from the downward and the upward components of flux from the installation. Flux from the fittings is divided between the lower and upper hemispheres. The ratio of the downward flux emitted from the fittings to the total lamp flux, is known as the *downward light output ratio* (D.L.O.R. symbol η''). Similarly the ratio of the upward flux emitted from the fittings to the total lamp flux is known as the *upward light output ratio* (U.L.O.R. symbol η').

The total flux reaching the working plane consists of that part which is directly incident on the working plane plus that part which reaches it after inter-reflection. The lower hemisphere flux which is utilised contains a direct component and an inter-reflected component, while the upper hemisphere flux which is utilised will consist entirely of inter-reflected flux within the space between ceiling and walls.

For the calculation of both the direct and inter-reflected components, certain assumptions are made and conventions adopted. It has been shown that the inter-reflected components calculated for a square room will apply, with sufficient accuracy, to rectangular rooms of the same height and surface reflectivities, provided equivalent dimensions are used. These equivalent dimensions, the geometric mean, are called the *room ratio* or *room index* and the symbol used is K_r.

$$K_r = \frac{LW}{(L + W)H_m}$$

where L and W are the length and width respectively, and H_m is the mounting height of the fittings above the working plane.

As a convention, a regular square arrangement of fittings is assumed at a uniform spacing/mounting height ratio with one half the normal spacing from each of the walls of the square room of given room index. The distance of the outer rows of fittings from the walls of a building affect both the distribution of the available light flux and its utilisation. There will be occasions when it is desirable to locate the outer rows of fittings closer to the walls than the conventional half-spacing distance, so as to increase wall luminance and work-plane illumination near the walls. If the wall to outer row spacing is reduced to less than half the spacing in the rows, then the overall utilisation will be smaller and the number of fittings may need to be increased over the value obtained from Utilisation Factor data published by the manufacturers. It should be noted that in these circumstances, although the utilisation factor is lower, the quality of an installation will probably be enhanced.

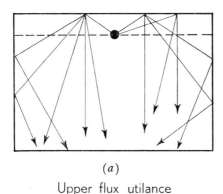

(a)

Upper flux utilance

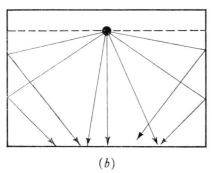

(b)

Lower flux utilance

Fig. 9.1   Utilisation of light flux received by the working plane
(a) Initially emitted upwards
(b) Initially emitted downwards

The distribution of light in the lower hemisphere is expressed in terms of the direct light incident on the working plane, and that proportion of the total downward flux from a conventional installation of lighting fittings which is directly incident on the working plane is known as the *direct ratio* (D.R.). The proportion of the total downward flux from the fittings which reaches the working plane, some directly and some after inter-reflection, is known as the *lower flux utilance* (symbol U''). Similarly the proportion of the total upward flux which finally reaches the working plane after inter-reflection is known as the *upper flux utilance* (symbol U'). The downward coefficient is the ratio of that part of the downward flux from the fittings which reaches the working plane to the total flux from the lamps, and the upward coefficient is the ratio of that part of the upward flux from the fittings which reaches the working plane to the total flux from the lamps (Figs. 9.1(a) and 9.1(b)).

Using these definitions, the basis of the B.Z. method can be stated by the equation:

$$\text{U.F.} = U''\eta'' + U'\eta'$$

or $\quad$ U.F. = D.C. + U.C.

$$= \text{L.F.U.} \times \text{D.L.O.R.} + \text{U.F.U.} \times \text{U.L.O.R.}$$

The D.L.O.R. and the U.L.O.R. are obtained from the photometric data for the fitting.

Ceiling mounted fittings. For ceiling mounted fittings it is assumed that the whole of the upward light flux falls on the ceiling and therefore both the upper and lower flux utilance values can be prepared and presented in tables to cover a wide range of conditions and the utilisation factor can be obtained as described earlier, i.e.

$$\text{U.F.} = \text{U.L.O.R.} \times \text{U.F.U.} + \text{D.L.O.R.} \times \text{L.F.U.}$$

Suspended fittings. For those installations in which the lighting fittings are suspended from the ceiling, the inter-reflected light calculations are made only for the space between the working plane and the plane of the fittings (Fig. 9.2). The space above the plane of the fittings is replaced by an equivalent ceiling which has an effective reflection factor less than that of the actual ceiling.

In general, where the suspension length, H_s, is less than one-sixth of the ceiling height above the work plane, the fittings may be regarded as ceiling mounted.

It can be shown that the light lost by absorption within the space above the fittings, known as the *ceiling cavity*, is the same as that which would be lost on an imaginary ceiling at the same height as the fittings, when this equivalent ceiling has an effective reflection factor given by the formula

$$R_e = \frac{A_c R_a}{A_c R_a + A_t(1 - R_a)}$$

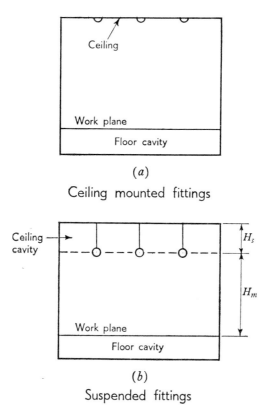

(a)

Ceiling mounted fittings

(b)

Suspended fittings

Fig. 9.2   The cavity method for installation design

where R_e = effective reflection factor for the equivalent ceiling

R_a = average reflection factor of all the actual surfaces within the ceiling cavity

A_c = plan area of the ceiling

A_t = total area of all surfaces within the ceiling cavity.

The average reflection factor (R_a) of the actual surfaces must be carefully estimated or measured, particularly if the cavity height is great or if the lighting is mainly indirect. Room index K_r is calculated using H_m, the mounting height, the distance between the work plane and the plane of fittings.

Alternatively, the double alignment nomograms, Fig. 9.3 and Fig. 9.4, may be used to determine the *cavity index* K_c and the effective reflection factor of the equivalent ceiling R_e. A straight line across the chart (Fig. 9.3) intersecting the room length and room width scales at the appropriate values, intersects the pivot line at the pivot point. A straight line through this pivot point and the appropriate cavity height will intersect the cavity index scale at the required value. The same pivot point may be used to determine the

5*

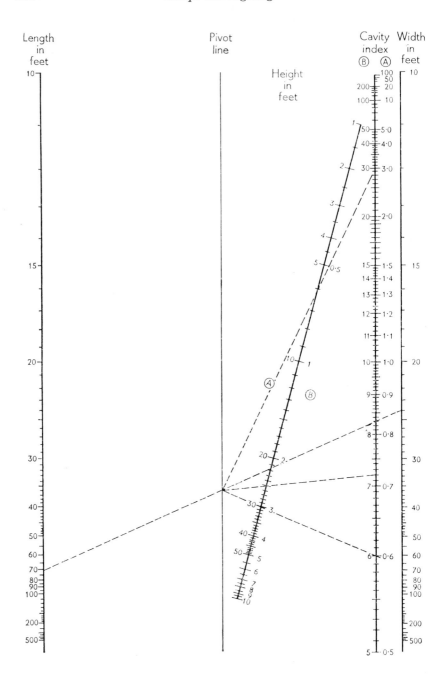

Fig. 9.3   Nomogram for obtaining cavity index

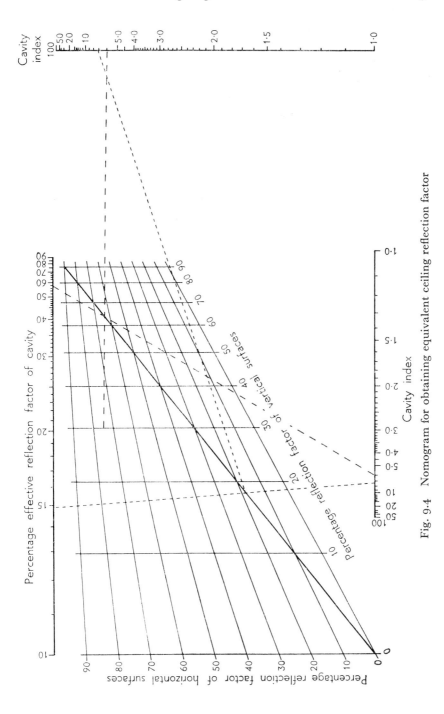

Fig. 9.4   Nomogram for obtaining equivalent ceiling reflection factor

floor, ceiling and room cavity indices. The height axis is graduated with two sets of values. Whichever scale is used the same scale should be used on the cavity index axis when reading the result. The starting point for the other nomogram (Fig. 9.4) is in the lattice on the left-hand side in a position appropriate for the reflection factors in the cavity. The first alignment between this point and the cavity index scale on the right-hand side intersects the bold diagonal line in the lattice at the pivot point. A straight line through this pivot point and the appropriate value on the cavity index scale at the bottom of the chart intersects the effective reflection factor scale at the required value.

Having determined the value of R_e the upper and lower flux utilance can be read from the same tables as those used for ceiling mounted fittings.

Luminous ceilings. The design of wall-to-wall uniformly diffusing luminous ceiling installations can be achieved, as with other types of installation, provided the utilisation factor can be calculated. If the ceiling cavity and the translucent ceiling material enclosing the lighting fittings is considered as being the source of light, emitting all its flux in the lower hemisphere, for given conditions of room surface reflection factors and room index, utilance tables can be prepared as for other types of installation.

To treat the ceiling as the source, its light output ratio must be determined and as it also serves as a reflecting surface within the room, its effective reflection factor is required.

The effective reflection factor of the luminous ceiling can be determined using the formula

$$r + \frac{t^2 R_e}{1 - r R_e}$$

where r = total reflection factor of the translucent ceiling material and its supporting framework

t = total diffuse transmission factor of the translucent ceiling material and its supporting framework

and R_e = effective reflection factor of the cavity, determined by the same method as that used for obtaining R_e for suspended lighting fitting installations.

The remaining factor required to calculate the U.F. for the luminous ceiling installation is the light output ratio of the combined cavity, translucent material and primary light sources. This is obtained using the formula

$$\eta = \frac{t(\eta'' + \eta' . R_e)}{1 - r . R_e}$$

where η'' is the upward light output of the fittings in the cavity and η' is the downward light output ratio of the fittings in the cavity.

A table of values of utilance for wall-to-wall luminous ceilings is given as Table 9.1.

TABLE 9.1

Utilance of Wall-to-Wall Luminous Ceiling

Room index	Effective reflection factor of luminous ceiling	Effective reflection factor of working plane 10%				Effective reflection factor of working plane 30%			
		Reflection factor of walls				Reflection factor of walls			
		50%	30%	10%	0	50%	30%	10%	0
(k_r)	(R_d)	Utilance							
0·6	70%	·38	·32	·27	·25	·39	·33	·27	·26
	50%	·37	·32	·27	·25	·38	·32	·27	·25
	30%	·36	·31	·27	·25	·37	·31	·27	·25
0·8	70%	·49	·42	·36	·35	·51	·43	·37	·36
	50%	·48	·42	·36	·34	·50	·42	·36	·34
	30%	·47	·41	·36	·34	·48	·41	·36	·34
1·0	70%	·58	·51	·46	·43	·61	·52	·47	·44
	50%	·57	·50	·45	·43	·59	·51	·45	·43
	30%	·56	·49	·44	·42	·57	·50	·44	·43
1·25	70%	·65	·57	·52	·50	·69	·60	·53	·51
	50%	·63	·56	·52	·50	·66	·58	·52	·50
	30%	·61	·56	·51	·49	·63	·57	·51	·50
1·5	70%	·71	·64	·58	·56	·76	·67	·60	·57
	50%	·69	·63	·58	·56	·73	·65	·59	·56
	30%	·67	·62	·57	·55	·70	·63	·58	·56
2·0	70%	·78	·72	·67	·65	·85	·77	·69	·66
	50%	·76	·71	·66	·64	·82	·74	·68	·65
	30%	·75	·70	·65	·63	·80	·72	·66	·64
2·5	70%	·84	·78	·73	·71	·91	·84	·77	·74
	50%	·82	·76	·72	·70	·88	·80	·74	·72
	30%	·80	·75	·71	·70	·85	·78	·72	·70
3·0	70%	·87	·82	·78	·76	·96	·88	·83	·79
	50%	·85	·80	·77	·75	·91	·84	·80	·78
	30%	·84	·79	·76	·74	·89	·83	·77	·77
4·0	70%	·92	·88	·84	·82	1·03	·97	·91	·87
	50%	·90	·86	·83	·81	·98	·92	·88	·86
	30%	·88	·84	·82	·80	·95	·89	·86	·84
5·0	70%	·95	·91	·88	·86	1·07	1·01	·97	·95
	50%	·93	·89	·87	·86	1·01	·96	·93	·92
	30%	·91	·88	·86	·85	·98	·93	·91	·90

The procedure for calculating the U.F. is as follows:

(1) Calculate the light output ratio.
(2) Calculate the effective reflection factor R_d.
(3) Read the utilance from Table 9.1.
(4) Multiply the utilance by the L.O.R. to give the U.F.

Alternatively the data presented in Figs. 9.5, 9.6 and 9.7 may be used to calculate the U.F. for a luminous ceiling installation. The formula for R_e, the effective reflection factor of the cavity, can be re-written in terms of the ratio A_c/A_t, the area of the cavity to the total area of all the surfaces within the cavity. Curves may then be drawn relating A_c/A_t and R_e for a series of values of R_a, the average cavity reflection factor, thus allowing the values of R_e to be read off for any given value of R_a and A_c/A_t (Fig. 9.5).

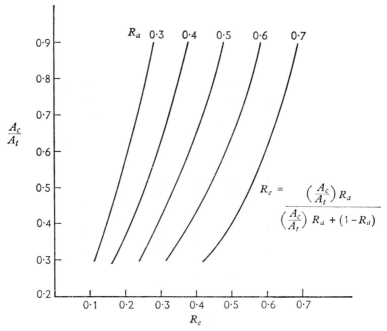

Fig. 9.5   Relation between values of effective reflection factor R_e of the cavity and area ratio A_c/A_t

Similarly for the translucent ceiling material being used, the effective reflection factor of the luminous ceiling R_d can be plotted against R_e and using the value of R_e taken from the first graph (Fig. 9.5) the value of R_d can be determined (Fig. 9.6). Also values of light output ratio may be plotted against R_e for the ceiling materials and types of fitting (Fig. 9.7). Thus, using again the value of R_e read from Fig. 9.5, the L.O.R. for the ceiling is obtained. The procedure for calculating the U.F. is that already given. The data

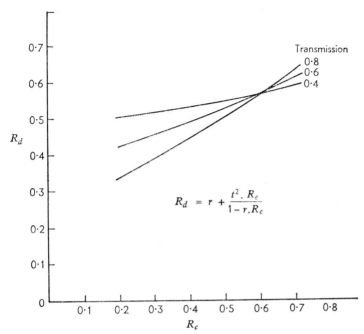

$$R_d = r + \frac{t^2 . R_e}{1 - r . R_e}$$

Fig. 9.6　Relation between values of effective ceiling reflection factor R_e and effective reflection factor of a luminous ceiling R_d

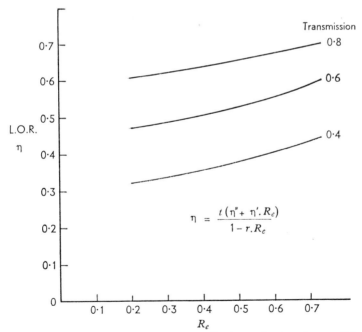

$$\eta = \frac{t\,(\eta'' + \eta' . R_e)}{1 - r . R_e}$$

Fig. 9.7　Relation between values of effective reflection factor of the cavity and the light-output ratio of a luminous ceiling

given in Figs. 9.5 to 9.7 is for bare fluorescent tubular lamps and the translucent materials data applies to materials such as thin P.V.C. film or $\frac{1}{8}$ in. acrylic sheet with transmission factor t varying from 0·4 to 0·8.

From the formula for the L.O.R. of a luminous ceiling it will be readily appreciated that the reflectivity of the various surfaces within the ceiling cavity is of considerable importance. It is therefore necessary to maintain these surfaces at high values of reflection factor. Also, when calculating R_e and r all surfaces within the cavity must be included. Thus any obstructions such as trunking, piping, suspension gear, etc., must be taken into account.

Overall louvered ceilings. The utilisation factors for overall louvered ceiling installations could be calculated similarly to those for luminous ceilings but the wide variety of types of louver and louver materials available introduces a very large range of variables. The transmission and reflection properties of various louver systems introduce modifications to the intensity distribution of the primary light sources and the light output ratio of the ceiling, and bring about conditions for which no simple formulae for calculating L.O.R. and R_d, the effective reflection factor, have so far been devised.

Utilisation factors for one particular set of conditions are given in Table 9.2 and the effects on L.O.R. of louver shielding angle and effective louver reflection factor are given in Fig. 9.8.

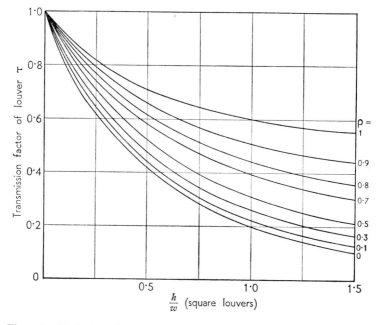

Fig. 9.8   Variation of transmission factor of louver with cell dimensions and reflection factor of louver material

TABLE 9.2

Utilisation Factors for Wall-to-wall Louvered Ceilings

Ceiling cavity reflection factor   0·75
Louver surface reflection factor 0·75
Effective working plane reflection factor   0·1

Room index	Wall reflection factors		
	0·5	0·3	0·1
0·6	·19	·16	·15
0·8	·23	·20	·19
1·0	·25	·22	·21
1·25	·27	·25	·24
1·5	·30	·26	·25
2·0	·32	·30	·29
2·5	·33	·31	·30
3·0	·34	·32	·32
4·0	·35	·34	·33
5·0	·36	·35	·34

Installation design data. To design a lighting installation by the lumen method the following factors must be known or determined:

(a) Room index K_r
(b) Surface reflectivities
(c) Required working plane illumination (E_{av})
(d) Utilisation factor (U.F.)
(e) Maintenance factor (M.F.).

Room index is calculated using the formula given earlier.

Where suspended fittings are employed, the ceiling reflection factor used in the calculations is the effective reflection factor of the equivalent ceiling, R_e. Where the installation has a luminous ceiling the effective reflection factor of the luminous ceiling R_d is used. The effective reflection factor of the working plane is obtained using the same formula as for calculating the effective reflection factor of the equivalent ceiling, the cavity data used being that for the floor cavity instead of the ceiling cavity. In tables of utilance and utilisation factors this has been referred to as the floor reflection factor but it is more correct to use the term effective reflection factor of the working plane. It is sometimes taken as the average reflection factor of all the horizontal surfaces of furniture at working plane level and that of the floor.

Surface reflectivities should be specified by the client or alternatively the installation designer should choose values suitable for the room's purpose. It should be borne in mind that high surface reflectivities provide high utilisation. Further advice on this subject is given in publications dealing with the choice of colours used in decoration (see *Bibliography*).

Utilisation factors for fittings are generally published by the fittings manufacturer or they can be calculated as already described, provided the data required to calculate the direct ratio and downward light output ratios are available. Utilisation factors are generally given for the following room conditions:

K_r = 0·6, 0·8, 1·0, 1·25, 1·5, 2·0, 2·5, 3·0, 4·0 or 5·0
Surface Reflectivities

Ceiling	·75	·75	·75	·50	·50	·50	·30	·30
Walls	·50	·30	·10	·50	·30	·10	·30	·10
Effective working plane	·10	·10	·10	·10	·10	·10	·10	·10

Where the working plane reflection factor differs from 0·10, the multiplying factors in Table 9.3 can be applied.

TABLE 9.3

Correction Factors for Various Effective Working Plane Reflection Factors
$(10\% = 1·00)$

Reflection Factor		Room Index								
Effective Ceiling	Wall	0·6	0·8	1·0	1·25	1·5	2·0	2·5	3·0	4·0	5·0

(table columns: Effective Ceiling, Wall, 0·6, 0·8, 1·0, 1·25, 1·5, 2·0, 2·5, 3·0, 4·0, 5·0)

Effective Ceiling	Wall	0·6	0·8	1·0	1·25	1·5	2·0	2·5	3·0	4·0	5·0
20% effective working plane reflection factor											
75	50	1·03	1·03	1·04	1·04	1·05	1·05	1·06	1·06	1·07	1·07
	30	1·01	1·02	1·02	1·03	1·04	1·04	1·05	1·05	1·06	1·07
	10	1·01	1·01	1·02	1·02	1·03	1·04	1·04	1·05	1·05	1·06
50	50	1·02	1·02	1·03	1·03	1·03	1·04	1·04	1·04	1·04	1·05
	30	1·01	1·01	1·02	1·02	1·02	1·03	1·03	1·04	1·04	1·04
	10	1·01	1·01	1·01	1·02	1·02	1·02	1·03	1·03	1·04	1·04
30	30	1·01	1·01	1·01	1·02	1·02	1·02	1·02	1·02	1·02	1·03
	10	1·00	1·01	1·01	1·01	1·01	1·01	1·02	1·02	1·02	1·02
30% effective working plane reflection factor											
75	50	1·05	1·06	1·07	1·09	1·10	1·11	1·12	1·13	1·14	1·15
	30	1·03	1·04	1·05	1·06	1·07	1·09	1·10	1·11	1·13	1·14
	10	1·01	1·02	1·03	1·05	1·06	1·07	1·09	1·10	1·12	1·13
50	50	1·04	1·05	1·05	1·06	1·07	1·08	1·08	1·09	1·09	1·10
	30	1·03	1·03	1·04	1·04	1·05	1·06	1·07	1·07	1·08	1·09
	10	1·01	1·02	1·02	1·03	1·04	1·05	1·06	1·06	1·07	1·08
30	30	1·02	1·02	1·03	1·03	1·03	1·04	1·04	1·05	1·05	1·05
	10	1·01	1·01	1·02	1·02	1·02	1·03	1·03	1·04	1·04	1·05

For conditions corresponding to other values intermediate between those tabulated, utilisation factors may be obtained by linear interpolation.

In addition to the tables of utilisation factors, polar curves of intensity distribution, maximum spacing/mounting height ratio at which the fitting may be used and some notes on its construction and the type of installation for which it is most suited, are generally published by the manufacturers. An example of such data is given in Fig. 9.9.

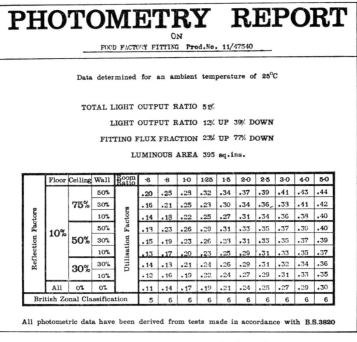

PHOTOMETRY REPORT
ON
FOOD FACTORY FITTING Prod.No. 11/47540

Data determined for an ambient temperature of 25°C

TOTAL LIGHT OUTPUT RATIO 51%

LIGHT OUTPUT RATIO 12% UP 39% DOWN

FITTING FLUX FRACTION 23% UP 77% DOWN

LUMINOUS AREA 395 sq.ins.

	Floor	Ceiling	Wall	Room Ratio	·6	·8	1·0	1·25	1·5	2·0	2·5	3·0	4·0	5·0
Reflection Factors	10%	75%	50%	Utilisation Factors	.20	.25	.28	.32	.34	.37	.39	.41	.43	.44
			30%		.16	.21	.25	.23	.30	.34	.36	.33	.41	.42
			10%		.14	.18	.22	.25	.27	.31	.34	.36	.38	.40
		50%	50%		.13	.23	.26	.29	.31	.33	.35	.37	.39	.40
			30%		.15	.19	.23	.26	.23	.31	.33	.35	.37	.39
			10%		.13	.17	.20	.23	.25	.29	.31	.33	.35	.37
		30%	30%		.14	.13	.21	.24	.26	.29	.31	.32	.34	.36
			10%		.12	.16	.19	.22	.24	.27	.29	.31	.33	.35
	All	0%	0%		.11	.14	.17	.19	.21	.24	.25	.27	.29	.30
British Zonal Classification					5	6	6	6	6	6	6	6	6	6

All photometric data have been derived from tests made in accordance with B.S.3820

Fig. 9.9 Standard photometric data sheet

Task illumination has already been discussed in Chapter 2 and for many applications reference to the I.E.S. Code enables the designer to fix the value appropriate to the purpose. An allowance must be made for the depreciation in luminous output of the lighting fittings, due to fall-off in lamp lumens over life, collection of dust and dirt on lamps and fittings, and reduction in the reflectivity of room surfaces due to the collection of dirt which inevitably reduces the installation efficiency during service. An allowance is made for the fall-off in lamp lumens through life, by using the 'lighting design lumens' for the lamps, obtained from manufacturer's data, and a maintenance factor is applied to allow for the depreciation due to the collection of dirt on the lamps, lighting fittings and room surfaces.

The value of the maintenance factor to be used when designing an installation is governed by a number of other factors which include

(1) the location of the installation
(2) the purpose of the building
(3) the type of lamp and lighting fitting employed
(4) the interior surface finishes and reflection factors

(5) the method of lamp replacement
(6) the cost of cleaning, and
(7) the installation running cost.

With the passage of time the lighting fittings in the installation collect dirt and their light output falls. The optimum economic cleaning interval occurs when the cost of the light lost due to the dirt collection equals the cost of cleaning the lighting fittings. The maintenance factor is the resultant of these separate main parts relating (a) to the collection of dirt on the lamps and on the lighting fittings (b) depreciation of the room surfaces, and the values of each part are governed by the cleaning interval.

To assist a rapid determination of the maintenance factor, the I.E.S. have prepared tables, and from a knowledge of items (1) to (7) above the appropriate value can be obtained.

Examples of Installation Design

(1) *A large general office located in a town centre and clean situation.* Required working plane illumination, 30 lm/ft². Dimensions of office, 24 ft wide and 60 ft long. Height of ceiling, 11 ft. Suspension distance of fitting from ceiling, $H_s = 1$ ft. Surface reflection factors—walls 50%, ceiling 70%, effective working plane 10%.

Room index $K_r = \dfrac{W \times L}{H_m(W + L)} = \dfrac{60 \times 24}{7 \times 84} = 2\cdot45$

Cavity index $K_c = K_r \times \dfrac{H_m}{H_s} = 2\cdot45 \times \dfrac{7}{1} = 17\cdot15$

From Table 2 of I.E.S. Report No. 2, the effective ceiling reflection = 60%.

The utilisation factor from the table for the fitting selected, a louvered diffuser fitting with two 5 ft 80 W tubular fluorescent lamps and BZ 3 classification, is 0·48, interpolating between the tabulated values for effective ceiling reflection factors of 50% and 70%.

Assuming that an economical cleaning period of nine months has been determined for the installation, and assuming the room surfaces will be cleaned every 12 months the maintenance factor is found to be 0·77.

Hence the total flux required

$$F = \frac{30 \times 60 \times 24}{0\cdot48 \times 0\cdot77} = 117{,}000 \text{ lumens.}$$

Hence the number of fittings required

$$N = \frac{117{,}000}{4500 \times 2} = 13$$

assuming lighting design lumens per lamp = 4500.

For symmetry, 12 or 14 fittings would be used, preferably 14 so as to ensure the maintenance of the illumination design value of 30 lm/ft².

Thus two rows spaced 12 ft apart with 7 fittings per row spaced 8 ft 6 in.

between centres could be adopted. The spacing/height ratio between the rows is 1·2, just within the maximum of 1·25 recommended for the type of fitting selected, and hence the diversity of working plane illumination should be quite acceptable.

(2) *Light machine shop located in a dirty industrial area.* Dimensions, 120 ft long and 64 ft wide with flat roof of height 26 ft, work plane 3 ft above floor. Roof glazing covers 33% of total roof area. Reflection factors—walls 30%, ceiling 70%, effective working plane 10%.

It is decided to use industrial open top reflector fittings employing two 5 ft 80 W tubular fluorescent lamps. Fittings suspended 3 ft from ceiling.

From the I.E.S. Code the working plane illumination recommended is 30 lm/ft² and this value is to be maintained in service conditions.

The effective reflection factor of the horizontal ceiling area, assuming the glass reflection factor is 0·1, will be

$$0{\cdot}7 \times \frac{2}{3} + 0{\cdot}1 \times \frac{1}{3} = \frac{1{\cdot}4}{3} + \frac{0{\cdot}1}{3} = 0.5$$

From the nomogram, Fig. 9.3, the ceiling cavity ratio is 13.9.
Room index

$$K_r = \frac{120 \times 64}{20 \times 184} = 2{\cdot}08$$

From the nomogram, Fig. 9.4, the reflection factor of the equivalent ceiling R_e is 0·45.

The utilisation factor for these conditions (from manufacturer's published data) is 0·51.

Total lamp flux required

$$F = \frac{120 \times 64 \times 30}{{\cdot}51 \times \text{M.F.}}$$

Assuming that the economical cleaning period for the installation has been found to be every six months, that a system of bulk replacement of lamps is anticipated, and walls are to be cleaned or redecorated every two years, the maintenance factor will be 0·75.

The total flux

$$F = \frac{120 \times 64 \times 30}{{\cdot}51 \times {\cdot}75} = 600{,}000 \text{ lumens}$$

Number of fittings required,

$$N = \frac{600{,}000}{5000 \times 2} = 60$$

assuming that the lighting design lumens per lamp = 5000.

As a symmetrical arrangement of fittings is desirable for this installation 60 fittings would be used.

These fittings can be arranged in 6 rows of 20 ft spacing between rows at approximately 6 ft 4 in. between the centres of the fittings in the rows.

The spacing/height ratio will be $\frac{20}{20} = 1$, well within the maximum value of 1.25 required for an acceptable working plane illumination diversity.

Predicting discomfort glare ratings. It will be evident that the 'lumen' method of lighting installation design is a limited one in that it does not give any indication of brightness of the work surfaces, or whether there may be objectional contrasts which could be a cause of discomfort.

This limitation may be overcome, in part, by assessing the discomfort glare index for the installation.

The glare formula. The procedure for doing this is set out in the I.E.S. Code and is based upon an empirical formula developed by the Building Research Station as a result of research carried out there. The formula is:

$$G = \sum \frac{B_s^{1 \cdot 6} \omega^{0 \cdot 8}}{B_b} \cdot \frac{1}{p^{1 \cdot 6}}$$

where G = glare constant for the installation

   B_s = luminance of each individual source in ft-L

   ω = solid angle subtended by each individual source at the eye (steradians)

   B_b = background luminance of the whole surroundings (ft-L) defined as that uniform luminance of the surroundings which would produce the same illumination on a vertical plane at the observer's eye as does the actual field, excluding the glare sources.

   p = position index for each individual source.

In order to obtain numerically convenient values, the glare constant as defined in the B.R.S. formula is expressed as a glare index $= 10 \log G$.

The glare index system. In a practical installation the glare assessment is made for an observer who is sitting at the mid-point of one side of the room, looking straight ahead along a horizontal sight line, and the total glare is taken to be the sum of that due to each source taken separately.

The glare index can be derived from the basic formula, but the procedure is lengthy. Therefore tables were prepared of glare index for installations covering a selected range of room dimensions, light distributions, and room surface reflectivities, whilst keeping the total downward flux from the fittings, the height of the fittings above a 4 ft eye level, and the fitting luminous area at certain chosen constant values. The selected ranges were chosen so as to cover the range of lighting installations generally met in practice. Conversion terms were also derived to take account of variations in a practical installation of those factors which are of fixed value in the glare index tables.

The factors chosen to have fixed values in the tables are:

(1) the downward flux F at 1000 lumens,
(2) the fitting luminous area A at 100 in^2,
(3) the height of the fittings above a 4 ft eye level H, at 10 ft.

The values of initial glare index in the tables were computed for a basic installation for each of the ten defined light distributions (BZ 1–10), four defined fittings flux fraction ratios, 0, 0·33, 1·0 and 3·0, and selected combinations of room dimensions and reflection factors. There is one table for each of the classified distributions.

Thus the glare index for an installation is obtained by reading from the appropriate table, opposite the room dimensions and surface reflectivities, the initial glare index and then applying the appropriate conversion terms taken from another table. The information required is as follows:

(1) *Lighting fittings*
The light distribution expressed as a BZ classification.
Total light output from the fitting in lumens.
Fittings flux fraction ratio (i.e. proportions in the upper and lower hemispheres).
Luminous area A of the fittings.
Mounting height H above a 4 ft eye level.

(2) *Room surfaces*
Reflection factors of ceiling, walls and floor.

(3) *Room dimensions*
The dimensions X and Y across and parallel respectively to the line of sight and expressed in terms of the height H above a 4 ft eye level.

The data for the lighting fittings is generally provided by the fittings manufacturer. The procedure is as follows:

(1) The table appropriate to the BZ classification of the fitting is selected.
(2) The room dimensions X and Y are determined in terms of the fitting height above a 4 ft eye level.
(3) The value of the initial glare index for the particular room dimensions, fittings flux fractions and room reflection factors is read from the selected table, interpolating where necessary.
(4) When linear fittings are used, having different endwise and cross-wise distributions, the appropriate conversion term given on the right-hand side of the table is added to or subtracted from the initial glare index.
(5) Add algebraically the conversion terms for luminous flux F, area A, and mounting height H.

The value obtained in this way is the glare index for the installation. Having determined the installation glare index, it can then be compared with the value of the limiting glare index which has been assessed as appropriate for that type of location. These limiting values are given in a Schedule in Part III of the Code.

Additional notes on the limiting glare index system
(1) The luminous area A of fittings is defined as follows: BZ 1 to BZ 8, the orthogonally projected area (in in²) at 0°, i.e. as seen vertically beneath the fitting. BZ 9 and BZ 10, the maximum orthogonally projected area at 90°, i.e. when viewed horizontally from the sides.

(2) For convenience, and to avoid interpolation of tabulated values, the values of the conversion terms for F, A and H can be plotted as graphs, which can be used more quickly and more accurately than tables.

(3) When planning an installation in which fittings having non-symmetric distributions are used, if the normal viewing direction of the occupants of the room is fixed, and it is found that the glare index is higher than the recommended limit, it is sometimes possible to reduce the glare index by re-orientating the fittings.

(4) It should be noted that the assessment of glare is complex and the influence of the various factors which are involved is not a single proportional change. Therefore if one or more of the parameters is changed the full procedure for determining the glare index, given above, must be carried out. If a particular type of fitting is found unsuitable for one installation it does not follow that it is necessarily unsuitable for another. Also, if a particular fitting in a given installation produces a glare index very much lower than the recommended limiting value, it is not necessarily a better lighting installation than that in which some other lighting fitting gives a glare index just below the recommended limit. The recommended limits have been set according to the nature of (and conditions demanded by) the occupation, and there is no great virtue in a glare index considerably lower than the recommended limit.

Example.   A Sheet Metal Works

Dimensions: 120 ft long, 60 ft wide with fittings mounted at 24 ft above the floor.

Room reflection factors: ceiling 50%, walls 30%, effective working plane 14%.

Fittings: fluorescent lamp fittings BZ 4 classification mounted in rows parallel to the longer side of the factory.

Flux fractions: $\dfrac{0}{100}$

Total downward flux, 6000 lumens.
Luminous area, 720 in^2.

H will be $24 - 4 = 20$ ft, $Y = 6H$ and $X = 3H$.

Initial Glare Index from tables $= 23 \cdot 6 + 1 \cdot 3$ for endwise viewing.

Conversion terms:
$F = +4 \cdot 7$
$A = -7 \cdot 0$
$H = +1 \cdot 0$
Total $-1 \cdot 3$

Installation glare index 23·6.

The limiting value recommended for a sheet metal works is 25 and therefore the designed installation will be satisfactory.

Suppose, however, that the factory is a woodworking shop where the

recommended limit is 22. The condition can be met by raising the height
of the fittings to 34 ft as follows:

$H = 30$ ft, $Y = 4H$ and $X = 2H$.

Initial glare index from tables $= 20·7 + 0·5 = 21·2$.

Conversion terms:

$F = +4·7$ as before

$A = -7·0$ as before

$H = +1·6$

and Glare Index $= 21·1 + 4·7 - 7·0 + 1·6 = 20·5$

within the recommended limit of 22.

CALCULATION OF DIRECT ILLUMINATION

Where values of illumination at specific points in an installation are required,
the lumen method cannot be applied. Instead, the direct illumination at the
point due to all the sources contributing to the illumination is first calculated,
and a component is added to allow for the light reflected from the room
surfaces.

Illumination from point sources. The calculation of direct illumination
is based upon the concept of the point source, the intensity I of the source in
the significant direction, and the application of the inverse square and
cosine laws. Thus

$$E = \frac{I \cos \theta}{d^2}$$

where d is the distance from the source to the point and θ is the angle between
the incident ray of light and the normal to the receiving surface (Fig. 9.10).

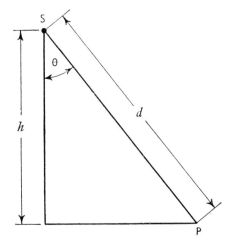

Fig. 9.10   Illumination from a point source

Since $d = h/\cos \theta$ the equation can be written as

$$E = \frac{I \cos^3 \theta}{h^2}$$

a form frequently found in practice to be more convenient to apply.

For example, taking a point source at a height $h = 12$ ft above a horizontal surface, emitting uniformly in all directions an intensity of 1600 cd, then the illumination at a point on the surface distance $s = 4$ ft from the point vertically below the source will be given by:

$$E = \frac{I \cos^3 \theta}{h^2}$$

where $\quad I = 1600$ cd

$\quad\quad\quad h^2 = 144$

$$\theta = \tan^{-1} \frac{s}{h} = \tan^{-1} \frac{4}{12} = 18\cdot4°$$

and $\quad \cos^3 \theta = \cdot855$

$$E = \frac{1600 \times \cdot855}{144} = 9\cdot5 \text{ lm/ft}^2$$

In the practical case any source will have finite size, and as the size of the source relative to the distance increases, the value obtained using the inverse square law to calculate illumination will be less and less accurate. The point at which the inverse square law can no longer be applied will depend upon the order of accuracy required.

The calculation of the direct illumination due to long continuous or broken lines of tubular fluorescent lamp fittings at points on a surface where the distance of the line of fittings to the surface is small compared with the length of the line of fittings is an example where the inverse square law cannot generally be applied directly to obtain answers of acceptable accuracy. Therefore other methods have been devised to overcome this limitation and one such method is described below.

Calculation of direct illumination from linear sources. The accurate calculation of illumination at a point on a surface due to a linear source depends upon a knowledge of the axial intensity distribution, the intensity distribution in a plane normal to the axis and the geometry of the point of interest and source position. As those parts of the source remote from the illuminated point of interest will be less effective than nearer parts of the source, it is evident that the shape of the axial intensity distribution curve is of particular importance. Also the intensity in any given direction of any short element of a uniform linear source is proportional to the total intensity of the source (i.e. due to a finite length) in the same parallel direction. That fraction of the total intensity of the source which sums up the influence of all the individual source elements on the illumination at the point of interest according to their angular relation to that point and the characteristic type of axial distribution of the source is termed the *aspect factor*. The shape of the axial intensity distribution curve for practical linear sources is usually similar

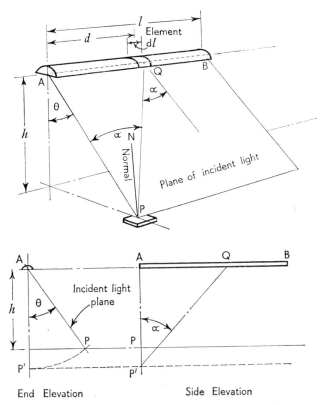

Fig. 9.11   Geometrical relationships of factors contributing to
the illumination from linear sources

in all inclined planes passing through the source axis, the scale of magnitude
of the curve in any particular case being defined by the value at the nadir,
which is the same as that given by the transverse polar curve at the angle of
the inclined plane (Fig. 9.12) through the source axis and the point of interest.

The illumination calculations can be made easily and quickly if data
expressed in terms of the source axial intensity distribution are pre-calculated
and tabulated. A classified range of axial intensity distributions covering the
practical range of distributions has therefore been prepared. These distributions are defined in terms of the cosine powers and are designated distributions
A, B, C, D and E, where for distribution

$$A \qquad I_\alpha = I_\theta \cos\alpha$$

$$B \qquad I_\alpha = I_\theta \frac{(\cos\alpha + \cos^2\alpha)}{2}$$

$$C \qquad I_\alpha = I_\theta \cos^2\alpha$$

$$D \qquad I_\alpha = I_\theta \cos^3\alpha$$

$$E \qquad I_\alpha = I_\theta \cos^4\alpha$$

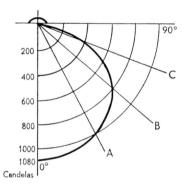

Transverse polar curve

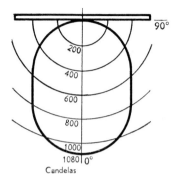

Axial (vertical) polar curve

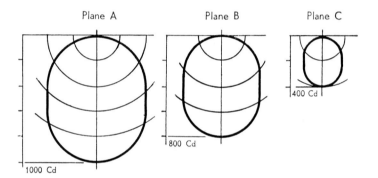

Polar curves in inclined axial planes A, B & C: the maximum in each case is the value from the transverse polar curve and the shape is similar to the axial (vertical) curve

Fig. 9.12   Polar curves of axial plane light distribution at various angles of elevation

where I_α is the axial intensity at any angle α and I_θ the intensity of the transverse polar distribution at angle θ, that angle between the vertical axial plane and the inclined plane through the point of interest.

The axial intensity distribution for practical lighting fittings can be classified by plotting the axial intensity distribution on rectangular co-ordinates and comparing this with the classified distributions given in Fig. 9.13, the fitting being classified by reference to the nearest standard curve A, B, C, D or E.

It can be shown that the illumination E_{pl} at any point on a plane parallel to the axis of a linear source may be given by the equation

$$E_{\mathrm{pl}} = \frac{I_\theta}{lh} \cos \theta \cos \phi \ (\mathrm{AF}) \qquad (\text{Fig. 9.14})$$

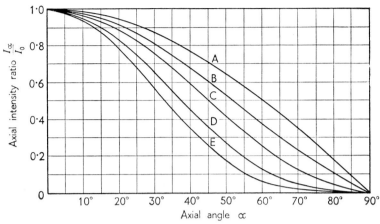

Fig. 9.13   Classification of axial intensity distributions

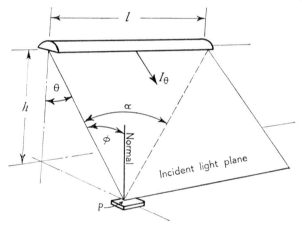

Fig. 9.14   Illumination at a point on a surface parallel to a linear source

where θ = the angle made by the incident light plane with the vertical, or nadir, of the transverse polar curve

ϕ = the angle made by the normal to the plane of interest with the plane of incident light

l = the length of the source (or fitting)

h = the height of the source axis above the horizontal plane through the point of interest

I_θ = the intensity of the total source, normal to the source axis, in the incident light plane

AF = the aspect factor.

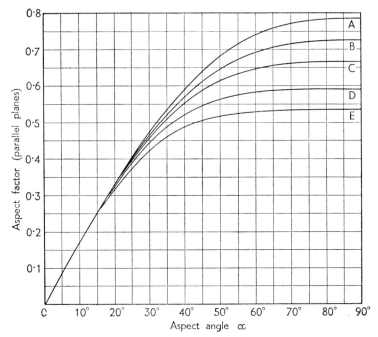

Fig. 9.15   Aspect factors (AF) parallel planes

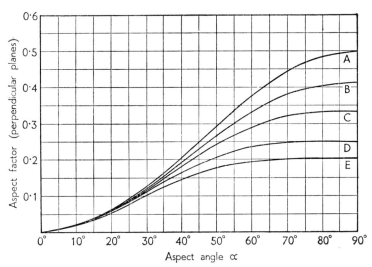

Fig. 9.15(a)   Aspect factors (af) perpendicular planes

In the equation I_θ is found directly from the transverse polar curve for the fitting, l, h, θ and ϕ are directly determined from the geometry of the installation, leaving only the aspect factor AF to be determined. Values of aspect factors can be read off from the graphs in Fig. 9.15 from the curve appropriate to the axial distribution.

The *aspect angle* α for any point Q (Fig. 9.11) on the source is measured in the incident light plane passing through the source axis and the point of interest P.

The incident light plane is defined by angle θ, and h is the height of the source axis above the horizontal plane through the point of interest, d is the distance of the point concerned on the source axis from the plane through the point of interest that is perpendicular to the source axis.

The aspect angle α can be found either graphically (Fig. 9.11) or from

$$\tan \alpha = \frac{d \cos \theta}{h}$$

Similarly, the illumination on a point on a plane perpendicular to the source axis is given by the formula

$$E_{\mathrm{pr}} = \frac{I_\theta}{lh} \cos \theta (\mathrm{af}) \qquad (\text{Fig. 9.16})$$

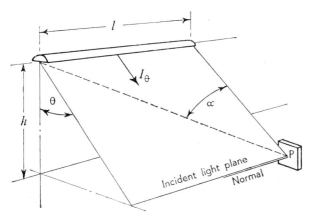

Fig. 9.16 Illumination at a point on a surface perpendicular to a linear source

where the symbols have the same significance as given for the illumination on a parallel plane and (af) is the aspect factor term for planes perpendicular to the source axis. Values of (af) are given on Fig. 9.15(a).

Example. To determine the illumination at a point P, Fig. 9.17(b), on a surface parallel to a linear source which is 25 ft long and 5 ft above the horizontal surface, the point P being at a distance of 2 ft from a point vertically

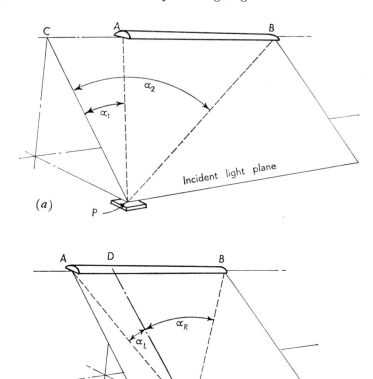

Fig. 9.17 Illumination at a point on a surface
(a) Beyond the end of a linear source
(b) Within the length of a linear source

below the source, 10 ft from one end of the source and 15 ft from the other end. Assume the axial distribution is distribution D and that $I_\theta = 150$ cd per foot length of the source.

$$E_{pl} = \frac{I_\theta}{h} \cos \theta \cos \phi \, \text{A.F.}$$

$$\tan \theta = 2/5 = 0\cdot4 \qquad \theta = 22° \qquad \cos \theta = 0\cdot927$$
$$\phi = \theta \qquad \cos \phi = 0\cdot927$$

$$\tan \alpha_1 = \frac{d_1 \cos \theta}{h} = \frac{10 \times 0\cdot927}{5} = 1\cdot854$$

$$\alpha_1 = 61\cdot5° \quad \text{and} \quad \text{A.F} = 0\cdot584$$

Therefore $E_{pl_1} = \dfrac{150}{5} \times (0.927)^2 \times 0.584 = 15.9 \text{ lm/ft}^2$

$$\tan \alpha_2 = \dfrac{d_2 \cos \theta}{h} = \dfrac{15}{5} \times 0.927 = 2.781$$

and $\alpha_2 = 70.2°$

and A.F. $= 0.588$

$$E_{pl_2} = \dfrac{150}{5} \times (0.927)^2 \times 0.588 = 16 \text{ lm/ft}^2$$

The total illumination at the point is $15.9 + 16 = 31.9 \text{ lm/ft}^2$.

Where the point of interest lies beyond the end of the source the illumination is calculated for a source of extended length equal to the distance of the point from the remote end of the source measured in a line parallel to the source. From this value is subtracted the illumination due to the extended part of the source only. Thus if the length of the extended source is $l + l_1$ where l is the true source length then, from Fig. 9.17(a).

$$E_{pl} = E_{pl_1} \text{ (due to } l + l_1) - E_{pl_2} \text{ (due to } l_1)$$

Illumination from area sources. In many instances a source may be so extensive as viewed from the receiving point that it cannot be treated as a single unit possessing an intensity. In such cases the area may be divided into small elements which can then be treated as point sources and the illumination due to the whole area obtained by a summation of the illumination due to each element. If there is a simple mathematical relationship between the intensities of the small elements of the extensive source, the illumination due to the whole source may be obtained by simple integration.

Many extensive sources may be considered as being of uniform luminance, that is, every element of the surface is of the same luminance irrespective of the angle of view or position on the source; such a source is known as a perfect diffuser. The sources to be considered will be treated as plane surfaces, however, and the results may be applied to any source possessing the same luminance conditions as viewed from the receiving point, provided the boundary of the source as seen from this point is the same as that for the plane source.

Plane surface source of infinite extent. The illumination on a plane parallel to a perfectly diffusing source of infinite extent may be obtained as follows:

Since the luminance of a perfect diffuser is equal in all directions, the luminous flux it emits must bear some simple relation to its luminance.

In Fig. 9.18, take the small element S of a perfect diffuser of luminance B and area a. Consider the point P on an imaginary sphere of radius r, the angle between SP and the normal to the surface being θ. Consider an elementary zone of the sphere around the point P and of angular width $d\theta$. Since the area of the zone is $2\pi r^2 \sin \theta \, d\theta$ the total solid angle it subtends at S is $2\pi \sin \theta \, d\theta$. Since the luminance of the surface at S is B, and apparent area in the direction SP is $a \cos \theta$, its luminous intensity in that direction and in all other directions passing through the elementary zone is $aB \cos \theta$.

6+

Thus, the total flux emitted from surface S within the solid angle subtended by the zone, is $aB \cos \theta \times 2\pi \sin \theta \, d\theta$, and the total flux over the whole hemisphere will be

$$\int_0^{\pi/2} 2\pi aB \cos \theta \sin \theta \, d\theta = 2\pi aB[\tfrac{1}{2} \sin^2 \theta]^{\pi/2}$$

$$= \pi aB$$

Thus, the flux in lumens emitted per unit area from a perfectly diffusing surface of luminance B is πB where B is expressed in candelas per unit area.

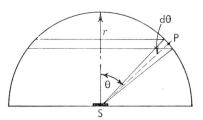

Fig. 9.18   Luminous flux emitted from a perfect diffuser

The illumination of the small element of the receiving surface at P (Fig. 9.19) due to the differential element of area dA is

$$dE_P = \frac{B}{D^2} \cos \beta \cos \alpha \, dA$$

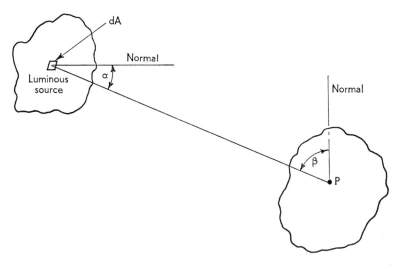

Fig. 9.19   Illumination of a small element due to a differential element dA

Similarly (Fig. 9.20)

$$dE_p = \frac{Bx^2}{(r^2 + x^2)^2} 2\pi r . dr$$

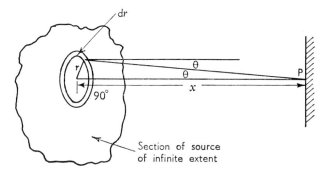

Fig. 9.20   Illumination from a source of infinite extent

since

$$dA = 2\pi r . dr \qquad \cos \beta = \cos \alpha = \cos \theta = \frac{x}{\sqrt{r^2 + x^2}}$$

$$D^2 = (r^2 + x^2)$$

The total illumination at P is

$$E_p = \pi x^2 B \int_0^\infty (r^2 + x^2)^{-2} 2r . dr$$
$$= -\pi x^2 B [(r^2 + x^2)^{-1}]_0^\infty$$
$$= \pi B$$

Thus, it should be noted that the illumination is independent of the distance x and is dependent only upon the luminance of the source. Since

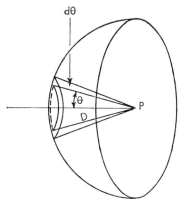

Fig. 9.21   Illumination at the centre of a hemispherical source
of uniform luminance

also the flux per unit area emitted by a perfectly diffusing surface is πB it follows that the illumination due to a perfectly diffusing surface is equal to the flux emitted per unit area. Similarly it can be shown that the illumination at a point P at the centre of a hemispherical source, Fig. 9.21, of uniform luminance is πB.

Illumination from a circular disc source. The illumination from a perfectly diffusing circular disc (Fig. 9.22) may be determined using the same equation

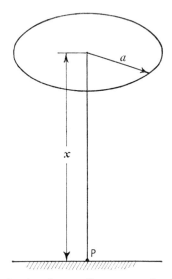

Fig. 9.22   Illumination from a disc source of uniform luminance
at a point below the centre of the source

used for the infinite source except that the integration is over the limits zero to a, where a is the radius of the disc.

Thus
$$E_{\mathrm{P}} = -\pi x^2 B[(r^2 + x^2)^{-1}]_0^a$$
$$= \pi B \frac{a^2}{a^2 + x^2}$$

This is the illumination on a plane parallel to the disc source and on a line perpendicular to the centre of the source.

It can also be shown that the illumination at any point on the surface of a sphere due to a circular disc source is constant for all positions on the surface, and that this is equal to the illumination on a horizontal surface at the point on the sphere surface.

From this it follows that, provided the correct dimensions are used, the simple formula for the illumination at a point on a surface perpendicularly below the centre of the source may be used to determine the illumination at any point on a horizontal plane.

Since the angle γ subtended by the constant arc AB (Fig. 9.23) is independent of the position of P on the circular arc below AB and the line NP bisects the angle HPJ, the illumination at any point P on the sphere wall is the same as at any other point and thus the illumination is the same as at C.

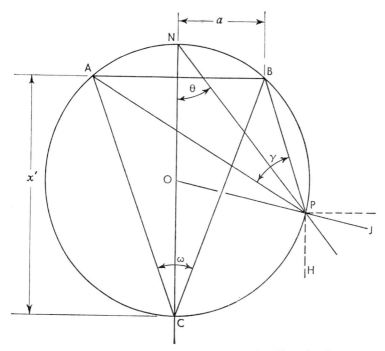

Fig. 9.23   Illumination from a disc source of uniform luminance at any point on a parallel plane below the source

Therefore $\quad E_{\mathrm{C}} = \pi B \left(\dfrac{a^2}{a^2 + x^2} \right) \quad$ and $\quad E_{\mathrm{P}} = \pi B \left(\dfrac{a^2}{a^2 + x^2} \right)$

but it should be noted that the value of x is not the same in each case.

$$E_{\mathrm{P}} = \pi B \left(\frac{a^2}{a^2 + x^2} \right)$$

can be written as

$$E_{\mathrm{P}} = \frac{\pi B}{2}(1 - \cos \omega) = \frac{\pi B}{2}(1 - \cos \gamma)$$

and the value of γ can be obtained by simple construction and measurement, or alternatively the distance x' can be measured.

Illumination from rectangular sources. Illumination resulting from a perfectly diffusing rectangular source may be obtained by integration over the boundary limits of the source, and as rectangular co-ordinates most easily define the boundaries of the source it involves the evaluation of a double integral using the same basic equation as used before.

There are two cases, one where the illuminated surface is parallel to the plane of the source and the other where the illuminated plane is perpendicular to the plane of the source. For the first condition, i.e. illuminated surface parallel to the plane of the source and with the point P (Fig. 9.24) on a perpendicular erected at one corner of the source:

$$E_P = \frac{B}{2} \left[\left(\frac{h}{\sqrt{h^2 + s^2}} \sin^{-1} \frac{w}{\sqrt{w^2 + h^2 + s^2}} \right) \right.$$
$$\left. + \left(\frac{w}{\sqrt{w^2 + s^2}} \sin^{-1} \frac{h}{\sqrt{w^2 + h^2 + s^2}} \right) \right]$$

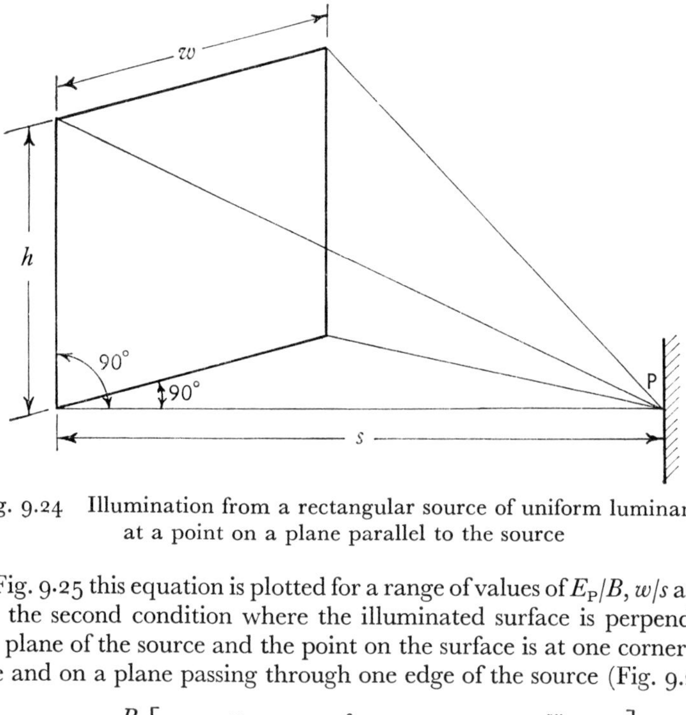

Fig. 9.24   Illumination from a rectangular source of uniform luminance at a point on a plane parallel to the source

In Fig. 9.25 this equation is plotted for a range of values of E_P/B, w/s and h/s. For the second condition where the illuminated surface is perpendicular to the plane of the source and the point on the surface is at one corner of the source and on a plane passing through one edge of the source (Fig. 9.26):

$$E_P = \frac{B}{2} \left[\tan^{-1} \frac{w}{s} + \frac{s}{\sqrt{h^2 + s^2}} \sin^{-1} \frac{w}{\sqrt{w^2 + h^2 + s^2}} \right]$$

In Fig. 9.27 this equation is plotted for a series of values of E_P/B, w/s and h/s, where B is measured in cd/ft^2 and 1 cd/ft$^2 = \pi$ftL.

Although Figs. 9.25 and 9.27 give the illumination for a point on a plane perpendicular to one corner of the source many problems are concerned with points offset from the perpendicular or within the area bounded by the planes perpendicular to the boundaries of the source.

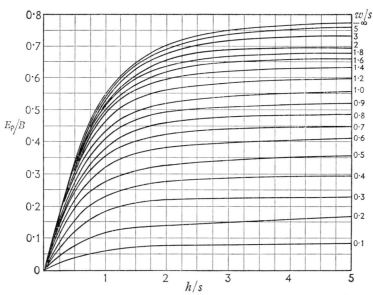

Fig. 9.25   Illumination from a rectangular source of uniform luminance
at a point on a plane parallel to the source

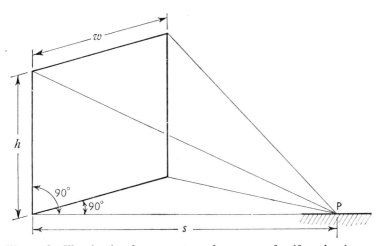

Fig. 9.26   Illumination from a rectangular source of uniform luminance
at a point on a plane perpendicular to the source

Where the point lies on a perpendicular within the boundaries of the source
the source may be divided into four components and the total illumination is
obtained by adding the component illuminations (Fig. 9.28(a)).

Thus E_P total $= E_{PA_1} + E_{PA_2} + E_{PA_3} + E_{PA_4}$

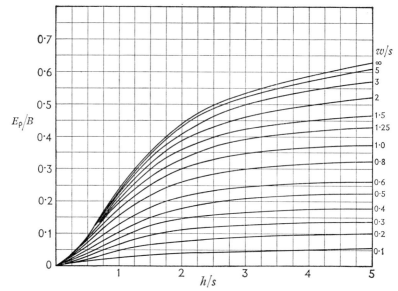

Fig. 9.27   Illumination from a rectangular source of uniform luminance
at a point on a plane perpendicular to the source

the receiving point being in each instance on a perpendicular at one corner
of a component area.

Where the point is on a perpendicular outside the boundaries of the source,
the source is extended so that its boundary coincides with the perpendicular
to the point. The illumination for the extended source areas $A_1 + A_2 + A_3 +
A_4$ (Fig. 9.28(b)) is calculated first. Then the illumination for the portions
$A_2 + A_4$ and $A_3 + A_4$ are calculated and subtracted from the first value.
As the value for A_4 has now been subtracted twice, the value for A_4 is then
added to give the value for the true source.

Thus $E_{PA_1} = E_{P(A_1 + A_2 + A_3 + A_4)} - E_{P(A_2 + A_4)} - E_{P(A_3 + A_4)} + E_{P(A_4)}$

Flux transfer.   So far this section has been concerned with a determination
of direct illumination at a point, and, as stated earlier, the total illumination
resulting from the direct and inter-reflected illumination within a room may
be required.

A determination of the inter-reflected component is generally accomplished
on the basis of a total flux transfer between one surface and another. In
the preceding sections methods of calculating the illumination due to large
area diffuse sources have been presented in the form of a ratio E_P/B. When
the value of B is unity this ratio is known as the *configuration factor* of the source
with respect to the point on the illuminated surface. It can be regarded as
equivalent to the flux density (illumination) at a point P on a surface 1 due
to uniformly diffusing surface 2 of unit emittance and the symbol used is C_{12}.

If the illumination values at a large number of points on a surface covering

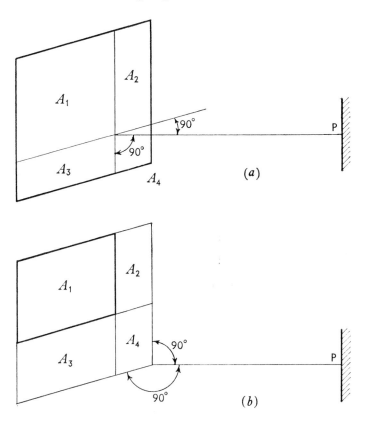

Fig. 9.28   Illumination at a point not opposite one corner of a
rectangular source of uniform luminance

the whole of its area are determined and summated, the result enables the
total flux transferred from one surface to another to be obtained, and when
B is unity the ratio of the received to the emitted flux is called the *form factor.*

Form factors for surfaces parallel to one another are given in terms of the
ratio *a/h* and *b/h* (the length and width to height ratios), and can be read
from the chart, Fig. 9.29. Similarly, for surfaces perpendicular to one another,
form factors can be read from Fig. 9.30.

Design from a specified luminance pattern.   Where it is desired to
design an installation from a specified luminance pattern, there are two main
problems:

(1) a determination of the initial or direct flux to each of the room surfaces;
(2) a determination of the number, arrangement and intensity distribution
of the lighting fittings.

The simple case can be expressed by the statement that the final illumination of the ceiling, walls and floor, will be given by the direct illumination of
6*

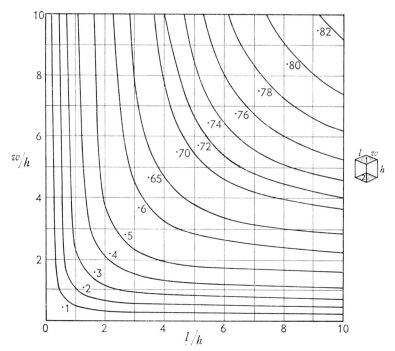

Fig. 9.29   Form factors for surfaces parallel to one another

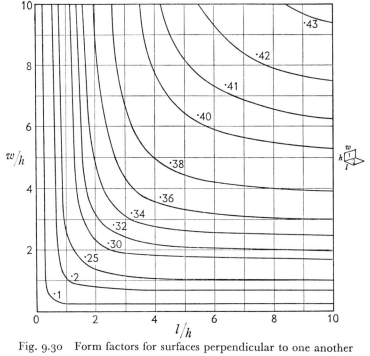

Fig. 9.30   Form factors for surfaces perpendicular to one another

the surface plus an inter-reflected component. For each surface the inter-reflected component due to each of the other room surfaces can be obtained by calculating the illumination on the surface, due to the final luminance of each of the other surfaces. If it is assumed that the surfaces are uniformly emitting and of unit emittance, then the flux transfer from one surface to another will be given by the form factor of one surface with respect to the other and the illumination of the surface will be the product of the form factor and the emitting surface luminance.

This is expressed by the three equations

$$(1) \quad E_w = E_{ow} + (f_{ww}L_w + f_{cw}L_c + f_{fw}L_f)$$

$$(2) \quad E_c = E_{oc} + (f_{wc}L_w + f_{fc}L_f)$$

$$(3) \quad E_f = E_{of} + (f_{wf}L_w + f_{cf}L_c)$$

where E_w is the final illumination of the walls
           E_c is the final illumination of the ceiling
           E_f is the final illumination of the floor
           E_{ow} is the initial illumination of the walls
           E_{oc} is the initial illumination of the ceiling
           E_{of} is the initial illumination of the floor
L_w, L_c and L_f are the final luminance of the walls, ceiling and floor respectively.
           f_{ww} is the form factor of one wall with respect to the other three walls.
           f_{cw} is the form factor of the ceiling with respect to the walls.
           f_{fw} is the form factor of the floor with respect to the walls.
           f_{wc} is the form factor of the walls with respect to the ceiling.
           f_{fc} is the form factor of the floor with respect to the ceiling.
           f_{wf} is the form factor of the walls with respect to the floor.
and f_{cf} is the form factor of the ceiling with respect to the floor.

Since the room surfaces are symmetrical $f_{cw} = f_{fw}$, $f_{cf} = f_{fc}$ and $f_{wc} = f_{wf}$. Form factors may be read from the graphs Figs. 9. 29 and 9.30. Thus if L_w, L_c and L_f are specified and since $E_w = L_w/\rho_w$,

$$E_f = \frac{L_f}{\rho_f} \quad \text{and} \quad E_c = \frac{L_c}{\rho_c}$$

where ρ_w, ρ_c and ρ_f are the average reflection factors of the walls, ceiling and floor, it is an easy matter to determine E_{ow}, E_{oc} and E_{of}.

The total flux required at each of the room surfaces will be

Walls: $E_{ow}A_w = F_w$
Ceiling: $E_{oc}A_c = F_c$
Floor: $E_{of}A_f = F_f$

where A_w, A_c and A_f are the areas of the walls, ceiling and floor respectively.
The direct ratio for the installation will be $F_f/(F_w + F_f)$.

If a conventional array of fittings is acceptable, by reference to I.E.S. Report No. 2, Table 6, the BZ classification of the fittings required to satisfy the luminance specification can be obtained.

For arrangements of fittings other than the conventional array, more extensive data on direct ratios for alternative arrangements are needed.

CHAPTER 10

Incandescent Lamps—General Principles

Introduction. The principle of the incandescent tungsten filament lamp is based on the fact that when an electric current is passed along a conductor, the resistance to its passage produces heat. If sufficient electrical energy is supplied to raise the temperature above approximately 500 °C, light is emitted as well as heat.

Fig. 10.1 shows an incandescent tungsten filament lamp. The light emitting

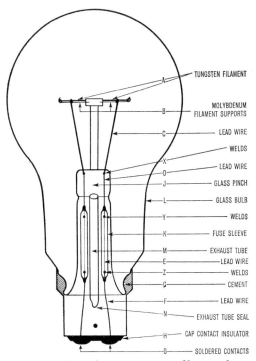

Fig. 10.1   Incandescent tungsten filament lamp

filament consists of a spiral of tungsten wire A. This is supported by molyb-denum wires B, and its ends are connected to the lead-wires C, D, E, F which terminate at the contacts of the cap G to which they are soldered. The lead-wires consist of a nickel portion C which is welded at X to a copper plated nickel-iron section D which is fused into the glass 'pinch' J forming an air-tight seal. The outer end of this section is welded at Y to a fine monel fuse E which is hermetically sealed into a glass sleeve K. The other end of the fuse is welded at Z to the copper wire F which passes through the cap to the contact G. The contacts are insulated from each other and from the brass cap shell by a black glass insulator H. Before the cap is cemented, the glass bulb L is evacuated through the exhaust tube M which, in the case of vacuum lamps, is then sealed off at N. Gas-filled lamps are filled with gas after evacuation, before sealing off.

The filament

Choice of Materials. The spectral power distribution of the energy radiated by a 'black body' (see Chapter 4) at different temperatures is represented by the curves in Fig. 10.2. It will be seen that as temperature rises, the

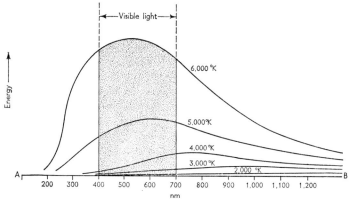

Fig. 10.2 Spectral power distribution of black body at various temperatures

output of energy also rises, but, what is more important, the proportion of energy given out as visible light increases. It will also be seen that with increasing temperature the colour of the light changes; the energy emitted as light spreads more evenly over the visible spectrum passing from pre-dominantly red at the lower temperatures to a whiter light which approaches the colour of daylight. As most materials which can be used as 'thermal radiators' have light emitting characteristics similar to those of the black body, it will be seen that the highest possible temperature is desirable for two reasons:

1. The efficiency, in lumens (lm) of light emitted per watt (W) of energy consumed, is higher; in other words the light is cheaper.
2. The colour of the light is whiter and nearer to daylight.

The choice of materials which will withstand high temperatures is very limited; electric lamp filaments have been made from the following materials, the last four having been used for commercially produced lamps.

	Melting Point °C
Platinum	1773
Osmium	2700
Tantalum	2900
Tungsten	3380
Carbon	3600

(Iron and steel melt at 1200 °C to 1500 °C and boil below 2900 °C.)

It is not practical to operate any filament at temperatures approaching its melting point, due to the high rate of evaporation at these temperatures. (Many solids can evaporate without melting, although in most cases at ordinary temperatures this happens so slowly that it cannot be detected. Familiar examples, however, are the evaporation of dry snow and the disappearance of naphthalene 'moth balls'; in the latter case the smell of the vapour is noticeable.) When evaporation occurs as a result of operating at a high temperature, not only does the filament become thinner, resulting eventually in failure, but the evaporated material settles on the inside of the bulb, causing it to darken. This deposit absorbs some of the light and, as it increases in thickness, the efficiency of the lamp decreases. Although the melting point of the earlier carbon filament is very high, the rate of evaporation is so great that it cannot be operated at temperatures in excess of about 1850 °C, at which its efficiency is only 2 to 3 lm/W. The useful life of this type of lamp was more often terminated by the excessive darkening of the bulb than by filament failure.

Tungsten is the next obvious choice and it was found that filaments made from it could be operated at a temperature several hundred degrees higher than that of carbon and still give reasonable life without excessive blackening of the bulb. This increased temperature enabled the efficiency to be trebled.

The electrical conductivity of tungsten determines, within close limits, the diameter and length of the filament wire for a given voltage and wattage rating. For mains voltages a length of wire which varies from about a yard in the case of the lower wattages to nearly two yards for 1500 W is required. In early lamps this was mounted in the form of 'hairpins'; mains voltage lamps required a 'squirrel-cage' of 9 or 10 hairpins, necessitating 17 or 19 supports, in addition to the lead-wires (Fig. 10.3).

The tungsten metal is prepared in the form of powder, pressed into bars approximately ⅜ in. square by a foot long (modern developments are moving in the direction of much larger bars), which are strengthened by heating in an electric furnace, and sintered by passing a current of several thousand amps through them. These rods are swaged down to about 1/16 in. diameter, after which they are drawn down to the required size through diamond dies. One rod can produce several miles of wire which may have a diameter as small as half-a-thousandth of an inch. This has a tensile strength several times that of steel.

The wire must be very uniform in diameter. As the same amount of current passes along its entire length any thin spot will be hotter because of its higher resistance. At such a hot spot increased evaporation will occur, leading to further thinning and still higher temperature. This 'compound interest' effect leads to rapid failure.

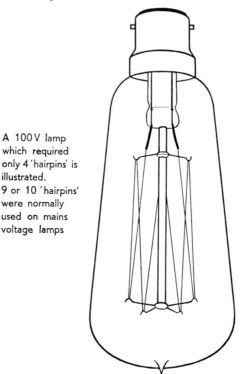

A 100 V lamp which required only 4 'hairpins' is illustrated. 9 or 10 'hairpins' were normally used on mains voltage lamps

Fig. 10.3   Early vacuum lamp using squirrel-cage filament

Filament evaporation.   We have seen earlier that it is desirable to operate the filament at a high temperature, but to limit the degree of evaporation. Evaporation is caused by some molecules of a substance having greater velocities than others, thus enabling them to break away from the surface. This process can be hindered by placing molecules of another substance near that surface. This effect can be illustrated by the fact that water boils at lower temperatures at high altitudes where air pressure is lower, for there are fewer air molecules, making evaporation easier. The evaporation from a tungsten filament can be reduced by filling the lamp bulb with a suitable gas. The gas must be one which does not attack the filament.

Coiled filaments.   When the filament is in the form of straight wire, as in the case of the 'squirrel-cage', the gas can circulate freely round it. The heat energy thus removed by convection has to be provided by additional watts input to the lamp. This results in a loss of efficiency which is greater than the gain obtained by operating the filament at a higher temperature.

This difficulty was overcome with the discovery that heat loss can be reduced by using the filament in the form of a spiral, whose outer surface alone is cooled by the gas.

The introduction of gas into lamps with coiled tungsten filaments enables them to operate at temperatures several hundred degrees higher than those of vacuum lamps.

The ratio of the surface area of the filament to its cross sectional area decreases as the size increases, hence the larger the filament (and the greater the wattage) the less the relative cooling effect and the higher the efficiency.

The efficiency of mains voltage gas-filled lamps with wattage ratings of 60 and upwards is higher than that of vacuum lamps, ranging from between 10 lm/W and 11 lm/W in the case of 60 W, to nearly 20 lm/W for 1500 W. In the case of lower wattage lamps having finer wire, the cooling effect of the gas outweighs any increase of efficiency which would have been made possible by operating at a higher temperature. With single-coil filaments 25 W and, more particularly, 15 W lamps are relatively inefficient as gas-filled lamps. The 40 W single-coil gas-filled lamp is slightly less efficient than its vacuum counterpart, but the public preference for the whiter light due to the higher operating temperature resulted in the withdrawal of the 40 W vacuum lamp from the market.

Extreme accuracy of coiling is of paramount importance. It is easy to see the effect of irregular pitch in the case of a spiral electric fire element; where the turns are close together the element is hotter than where they are pulled out. A section of a lamp filament with turns too close together will similarly overheat at that point, leading to early failure. Widely spaced turns will cause undue cooling by the filling gas with consequent loss of efficiency. The permissible variation of the spaces between turns of filaments made from the finer wire sizes is only a few millionths of an inch.

It will be apparent that the filament coil must retain its form throughout the life of the lamp. When a coiled filament is mounted in a lamp, several hundred turns of the coil may lie between two adjacent supports, and one of the greatest achievements in the development of gas-filled lamps has been to produce filaments which are stable under such conditions at temperatures of 2500 °C and over.

The wire is coiled by winding it round a mandrel of steel or molybdenum. The drawn wire has a fibrous structure (Fig. 10.4), which is retained after coiling. The coiled wire is 'set' on the mandrel by passing it through an electric furnace, and after cutting to the required length, the mandrel is dissolved away and the finished filaments furnaced in molybdenum boats. This heat treatment removes all the strains left in the wire due to cold working during wire drawing and coiling, and leaves it in such a condition that crystal growth occurs at the operating temperature of the filament in the lamp. This results in the formation of crystals which may be large enough to extend along the filament for several millimetres, as if that part of the filament had been cut out of a single crystal; this can usually be seen clearly with the naked eye in a lamp filament at the end of its life. While crystal growth is taking place the wire can lengthen, causing the filament to sag between the supports. In early coiled filament lamps crystal growth occurred during much of the life of the lamp and excessive sag resulted, the loss of efficiency being very serious. Modern wire for general service lamps is made

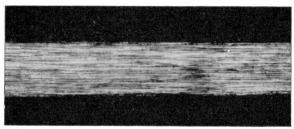

Fig. 10.4   Microphotograph of drawn tungsten wire showing fibrous structure

from tungsten powder to which small quantities of substances such as alumina or silica have been added. These substances have the effect of cleaning up the boundaries between the crystals, thus allowing very rapid crystal growth which takes place in a fraction of a second when the lamp is lit for the first time. A stable filament is thus produced, which does not sag appreciably further during the life of the lamp.

Fig. 10.5 (a) shows a microphotograph of a section through several turns of a filament which has not been lit. Fig. 10.5 (b) shows a similar filament after lighting up, when crystal growth is complete; the boundary between two crystals can be seen.

Another method of producing non-sag wire is to use a powder additive (usually thoria) which prevents any grain growth taking place, the filament thus having a fine-grain structure. Thoriated wire was for many years the standard lamp wire, but it has now been almost entirely superseded by the larger crystal type. It has, however, an application for some Rough Service vacuum lamps.

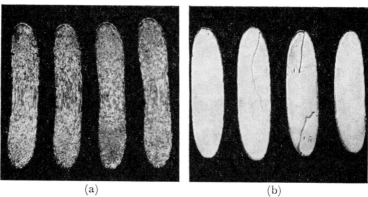

(a)   (b)

Fig. 10.5   Microphotographs of coiled tungsten filaments
before and after lighting up for the first time

Coiling the filament has other advantages. It results in a reduction of the length of the filament from approximately a yard of straight wire (in the case of 15 W to 100 W lamps) to two inches or less of spiral, and this shortened filament requires fewer supports. Each support conducts some heat away from the filament and the energy thus lost has to be supplied by extra wattage consumed by the lamp. Thus the reduction in the number of supports from the 17 to 19 used in 'squirrel-cage' lamps with uncoiled wire, to the five usually employed for a coiled filament, contributes to increased efficiency. Further, the simplified construction with its reduced manufacturing cost has been of great value in the development of modern high-speed machinery. These advantages apply to vacuum as well as gas-filled lamps.

Coiled-coil filaments. The success of the gas-filled coiled filament lamp led to attempts to reduce the effective surface of the filament still further. This was achieved with the coiled-coil filament, where, after winding the wire into a single primary coil, it is then coiled again into a secondary coil as shown in Fig. 10.6. This reduces the length to about one inch, and only two or three supports are necessary.

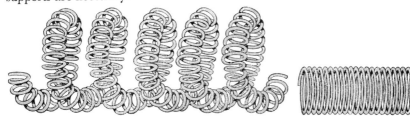

Fig. 10.6 Coiled-coil filament and single-coil filament

Coiled-coil filaments can be run at efficiencies as much as 20% greater than those of single coil filaments of the same rating. This is achieved in the case of mains voltage 40 W lamps, the advantage over single coil filaments decreasing as the size of the filament wire and the wattage of the lamp increases.

Filling gases. Gases which do not attack tungsten are hydrogen, nitrogen and the rare gases of the atmosphere. The amounts of heat absorbed by different gases vary considerably. Because of its very high thermal conductivity, hydrogen is normally useless as a filling gas. It may, however, be used in special rapid-nigrescence lamps for signalling, where it is necessary for the light to be extinguished as quickly as possible when switched off.

The following gases occur in the atmosphere:

	Molecular weight	% of atmosphere by volume
Helium	4	0.0005
Neon	20	0.0015
Nitrogen	28	78.03
Argon	40	0.94
Krypton	84	0.0001
Xenon	131	0.000009

The molecular weight is a measure of the size of the molecules of the gas, and the bigger and heavier they are the more effective they are in preventing molecules of tungsten escaping by evaporation. As the molecular weight increases, the thermal conductivity of the gas decreases. Thus from both these points of view the higher the molecular weight the better. Unfortunately the increasing efficiency thus obtained is accompanied by an increasing tendency to ionisation. When ionisation occurs the gas in the lamp becomes conducting and the current passing may be much higher than that carried by the filament. Such excessive current can heat up the nickel/iron wire in the pinch until it melts or vaporises, causing a 'burst pinch' which may shatter the lamp. This tendency is much greater when lamps are run on direct current.

The obvious first choice is nitrogen on account of its abundance and cheapness, and it was in fact tried in carbon lamps before the other inert gases had been discovered in the atmosphere. It has little tendency to arc, and it is superior to the much rarer helium and neon, not only in depressing evaporation but also in its lower thermal conductivity.

The use of argon in place of nitrogen gives a considerable increase in efficiency, which justifies its use in general service lamps although it is many times more costly than nitrogen. It has a considerably greater tendency to ionisation, but this is very greatly reduced by admixture with a small quantity of nitrogen. The percentage of nitrogen is kept as low as possible in order to obtain maximum efficiency but, to prevent arcing and possible shattering of the lamp at the end of life, fuses are incorporated in the lead-wires, as shown in Fig. 10.1.

Krypton, which has a thermal conductivity only half that of nitrogen is too costly for general service lamps but finds application for such purposes as miners' lamps, where the utmost efficiency is required since the power supply has to be carried in the form of batteries, the weight of which must be kept at a minimum. As these lamps are designed for low voltages, ionisation does not occur. Xenon, which would be even more efficient, is excessively rare and correspondingly expensive.

It has been mentioned that the filling gas must not attack the filament. It is also absolutely essential that the gas is extremely pure, as very small amounts of some substances can have disastrous effects. For example, a minute trace of water vapour left in the lamp after manufacture or introduced with the gas, attacks the filament, forming hydrogen and tungsten oxide. The latter settles on the bulb where, at the lower temperature, it reacts with the hydrogen to produce tungsten, which remains on the bulb, and water vapour which again attacks the filament.

Glass components

Lead oxide and lime-soda glasses. Clear transparent flint glass had been invented 200 years before the advent of the incandescent filament lamp. Such glass, containing about 30% of lead oxide, is used for the glass pinches of modern general service lamps, as it has the valuable property of high electrical resistivity. This is necessary when the glass is used to support lead-wires a few millimetres apart, in a high-temperature environment, with mains voltages of 200 V to 250 V between them.

The bulbs however are now made with the cheaper lime-soda glass.

In order to maintain the vacuum or gas filling within the bulb, the lead-wires must form an hermetic seal with the glass. Early lamps were manufactured with a short length of platinum wire in the pinch, but the high cost of this metal inevitably led to a search for cheaper material, and a copper-plated, or clad, nickel-iron alloy is now universally used for lamps with lead glass pinches.

Borosilicate glass. The compact light sources of projector lamps entail comparatively high wattages in very small bulbs which thus have to withstand much higher temperatures. For this purpose hard borosilicate glass is used, with lead-wires made of tungsten to match the expansion behaviour of the glass (Chapter 13).

The low thermal expansion of this glass makes it very suitable for sealed beam and other specialised types of lamps which may be subjected to sudden changes of temperature in use (Chapter 15).

Fused silica. The arc tubes of high-pressure mercury vapour lamps (Chapter 18) operate at temperatures approaching 1000 °C at pressures of about 10 atmospheres. For such conditions transparent fused silica (quartz) is used. This has a negligible thermal coefficient of expansion and the current is carried through the pinch by lengths of molybdenum foil about 0.001 in. thick.

Bulbs of fused silica, or quartz, are used for tungsten-halogen lamps because of the high temperatures required. Earlier reference has been made to the evaporation of tungsten from the lamp filament and its subsequent deposition on the bulb. If the gas in the lamp contains a small quantity of iodine, or other halogen, and the bulb is maintained at a sufficiently high temperature, the halogen prevents the tungsten from depositing on the bulb by forming a tungsten-halide in the vapour phase. This halide is decomposed by the much higher temperature near the filament, on which the tungsten is redeposited, liberating the halogen for another reaction cycle.

The important class of lamps utilising this principle is described fully in Chapter 15.

Glass bulbs. Clear lamp bulbs whether produced singly by highly-skilled hand-blown methods, or in torrents from the latest type of 'ribbon' bulb blowing machines, have smooth surfaces and absorb very little of the light passing through them. The high temperature of the compact coiled filament results in very high brightness which is not modified by the clear bulb. Such lamps are therefore little used for general lighting applications.

Early attempts to reduce the glare from the unobscured filament used bulbs frosted on the outside. The roughened surface was difficult to keep clean but this problem was overcome by the advent of the 'pearl' bulb which is frosted (etched and fortified) on the inside. The effect is to give an apparent increase in size of the light source to an area of several square inches. The loss of light is negligible, in the region of 0·5%.

A more recent extension of the technique is the modern 'inside-white' coated bulb which affords still greater diffusion of the filament image by a coating of finely divided silica, titania or the like, on the inside of the bulb. A loss of efficiency of from 4% to 8% may be incurred, according to the nature of the coating used and degree of diffusion provided.

By the application of lacquers, vitreous enamels, pigmented coatings, to the inside or outside surface of clear bulbs, or by use of coloured glass bulbs, a very wide variety of incandescent lamp colours and finishes are available. The colour of the light from the lamp is modified by filtering out some unwanted colour, which inevitably results in reduced efficiency. In view of the low proportion of blue light in the lamp spectrum (Fig. 10.7), the efficiency of lamps of this colour is particularly low, more than 90% of the light being lost.

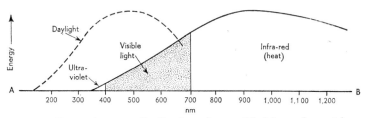

Fig. 10.7   Spectral power distribution of a gas-filled incandescent lamp

Caps.   The B.C. (bayonet) cap is the standard in this country for general service up to 150 W; it is also widely used in France. It makes lamp replacement very easy. It is not suitable for heavy currents which would weaken the lampholder contact plunger springs; E.S. (screw) caps are accordingly used for 200 W and upwards. The E.S. cap is used for 200 W and is also the standard cap for smaller lamps in many parts of the world. For 300 W and larger, the G.E.S. cap is used in order to ensure adequate mechanical strength (Fig. 10.8).

The caps must be so constructed and fitted to the lamp that they will withstand the torsion test specified in BS 161, i.e. 25 lb in. (3·0 Nm) for B.C. and E.S. caps and 45 lb in. (5·0 Nm) for G.E.S. caps, both before and at the end of life.

Pre-focus caps are used for a number of types of lamp in optical systems where, when the lamp is replaced, the filament of the new lamp must be in the exact position occupied by that of the lamp which has been removed. To ensure this each lamp filament must be positioned in strict spatial relation to its cap. This is usually achieved by cementing a brass sleeve on to the lamp bulb and then fixing the cap to the sleeve in an optical jig. A recent development has been the introduction of projector lamps with valve-type bases in which, prior to sealing in the bulb, the filament is mounted on a pressed glass base and accurately positioned with respect to its contact pins. The contact pins ensure an accurate and interchangeable location in the holder.

Improvements in capping cements enable them to withstand an operating temperature of 210 °C.

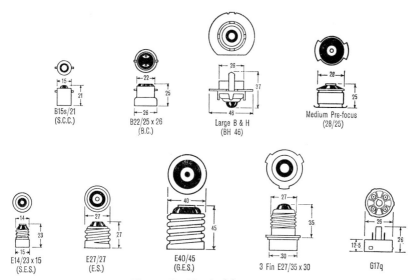

Fig. 10.8   Typical lamp caps

Life, lumen output and efficiency. In order to get the maximum possible efficiency from a gas-filled lamp we require the filament to be very accurately made from uniform wire of good non-sag quality, supported on the minimum practicable number of supports and operating in pure, inert gas.

When the utmost care has been taken of these points to produce a good quality lamp, its life will depend on the operating temperature of the filament. As this rises the efficiency increases and the length of life decreases, the relation between life, lumen output and efficiency being as shown in Fig. 10.9.

The British Standards Institution committee responsible for the general service lamp specification (BS 161) has decided on a life of 1000 hours. It points out, however, that it is impossible to fix upon a single designed life that will be most beneficial to all classes of users, for all lamp wattages. Factors which have to be taken into account are the cost of electricity and lamps and the labour cost of replacements. The latter cost hardly arises with domestic lighting but can be of major consequence in, say, an industrial high-bay installation.

The economics of efficiency and life can be illustrated for 100 W lamps as follows. During the life of 1000 hours it consumes 100 kW. Reference to Fig. 10.7 will show that reducing the efficiency by 10% (i.e. increasing the cost per lumen 10%) doubles the life (halving the cost of the lamp). At 2d. per unit the cost of 10% loss in efficiency is 1s. 8d. which is considerably more than half the cost of the lamp. It will be obvious that the higher the wattage and the higher the cost of current the more important it is to use lamps at the highest possible efficiency. In Norway, where hydroelectric power is very cheap, some lamps are designed for a life of 2500 hours. On the other hand, in the U.S.A. there is a range of general service lamps with a life of 750 hours.

For a life of 1000 hours, the 100 W single-coil lamp operates with a filament temperature of about 2500 °C with an efficiency of 12·5 lm/W. The spectral power distribution is shown in Fig. 10.7. This emphasises that a large proportion of the radiant energy is emitted in the infrared region as heat. It also shows that in the visible region there is a preponderance of red-orange light compared with daylight. This warm colour quality of the incandescent gas-filled lamp is well suited to most domestic lighting purposes.

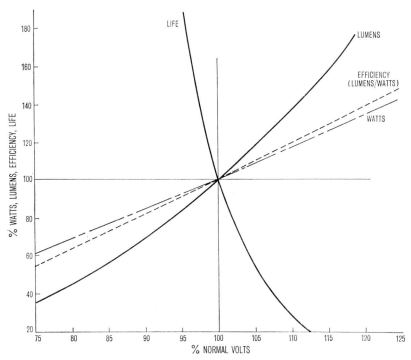

Fig. 10.9 Effect of voltage variation on the performance characteristics of the incandescent lamp

There are many important applications for incandescent lamps outside the fields of general and domestic lighting which demand a different balance between efficiency, life and lamp cost. Examples are to be found in photographic and projector lamps where precision construction to optical standards must be combined with high colour temperatures and light-output efficiencies (discussed in Chapters 11 and 13) and in vehicle lighting lamps with their emphasis on rugged construction, compact dimension and suitability to fittings optics (Chapters 11 and 14).

Quality control. The greatest care in manufacturing, meticulous accuracy of components, purity of filling gas and scrupulous cleanliness throughout assembly is necessary to obtain optimum lamp life and efficiency.

Modern statistical quality-control techniques help to ensure that possible causes in variation are at all times under close surveillance and control. A variation may take the form of a general drift away from a target, or a widening spread of individual results with the average still on target. At all stages of manufacture, from tungsten powder to finished lamps, samples of components and sub-assemblies are taken from the production lines and are critically examined, a record being made of the findings. These records provide a continuing picture of the quality of every process and statistical analysis indicates when a parameter, which may still be within the control limits, is showing an undesirable drift. This enables corrective action to be taken and become effective before defective parts are produced in quantity.

The final machine on each production group is equipped to carry out tests of a number of electrical characteristics of the finished lamp, such as filament rating, cap insulation and correctness of wiring connections within the lamp. Lamps failing to pass are automatically ejected from the machine. In addition, prior to the packing operation, lamps are subjected to a critical visual appraisal by skilled inspectors.

CHAPTER 11

Optics in Lamp Design

Introduction. In Chapter 6 reference is made to the basic laws and principles of light control but it will be helpful to discussion of the optical aspects of lamp design to make a preliminary reference to them.

When a ray of light meets the surface of a medium different from that in which it has been travelling, part will be reflected, part will be transmitted through the new medium, and part will be absorbed by the new medium. All three effects occur but usually one is very much more, or very much less, important, than the other two. Thus, with a piece of glass in a window, the amounts transmitted and reflected are quite noticeable and the amount absorbed is negligible; while, with a mirror, the amounts absorbed and transmitted are both negligible.

When the surface is polished and flat the basic laws of reflection and of refraction apply and are easily demonstrated. When the surface is flat but unpolished, the surface may be considered to be made up of many minute polished flat surfaces, which are lying in different random planes and the reflected rays from the separate surfaces therefore travel in many different directions. Such an unpolished surface is called diffuse and when considering the reflected pattern as a whole, the laws of reflection appear not to be obeyed, in this instance. When the surface is polished but curved, one may imagine the surface again to be made up of many minute polished flat surfaces lying in planes which are related one to another according to a certain law, which describes the curve itself and to which all the minute individual surfaces are tangent. Rays meeting these tangential surfaces are reflected and refracted according to the four laws given and one can therefore translate these geometrically, for any ray meeting any curved surface, by drawing tangents, or normals, at the point of incidence of the ray.

This is very interesting and important, for it means that not only can the behaviour of a ray of light meeting a curved surface, such as that of a lens, be determined but so also can the reverse, i.e. the surface curvature which will cause the ray to follow the required path.

The amount of light reflected at a surface depends on many factors, including the degree of uniformity of the surface (polish), its colour, the inherent power of the medium to reflect and the angle of incidence of the light at the surface. Thus, with coloured surfaces there is a reduction in the amount of light reflected, since only light of the same colour as that of the surface is reflected, other colours being absorbed. Even when there are no marked colour differences between surfaces such as polished iron, nickel and silver; there are differences in the amount of light reflected, due to the different reflectivities of these metals. The last of these factors, the angle which the incident light makes with the surface, is of particular interest in cases of transparent media, such as glass or water, and of polished surfaces of opaque media such as wood or metal. In the latter case, provided that the polish itself is transparent and of appreciable thickness, the surface will behave like that of a transparent medium, that is, the amount of light reflected will increase with the angle of incidence (the angle between the incident ray and the normal to the surface) and this can easily be demonstrated.

Not so obvious, but still an important factor in determining the amount of light reflected, is the refractive index of the material of the transparent surface. The law governing this, derived by Fresnel, gives the ratio of the incident light reflected normally by a transparent surface as equal to

$$\left(\frac{n_1 - n_2}{n_1 + n_2}\right)^2$$

where n_1, n_2 are the refractive indices of the two media.

As an example, one can consider a piece of window glass with a refractive index of 1·52, in air (with an index of 1·0), and one sees from this expression that the fraction of light reflected is about 1/25, or 4%. This applies to each surface of the glass, thus there is a total of about 8% reflected, *at normal incidence*; or, one can say there is a loss of light of 8% on transmission through an ordinary window, in air. This is true on the basis that the amounts reflected, transmitted and absorbed add up to 100% of the incident light. For other angles of incidence the loss is higher and increases with the angle.

These factors then affect the quantity of light reflected and of course, in the case of transparent surfaces, they must affect the amount of light transmitted after refraction, when this occurs. Other factors affect the quality of the light in some way and one could go on to consider diffraction, dispersion, and polarisation. However, for purposes of background relevant to lamp design only one other factor of importance remains and this is interference, of which use can be made in dealing with problems of heating which can arise in optical systems of high efficiency. To complete this survey therefore note must be taken of the effect of the change of phase which occurs when light travelling through a medium of low refractive index, meets a medium of higher index. In this case, the reflected ray suffers a change of phase of 180° and is therefore completely out of phase with the incident and refracted rays. When the ray passes from a high to a lower index medium no such change occurs.

An electric lamp is basically a device comprising a light source of some kind within a transparent, or translucent envelope (the main functions of which are to protect the source from physical damage and chemical attack), and which is fitted with a convenient means of electrical connection and mechanical location such as bayonet, or screw cap. Optical requirements in lamp construction are related directly to specific applications for which the lamp is to be designed. Nowadays some part, often a major part, of the optical system of a piece of lighting equipment may be incorporated within the lamp envelope. Discussion will be confined to lamps of the projection and photographic type, which are used mainly for one of two purposes; the production of high quality, usually highly magnified images on a viewing screen, or the production of high-intensity beams for illumination purposes.

Enlarging. The first application from the lamp making point of view is perhaps the simplest—the enlargement of photographic negatives. The form of lamp used is of conventional appearance, with a large-area source of light in a diffusing envelope, the surface of which is intended to act as the source itself, as far as the optical system is concerned. The primary requirement is to distribute the light as evenly as possible over the negative, so that the only variation in light reaching the print paper is due to the photographic image on the negative. Sometimes a further diffusing plate, or a condenser lens, is used in order to avoid any possibility of the production of the faintest image of the light-source on the negative and hence in turn on the printing paper. The diffuser and negative are placed as close to the lamp as is convenient, in order to obtain maximum illumination of the negative which must not protrude beyond the edges of the diffusing screen. The filament of the lamp is run at an excess voltage in order to increase the light output and reduce process time. The life of the lamp is 100 burning hours.

It will be noted that the light reaching the printing paper has actually passed through the object (the negative) to be enlarged (Fig. 11.1). This is called *diascopic projection* and is used most commonly in the cinema, also for

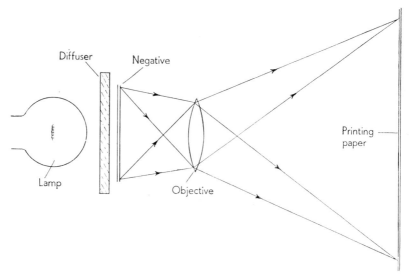

Fig. 11.1   Enlarger system

home cine and slide projection. The scheme is efficient optically because nearly all of the light directed towards the negative by the lamp and diffuser is used; the only losses being those of absorption and reflection by the lens components and the negative material. Thus a high screen, or print illumination results, except where the light is masked by the negative image and the screen image therefore has high contrast—which is of great value in slide and cine projection, where high magnifications are required.

Episcope. Before considering the diascopic system further, reference should be made to the use of another form of projection—the episcopic—but this is comparatively rare, owing to its poor efficiency. This is due to the fact that only the light *reflected* from the object is used and as most of these objects (pages of a book, drawings, etc.) have diffused surfaces, only a small percentage of the light directed on to them can be collected by the projection lens. Satisfactory contrast in the screen image is difficult to obtain even when high-efficiency, high-powered lamps are used to boost the illumination of the object and a further problem of overheating often arises from the use of such lamps. The optical system is quite elementary: a simple plain mirror behind the lamp reflects light, which would otherwise be lost, in a forward direction towards the object but this is mainly lit directly from the lamp, with no need for diffuser, or condenser system, owing to the diffuse nature of the object itself.

Slide projection. Reverting now to diascopic projection one comes to the use of film transparencies of the various 35 mm and 'Instamatic' still formats. These are all derived from the old 'magic lantern' arrangement and it may be of interest to consider this subject historically, from the point of view of lamp construction. The optical scheme is basically as shown (Fig. 11.2).

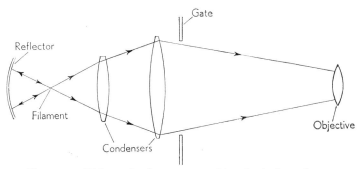

Fig. 11.2   Slide projection system, with spherical condensers

Since both high magnification and high screen illumination intensities are required it is desirable that most of the rays of light should pass through the transparency and be directed towards the objective lens. This would have been most simply achieved using a source of light which was the same size as the transparency and sited close to it. This was, however, impractical since the required brightness of a source of such dimensions required an undesirably high wattage, the heat from which would burn the transparency. A solution was provided by an optical system comprised of one or more positive lenses (condensers), of short focal length and with a diameter equal to the transparency diagonal. This produced an image of the source approximately on, or within, the objective lens itself.

There is another way of considering this system: the condenser produces an enlarged virtual image of the source which is 'seen' by the transparency, this virtual source being large enough to subtend the same angle at the centre of the objective, as the transparency itself. Thus, most of the light shed on the transparency is directed into the objective. Of particular interest to the lamp maker was the possibility of using a smaller source, because this could better be exploited to produce filaments of high intrinsic brightness, using techniques which were developing in the industry in step with the increasing popularity of transparency projection. Flat 'grid' shaped filaments of singly and doubly-coiled wire segments were used, to be followed by the biplane filament. Light output was raised to the limits of acceptable burning lives, usually around 25 hours.

Owing to the fact that condenser lenses of large aperture (i.e. large diameter and short focal length) were difficult and expensive to make, only systems of relatively long focal length were available. The magnification of the filament image was only moderate and filaments with an area of approximately 10 mm × 10 mm were satisfactory. With filaments of such size the brightness of the screen was directly proportional to lamp wattage. This feature relieved the lampmaker of the problems which would have arisen had smaller filaments been required. For any design of filament, with a given life, wattage and efficiency, the length of straight tungsten wire from which the filament is made depends mainly on the operating voltage. There are several limiting factors to the possible reduction in size of such a filament (mechanical limitations of coil pitch and diameter: also electrical limitations regarding short circuiting and the prevention of arcs) and it should be noted that the filaments used in the systems developed before the last war were restricted to 100/130 V supplies. It was not until about 1945 that a satisfactory mains voltage (200 V to 250 V) biplane filament emerged.

With optical systems of this type, biplane lamps of wattages between 400 and 1200 are still in use. In a typically modern design, the 'Trufocus' lamp has its filament position accurately fixed with respect to a 4-pin valve-type base and incorporates a mirror within the lamp envelope, in close proximity to the filament. This replaces the rear mirror of the conventional optical system, with enhanced efficiency. The 'proximity' mirror does not need cleaning and is accurately aligned in relation to the filament—two useful advantages over the conventional rear mirror.

The condenser lens, or system of lenses, converts a divergent beam of light from the source into a convergent beam, centred on the objective lens. While the angle subtended by the condenser system can easily be made to suit the objective (which has an aperture not greater than $f2\cdot8$), difficulty exists in arranging this source-system to subtend a large angle, which we can call the collection angle, at the source. Even when a rear mirror is used, only a relatively small part of the total radiation from the filament is utilised.

Modern systems make use of lenses of large diameter and of much shorter focal length. These lenses are specially figured, or contoured, to shapes which are not simply parts of spheres. The shapes used are formed by the rotation of a conic section about its axis, and the cross-sectional shape of such a lens is a parabola, hyperbola, or ellipse. The properties of *aspheric* lenses, as they are called, have been known for many years. At one time these shapes were known as 'Descartes' ovals', since Descartes (1596–1650) 'discovered' them. However, until recently, it had not been possible to make them with sufficient accuracy, with deep enough curvature, or with highly polished surfaces.

The deeper curvature of the aspheric lens changes the vergence of a beam to a much greater extent. This is of great advantage, since this bending of the rays can be achieved over a smaller distance, using one aspheric lens alone, or in conjunction with a weak field lens; instead of using three, or more spherical lenses, which lose more light by reflection, due to the greater number of air-to-glass surfaces.

Fig. 11.3 shows a typical arrangement employing an aspheric lens as the first lens close to the lamp, with a wide angle of collection at the filament.

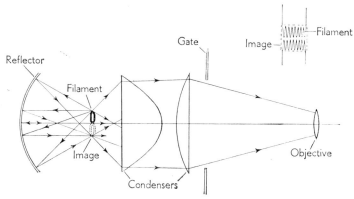

Fig. 11.3   Slide projection system, with aspheric condensers

The lens diameter can thereby be reduced which is advantageous to the cost, size and weight of the equipment. The rear, or proximity, mirror can be enlarged also to collect more light and finally the filament area can be reduced. This last feature is of great interest, for several gains are to be made by using smaller filaments. A smaller area of filament is achieved by lower voltage and wattage and this can, by careful coiling methods, produce filaments of brightness similar to that of the older designs of high wattage filaments. Lower wattage requires less cooling of the lamp envelope, which itself will be smaller, allowing the aspheric lens to be placed even nearer to the source.

At the time these optical improvements were being made, a new coiling technique was developed resulting in a more compact filament source which was optically nearly solid. This was done by coiling the filament wire on a flattened mandrel wire, which produced the shape illustrated. These coils were first intended for miniature cine projection and it was felt that they were probably too small in area for slide projection. Experimentation with the rear mirror in a conventional projection system showed that such filaments were too dense for light reflected from the rear mirror effectively to pass through towards the condenser and that this light must be directed to one side, or above the filament itself, in order to be of much practical use. A scheme was then devised, whereby the filament is set just below the axis of the system, allowing the rear mirror to form an image of the filament just above the axis, effectively doubling the area of the source. A slight revision of the design of the aspheric lens produced a system of much enhanced efficiency. For example, a 150 watt flat-filament of this sort, has a height-to-length ratio of 1:2; producing, with the filament image from the rear mirror, a square-shaped source (about 6 mm × 6 mm) ideally suited to 35 mm slide projection. It can provide screen illumination equal to that from previous systems using a 500 W biplane lamp. The arrival of the tungsten-iodine lamp coincided with these developments and manufacturers of projection equipment soon realised the possibility of further advances with this new lamp, which was even smaller in size, had a 'whiter' light output, longer life, a 100% maintenance of light output, and hardly any need for cooling.

Improvements in present-day glass processing have resulted in satisfactory aspheric lenses at an economic cost and the resultant optical systems have facilitated equipment miniaturisation. The smaller systems require greater precision in filament geometry which has been provided by devices such as the 'Trufocus' base. The trend towards higher efficiencies from lower voltages has reached its present peak with the tungsten-iodine lamp.

Cine projection. Interest covers the 16 mm; and the standard 8 mm and 9 mm format, but progress is mainly seen in practice with 8 mm. Recently, this has blossomed into the 'Super 8' system, which seems likely to supersede the other formats for most applications.

The discussion on slide-projection systems has shown how the light source is magnified to approximately the size of the slide and the light from this secondary source channelled through the transparency, towards the objective lens, by forming an image of the source in the centre of the objective. This means that the focus and aperture of the condenser system are determined by the focus and aperture of the objective. It also means that the latter cannot very well produce an image of the source on the screen. The obvious difference between slide and cine format is one of size and therefore a higher degree of magnification is desirable with cine projection. This, in turn, requires a higher relative illumination of the cine transparency, and a large collection angle is required by the optical system. The film must now be placed in the 'waist' of the beam projected by the system in the direction of the objective and for maximum efficiency, the condenser system must subtend the same angle at the film as does the objective (Fig. 11.4).

Several methods of satisfying this condition have been devised, the first being a system very like that for slide projection shown in Fig. 11.2. As in slide projectors, lamps with large filaments were first used, collection angles were low and a considerable part of the available light escaped collection. Indeed only a small part of the light collected found its way into the film gate. The need for smaller filaments and optical components produced a series of low voltage lamps, of which the latest version is the 12 V 100 W, in a 25 mm

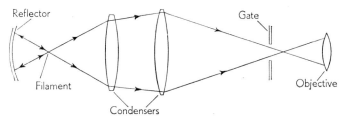

Fig. 11.4   8 mm projection system with spherical condensers

diameter, tubular bulb. This has a flat-mandrel filament, of area about 4 mm by 2·5 mm, normally used with a system of condenser lenses of just over an inch in diameter. The advent of aspheric lenses led to further reduction in condenser size, aided by the development of an even smaller projection lamp of suitable rating—12 V 100 W, in tungsten-iodine. These systems are designed to suit objectives of fairly high aperture (f1·3 to f1·4) and short focal length, about one inch maximum, which produce the high magnification and illumination intensities required.

A second approach to the problems involved resulted in an altogether new design of projection lamp. It was thought that the property of the ellipsoidal mirror could be used to transfer the radiation from the filament at one focal point, F_1, to the film at the second focus, F_2. Owing to the relative sizes of film, lens and lamp it was considered most practical to incorporate part of the ellipsoid into the lamp itself, either as a fixed part of the envelope which could be silvered, or as a separate, but internal, mirror. A range of lamps appeared with small filaments of wattage between 50 and 150, all at low voltage. The 'Truflector' lamp is the best example of the separate internal mirror, which can be contoured to suit a particular objective lens aperture (Fig. 11.5).

These new lamps required little cooling, but two problems remain. The method of funnelling the light down to the size of the film image meant that the light source was imaged near the plane of the film and in some cases undesirable variations in colour and intensity on the screen arose (known as 'banding'). This has been to some extent overcome by placing the film aperture slightly off the second focal point, thus defocusing the filament image and reducing banding, with some loss of light. Sometimes the design of the mirror and construction of the lamp allowed a second mirror of spherical form to be sited between the filament and the film gate, so collecting the light which was otherwise lost. This is shown in dotted lines in the diagram, the mirror in this case being a section of a sphere, with the filament at the centre. Rays of light within the angle B are reflected back to the filament,

7+

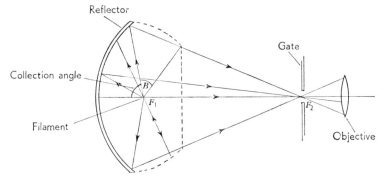

Fig. 11.5   Truflector projection system

a good proportion of them passing through it, to be reflected forward again by the ellipsoidal mirror. Such an arrangement increases the amount of light passed to the lens; in addition, the light from the spherical mirror which passes through the filament (via the gaps between turns), reduces the contrast in any filament image on the screen and hence banding is practically eliminated.

The second problem, less easy of solution, arose from the high efficiency of the ellipsoidal mirror system, which roughly doubled the screen illumination hitherto obtained. As well as light, heat is reflected towards the film gate and undesirable temperature rises in this region result. While the new lower wattage lamps required less cooling and some of the available cooling draught could be diverted towards the gate, projection at low frame speeds, or of stationary film sometimes required a reduction of the power to the lamp, or the interposing of heat filters.

A relatively recent answer to this problem is provided by the use of a mirror which is a selective reflector, with poor reflectivity for heat radiation. Such mirrors are known as *dichroic* or *cold-light* mirrors, and these have hitherto been used only in very sophisticated apparatus, because of their high cost. Expensive apparatus is necessary to manufacture dichroic mirrors and the processes involved are highly skilled and time-consuming, but the heat problems in cine projection have forced more attention to them. As a result more mechanised techniques are being devised for their manufacture, which will reduce cost and extend their range of application.

This book is not appropriate to a detailed explanation of the principles and methods of manufacture of the dichroic mirror but a general idea of how it operates can be given. Light, just as heat, X rays, etc., is a form of electro-magnetic radiation; the distinguishing characteristics of each form being the wavelength of the radiation. One band of wavelengths referred to as 'visible light' enables us to see objects on which this radiation falls because of the eye's peculiar sensitivity to this band. Other bands of wavelengths do not have this effect, but may affect a photographic material (infrared, X rays, ultraviolet, etc.) or a wireless aerial; or again, with infrared, there is a heating effect which our bodies can feel.

A dichroic mirror is made from a transparent base, usually of thin glass, which is curved as may be required and which, as seen previously, has very low absorption, very high transmission, and reflects from both surfaces about 8% of the normally incident light, when surrounded by air. On one surface of the base a series of alternate layers of two different transparent materials are laid, and there may be about twenty layers in all, for the mirrors currently used in lamp making. The materials are selected principally for their refractive indices, which must bear a specific relationship to that of air (1·0) and the glass (1·52). One material may be, for example, magnesium fluoride with an index (1·38) between that of air and glass and the other, for example, zinc sulphide (2·3) with an index above that of glass. We thus have covering the glass face, known as the 'substrate', a series of alternate layers of refractive indices which are high and low, with respect to glass. The scheme is shown diagramatically and it is sometimes referred to as a 'multi-layer stack'. Further, the thickness of each layer must be precisely controlled so that the thickness, multiplied by the refractive index of the material, is equal to one quarter of the wavelength of the light to be reflected (Fig. 11.6).

Optical thickness of $= \frac{\lambda}{4} = n \times t$. where, n = refractive index
each layer $\qquad$ t = physical thickness

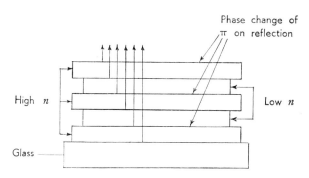

Fig. 11.6 Multilayer stack for cold mirror

It can be shown that the quarter wavelength thickness of the layer produces a difference in phase of 180° between the rays reflected from the upper and lower surfaces of the layer. Moreover, there are other changes, also 180° of phase, according to whether the radiation is passing from a low to a high index medium, or vice versa. If all the significant transmitted and reflected rays from each layer were included in the diagram with their phase indicated, it would be seen that the transmitted rays were equally divided—half in one phase and half 180° out-of-phase—so that they cancelled out; while the rays reflected on leaving the outermost layer were all in one phase. Transmission is cut down towards zero, while reflection rises towards 100% (in practice a dichroic coating will equal polished silver in reflectivity). At the same time the quarter wavelength factor for visible light will not affect heat radiation, since the heat rays have relatively long wavelengths and these pass through the coatings, more or less unhindered. It is found that a lamp with a dichroic mirror will produce not more than half the temperature rise at the film gate which is produced by a similar lamp, with a metallic mirror.

This discussion has covered two systems which are in current use—one being like the slide projection system and the other the mirror-condenser scheme. The latest developments relate to the use of the tungsten-iodine lamp in the first of these systems and attempts to use it in a mirror system, especially in connection with the 'Super 8' format. The 'Super 8' has, amongst other advantages over the Standard Eight format, a frame size roughly 20% larger in width and height, giving a 50% increase in area. This means, of course, a larger screen picture, or alternatively a brighter picture at the screen size obtained with the standard format. The increase in screen illumination is obtained simply by a larger aperture in the waist of the beam; provided that the waist is large enough in cross-section to fill the new aperture and that the distribution across the beam at the waist is even. Some fall-off in brightness from centre of screen to edge is expected however and is acceptable generally, since the centre of interest of the picture is usually near the geometric centre of the frame. A loss of 50% in brightness at a point near the corner, compared with the centre may be tolerated, while a loss of 30% is quite acceptable.

Both lamp makers and projection equipment makers are interested in getting more screen illumination from the larger film gate and variations in filament size, collecting angles for condenser systems, high aperture objective lenses and so on, are under investigation. Three approaches are in the main being made: one to combine a higher output, tungsten-iodine lamp with a double condenser lens system; another to produce a combination mirror-condenser lamp of the Truflector type and thirdly, to fit a small tungsten-iodine lamp in an external ellipsoidal mirror, thereby aiming to combine the advantages of dichroic mirror, tungsten-iodine lamp and Truflector design. In some systems it may be possible to use an objective lens with aperture of f1·0. More recently, a further development has appeared in the form of a sealed-beam version of the Truflector lamp, and this is producing the best performance at the time of writing, due to the simplicity and efficiency of its optical construction.

Beam projection. It is probably true to say, with optical considerations in mind, that the larger the lamp the less efficiently it tends to be used. This has been the case with lamps used for projection of images and the same applies to the lamps, generally of higher wattage, which are used for spot and floodlighting. It may be due to the high cost of manufacture of reflectors, prisms and lenses of a size suitable for these sources, or to the ease with which one can generally find a lamp of higher power to provide more illumination from an existing system. At the same time, the trend towards miniaturisation and the use of more efficient systems has been growing, perhaps following the example given by the projector lamp applications already discussed.

An example is the photoflood lamp. This has been reduced somewhat in size over the years, for it started simply as an overrun domestic lamp (frosted bulb) which needed only a simple reflector, sometimes just a flat piece of sheet metal behind it, to throw some of the stray light in the right direction. With reduction in bulb size better reflectors came along and then the envelope shape was changed so that the parabolic contour behind the filament would project a parallel, or nearly parallel, beam of light. This envelope was internally aluminised over the area of parabolic contour and usually frosted over the area where the beam passed out of the bulb. The latest example of this is a 375 W lamp, which equals the previous 500 W lamp in output, has a life of three hours instead of six and is much more convenient to handle because of its smaller size.

Tungsten-iodine lamps have made their mark in this field also and first appeared in a series of 'Sun-Guns' for photographic floodlighting in small studios, or for home cine work. There is a series of double-ended tubular lamps of about half-inch diameter, which produce a very useful amount of light using between 500 W and 1000 W. These lamps are placed in simple, near-parabolic reflectors and the beam covers an area of about 8 ft by 5 ft, at some 10 ft range. Another group of tungsten-iodine lamps have been introduced for use in the outdoor floodlighting of buildings and a considerable improvement in equipment performance has been made. It would not be appropriate here to discuss this in detail since the optical features of the lamp design are of little significance compared to the optics of the new fittings.

One of the most difficult of modern problems in projection is that connected with car headlamps. This has not yet been satisfactorily solved, for headlights still have to be 'dipped' to avoid dazzling approaching drivers. The difficulty arises from the fact that on most of our roads traffic in one direction is laterally displaced by only a few feet from traffic in the other direction and a headlight beam, with only a few degrees in spread, has a field which includes the approaching traffic. Even when beams are dipped downwards and away from the straight-ahead direction, stray light can still be a nuisance. Over the last 25 years continuous attention has been given to improving beam control in headlights, mostly in preventing the escape of stray light.

Modern headlight lamps contain two filaments, so disposed that one is at the focal point of the parabolic reflector, while the other is displaced vertically and laterally from it, causing the dipped or 'passing' beam to be deflected from the parabola axis when this latter filament is switched on in place of the main-beam filament. Various shielding devices have been used to prevent direct light from the dipped-filament from reaching certain parts of the reflector, such as a metal hood near the filament, or a shield over part of the lamp envelope. Shielding part of the reflector is also possible but presents practical difficulties if the shield has to be moved when the main beam is required.

These problems are predominantly the concern of the fitting manufacturer, except that the lamp maker has to position filaments very accurately with respect to some form of housing, or socket reference, so that lamp replacement can be carried out simply and without affecting beam characteristics on the road. The lamp maker has more responsibility with the sealed-beam type of headlight, where the lamp envelope comprises a pressed-glass parabolic reflector and a 'lens' or cover glass, sealed together round their periphery (cf. Chapter 15). In general the 'drive' filament is at the focus of the reflector and the lens is thus receiving light rays from it, via the reflector, in the form of a parallel beam. A shield between the filament and the lens prevents direct light from the filament passing through the lens, which is specially contoured to deflect parts of the beam, to give a required pattern of distribution to the emergent light. In this way small angular deflections can be arranged and both main-beam and dipped-beams are then more accurately controlled, although a more technically satisfactory system uses separate lamps for the two beams. This is of interest in connection with tungsten-iodine lamps, which are now being used for vehicle lighting. Separate, single-filament lamps are now in use in vehicle headlights and auxiliary lamps (e.g. fog and spotlamps), but twin-filament tungsten-iodine lamps are not easy to make satisfactorily and the problem of the stray light reflected from the envelope of present construction is increased when twin-filament designs are considered (see Chapter 15).

While the bulb size of the tungsten-iodine lamp is small in comparison with that of its predecessor, it follows that the envelope and adjacent external parts, such as the seals, caps, etc., which are so close to the light source, can cause considerable obstruction to the rays of light emitted. Hence careful attention is required in some applications to ensure that this does not reduce the inherently high lamp efficiency too greatly.

While considerable reductions in lamp dimensions have been achieved over the last few years, lamp envelopes will continue to incorporate optical components, thereby providing more light and better control. The tungsten-iodine lamp has so far been used more on traditional lines, because it has not yet been possible to equip these lamps with internal reflectors of suitable thermal and optical properties and of size large enough to compete with present-day projection systems.

CHAPTER 12

Lamps for General Lighting Service and Display

Introduction. Chapter 10 dealt with the basic principles governing the choice of materials used in the construction of incandescent electric lamps, together with general considerations of design and operating characteristics. It is now intended to cover in more detail aspects related to the range of lamps used for general lighting service and display ('GLS' lamps).

Vast numbers of incandescent electric light bulbs are in use today and it is estimated that in Britain alone there are at least 150 million lighting points in homes, quite apart from the considerable numbers employed for commercial, industrial and kindred purposes. It is evident therefore, that the modern range of lamps for general lighting service must not only be capable of application to a wide variety of environmental conditions and lighting situations but must also embody high standards of safety and reliability. In addition, they must be readily available at economic prices.

Approximately 250 million incandescent general lighting service lamps are produced in Britain yearly, at the present time. In most instances the cost to the consumer is only a fraction of the cost applicable some 40 years ago, notwithstanding the considerable increase in the cost-of-living index during this period. In fact in 1922 the average manual worker had to work 5 hours to earn enough money to pay for one lamp of 100 W rating, while today the same class of worker need only work for about 15 minutes to be able to make an equivalent purchase—a good example of the achievements of progressive industrial technology.

Construction and design

Wire and coils. Chapter 10 dealt in detail with metallurgical aspects of wire and coils; available wire types and coil forms. Reference was made in this chapter to the importance of additions at the powder stage, to assist clean-up of the grain boundaries, hence assisting rapid crystal growth and subsequent coil stability. Developments in recent years include the introduction of a special washing process with hydrofluoric acid for the tungsten powder, prior to pressing. This has the effect of enhancing grain boundary clean-up and still further improving ultimate coil stability.

The avoidance of split-wire has always been a difficult problem for drawers of tungsten wire, and necessitates a high level of process control. The ability to provide this control has been improved by the availability of machines which can monitor for splits on a continuous, non-destructive basis, even on very small diameter wire.

The search for improved anti-vibration wires continues and a fairly recent development is the introduction of tungsten wire, containing 3% rhenium, for some rough-service applications. This wire has a small grain structure but is not as prone to sag as the thoria-doped wire mentioned in Chapter 10.

Turning now to coils, the predominant coil forms in general use continue to be 'single coil' and 'coiled coil'. Here the main emphasis of research and development effort is in the direction of improving mechanical and dimensional stability, to the standards necessary for modern high-speed lamp-assembly machinery.

Mount designs. Lamp makers have always exercised a high degree of ingenuity in devising coil and mount forms—often of great complexity—to suit special purpose applications. The keynote, however, of the designs employed for

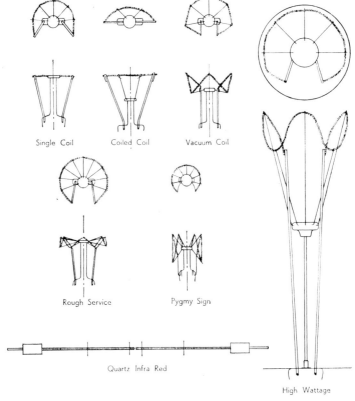

Single Coil　Coiled Coil　Vacuum Coil

Rough Service　Pygmy Sign

Quartz Infra Red

High Wattage

Fig. 12.1　GLS mount designs

general lighting service lamps is the simplicity demanded by the requirements of high-speed assembly machinery. Fortunately, by attention to design detail and choice of materials, this simplicity has been achieved without sacrificing the essential 'fitness-for-purpose' in lamps used for such a wide variety of lighting applications.

Design detail is best appreciated by references to Fig. 12.1.

It will be noted that the coiled coil construction employs fewer supports than the single coil and that the filament is pendant from the support hub. This is to reduce the operating temperature of the support hub. A pendant mount is not usually necessary with the longer length, single coil filament. For wattages of 300 and above, it is normal practice to use a borosilicate hub glass because of the higher operating temperature in these lamps. This, in turn, requires a different cane construction from the lower wattage types, in view of the lower coefficient of expansion of the borosilicate glass. The usual method is to attach the hub to the lamp stem with a nickel/iron alloy rod, which has an expansion coefficient compatible with both lead and borosilicate glasses. The metal rod also imparts a desirable resilience to the mount. For wattages above 300 W, it is normal to incorporate a heat-baffle disc— mica, or metal—to minimise the cap temperature in operation.

Lamps for rough service application incorporate many more supports than the equivalent wattage, general-service, lamp.

Glasses. Typical compositions of the three main types of glass in common use for lamps in the general lighting service category are provided in the Table below.

Typical Glass Compositions

	Lead	Borosilicate	Soda Lime
	%	%	%
SiO_2	56·0	75·5	72·5
Al_2O_3	1·3	2·2	1·3
PbO	30·0		
Na_2O	4·5	4·0	} 16·3
K_2O	8·0	1·8	
CaO			6·5
MgO			3·0
B_2O_3		16·5	
Softening point	630 °C	775 °C	710 °C
Coefficient of expansion	90×10^{-7}	$37·5 \times 10^{-7}$	92×10^{-7}

Soda-lime silicate glasses are employed almost universally for the bulbs of this range of electric lamps. As will be seen from the table, this glass has a reasonably high softening point and a good compatibility of expansion coefficient with the lead glass normally used for the flare tubing, on to which the bulb is sealed during the lamp manufacturing process. In addition, soda-lime bulbs of good optical clarity can be produced and processed on high-speed machinery from relatively inexpensive materials.

7*

Lead glasses are normally used for the flare-tubing support-cane and exhaust-tube components of electric lamp bulb assemblies (see Fig. 10.1). They have lower softening and annealing temperatures than soda-lime glass. The coefficient of expansion is such that reliable vacuum-tight seals can be produced with 'dumet' lead wire (see below), used to conduct electricity to the interior of the lamp. Lead oxide, a major constituent of the glass is very expensive. It assists in reducing glass conductivity at lamp operating temperatures and hence the risk of electrolysis across the lamp stem-pinch.

Borosilicate glass, which is of similar composition to the well-known 'Pyrex'-type of glass, is expensive to produce but is necessary for high-temperature applications. The low coefficient of expansion imparts good resistance to the temperature extremes which are often encountered when lamps are used in outdoor locations. The main use for this glass in the GLS lamp range is for lamps of sealed-beam construction (Chapter 15, Fig. 15.9), for example, spot and flood lamps. It is also used for the hubs, into which filament supports are inserted, in the higher wattage range of conventional lamp construction. In addition to the three glasses mentioned above, clear fused silica (quartz) is used for the bulbs of highly loaded infrared lamps, used for a variety of industrial and commercial applications.

Lead wires and hermetic seals. All incandescent lamps employing tungsten filaments must necessarily incorporate a hermetic seal, through which electrical conductors convey power to the filament. In the early days of lamp making and for a considerable period thereafter, pure platinum wire was the electrical conductor most commonly used for this purpose. It was a great advance in lamp-making technique when 'dumet' was introduced. Dumet, which is much cheaper than platinum, has a coefficient of expansion slightly lower than lead-glass and is a nickel/iron alloy wire surrounded by a copper sheath, or plating and usually externally coated with anhydrous sodium borate. The borate coating protects the copper from excessive oxidation or corrosion during storage. It also combats excessive oxidation during the stem-making process, acting as a flux to assist the production of a properly wetted glass/wire seal. A typical composition for dumet is 72% nickel/iron (42:58—nickel:iron), 28% copper.

A different form of vacuum seal construction is employed in the borosilicate sealed-beam type lamps used as reflector spot and floodlights. Here, feather-edged nickel/iron thimbles are pressed into the base of the reflector pressing, as illustrated in Fig. 12.2.

In the borosilicate glass lamps of conventional bulb construction such as B1 floods, the usual vacuum sealing conductor material is tungsten rod.

Finally, with very low expansion materials such as fused silica, an entirely different seal construction is necessary. There are several possible alternatives but the one most commonly employed is a molybdenum foil seal as illustrated in Fig. 12.3.

This seal form which is also used in high-pressure discharge lamps is capable of carrying high current loadings. The maximum safe operating seal temperature in air, is of the order of 350 °C.

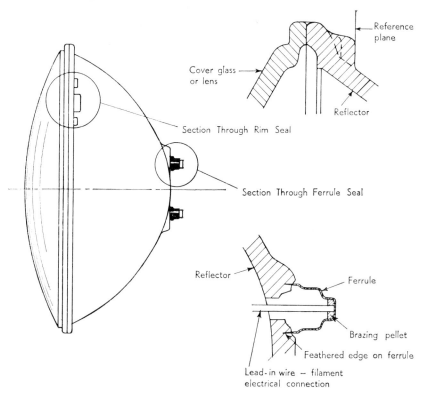

Fig. 12.2   Sealed-beam lamp

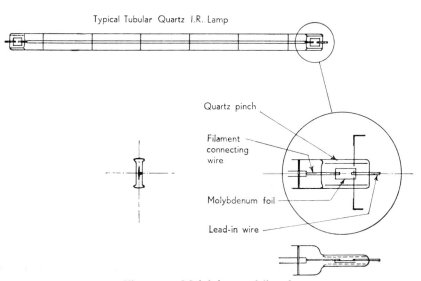

Fig. 12.3   Molybdenum foil seal

Bulbs—sizes, shapes and finishes

Sizes

It has always been the objective of lamp manufacturers to seek benefits in economic production and versatility of application by reducing bulb sizes to the minimum consistent with safe operation. The main difficulties in the way of this—namely, materials quality and processing quality—have been progressively diminished by improvements in lamp making techniques, with the result that during the past 25 years there has been a gradual reduction in sizes, as illustrated in Fig. 12.4.

Further reductions in bulb sizes would be possible without infringing the margins necessary for safe cap temperature in operation, for instance, by the adoption of krypton/nitrogen gas-filling mixtures but at the present cost of krypton this is decidedly uneconomic.

Shapes

The familiar pear-shaped bulb, which has remained substantially unchanged for the past 50 years, is still the predominant shape for domestic and industrial incandescent, general lighting service lamps. In recent years, however, there has been a considerable and continued growth in the popularity of the mushroom-shaped bulb.

Other shapes, which although not new are growing in popularity, are candle-shapes, both plain and twisted, and the small, round bulbs employed in multi-arm chandeliers and other decorative, domestic fittings.

The bulb shape for the range of reflector lamps used for display purposes is, of course, governed by optical requirements and here the reflector form is essentially parabolic.

Bulb coatings

It has been the practice for many years to reduce the glare of the incandescent filament by inside frosting of the lamp bulb and this is achieved with only a nominal (less than 1%) reduction in light output, compared with a clear bulb. To go beyond this and largely eliminate glare by improved diffusion has in the past meant the use of opal glass, which is not only expensive but also cuts down light output by some 20%. In recent years developments in internal bulb coating have been such that by the use of inorganic coating materials, such as finely divided silica, or titania it is possible to obtain virtual obscuration of the bright filaments, with only a small reduction in light output. The loss in light output is as low as 4% if silica coatings are used. The coatings are applied to the lamp bulbs prior to sealing-in, either as a suspension, or by the controlled burning of silica, or titanium compounds. They are widely used in conjunction with the mushroom-shaped bulbs mentioned earlier.

The use of 'natural' coloured glass bulbs to obtain a coloured light source is very expensive and except for special applications is being largely superseded by inside colour coatings of inorganic pigments.

It will be appreciated that all coloured incandescent lamps must operate at a reduced efficiency because of the filter effect of the pigment, or coloured

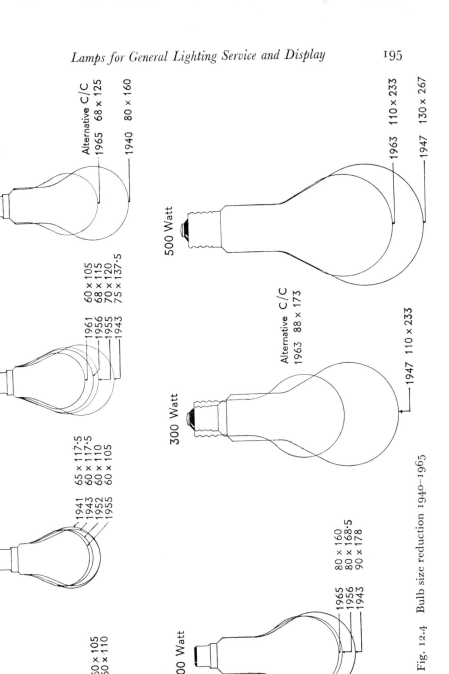

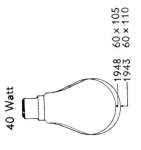

Fig. 12.4 Bulb size reduction 1940–1965

glass. This reduced efficiency of light output is accompanied by higher bulb temperatures, so that it is usual to confine coloured lamps for outdoor operation to the lower wattage range. Bright, saturated colours are not possible with pigment-coloured lamps.

The increasing need of lamps with directional beam properties for display purposes is met by the range of parabolic blown-bulb and pressed-glass (sealed-beam) lamp designs, incorporating highly reflective coatings on the inside of the bulb. The coating is usually applied by the controlled evaporation in a vacuum of aluminium, or silver and maintains a high degree of reflectance throughout the life of the lamp.

Caps and capping cement. The range of caps employed for GLS lamps is illustrated in Fig. 12.5.

Bayonet caps are standard for lamps 15 W to 150 W, E.S. caps are stan-

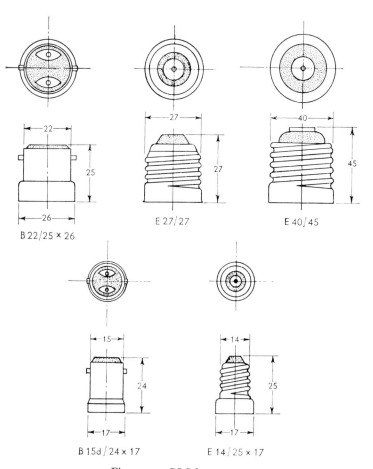

B 22/25 × 26

E 27/27

E 40/45

B 15d / 24 × 17

E 14 / 25 × 17

Fig. 12.5   GLS lamp caps

dard for 200 W lamps and G.E.S. caps for 300 W to 1500 W lamps. Lamps used for decoration and display use a greater variety of caps, for example, in the smaller bulb lamps such as candles and 45 mm round; small bayonet caps and small edison-screw caps are commonly used in fittings for decorative applications.

British Standard Specifications (BS 98, 'Screw Lamp Caps and Lampholders' and BS 52, 'Bayonet Lamp Caps and Lampholders') provide recommendations for maximum lamp wattage and current for different lamp cap/holder combinations.

It is important to safety and efficient operation over long service lives that the lamp cap should remain firmly attached to the lamp bulb. British Standard Specifications include a requirement that B.C. and E.S. capped lamps should withstand a torsion test of 25 lb in. and G.E.S. caps 45 lb in., both at the beginning and end of life. Caps are usually attached to the bulb by means of a cement, compounded of a thermosetting resin and inert, inorganic filler. Some manufacturers include in the capping cement a small amount of silicone resin to enhance resistance to bond failure when lamps are stored, or operated for long periods, under excessively humid conditions. It is also common practice to provide a moulded keyway in the shape of the lamp seal, to reduce the likelihood of torsion failure. Process control of the capping-cement baking operation can be assisted by the incorporation of a temperature indicator dye, which changes colour when baking is complete. Temperature of operation is a limiting feature of cement-bonded caps but capping cements have now been developed which can withstand operating temperatures up to 210 °C. In some special applications where service conditions are particularly onerous and it is convenient to use screw caps, a mating thread profile is moulded into the lamp bulb seal. The cap is then screwed on and permanently fixed, by means of a coating of silicone resin.

Standardisation. Standardisation is of paramount importance both to the industry and to the user. From the lamp manufacturer's standpoint it is necessary to achieve a high degree of standardisation of component dimensions for economic operation of high-speed machinery. The user, aside from considerations of price and availability, is primarily interested in interchangeability in fittings, operating characteristics and performance.

The lamp industry has always been assisted by the co-operation of fittings and accessory manufacturers, user representatives, Government Departments and the British Standards Institution in establishing practical and significant lamp specifications. The British Standard Specification for General Lighting Service lamps covers dimensions, operating characteristics and minimum performance levels, for compliance by the finished product.

British Standard Specifications are subject to continuous review and improvement, for example, the latest revision of the specification covering 200 V to 250 V Tungsten Filament General Service Electric Lamps (BS 161 amendment No. 6), includes two noteworthy additions. The more important of these is the introduction of a mandatory restriction in maximum lamp cap temperature rise, for a range of wattages and caps, to safeguard operating safety and reliability. The other is the provision of templet drawings, to assist manufacturers in the design of fittings dimensionally compatible with the lamp specification.

Most large manufacturers claim conformity of their GLS lamps with the appropriate BS specification and many hold 'BSI Licences' to support this. The British Standards Institution exercises a systematic check on the test levels and procedures of manufacturers operating the licensing scheme by a site-inspection scheme. This inspection is backed up by an open-market purchase of selections of the manufacturers' products. Failure to comply with the minimum test standards involves withdrawal of licence.

Operating characteristics. As mentioned in Chapter 10, most lamps for general lighting are designed to give a rated life of 1000 hours for reasons of economic operation, with the present price of electricity balanced against the cost of lamp replacement. They are also designed for universal burning (i.e. in any position), although optimum life quality is usually obtained in the 'cap up' position. Departures from this optimum, when operated in positions other than 'cap up', are normally greater for single coil lamps than coiled-coil lamps.

Details of dimensions, initial and through life light outputs, and minimum quality standards for general lighting service lamps are covered by a range of British Standard Specifications, to which reference is made in an Appendix.

The effect on initial characteristics (light output, etc.) of departures from rated voltage is shown in Chapter 10, Fig. 10.9. As a rough guide it is useful to bear in mind that 1% change in applied volts modifies watts by $1\frac{1}{2}\%$, efficiency (lumens per watt) by 2% and light output (lumens) by $3\frac{1}{2}\%$.

The main factors affecting lamp life are operating voltage and operating environment.

The relationship between lamp life and operating voltage is given by the following equation:

$$L_0 = L \left[\frac{V}{V_0}\right]^n$$

where L_0 = life, at rated voltage

L = life, at operating voltage

V_0 = rated voltage

V = average operating voltage

n = 13, for vacuum lamps and 14, for gas-filled lamps.

This exponential relationship between lamp life and voltage translated into a practical example means, that for every 5% increase in operating voltage over rated voltage, the lamp life is approximately halved.

The effect of operating environment on life is less easily assessed but the best results are obtained when incandescent lamps are operated in well ventilated surroundings, free from vibration, or shock. The standard range of general lighting service lamps will tolerate reasonable departures from the ideal but for those environments where vibration and shock are inescapable a range of 'rough-service' lamps is manufactured. These lamps normally use filaments made from special anti-vibration wires, referred to earlier and in addition, employ a multi-support construction. The efficiency is some 15% below that of the standard range lamps. Special environmental conditions—heat, vibration, humidity—are considered in Chapter 7.

Applications. Reference to Fig. 12.6 will provide some idea of the diversity of lamps now available for general lighting service and display.

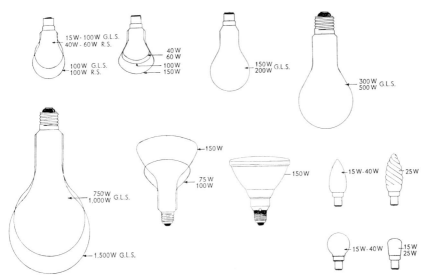

Fig. 12.6 Lamps for general lighting service and display

Most of the types illustrated are non-directional light sources and where the application extends beyond the utilitarian provision of light, are usually employed in conjunction with directional, or decorative fittings, or shades.

In recent years, however, there has been a considerable extension of the use of lamps with built-in reflectors, for a wide variety of lighting situations. Apart from the improved directional properties and the elimination of fittings maintenance, lamps with internal reflectors also offer compactness and flexibility suited to the constantly changing requirements of display lighting in many applications.

Blown bulb, reflector lamp types have been available for many years but their use has largely been limited to indoor and under-cover lighting. The introduction more recently of reflector-type lamps of sealed beam construction, which are made from borosilicate glass pressings giving higher beam intensities and able to withstand outdoor operation without the need for enclosed fittings, has greatly extended their use. Coloured fronts can also be incorporated in lamps of sealed-beam construction thus further increasing the scope for outdoor effects, lighting of gardens, buildings, etc.

An interesting new development which can be applied to lamps of sealed-beam construction is the incorporation of dichroic coatings (see Chapter 11). A multi-layer, interference (dichroic) film, is evaporated on to the inside surface of the lamp before assembly to provide a light reflecting surface at least as efficient as silver, or aluminium but which has the advantage of allowing unwanted infrared radiation to be transmitted rearwards out of the lamp. The resulting light beam is therefore much cooler and the heating effect at the illuminated surface is reduced, to approximately 50% of normal values. The main use of this technique is currently in lamps for photographic and projection use but there is obvious scope for application in the display lighting of heat-sensitive merchandise and for medical purposes.

Dichroic coatings can also be applied to the front of the lamp (cover glass) through which light is transmitted, in order to modify the colour of the emitted light. By contrast with coloured glass, dichroic coatings do not absorb radiation of the transmitted colour and hence a more efficient coloured light source is obtained, free from fading.

Safety in Application. Modern incandescent electric light bulbs have a considerable safety advantage over the combustion-type light sources (candles, oil lamps, etc.) which they have largely superseded.

The inherent safety of the electric light bulb springs from several aspects of design and it is convenient to consider these, under three main headings.

Electrical safety. The main danger is that of electric shock and manufacturers take great care to ensure that lamps are electrically safe. For lamps fitted with bayonet caps, the effective insulation of the cap shell from the cap contacts virtually eliminates the chance of an electric shock should the shell be touched when being inserted (accidentally) into a 'live' holder. Notwithstanding these design and manufacturing precautions, however, in the interests of ultimate safety, there is some responsibility on the part of the consumer to ensure that correct practice is observed. The golden rules are that lamps should never, knowingly, be inserted into 'live' holders; that metal holders should always be earthed and that skirted holders which shroud the cap, are safer than unskirted holders.

In the case of screw caps, should the holder be wrongly connected, the shell is 'live' to earth during the normal operation of the lamp and design precautions are taken to prevent the possibility of accidental shock. Caps and bulbs are matched such that the cap shell is inaccessible when screwed into the holder. Danger from shock whilst screwing into a 'live' holder is minimised by the use of a skirted holder, or as is more usual on the Continent, by the use of a screw holder so designed that the lamp cap shell only makes electrical contact when screwed fully home.

Another contingency is that of excessive surge currents due to internal arcs, for example, when the lamp fails. Protection against this hazard is provided by the incorporation of internal fuses (see Chapter 10, Fig. 10.1).

Fire risk

Much effort is directed toward eliminating any fire hazard from the use of an electric light bulb for normal lighting purposes. Nothing that the manufacturers can do, however, alters the fact that an incandescent light bulb radiates most of its energy in the form of heat and hence they must not be operated in close proximity to, or contact with, flammable materials. An important step forward has been made by the recent adoption of maximum values for cap temperature rise throughout the range of general lighting service lamps together with the recommendations concerning the maximum wattage loading for the various types of fitting. It is important that these recommendations should not be exceeded. The risk of fire being caused by the accidental breakage of the glass envelope whilst the lamp is switched on is very small, since when the tungsten filament is exposed to oxygen in the atmosphere, the filament rapidly evaporates into a cloud of tungsten-oxide smoke. None the less, electric light bulbs should never be operated 'bare' in explosive, or flammable vapour atmospheres.

Explosions

Violent lamp failures due to fracture of the glass envelope of the lamp can occur, due to manufacturing defects, thermal shock, mechanical shock and surface damage (scratches) to the glass bulb.

Explosive failures due to manufacturing defects are nowadays very rare since stress patterns, uniformity of bulb-wall thickness and process treatments are kept under close control. Furthermore, the chance of scratch-damage weakening the glass envelope is also largely eliminated by present manufacturing techniques.

Failures due to thermal shock, caused for example, by water dripping on to a hot lamp bulb, can sometimes occur and some discrimination in the choice of fittings is necessary, especially for the higher wattage lamps in outdoor locations. The risk of thermal-shock failure can be reduced by the use of the more expensive borosilicate glass, which as mentioned earlier, has a lower coefficient of thermal expansion. In some special cases the glass bulb is coated with a silicone resin to minimise heat-transfer from water droplets.

Scratch-damage to the envelope, caused by abrasion against a glass outer shade, or a ceramic holder skirt has occasionally been known to promote explosive failure.

CHAPTER 13

Lamps for Photography and Projection

Expendable photoflash bulbs. Photoflash bulbs emit a high level of illumination, of controlled colour temperature, for a short period of time and they are primarily designed as a light source for the exposure of photographic film materials.

A glass bulb is filled with a highly combustible material, usually zirconium foil, or wire in a finely shredded state. Into the midst of this foil is introduced a filament igniter, mounted between a pair of lead-in wires coated with a primer paste, made from finely milled zirconium powder and powerful oxidising materials.

The complete assembly is sealed into the bulb, under pressure, in an oxygen atmosphere.

When the bulb is fired, the filament is charged with an electrical current and becomes heated, this causes the primer paste to ignite and small pellets of burning primer are thrown off. This, in turn, triggers explosive combustion of the finely shredded foil in the oxygen atmosphere within the bulb— causing, by very careful quality control throughout production, a pre-determined flash of known duration and light output.

Fig. 13.1 illustrates the amount of light emitted at any given interval of time during the period of the flash cycle, from a Type 1B bulb. The value of

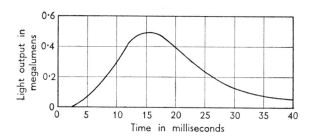

Fig. 13.1   Type 1B—lumens/time curve

the light intensity in mega lumens is plotted on the vertical scale. The horizontal scale is plotted in time measured in milliseconds.

Three primary factors can be deduced from the diagram, namely:

(1) The rapidity with which the bulb reaches the peak and half-peak light outputs and hence, an indication of the type of camera synchronisation to which it is suited.

(2) The total light output in mega lumens, which is a measure of the effective range of the flash.

(3) The duration of the light output at the full, or half-peak values, which determines the most effective shutter speed to be used.

Although bulbs of the type used mainly by press and commercial photographers, are of comparatively large dimensions, due to the high light outputs necessary, considerable miniaturisation has taken place in recent years in the bulb size used by the amateur. The development work involved has been successful not only in reducing bulb size with consequent assistance to equipment portability but additionally increases in performance have been made.

Fig. 13.2 illustrates the size and differences in the design of the two popular photoflash bulbs currently used by amateur photographers. Type 1 has the

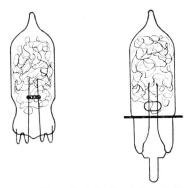

Fig. 13.2   Photoflash bulbs AG and Type 1

European capless base and the AG type has the smaller base, first adopted in the U.S.A. The light outputs of the latest versions of the Type 1 and AG bulbs in both clear and blue finish, are identical; thus the same Guide Number (the Guide Number system is explained later in this chapter) is utilised, for any given film and shutter speed, for all four types of bulbs.

Whilst the miniaturisation of photoflash bulbs has made them more convenient to store and to carry, difficulties are sometimes reported in 'handling', causing them to be incorrectly seated in the reflector socket. Another problem familiar to the designers of both photoflash bulbs and the equipment in which they are used, is that of providing for the rapid repetition firing of bulbs. Magazine units and turrets have been designed with varying degrees of success from the aspects of both cost and reliability.

The recently introduced flashcube design appears to offer an effective solution to these problems (see Fig. 13.3).

The flashcube consists of four tiny flashbulbs, each accurately aligned within an integral reflector. The bulbs and reflectors are encased within a transparent plastic protective shield, to form a cube, each vertical face of which is $1\frac{1}{8}$ in. square. Cameras designed to accommodate the flashcube incorporate a device automatically to rotate the cube, after taking a flash picture.

Fig. 13.3   Flashcube

Electronic flashtubes.   For the professional photographer taking many photographs, it may be inconvenient to carry and replace bulbs after each flash. An alternative exists in the electronic flashtube (see Chapter 19) which derives its light by the discharge of energy into a gas contained in the tube. This is not destructive and the tube may be used for many thousands of flashes. The flash duration may be modified over considerably wider limits than the flashbulb and it thus finds more application in science and industry.

For the amateur photographer many portable units are available ranging from approximately 15 joule to 500 joule output. The usefulness of the lower rated units is questionable since the smallest photoflash bulb approximates in output to a 150 joule flashtube. Battery and power unit costs are considerable, amounting to some £30 to £50 for a 100 joule to 150 joule unit and hence the advantages of electronic flash relate to its convenience, or economy, with large numbers of shots.

The Guide Number System.   The manufacturers of photoflash bulbs issue guide numbers for their products. These can be used in two ways; firstly, to determine the correct flash-to-subject distance, with the aperture of the camera lens diaphragm set at a particular stop (f number) and secondly, to ascertain the correct lens aperture for a particular flash-to-subject distance.

Photoflash application.   The applications for photoflash photography are numerous: at functions and parties, for pictures outdoors at night which could not otherwise be taken at all, or for which a time exposure of considerable duration would be required; and for arresting movement in action shots, being amongst the more obvious. Less obvious, but equally useful is the facility of using flashbulbs to 'fill-in' shadows. The 'fill-in' flash technique should always be used on both dull and sunny days, for portrait work out of doors. It can be useful for indoor shots too—an indoor scene against a sunlit window is a typical example.

Studio and photoflood lamps—requirements and usage. In Chapter 10 the general principles and methods of construction of incandescent lamps have been explained and information given concerning lamp types, including those specifically designed for photographic applications. The intending user of photographic incandescent light sources may be assisted if the information in that chapter is now augmented, particularly from the viewpoint of the usage of such lamps.

Lamps for photography are used in conjunction with either colour or black and white film and they must be selected for the particular application.

Class CP lamps are designed to operate at a given colour temperature, at their rated voltage and are for use with colour film (other than artificial light types for amateur use, e.g. Kodachrome A) which is balanced to a colour temperature of 3250 °K. The lamp filaments must operate at very high temperatures to meet this need and due to the consequent high rate of the evaporation of the tungsten, the useful lamp life is relatively short. These lamps are used extensively by the professional in film studios where the film stock requires this colour temperature illumination for a balanced interpretation of colour.

Before lamps of controlled colour temperature were available, it was necessary to correct the colour of the light emitted by using colour filters over the lens of the lamp housing; for example, arc-lamp fittings required a yellow filter and tungsten lamps a blue filter. Besides cutting down light these were not entirely satisfactory as the colours tended to fade.

Artificial light film (e.g. Kodachrome A) which is used by the amateur, requires lamps of an even higher colour temperature, i.e. 3400 °K.

When monochrome film stock is used the colour temperature of the lamp is unimportant but not so the light output, therefore lamps for this application are usually designed to operate at about 3000 °K, with resultant increase in lamp life.

Many different lamp types are used in film studios today, from 1 kW to 20 kW and a series of smaller lamps in the 'CP' range.

In the case of the higher wattage lamps, which are used to project large *splashes* of light some distance from the actual scene (it is common practice to put lamps on a gallery around a set), the current rating is greater than that which conventional caps have been designed to carry, e.g. the 10 kW lamp current approaches 100 A. These lamps are therefore fitted with a base of a 'Bipost' construction. The two contact members consist of copper thimbles, the rims of which are sealed into a hard-glass pressing which, in turn, forms the base of the lamp (see Fig. 13.4).

This form of construction has an additional advantage in that the filament can be located accurately in relation to the Bipost pins during lamp assembly and hence to the holder and reflector in the fitting. The lamp houses incorporate a lens and a mirror; the mirror and lamp holder assembly are usually integral and moveable, with respect to the lens. Thus the beam can be adjusted easily from a narrow spot, to a wide flood.

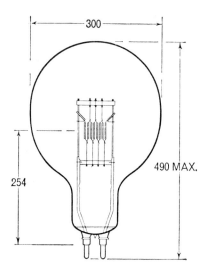

Fig. 13.4   A 10 kW studio lamp, showing Bipost (Bi38) base

It is important to maintain light output and colour temperature as long as possible throughout the lamp life. During the burning of the lamp, tungsten is deposited from the filament on to the wall of the bulb, reducing both the light output and colour temperature. In order to minimise this effect a small quantity of coarse tungsten powder is inserted in the bulb and at suitable intervals through life the lamp is removed from the fitting and shaken, causing the tungsten crystals to scour any deposits from the bulb wall.

Film studios require controlled uniformity and standards of performance from their lamps and fittings. Arising from this the British Standards Institution, in collaboration with users and lamp manufacturers, has produced a BS 1075, for lamps and BS 2063, for fittings.

The requirements for television studios differ slightly from those of film studios and therefore a separate British Standard for fittings is being prepared to cover their requirements.

Lamps of lower wattages giving illumination of high colour temperature have very short design lives, that of the 240 V 275 W photoflood (PP/1) being only 2 to 3 hours. These lamps, however, are extremely useful, since they produce high light output at high colour temperature, for use in portrait studios and for indoor photography by the amateur. They are normally used in conjunction with reflectors. Reflector photoflood lamps (Fig. 13.5), incorporating their own built in reflectors are also in common use, as simple directional light sources.

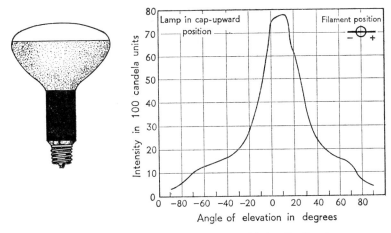

Fig. 13.5   A Reflector Photoflood lamp, with its distribution curve

The life of photoflood and reflector photoflood lamps can be prolonged if a series/parallel circuit is used (Fig. 13.6). In such circuits, lamps can be operated at a reduced load while composing the picture and then switched to full brilliance for the actual exposure.

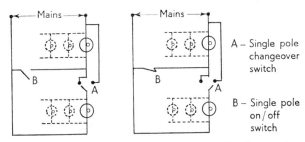

Fig. 13.6   Series parallel circuit for photoflood operation

In addition to the lamps already described, a sealed-beam photoflood lamp is available for use with cine cameras. This lamp, rated at 240 V 600 W (10 hours average life), has been designed for use with cameras having wide-angle lenses, the lamp giving axial coverage to half-peak beam candlepower of 28°, and a horizontal coverage to half-peak beam candlepower of 58°. The peak beam candlepower is 17,500 cd, with a colour temperature of 3400 °K (Fig. 13.7).

This lamp is used in 'cine guns' and can be affixed to either cine cameras (for which it was specifically designed), or still cameras.

Tungsten-halogen floodlights.   Whilst photofloods and reflector photo-floods perform a useful function as light sources for the photographer, tungsten-halogen lamps specifically designed for photographic purposes are now available and have certain advantages. Elsewhere in this Manual a

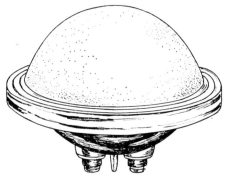

Fig. 13.7   A sealed-beam cine floodlamp

chapter has been devoted to these lamps and this should be read so that the principles of their operation may be fully understood (Chapter 15). However, the results of the development activities can be summarised briefly as follows:

(a) They are much smaller in dimensions than conventional incandescent lamps of similar rating.
(b) Their design can, in general, be arranged to produce double the life of conventional lamps, while at the same time having increased efficiencies of up to 30%.
(c) There is no significant fall-off in colour temperature or light output during life.

The 120 V 650 W, 240 V 800 W and 240 V 1000 W versions were designed primarily for the photographer. Their advantages, over conventional type tungsten filament lamps, of constant colour temperature and lumen maintenance are important for it will be readily understood that if the colour temperature drops appreciably the colour rendering will also change—this, of course, does not apply when monochrome film stock is used—and that loss of light output during the life of a lamp creates exposure problems. When these advantages are taken in conjunction with the portability, compactness and versatility of the lighting units (colloquially referred to as 'guns') that have been designed to make the best use of them, there can be no doubt that in future they will be used extensively. Film and TV studios, industrial and educational film units, professional photographers and the ever increasing army of amateurs devoted to both cine and still photography, whose common aim is to produce consistently good results, not only from the aesthetic viewpoint but from those of correct exposure and accurate colour balance, will find the use of tungsten-halogen lamps advantageous.

Lamps for projection of cine film and transparencies

Introduction.   In earlier chapters of this book the general principles and methods of construction of incandescent lamps are explained, including the optical considerations relating to designs employed in projection systems.

The large majority of projector lamps are of the incandescent filament type to specialised design and these aspects will now be discussed in more detail in relation to application requirements.

After the Second World War, photography, as a visual aid in education and as a pastime became widespread and in particular, the use of colour film increased. Parallel with this came technical advances, not only in sensitised materials but in photographic apparatus generally, including projectors and their associated light sources. In order to reduce the weight of projection equipment (and incidentally to reduce the price) an early post-war development was the introduction of projector lamps for use directly on 200/250 V mains supply. Previously, lamps of 110 V or 115 V rating had been generally accepted and operated from a transformer. This transition presented some difficulty for the lamp manufacturers but as design problems were overcome, the equipment manufacturers turned their attention to producing machines incorporating lamps of higher wattage, as these did not now require the use of a step-down transformer. (This demand for higher wattage lamps was stimulated by the conviction in the trade, especially in the U.S.A., that a projector incorporating a 750 W lamp was bound to give a higher screen illumination than a model using one of 500 W rating.) Little recognition was given to the percentage of light output which failed to reach the screen because of spillage round the outside of the 'film gate', due to the larger area of the higher wattage filament. This problem was intensified by the higher European voltages compared to the 115 V supplies in the U.S.A. Inevitably, the filament area of a lamp designed for 200 V to 250 V was larger than that of the equivalent 115 V filament; also the reduction in wire diameter necessitated by the higher voltage resulted in a lower filament temperature for given lamp life and hence, an appreciable drop in efficiency. Such disadvantages are inherent in filament lamp constructions for use on 200/250 V supplies.

Projector lamps must be designed as an integral part of an optical projection system, where the light has to be concentrated in a small area taken by the film to be illuminated. Their construction and assembly require extreme precision in lamp making. The tungsten wire must be wound very accurately and formed into the most compact filament possible. This filament must then be positioned in a precise manner in relation to a prefocus base, or some other locating point of the lamp, so that when the lamp is inserted into the lampholder the filament is accurately located on the optical axis of the projector.

Maximum light on the screen is the primary objective in projector performance and is obtained by operating the filament at the highest possible temperature compatible with an economical lamp life. Lamp efficiency increases as the filament temperature is raised. At the melting temperature of tungsten, the theoretical maximum efficiency approximates to 52 lm/W. The practical limit achieved with the most efficiently designed lamp is, however, in the region of 40 lm/W, mainly due to heat losses through the gas, leads, etc. Such a lamp would have a very short life in terms of minutes, impractical from the economic standpoint. The majority of standard projector lamps currently operate at efficiencies related to an average life of 25 hours and tungsten-halogen lamps (incorporating a regenerative halogen cycle), an average life of 50 hours.

Voltage control can have a great influence on lamp life. For example, a 50 hour life 12 V 100 W tungsten-halogen lamp, if operated at 13 V, would have an average life of only 25 hours. In addition an excess voltage (i.e. a voltage applied which is higher than the rated voltage of the lamp), in particular with mains voltage lamps, can cause an electrical arc across the filament with resultant violent failure. Consequently, most lamps above 100 V are internally fused to avoid a rapid surge across the lead wires, which could lead to a sudden increase of gas pressure and consequent bulb explosion. The fuse also protects the circuit and prevents blowing of the line-fuse.

High operating temperatures are attained in most projector lamps. For instance, a 1 kW lamp is designed for filament operation at approximately 2950 °C and it is located only about 18 mm from the wall of the glass envelope, which may begin to soften at temperatures above 500 °C. This lamp dissipates as much energy as a $1\frac{1}{4}$ horse-power motor. Therefore it readily will be appreciated that forced cooling is necessary to prevent damage to lamp and equipment.

Materials used in projector lamp manufacture are specially selected to withstand these high temperatures. For example, the supports of the filament can only be made from tungsten, or molybdenum. Most other metals would melt in such close proximity to a tungsten filament operating at a temperature higher than any other artificial heat ordinarily encountered by man, a temperature at which furnace bricks would melt, more than twice the temperature of molten steel.

There are more than 250 individual types of projector lamp listed in the industry and as the art of picture projection has progressed new lamps have been designed to greater precision, generally smaller in size than their predecessors and with more compact filaments of higher brightness. The majority fall into two main groups, mains voltage and low-voltage lamps.

Mains voltage lamps. Mains voltage lamps, operating between 200 V and 250 V in 10 V steps, are normally manufactured in ratings from 100 W to 1 kW. Ratings below 400 W generally employ filaments which are of coiled-coil (Fig. 13.8) configuration.

The light emitted from the filament is collected directly by the condenser lens. In most optical systems the emitted rearward light is collected by a mirror which redirects it back on to the filament. The reflected image is reversed, thus filling the spaces between the filament coil sections.

Lamps rated between 500 W and 1000 W usually have 'biplane' filaments (Fig. 13.8). In this case the filament is of single-coil winding in two planes, so that the gaps in the front row of coils are filled as far as possible by the rear row, thereby presenting an approximation to a solid source of light to the optical system.

In recent years the more popular ratings (i.e. 150 W, 300 W, 500 W, 750 W and 1000 W) have been improved by locating the filament structure on a valve-type base (Tru-Focus G17q). This type of construction ensures more precise positioning of the filament in relation to the projector optical system. Additionally, the 'snap-in' accurate alignment of the lamp in the keyed spigot, ensures that the lamp fits the lampholder only when properly positioned.

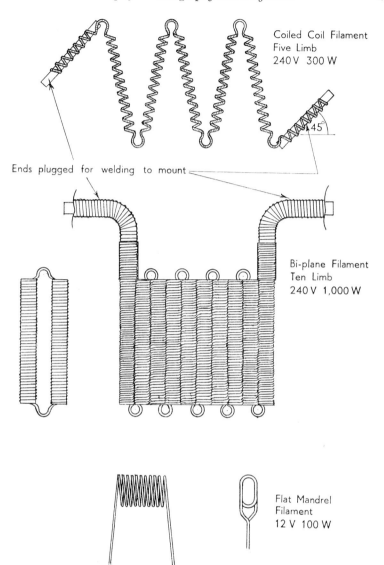

Fig. 13.8   Typical projector lamp filament formations

Utilisation of the valve-base on Tru-Focus types has dispensed with the older forms of lamp stem assembly and deeper base thereby considerably reducing overall lamp length (Fig. 13.9).

It has been followed by the introduction of the proximity-reflector lamp range. These lamps incorporate a miniature internal reflector, which is located immediately behind the filament. The reflector gathers light directly from the filament and redirects it through the gaps between the coils towards the optical system. The result is an initial gain in screen brightness of up to 30%, due to the high collection angle of the reflector. As the reflector is hermetically sealed against dirt and oxidation, it retains a high percentage of its initial efficiency throughout life. The lamps run cooler because there is no

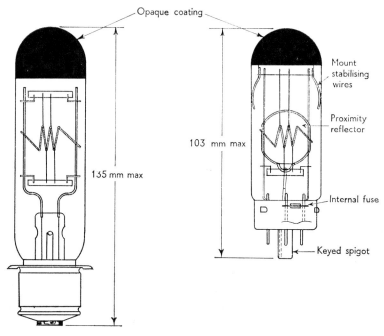

Fig. 13.9   Comparison to scale of conventional 300 W projector (lamp ref. A1/6) with valve-base proximity reflector type (ref. A1/201)

rearward radiation through the bulb, compared with the conventional system where the reflector is part of the projector. There is a reduced risk of bulb overheating and the relatively cool area on the lamp bulb behind the reflector preferentially collects most of the evaporated tungsten from the filament, thus increasing the efficiency maintenance of the light output throughout life.

Low-voltage lamps.   Low-voltage lamps mainly operate between 8 V and 30 V and in most applications they offer distinct advantages over mains voltage versions. The trend in Europe for 8 mm cine and slide projection is towards low-voltage lamps. As the design voltage is decreased from 240 V to, say, 24 V for lamps of the same wattage, the filament wire diameter is increased very considerably and the length is shortened. Thus the filament becomes much more robust and can be wound in a more compact form as, for example, the flat-mandrel filament (Fig. 13.8). The thicker wire also means that the efficiency, in lumens per watt can be increased for equivalent life, thus raising the light output and colour temperature. The flat-mandrel filament is particularly advantageous in projectors using a condenser system (see Chapter 10).

The practical effect of these advantages is that low-voltage lamps can replace mains voltage types of some three times their wattage consumption without loss of screen illumination while giving a 'whiter' light, due to the higher colour temperature at which their filaments operate. The lower wattage rating means that the projector operates at a considerably reduced temperature and any forced cooling can be directed mainly at the slide, or film, instead of at the lamp.

Low-voltage lamps can be sub-divided into three main categories: (a) flat-mandrel filament lamps, with either a Tru-Focus, or single centre-contact base; (b) Truflector lamps which incorporate their own integral optical system; (c) tungsten-halogen lamps. As these types have design features very peculiar to their applications, more details of their construction and design are given in the following section.

Applications of projector lamps. There are quite a number of film sizes for cine and still (diascope) projection but today five systems represent 95%, or more, of the total usage.

These are: 8 mm—cine; 16 mm—cine; 35 and 70 mm film projection slides and filmstrip—which will be discussed in turn.

8 mm cine. It has been stated that 8 mm film lacks sufficient definition for projection on screens more than 5 ft wide. This statement is open to question but it is certain that the brilliance of the projected image is of vital importance. For this reason leading lamp manufacturers have in recent years carried out considerable development work to improve the screen illumination and have met with much success. Illumination of the 8 mm format presents a formidable task. Light has to be concentrated on to a very small area which can then be magnified up to 250,000 times on the screen. The resultant picture must be clear and evenly illuminated with a reasonable uniformity of brightness from centre to corners of the picture.

Appreciation of the lamp developments which have taken place may benefit from a brief description of the film to be projected. There are two distinct 8 mm systems now in operation, (1) Standard 8, (2) Super 8 (Fig. 13.10).

Standard 8 has been in use since before the Second World War and consists of 16 mm film which is run through the camera twice, being exposed for only half the width at a time and reversed after exposure of the first half. After processing it is slit, joined and returned to the user in a continuous length of 8 mm film, ready for projection. The picture area to be illuminated is only 3·28 × 4·37 mm.

Super 8 is of recent development. It is 8 mm film supplied in a cassette for easy loading and is run through the camera in a continuous length. The perforations are smaller than Standard 8, allowing the picture area to be increased by approximately 50% to 4 × 5·36 mm. This permits more light to pass through the 'film gate' and the screen illumination can be considerably higher.

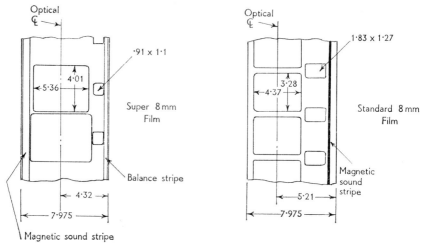

Fig. 13.10   Comparative dimensions (in mm) of 'Standard' and 'Super 8' cine film picture areas

Lamps available for Standard and Super 8 operate on similar principles, but because of the larger Super 8 format small changes in either lamp or projector optical design may be necessary in order that the film is evenly illuminated.

Attempts to improve the brilliance of the 8 mm format illumination have led to a number of distinctly different approaches. Two of these which have found wide and popular usage will be described.

The "integral mirror" system. Until a few years ago a condenser system was used with a lamp employing a large, high-wattage filament. The illumination was extremely poor and the system very inefficient. A 500 W lamp produced as an average 35 lm on the screen. This lamp had an output of 11,000 lm thus the utilisation efficiency was 0·3%.

With the advent of the 21·5 V 150 W Truflector lamp an illumination of 100 lm could be achieved with a similar objective, which increased the utilisation of available light to 2·5%, an increase of no less than eight-fold.

A comparison between a Truflector 150 W lamp and a condenser system using the 500 W lamp is shown (Fig. 13.11). Elimination of the external reflector and condensing lenses and the use of a shorter envelope permits the design of a smaller projector. The purpose of the internal reflector is to obtain a more efficient usage of the light from the filament. It does this by directing a high percentage of light on to the 'film gate', thus enabling the use of a small compact filament. The reflector, which is silver plated and made to great precision, is ellipsoidal in shape. The filament is positioned accurately at the first focus of the reflector and the 'film gate' is positioned at the second focus. The dimensions of the ellipse and filament are chosen so that the reflected light will fill the objective lens at the required focal distance.

A very important and efficient lamp operating on similar principles is the 'shaped-bulb' integral-mirror lamp, rated at 8 V 50 W (ref. A1/17). As distinct from the Truflector lamp it does not have an internal reflector but the rear portion of the bulb is moulded into an ellipsoidal shape. The front portion of the bulb is hemispherical in shape with the focus point within the

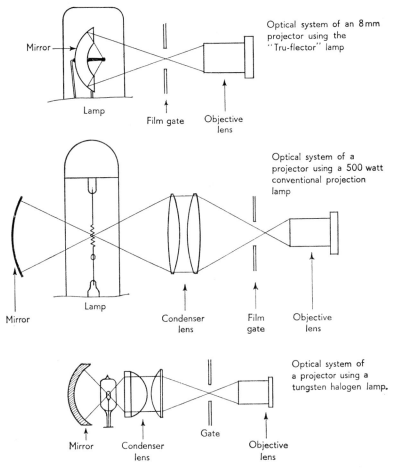

Fig. 13.11   Comparison of 8 mm cine optical systems utilising Truflector 150 W, conventional 500 W, and tungsten-halogen 100 W projector lamps

lamp, where the filament is located; this is also the first focus of the ellipse. The whole lamp is externally silvered with the exception of a circular aperture in the front of the bulb which allows the cone of light, gathered by the two reflecting surfaces, to emerge and be directed on to the film gate (Fig. 13.12).

The tungsten-halogen system.   The tungsten-halogen lamp has certain characteristics which are ideal for projection purposes. The 12 V 100 W lamp

8+

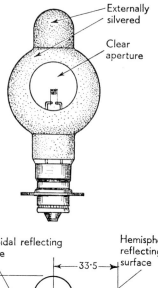

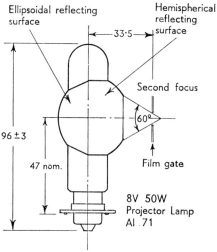

Fig. 13.12   A low-voltage, shaped-bulb, integral-mirror projector lamp

(ref. A1/215) has an increase in light output of 30% over the conventional lamp and at this increase in efficiency a double lamp life (50 hours average) can still be achieved. The virtual 100% lumen maintenance, due to the cleaning action of the halogen cycle is again a great improvement over the lamps it replaced, which had a fall-off in light output of up to 40% during life. Above all the diameter of the 100 W halogen lamp is only 11 mm compared with 25 mm for the conventional lamp. As can be seen from Fig. 13.11, the tungsten-halogen lamp is used with an aspheric condenser and a rear mirror. Due to the lamp's compact filament and small diameter, the light collection angle of the condenser is very large, resulting in a high utilisation of the light output. Again, as the lamp and condenser are very small and close together, the arrangement takes up little area, allowing the construction of compact-styled equipment.

With the light sources described, utilising low-voltage filaments and producing high-screen illumination, some increase in film temperature is inevitable. The lamps are of lower wattage than their predecessors and therefore the cooling can be directed to the 'gate'. Nevertheless with projectors incorporating slow running and still picture devices, film-burning may be possible, under certain conditions. Therefore, the Truflector lamp is manufactured in a version which incorporates a dichroic, heat-transmitting mirror (the principles of this are described in Chapter 10). The use of such mirrors reduce the film temperature by at least 40% thereby giving protection to the film against excessive heat. In the case of the tungsten-halogen lamp, the condensers absorb a proportion of the heat but some projector manufacturers coat one element of the condensers with a heat-reflecting layer, to reduce the heat reaching the film.

16 mm—ciné. The usage of 16 mm projection apparatus is limited, in the main, to semi-professional and educational requirements.

Lamps of the integral-mirror, Truflector type have been applied to this format in the U.S.A. but they have not yet been incorporated in a European projection equipment. The reasons for this are probably three-fold: (a) the number of machines sold is low, by comparison with 8 mm cine and 35 mm slide projector; (b) design, tooling and production costs are high; and (c) lamps in the 110/115 V and 200/250 V ranges, of 750 W and 1000 W rating produce a screen illumination which is generally acceptable. The problems of heating which can be encountered when lamps of this type are used for the projection of slides are minimised for the film travels rapidly past the 'gate', no individual 'frame' being exposed to the heat from the lamp for more than a fraction of a second.

35 mm and 70 mm film projection. The 35 mm film projector, widely used in the cinema, was designed with a carbon arc as the light source. Today there are many conversion installations where the carbon-arc is replaced with the xenon arc discharge lamp.

The xenon arc lamp offers simplicity in operation to suit the already semi-automated cinemas. The light on the screen is independent of the operator; once optically aligned no further focusing is required. Likewise the absence of fumes and electrode movement and mechanisms helps to reduce maintenance to the minimum. The xenon arc is also well accepted for its colour stability and rendition properties.

The more widely used lamp rating in this country is the 2 kw xenon lamp (reference Chapter 19) but there is continuing interest in higher lamp powers of 5 kw–8 kw. Lamps of this power are, however, less attractive economically at the present time. They are suitable for 70 mm systems which now make use of large carbon-arc equipment.

The tungsten-halogen lamp (Fig. 13.13) has played a major part in raising the standards of slide-projector illumination. The most popular rating at present in use is the 24 V 150 W lamp (ref. A1/216). This has a flat

mandrel filament of very high brilliance, because of the close winding. The
filament has a width to height ratio of 2:1 so that when the image from the
mirror (Fig. 13.14) is produced above the filament, the effective light source

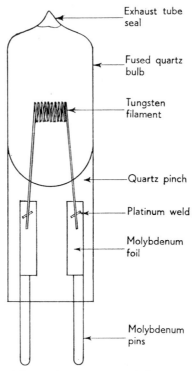

Exhaust tube seal

Fused quartz bulb

Tungsten filament

Quartz pinch

Platinum weld

Molybdenum foil

Molybdenum pins

Fig. 13.13   A low-voltage, tungsten-halogen projector lamp

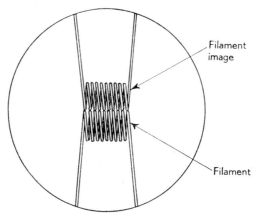

Filament image

Filament

Fig. 13.14   Rectangular filament images forming a square "effective" light source

is square. Such a lamp produces a screen illumination higher than obtained with the mains voltage 500 W lamp. This is partially achieved because the efficiency of the halogen lamp for a 50 hour life is 32 lm/W, whereas the 25 hour life 240 V 500 W lamp operates at 22 lm/W. This higher efficiency attains a 'whiter' screen illumination with the filament operating at approximately 3350 °K whereas the 500 W lamp operates at about 3100 °K. In addition the very much smaller filament of the tungsten-halogen lamps fills the objective evenly with much less spillage of light around the 'gate'. Because it is nearer to being a point source, the depth of focus on the slide is considerably increased, thus re-focusing the objective lens is not necessary when changing slides. A high overall definition is obtained, a condition which cannot be achieved when using lamps with a large filament area.

Assessment of future design considerations. During the past two decades photography, both as a pastime and as a tool for education and instruction, has shown a phenomenal increase in popularity and this may be expected to continue.

The advent of the larger 8 mm format has presented new and interesting problems for lamp designer and manufacturer. It can therefore be anticipated that this field will absorb much of the lamp development effort in the immediate future. Improvements can be expected in the design of integral mirror lamps so that their internal reflectors will be capable of gathering more light, redirecting it to fill objectives of apertures of the order of f1·0, with consequent increase in screen illumination and picture size. Dichroic-coated mirrors which reflect light and transmit heat are likely to be utilised more extensively and more lamps will be produced with a flat-faced glass envelope. Such lamps, incorporating reflectors of larger dimensions than hitherto, also permit the reflectors to be offset in the lamp, towards the film path. This allows the larger objectives, previously mentioned, to be filled and increases light output.

It is possible, however, that lamps of the regenerative cycle type will make the greatest impact on projector light output.

It is already known that lamps working with halogens other than iodine such as fluorine, have a regenerative cycle where the evaporated tungsten is redeposited on the hotter portions of the filament from whence it came, instead of on the cooler areas of the filament, as in the case of iodine lamps. This means that such lamps can have a reasonable life expectancy, operating at efficiencies nearer the theoretical maximum of approximately 50 lm/W.

A low-voltage lamp employing the regenerative principle, with a light output capable of producing 1000 screen lumens (when used in conjunction with a correctly computed optical system), has already been developed for use in slide and filmstrip projectors. There is also a possible application for 16 mm cine use.

Compact forms of metal-iodide discharge lamp (see Chapter 18), which operate at an efficiency very much higher than is possible with a filament lamp, will no doubt also make an impact on the semi-professional and professional market, where the inclusion of the necessary control gear can be accepted.

From the foregoing it will be appreciated that effective progress will continue to depend upon close co-operation between lamp designers and the designers of optical and projection apparatus, in a highly competitive environment.

Recommendations for care and replacement of projector lamps. In conclusion it should be stressed that it is to the benefit of the user, both professional and amateur, to consider the main factors to be taken into account when handling projector lamps, in order to ensure that satisfactory service and value for money are obtained. The following points may provide a useful reference:

(1) Check the cooling system frequently, to ensure that there is no obstruction, or deflection of the cooling air-stream.

(2) It is essential that projector lamps are operated at the correct voltage and therefore, if there is a voltage tapping adjustment on the projector, it should be checked. Should there be reason to suppose that the voltage supply is in excess of the rated value (i.e. 240 V, etc.) the transformer should be adjusted to the next highest voltage-tapping, or if mains voltage lamps are used they should be purchased in the next highest voltage (i.e. 250 V instead of 240 V). A 1% voltage overload may reduce the lamp life by 12%.

(3) The projector should not be moved whilst the lamp is alight, as a sudden shock can cause the filament to distort, due to the very high temperature at which it operates. After switching off, approximately 15 minutes should be allowed for cooling before the apparatus is moved.

(4) When handling valve-based lamps, it is also important to avoid damaging the connection pins. To insert the lamp into the projector the key, or ridge, on the central peg should be lined up with the keyway in the lampholder. The lamp may then be pushed straight into the holder; it should not be rotated, or moved in any other way.

CHAPTER 14

Lamps for Transport Lighting

Introduction. A wide range of lamps exists for specialised application in transport lighting. Maximum utilisation of light, space, weight and power together with reliability in service, are important design requirements.

Lamps actually mounted on, or in, vehicles are required to withstand the effects of shock and vibration while in many cases, providing the light source of an optical system, with the associated demands of precision assembly.

A further range of special lamps meets the various requirements of traffic control lighting and illumination of roads, airports, etc. Aspects related to street lighting are discussed in Chapter 32, under that heading.

Lamps for passenger cars

Headlights. There are several approaches to the problem of affording to the vehicle driver lighting adequate for modern fast driving, without causing too much glare to on-coming traffic.

A great proportion of vehicles now incorporate pressed glass 'sealed-beam' lamps which usually comprise two accurately located filaments within a glass reflector and lensed cover-glass assembly. One filament, normally rated 60 W at 12·8 V, is mounted transversely on the focal point of the parabolic reflector to provide the long-range driving beam. A second filament, rated 45 W, is disposed in the reflector above the horizontal axis and to one side of the vertical axis, so that its beam is deflected downward and to the near side. This 'meeting-beam' filament is mounted behind a shield which cuts off upward light from the filament (see Chap. 15, Fig. 15.7).

The pressed glass, sealed-beam automobile lamp has some important advantages over the conventional replaceable bulb type. The filaments are located more accurately relative to the reflector, for example 45,000 peak beam candelas can be achieved with a 60 W filament, compared with some 30,000 cd from a 50 W source by the separate lamp/reflector system. The much increased lamp volume reduces the blackening effect of filament evaporation to negligible proportions and as the reflector coating is contained within an inert atmosphere, it remains free from discoloration for many years. In addition, the intrinsic efficiency of the construction allows the life to be extended while still providing sufficient light output.

The basic sealed-beam vehicle headlight system consists of two 7 in.

diameter units, each containing two filaments, as described above and mounted on each side of the vehicle. An improved control of the 'passing-beam' pattern is obtained by using four units, usually of 5¾ in. diameter, mounted in pairs on each side of the vehicle. In this case the outer pair each contain two filaments in the configuration described for the 7 in. lamps and the inner pair of units each contain a single, axially mounted filament which produces a beam of high intensity and narrow-angle spread. The complete 'driving beam' combines the light from the two single-filament units with that from two 37·5 W 'driving-beam' filaments in the outer pair of units. The total power dissipated by the driving beam is 4 × 37·5 W. The 'meeting' beam is produced by two 50 W filaments, in the outer pair of units.

Before the general introduction of pressed-glass lamps, an improvement in the performance of separate lamp/reflector units was achieved by individually soldering, with optical assistance, a capped lamp into a metal-backed reflector fitting so as to produce optimum beam characteristics.

An earlier form of headlamp, which has not yet been completely superseded by the types so far described is known as the 'British Prefocus' (BPF) lamp. The general filament arrangement is similar to that of the pressed-glass lamp having two transversely mounted filaments: one of which is mounted on axis and the other, for the meeting beam, offset above, and to one side of, the driving filament. In order to ensure correct location of the filament relative to the separate reflector and to facilitate subsequent lamp replacement, a flange is soldered around the lamp cap whilst the filaments are held in the pre-scribed position. Clearly, the additive effect of the tolerances required for the separate components does not equal the precision of a pressed-glass unit. Fig. 14.1 illustrates a typical BPF lamp, rated 12 V, 50/40 W.

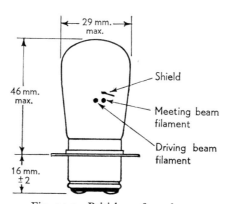

Fig. 14.1   British prefocus lamp

A variation of this construction designed for improved night driving on the more expensive class of vehicle, includes higher wattage filaments and in-corporates a larger diameter envelope with Unified European cap and prefocus flange.

Recent trends in headlamp design, influenced by both styling considerations and efforts to lower the bonnet so as to improve visibility, are towards a departure from the circular form. The use of a rectangular shape enables the fitting depth to be reduced from 7 in. to some 5 in. However, abandonment of the full paraboloid reflector, necessitated by conforming to the rectangular frontal section, diminishes optical efficiency to some extent. This may be compensated either by raising lamp wattage, or by use of higher output sources, e.g. tungsten-halogen lamps.

Auxiliary lamps. This classification embraces all lamps other than headlamps and may be sub-divided conveniently as follows:

Fog lamps and spotlamps

These lamps are usually considered together but have widely varying requirements. The fog lamp has to produce a beam of wide angle, even intensity, with no upward light, so as to minimise back-reflection from fog and mist; whereas, the spotlamp's function is to give a concentrated beam of narrow-angle divergence, for long-range vision.

Each need is separately met by a combination of lensing, shielding and filament arrangement. The fog lamp is usually designed with a transversely mounted filament and shield, in conjunction with a spreader lens, whereas the spotlamp has an axially mounted filament, which is capable of giving the required beam without lensing. Both types of lamp are produced in the pressed-glass construction as well as in separate lamp/reflector units.

Because of trends in vehicle design causing reductions in available space behind the front bumper, there has been increasing demand for shallower fittings, which in turn has led to the design of special lamps to meet this demand (Fig. 14.2).

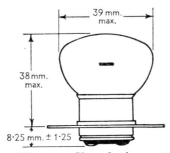

Fig. 14.2 Short fog lamp

The small dimensions of tungsten-halogen lamps are particularly attractive and this factor, together with their improved beam intensity, has resulted in a new range of high-performance spotlamp and fog lamp units.

Fittings designers have employed a variety of lamp mounting positions in an endeavour to achieve shallower housings. The halogen lamp offers both shorter length and smaller diameter which thereby increases the scope of the designer. Figs. 14.3 illustrates two of the types in use.

8*

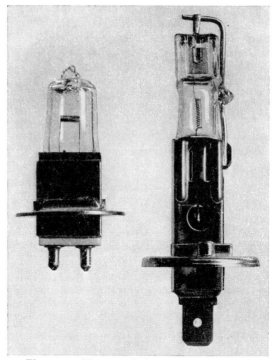

Fig. 14.3 Tungsten-halogen auxiliary lamps

Subsequent development work has led to further length reductions from those of the earlier halogen lamps, permitting designs using lamps aligned co-axially with the fitting. This demands the sacrifice of less reflector area than with other configurations.

The currently available halogen lamps are confined to single-filament types which find application in 4-headlamp systems, in addition to the auxiliary units described above. The single-filament limitation results from the difficulties encountered in producing halogen lamps of good quality having more than one filament: the introduction of a second filament causing interference with the functioning of the halogen regenerative process (refer to Chapter 15).

Stop/tail and direction-indicator lamps

Two basic designs exist which serve the needs of the 'stop', 'tail' and 'direction-indicator' functions. A single-filament version is sometimes used; for instance, in 'direction-indicator' units with amber-coloured covers, where the light output is not suitable for any other purpose. Alternatively the double-filament lamp is able to fulfil the dual role of stop (brake) light and tail (rear) light in a single housing, within a red cover. Both lamps are made with the high-wattage filament (stop, or direction indicator) accurately located, relative to the lamp cap, to provide correct focusing in the reflector. This is essential to achieve the high-intensity beams necessary for clear recognition of signals in bright sunlight.

The double-filament lamp is fitted with a cap having asymmetric (indexing) pins to ensure that it can only be inserted into the fitting socket with the filaments correctly connected. The tail filament is offset from the lamp axis, so as to produce a dispersed, low-intensity light beam, sufficient to give indication of vehicle dimensions at a reasonable distance.

This class of lamp is probably subject to the most severe mechanical shock (e.g. boot slamming) in vehicle applications and experience has shown that service performance can be much improved by the adoption of special constructional features in securing the filaments to the lead wires. Extensive testing in laboratory and service has led to the adoption of a clamped anchorage for the high-wattage filament and cold pressing for the low-wattage filament. This avoids the embrittlement problems which frequently arise from welding filaments of this size to the lead wires (Fig. 14.4).

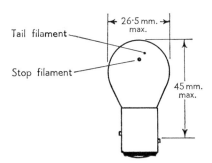

Fig. 14.4   Stop and tail lamp

Side, tail and number-plate lamps

These miniature lamps are produced in 15 mm and 18 mm diameter bulbs, fitted with the small and miniature bayonet caps (see Fig. 14.5).

The nominal standard rating is 6 W and best results are achieved by the use of a gas-filled design. This offers a vastly improved 'through-life' performance over the previously used vacuum lamp of similar rating which suffered from premature blackening of the envelope.

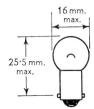

Fig. 14.5   Side and tail lamp

The 'wedge-base' or capless lamp (see Fig. 14.6) has more recently been introduced to these applications bringing with it advantages with respect to

(a) improved resistance to shock vibration;

(b) more accurate location of filament to reference plane (and therefore to fitting);

(c) corrosion resistance due to elimination of metal cap. The contact wires are nickel plated;

(d) reductions in length and weight; and

(e) operation at high humidities and ambient temperatures.

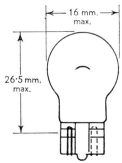

Fig. 14.6   Wedge-base lamp

The design obviates the need for a lamp cap and is held in the socket by means of spring contacts locating in grooves. The grooves are formed in the glass base by a mould which regulates the dimensions and shape within specified, internationally agreed, limits.

Electrical contact is effected by means of lead wires from the lamp which are pressed between the socket contacts and the glass base.

Panel indicator lamps

Low-wattage miniature lamps are normally used for panel illumination. As the light-output requirement is less onerous, it is customary to design these lamps with long lives to reduce the likelihood of replacement arising. Again, wedge-base lamps are being used for this purpose because of the benefits discussed above.

Wedge-base reflector lamps

A version of the wedge-base lamp is produced which incorporates a reflector (see Fig. 14.7). This enables the fittings manufacturer to make units without built-in reflectors with consequent space saving. Appropriate applications are found in 'reversing' light and 'interior reading' (or map) lights. The lamp illustrated is rated at 12 V 5 W and its optical performance is shown in Fig. 14.8.

Commercial vehicle lamps. Many lamps for commercial vehicles are required to overcome the problem posed by the 24 V systems frequently used in this class of transport. As described in the section dealing with aircraft

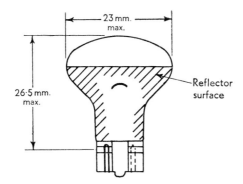

Fig. 14.7 Wedge-base reflector lamp

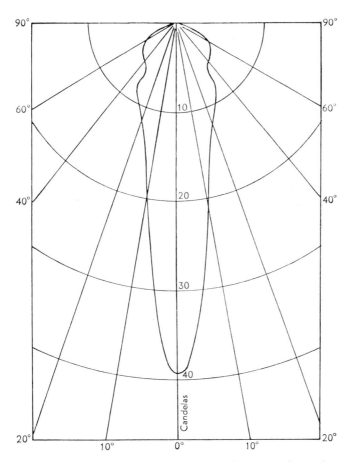

Fig. 14.8 Typical polar distribution of wedge-base reflector lamp

lamps, this higher voltage involves a greater wire length within a coil and this point is dealt with in different ways, as follows:

Headlamps

In order to produce the desired beam pattern filament lengths must be similar to the 12 V counterparts and this is achieved by the use of coiled-coil designs. By this method it is possible to produce lamps with physical dimensions similar to 12 V ratings and which satisfactorily meet the optical requirements.

Side, tail and indicator lamps

As the wattage ratings on commercial vehicle lamps are equivalent to those on 12 V systems, clearly the current ratings, and therefore filament wire sizes, are very much reduced. This fact, coupled with the increased length of wire, necessitates either the inclusion of an intermediate filament support or, as in some cases a double-bead construction which comprises two 12 V filaments connected in series.

Aircraft lamps.   Lamps designed for use on aircraft are perhaps subject to the most rigorous environment in service, due to the severe vibration conditions generated by the power units. The situation is aggravated by the fact that the supply at the lighting points is usually 28 V. As the length of wire in a filament is roughly proportional to the voltage, it will be appreciated that the 28 V filament is considerably longer and therefore less robust, than its 12 V counterpart used in motor cars. It is therefore essential, particularly on low-current ratings which have small filament wire diameters, to include intermediate supports.

The most common rating of aircraft lamp is the 28 V 0·04 A indicator, which is used for instrument-panel illumination. The application requires a lamp of small dimensions which will give reliable service under the vibration conditions described. Fig. 14.9 illustrates this lamp, which is made with two intermediate filament supports in a bulb of 5·6 mm diameter and an overall length of some 15 mm.

At the other end of the scale, sealed-beam lamps of up to 8 in. diameter are used to provide the pilot with local illumination sufficient for landing and

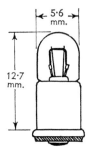

Fig. 14.9   28 V, 0·04 A, Aircraft panel indicator lamp

taxi-ing at night time. A typical lamp has two filaments, rated at 600 W and 400 W. These are operated simultaneously to produce the beam for landing, whereas the taxi-ing beam is provided by the 400 W filament alone.

Between these extremes of size there are several lamp types designed for specific functions, such as interior lighting and navigation lights of various sorts for location on wing-tips, tail, or fuselage. It should be noted that the wedge-base lamp, which has features of some importance in aircraft, i.e. minimum weight, dimensions, etc., has been introduced recently to this application.

Traffic control and road sign illumination. With the increase in traffic on our roads, together with the tremendous amount of extraneous lighting (shop-windows, advertising, etc.) traffic signals and signs can be very difficult to recognise and interpret. Because of this, new specifications are being tabled, to improve the quality of signals and signs. The specification for traffic signals is under review and as a result of recent work the current BS 873:1959 for road signs, may be amended.

Traffic signals. At present normal traffic lights use special rough-service mains voltage 65 W lamps, housed in simple parabolic reflectors. A prismatic front glass is made from the correct colour materials and is designed to eliminate 'phantom' effects. 'Phantom' is the term which describes the effect of the signal reflecting some external light (sunlight perhaps) and looking as if the signal is operating.

The new recommendations will suggest much higher intensities for signals to enable them to be visible in bright sunlight, or similar difficult visual conditions. Some signals will require to have two intensities; one for use during the day and one much lower, for use at night, this latter to eliminate any glare problem. Different intensities will be recommended for various types of route.

All this means that different high-efficiency light sources will be required and possibly, tungsten-halogen lamps will find yet another application.

Road signs. In the APLE Technical Report No. 2, the Worboy's Report and the recent M.O.T. recommendations to local authorities, proposals have been made to improve the lighting of road signs. It was felt that the existing recommendations (BS 873: 1959) were not sufficiently demanding especially in the section dealing with luminance variation across the sign. The Worboy's Report goes on to suggest the increased use of internally illuminated signs.

The lighting of a road sign has to be a compromise. On the one hand, the sign should be easy to see but, on the other hand, it should not be too bright and give rise to glare. It should be illuminated as evenly as possible and must also be easy to see during the day, when unlit.

A reasonable specification for the external lighting of a sign, derived from the publications referred to, is as follows: The average luminance over the whole area of the sign, should be about 10 ft L, with the maximum luminance not more than 150 ft L and minimum not less than 3 ft L. The luminance variation should not be more than 10 to 1. Recently, more definite recommendations to local authorities have been made by the Ministry of Transport, dealing with internally illuminated signs. In this the recommended luminance for the white portions of the signs, range from a maximum to minimum of 300 ft L to 100 ft L, for use in recognised display centres; down to 75 ft L to 25 ft L for a large sign, in an unlighted road.

The light source for any sign will be somewhat dependent upon the size of the sign. Fluorescent tubes in both normal and miniature forms, serve as good sources for both internally and externally illuminated signs. Their dimensions, luminous efficiency and long life are advantageous for this application. The Ministry recommendation for the colour of fluorescent tubes is Daylight (or Cool White). One difficulty is that the lamps are sometimes required to be started in low temperatures but by the careful selection of lamp type and gear, this problem can be overcome.

Airfield lighting. When a pilot is about to land his aeroplane, he needs to have plenty of information fed to him. The pilot will rely on radio information until he is a few miles from the airport, when he will start to use visual aids.

Approach lights will show him the positions of the runway and possibly an 'angle-of-approach' system will show him his correct glide-path. Once on the ground, a lighting system will indicate to him the path of the runway and when he has slowed down, another system will help him to taxi the aircraft to the unloading point.

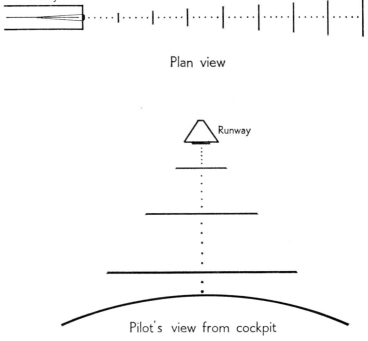

Fig. 14.10   Calvert 'line and bar' approach light system

Hence a whole variety of lighting units is required for lighting on an airfield, each type being highly specialised and most requiring a high degree of optical control.

Approach lights. These are lighting units, designed to give a beam of more than 10° in the vertical and 30° in the horizontal with a peak intensity of some 40,000 cd. They use a 200 W or 300 W lamp, with a prismatic lens, usually integral with the filament assembly as a sealed-beam unit. The approach-lighting system comprises a number of these units, arranged in a pattern which will give most information to the pilot. The most generally accepted pattern is that suggested by Calvert and is shown in Fig. 14.10. His system is a 'line and bar' arrangement where the line shows the correct landing direction and the bars show the horizontal.

It is essential that the lights can be dimmed so that, at night they can be set to operate efficiently without causing glare. In conditions of bad visibility, they can be run at peak intensity. A recent development enabling sodium lamps to be dimmed, has led to these lamps being used in an approach-light system. These lamps are the 200 W linear type, with the difference that the arc tube is enclosed within an infrared retaining glass tube. Round this there is wound a heater coil. Another glass tube encloses this assembly and has porcelain 3-pin caps at each end.

Angle-of-approach indication. The most usual visual approach slope-indicator system is that shown in Fig. 14.11.

It can be seen from the diagram that, if the pilot is too high, he will see two white horizontal lines; if he is too low, he will see two red horizontal lines. His correct angle of approach will be when he sees the far line red and the near line white.

Each unit uses a quite simple optical system to give its red and white beams. The light from three 200 W sealed-beam units is made to cross over at a slit, some 4 ft in front of the lamp housing. In front of each lamp is a filter/ spreader glass, the top half of which is red. This combines two functions, it provides the red part of the beam and also spreads the beam in the horizontal.

High-speed runway centreline lights. When the aircraft has just landed, it is travelling quite fast along the runway. The pilot needs to see the path of the runway and the centreline lights enable him to do this. These units need to give a beam of light, from $\frac{1}{2}$° to about 5° in the vertical, of some 3000 cd. The width of the beam in the horizontal should be more than 15°.

Positioned in the centre of the runway, they are recessed into the concrete so that an aircraft taxi-ing over them is not significantly affected. This means that a maximum of $\frac{3}{4}$ in. should protrude and this should be designed to enable the aircraft wheels smoothly to roll over the fitting.

A light source suitable for use in these fittings is a 200 W double-ended tungsten-halogen lamp. The lamp is prefocused because the optical design of the fitting requires that the lamp is positioned very accurately. Spade-end contacts of controlled length are used so that when inserted in the lampholder, the filament position is precisely located.

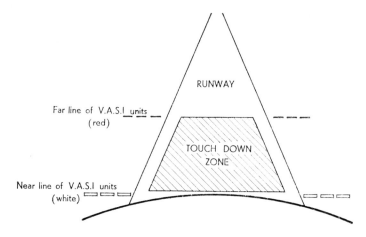

Pilot's view of the runway when
on the correct glide path

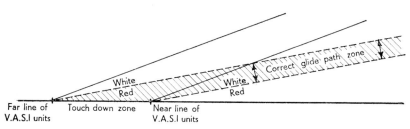

Side view of the glide path indication system at runway level

Fig. 14.11   The visual approach slope indicator (V.A.S.I.)

Centreline lights do not have to be run at rated current all the time. At night, the contrast between the light and the dark background increases visibility from the units but also introduces glare problems. Because of this, dimming becomes an essential feature to adjust the brightness to the optimum value for varying conditions.

Taxitrack fittings.   Another lighting system guides the pilot to the unloading point. He follows green dots of light down the path of a selected taxiway. These lights do not have to be as intense as the high-speed runway lights and a value of 15 cd of a defined green light is specified as adequate. The beam should be from 0° to 20° in the vertical and from $+35°$ to $-35°$ in the horizontal, the latter to allow for the curves in the taxitrack. A slightly greater protrusion above the surface of the runway up to 1 in. is permissible, as the aircraft will be travelling over them at a relatively low speed. Single-ended 45 W tungsten-halogen lamps are efficient sources for these fittings, because of their high luminous efficiency, long life and stability of output through life. '*Taking-off*'. In briefly describing airfield lighting systems, their use in the landing of aircraft has been discussed. When a pilot is taking off, he may be able to use the taxi-lights and the high-speed centreline lights in the reverse order. Because of this it is advantageous to design these units for bi-directional use.

Flashing beacons. Any tall building or tower near to the airfield should have some warning light on it, so that pilots can see the hazard at safe distance. The difficulty here is that the warning light cannot be serviced very easily. If the tower is very high the unit is likely to be inaccessible so the light source used must be very reliable, and have a long life. A new form of neon lamp has been developed from the linear sodium lamp construction especially for this application. They are 150 W lamps, with a life of 8000 hours and are used in a fitting giving a peak intensity of 2000 cd, over a wide beam. The visibility range of these lamps on a clear night is some 80 miles.

Interior lighting for public transport. The lighting in the passenger areas of all the various systems of public transport should firstly aim to give enough light to see by, without any discomfort glare. The second but scarcely less important aim should be to harmonise with an interior that is interesting and comfortable. This might sound like advice to a domestic-interior designer. To a certain extent, a passenger area is similar to a domestic area. People are required to remain in a confined space, sometimes for hours at a time. While there, they should be made to feel comfortable and relaxed. Comfort is not limited to aspects of the seat design; the passenger's visual comfort is a function of the overall design of the coach, of which the lighting is an important part.

Railway coach lighting. Two types of passenger train will be considered here; one is the long-distance through-train and the other the short-distance type. With the former, the passengers tend to make themselves at home because they may be there for some hours. Under these circumstances the analogy to 'domestic-interior design' is quite in order.

From a purely amenity point of view, a good level of illumination is needed to allow the passenger to read, write, glance round the carriage and see to move about.

At night, facilities for dimming the lighting level should be available, so that passengers can sleep. Under these conditions, a light to enable a passenger to read, without disturbing his neighbour, is a very useful addition to the general lighting.

The lighting system having these properties should be designed with the complete environment in mind. Too often in the past the carriage interior was designed and then, almost as an after-thought, the lighting added.

In the development of the proposed new British Rail Standard Carriage, a great deal of study was given to the lighting. The resulting system uses a combination of incandescent and fluorescent lamps. The main lighting is from a central suspended feature with 4 ft 40 W tubes above a perforated channel (Fig. 14.12). The incandescent reading lights (Fig. 14.13) are recessed in the base of the luggage rack. A special 24/28 V 6 W lamp was devised for this fitting, with a crown-silvered bulb to reduce direct light glare.

Fig. 14.12   The British Rail new Standard Coach, showing the fluorescent fittings in the centre of the ceiling, and the passengers' individual reading lights inset into the luggage rack

In trains designed for local transport, the passengers are only in the carriages for a relatively short period of time. Even though the question of environmental design is still important, it is less so than in the long-distance train.

Because of this, a simple overall system of lighting is adequate. A level of illumination of about 15 lm/ft² will enable people to read, or move about the carriage, with ease. Fluorescent lamps in suitable fittings are generally used, the scheme being designed to give the correct level of illumination without giving rise to any discomfort glare.

Bus lighting.   Once again distinction must be made between long- and short-journey buses. For the long-distance buses a similar arrangement to that used in long-distance trains will be suitable. A combination of general fluorescent lighting and incandescent individual spotlights can be used to achieve good results.

Shorter journey buses use general lighting only, usually from fluorescent lamps in suitable fittings. In this type of situation, where only low-voltage

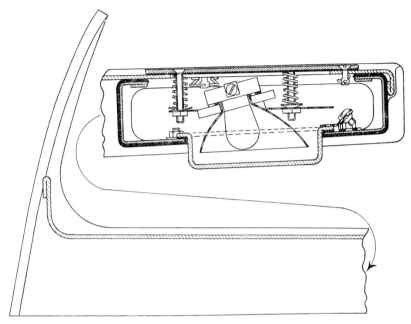

Fig. 14.13   Passenger reading light in luggage rack

d.c. supplies are available, the fluorescent lighting can be supplied from special transistor-invertors.

Aircraft lighting.   As with long-distance trains, considerable thought has to be given to the overall comfort of the passengers. Again, a combination of fluorescent and incandescent lamps can be used to achieve good lighting. The space restriction in an aircraft, makes it difficult to 'build-in' the lighting. There is also a strict weight limit which becomes a problem when the gear to operate the fluorescent tubes is considered. The problem is eased somewhat however because the gear can be made smaller than normal, as it is usually running at 400 c/s.

Considerations of economy in space and weight have led to special wedge-base, reflector lamps being developed for use as individual reading lights for the passengers. These are now being used in the VC 10 airliner.

CHAPTER 15

Incandescent Lamps—Recent Developments

Sealed-beam lamps. For many applications where a beam of light is required to be directed, incandescent lamps are used in conjunction with reflectors and in some cases reflector/lens combinations.

One of the major uses is for automobile headlights.

The early unit designs comprised a single-filament lamp located with its filament on the focal point of a parabola and the beam travelled through either, a clear, or simply fluted spreader lens (shown in Fig. 15.1).

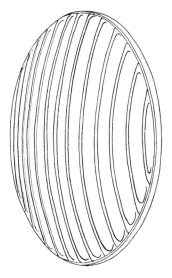

Fig. 15.1 Simple fluted lens

Later, as more cars were put on the road it became necessary to incorporate some kind of 'dipping' or 'meeting' beam arrangement to avoid dazzling on-coming drivers. Whilst many arrangements were tried, such as mechanical tilting of the headlight units, switching the offside lamp out, or a combination of both, the design offering the most advantages was that which incorporated into the lamp a second filament, to provide the dipping, or meeting beam.

In Britain and the U.S.A. this auxiliary filament is positioned above and to one side of the driving filament; the reflector and lamp combination being used in conjunction with a complex pattern of lenses, moulded into the headlight cover-glass (shown in Fig. 15.2).

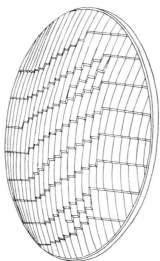

Fig. 15.2   Complex block lens for twin-filament headlight

The light from each portion of the reflector is directed and spread vertically and/or horizontally, as required by the various lens segments in the cover-glass, until the required composite beam patterns are produced. Design is complicated by the fact that both the driving and the meeting beams must pass through the same lens and the requirements for the two-beam patterns are quite different.

A typical requirement for a driving beam is shown in Fig. 15.3 and for a meeting beam in Fig. 15.4.

Fig. 15.3   Sealed-beam headlamp system—driving beam

Fig. 15.4   Sealed-beam headlamp system—meeting beam

The make-up of these beams, their definition at critical points and the deflection of the meeting beam relative to the driving beam, is primarily dependent on the filament position, with respect to the focal point of the reflector. A first step therefore was to prefocus the lamp and Fig. 15.5 shows the physical characteristics of the British prefocus lamp, for many years adopted almost universally in British vehicles.

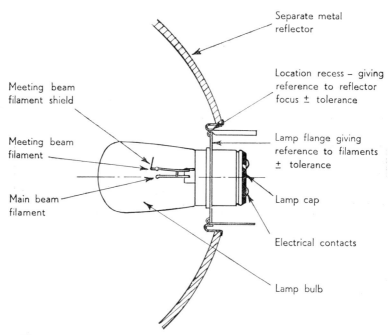

Fig. 15.5   British prefocus lamp in separate reflector

Even the close tolerances to which this design could be made are too wide for beam control requirements. To them must be added the tolerances between the lamp seating in the reflector and the designed focal point; together with any deviations from the design focal point, which may be exhibited by individual reflectors. In the design of the headlight unit the extremes of filament position must be taken into account and therefore the design must be something of a compromise.

Additionally, about 20% of the light from the filament is lost, due to obscuration by the bulb and cap. Also in service, the evaporated tungsten from the filament settles on the upper surface of the bulb and although the total light from the lamp is reduced only by 10% to 15%, at half-life (say about 2 years in service), the obscuration thereby presented to a large section of the reflector is of much greater consequence (Fig. 15.6) and the beam pattern is disturbed.

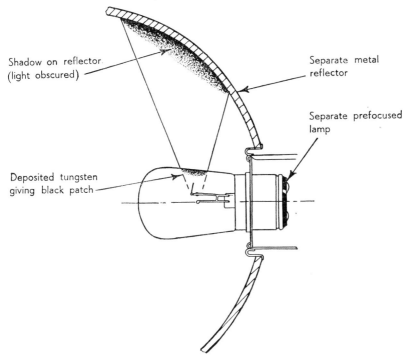

Shadow on reflector (light obscured)

Separate metal reflector

Separate prefocused lamp

Deposited tungsten giving black patch

Fig. 15.6   Effect of bulb blackening

Finally, due to oxidation and the deposition of dust and dirt, the reflector gradually loses efficiency, so that after 3 to 4 years service the beam intensity may be reduced to about 60% of the original value.

Most of the problems are brought about because the lamp design and the headlight unit design have been considered as two separate entities. When a combination design is considered, i.e. the reflector and the cover-glass form the bulb so that the whole headlight unit is the lamp, these disadvantages disappear, or are greatly reduced. This is the basic concept of the sealed-beam lamp design (Fig. 15.7).

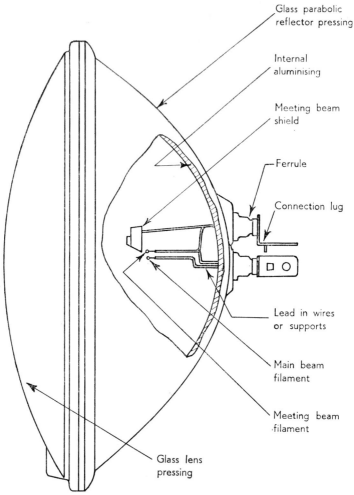

Glass parabolic reflector pressing

Internal aluminising

Meeting beam shield

Ferrule

Connection lug

Lead in wires or supports

Main beam filament

Meeting beam filament

Glass lens pressing

Fig. 15.7 Sealed-beam, motor vehicle lamp

In order to withstand the thermal stresses arising during manufacture and subsequently those encountered in service, both the reflector and the lens (cover-glass) are made from low-expansion borosilicate (hard) glass.

Similarly, to enable them to withstand the implosive pressures during manufacture and the explosive pressures in service, the glass pressing requires to be from 3 mm to 5 mm thick, dependent on the contour and diameter. This glass thickness has a secondary advantage in that it permits offsetting the reflector axis, relative to the mechanical axis of the unit, thus reducing the depth of cutting required in the lens.

The reflector surface is evaporated aluminium and is protected throughout the life of the lamp by the inert gas filling.

Prior to sealing, it is obvious that the filaments can be mounted very accurately with respect to the reflector and this is done in relation to the actual focus of the pre-tested glassware, rather than to the theoretical focal point. This system enables the filament to reflector tolerances to be reduced substantially, approaching one quarter of those required in the conventional separate bulb designs.

In the Anglo-American system the beam control is obtained by accurately-cut compound lenses on the cover-glass. These deflect and spread the filament images from separate portions of the reflector, so that the required beam intensity and pattern is fully developed a short distance in front of the lamp.

After sealing the cover-glass on to the reflector, the space between them is evacuated and then filled with a controlled pressure of argon-nitrogen gas mixture.

Needless to say, since there is not a separate bulb, there will be no stray reflections from it and the tungsten evaporation from the filament is spread so thinly on the large reflector surface that there is virtually no light loss throughout life. Light maintenance remains at between 98% and 100%, even towards the end of life, equivalent to several years in average service conditions.

Resulting from the summation of these factors the sealed-beam headlight construction provides greatly improved characteristics of beam control. The driving beam has initial intensities about 20% to 30% greater than those of the separate bulb type. The meeting beam has a sharper cut-off and higher intensities near to the horizontal, thus enabling the high-intensity point to be set $\frac{1}{2}°$ nearer to the horizontal. The effect on seeing distance is illustrated on Fig. 15.8. It will be noted that this permits a seeing distance of about 285 ft compared with 140 ft with the conventional separate bulb lamp.

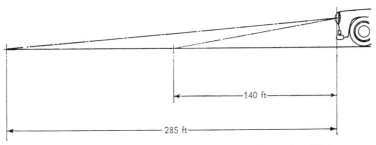

Fig. 15.8   Comparison between separate reflector headlight
and sealed-beam unit

Finally, there is practically no reduction in light output throughout the life of the lamp, compared with a reduction approximating to 50% in the case of the separate bulb unit, after about 4 years.

An increasing number of mains voltage spotlights and floodlights are also being made in the sealed-beam design in this country (Chapter 12). The construction of a typical 200/250 V 150 W (Type Par 38) lamp, is illustrated in Fig. 15.9. Spot and floodlamps of this nature provide beam characteristics

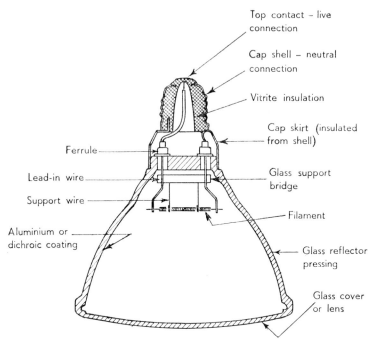

Top contact – live connection

Cap shell – neutral connection

Vitrite insulation

Cap skirt (insulated from shell)

Ferrule

Lead-in wire

Support wire

Aluminium or dichroic coating

Glass support bridge

Filament

Glass reflector pressing

Glass cover or lens

Fig. 15.9   Sealed-beam spot- and floodlight construction

of higher intensity and definition than the equivalent ratings of blown-bulb lamps. This is due to the greater precision with which the components are assembled and the superior reflector contour provided by the glass-pressing process. They are also of more rugged construction than blown-bulb lamps and can be operated outdoors without the necessity of enclosing fittings, due to their hard glass construction.

The range of lamp types, wattage loading, size and finish is likely to be extended considerably in the near future. The incorporation of selective-reflector coatings on the cover-glass, or the reflector to give a light beam with little heat, or of particular colour (see Chapter 10) is likely further to extend the range of application for this class of lamps.

In the projector lamp field an approach towards the sealed-beam concept in the form of the 21·5 V 150 W Truflector lamp and the 8 V 50 W shaped-bulb design have had widespread acceptance over recent years. It would be a logical step to consider a true sealed-beam development in this area although so far only the sealed-beam photoflood has achieved any appreciable recognition.

The sealed-beam approach does, of course, lend itself to other lamp types, e.g. aircraft landing lights, where the problems involved are somewhat similar to those in the automobile field.

The success of the sealed-beam unit lies in the concept of considering light-source and fitting as an entity, for precision-assembly; instead of as two separate components.

Miniature lamps. As well as considering the lamp and the fitting in conjunction it is sometimes fruitful to consider their combined simplification. Such an approach has led to the development of the capless (or wedge-base) miniature lamp.

It represents the outcome of a critical reappraisal of the conventional designs of lamp and socket, for long used in vehicle panel and number plate illumination and it has been aimed to overcome some of the shortcomings of the established system, e.g. cap corrosion, lamps coming unscrewed, inaccurate filament-to-holder positioning and some limitations in vibration behaviour.

Attention was directed to the function of each component in the conventional system. While the filament, lead wires and enclosing glass bulb were essential; the cap, capping cement and solder were considered to be expendable to the application requirements.

It was considered desirable to increase the glass-to-metal seal length, from about 1 mm (as in the conventional construction), to a minimum of three times this distance, to give greater reliability and freedom from leaks. A pinched-seal type of construction was therefore adopted. A glass-pinch shape was designed which could offer a satisfactory socket location and a means of positioning the lead wires, so that good electrical contact could be made. The new construction resulting from this extensive development project is the present-day wedge-base lamp, illustrated in Fig. 14.6.

The vibration resistance is markedly superior to that of the conventional product, as shown by comparison of the curves in Fig. 15.10. In a correctly designed holder this lamp cannot shake loose and the filament positioning tolerance relative to the holder is reduced to less than half that of the standard design. In addition, there is no cap to corrode and the lead-in wires are nickel-plated to prevent any trouble at that point.

Of necessity the introduction of such a radical design change has taken place over an extended period, since a new range of sockets to accept it had also to be designed and tested under a variety of environments. In Britain it is being adopted extensively for both interior and exterior vehicle illumination and will, it is believed over a period of time, largely supersede the capped designs.

The same base, minus the exhaust tube has been adopted by the Americans in the design of photoflash bulbs of the AG type also now widely used in Europe.

Of course design and development does not stand still, and the larger glass volume which the wedge-base design permits has led to the development of reflectorised versions, such as the type shown in Fig. 14.7 (Chapter 14).

For the future, extension of the wedge-base principle to other lamp types may be foreseen particularly where a reduction in overall length is required, or where trends in styling concepts and technical features require the use of non-conventional designs, e.g. of rectangular shape.

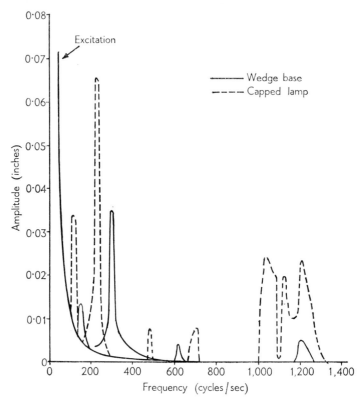

Fig. 15.10   Vibration characteristics of wedge-base and MES capped lamps

Halogen lamps

Introduction. To appreciate fully the significance of halogen additions in incandescent lamps, it is useful to review the factors which influence the intrinsic quality and general design features of normal tungsten filament lamps.

As explained earlier (Chapter 10), the conventional coiled tungsten filament incandescent lamp radiates energy over a continuous spectrum, substantially from 300 nm to 1200 nm. The proportion of the total energy radiated in the visible region, from 400 nm to 700 nm is dependent upon the filament temperature (Fig. 10.2), and it is seen that the higher the filament temperature, the greater is the proportion of the energy radiated in the visible region (although at best this is only a few percent of the total energy). From this it would appear that filaments should run at temperatures approaching the melting point of tungsten to give maximum efficiency. However, as the luminous efficiency (or temperature) increases, the rate of evaporation increases very sharply, shortening the lamp life; life being proportional to efficiency (Fig. 10.9). Also the evaporated tungsten deposits on the bulb wall causing progressive reductions in light output through life. Filling a lamp with an inert gas suppresses the rate of tungsten evaporation at any given luminous efficiency (or filament temperature); the higher the filling pressure the lower the rate of evaporation, resulting in longer life. The relationship of lamp life to gas-filling pressure, using nitrogen, argon or krypton for a constant value of efficiency, is shown in Fig. 15.11. Usually a lamp is filled

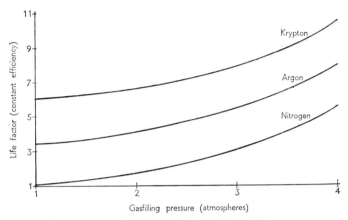

Fig. 15.11   Relationship of life and gas-filling pressure

with argon, having nitrogen added to prevent an arc forming in the filling gas which would destroy the filament. The argon content is maintained as high as possible; typical proportions for general lighting service lamps are 93% argon and 7% nitrogen, at a pressure of about 700 mm.

Krypton filling gives a considerable gain over argon/nitrogen mixtures but it costs some 2000 times more. Hence, it is used only in special lamps such as coal-miners' headlamps, where efficiency is of paramount importance and the high cost can be tolerated.

The design of an incandescent lamp is therefore based upon a compromise of luminous efficiency, life and cost. For general lighting service lamps the life is usually set at a level best suited to the economics of operation. The highest intrinsic quality is attained by the design of the filament arrangement to give minimum losses and filling with a mixture of highly purified argon/nitrogen gas, at atmospheric pressure. Lamps used in photographic work, however, require filament temperatures of 3400 °K and these lamps are sometimes pressure filled, which is a more difficult and costly process in production but gives increased life. The minimum bulb size of a conventional lamp is also fixed, as sufficient surface area must be available to receive the evaporated tungsten from the filament during life without unduly obscuring the light; even so, at half-life the light output usually falls by about 10%.

To achieve further improvements in the incandescent lamp, a new filament material is required which would permit either a higher operating temperature without undue evaporation, or an extension of the life of the lamp. The latter course has been realised to some extent by the development of the incandescent lamp using a regenerative halogen cycle.

The regenerative cycle. The conventional incandescent gas-filled lamp loses filament material by evaporation; some of the tungsten atoms leaving the hot filament collide with gas molecules and are returned to the filament, while others escape and deposit on the bulb wall. When a halogen is added to the filling gas, and if certain temperature conditions are established, a regenerative chemical reaction is formed between tungsten and halogen. The simplified action of the regenerative cycle is as follows: Tungsten is evaporated from the incandescent filament and some portion of this diffuses towards the bulb wall. Within a specific zone between the filament and bulb wall, where temperature conditions are favourable, the tungsten combines with the halogen. The tungsten halide molecules diffuse towards the filament where they dissociate, the tungsten being deposited back on the filament and the halogen becoming available for a further reaction cycle.

Expanding this to give further detail, consider an incandescent filament positioned along the axis of a closed tube containing an inert gas and one of the halogens. The filament will normally operate at around 3000 °K, and from the filament to the bulb wall there will be a temperature gradient through the fill gas. This gradient can be divided into three zones, extending radially from filament to bulb wall, with limiting temperatures dividing them. Within the zone, or layer, immediately surrounding the filament there are no reactions, the inert filling gas and halogen being present as two separate components. The next zone contains halogen and tungsten atoms (with the fill gas), both recombination of the halogen atoms and formation of tungsten halides will take place. Towards the high-temperature limit, there will also be thermal dissociation. Beyond the lower limiting temperature of this zone to the bulb wall, there is no thermal dissociation and recombination of halogen atoms and formation of tungsten halide is completed—mainly at the bulb wall. The tungsten halides formed in the two outer zones diffuse towards the filament, where they dissociate into the halogen and tungsten (Fig. 15.12).

The regenerated tungsten is not in most cases deposited directly back on to the filament but is liberated in the inner zone, where the tungsten vapour density is enhanced. While radial diffusion of tungsten is restricted, axial diffusion along the high temperature zone continues with tungsten being transported and redistributed along the filament in this way.

All halogens, iodine, bromine, chlorine and fluorine are capable of supporting a regenerative cycle in a tungsten filament lamp, the main differences between them being the temperatures at which the various reactions in the cycle may take place and the extent to which they react with components, or with impurities, inside the lamp. At the present time the theoretical and practical aspects of iodine additions are well established and tungsten-bromine lamps have been made successfully. Chlorine and fluorine additions are under active investigation but there are formidable practical problems. Theoretically a tungsten-fluorine cycle should give the optimum performance and approach infinite lamp life.

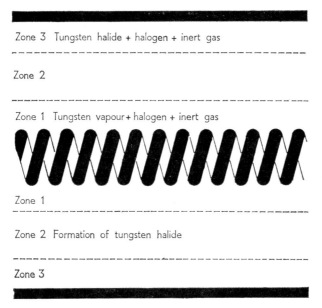

Zone 3 Tungsten halide + halogen + inert gas

Zone 2

Zone 1 Tungsten vapour + halogen + inert gas

Zone 1

Zone 2 Formation of tungsten halide

Zone 3

Fig. 15.12   Simplified mechanism of the halogen regenerative cycle

Tungsten-iodine lamps.   Of the possible tungsten-halogen lamps, the iodine lamp has been the most widely developed. This is due mainly to the fact that the temperatures required to maintain the regenerative cycle are well suited to practical lamp design and the difficulties of processing and handling the least formidable. The boundary temperature of the previously mentioned zones have been determined and for a satisfactory iodine regenerative cycle the tungsten filament must run at a minimum temperature of 2000 °K, with the bulb wall at least 250 °C. Iodine quantity is variable, dependent upon the amount of tungsten to be regenerated; this in turn being related to filament temperature, type of inert gas filling, cold-gas pressure, and overall lamp loading. The greater the proportion of iodine vapour in a lamp, the greater is the light lost due to absorption, which is selective in the green. Hence, there is an optimum quantity to maintain satisfactory regeneration but with minimum absorption, for each design.

The main limitation to the life of a tungsten-iodine lamp is caused by differences in temperature along the filament. While there is no loss in filament weight by radial diffusion of tungsten, axial diffusion still occurs. Also since the hot spots lose tungsten at a greater rate than that at which they receive the redeposited metal while a reverse procedure operates at the cold spots; tungsten migrates from the hot, to the cold spots. Eventual failure is due to fusing of a thin portion of the filament—often at switching.

9+

The relationship of life to filament temperature and differences in temperature, is given by the formula:

$$L \propto \frac{T^{-32}}{\Delta T}$$

where L = lamp life

   T = average filament temperature

   ΔT = temperature differences between hot and cold turns.

The improved efficiency and life of a tungsten-iodine lamp over a conventional incandescent lamp does not, in fact, arise directly from the redeposition of tungsten on to the filament. The regenerative cycle prevents the accumulation of tungsten on the bulb wall and this permits changes in geometry and size which, in turn, result in increased efficiency and life. Generally the volume of a tungsten-iodine lamp is very much less than that of an equivalent conventional type, for example a 1·5 kW tungsten-iodine floodlamp is only about 1% of the volume of its conventional counterpart (Fig. 15.13).

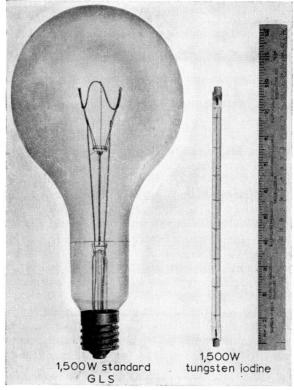

1,500W standard
G L S

1,500W
tungsten iodine

Fig. 15.13.   Comparative sizes of G.L.S. and tungsten-iodine lamps

The necessity to maintain the bulb wall of a tungsten-iodine lamp at a minimum temperature of 250 °C, has to some extent dictated the loading, size and configuration of the practical lamp. It would not be possible for instance, to make a lamp with a useful regenerative cycle, in the familiar pear-shaped bulb. Generally the tungsten-iodine lamp is formed by sealing a straight coiled-tungsten filament into a fused silica (quartz) tube with the filament running down the centre.

The respective diameters of the filament and the tubular envelope are very important design factors. Not only must the minimum temperature conditions be satisfied but the tube diameter should be such as virtually to prevent convection currents in the gas filling, to reduce losses through the gas and to improve efficiency. The theoretical aspects of this effect were developed by Langmuir in 1912, this experimental work indicated that the immediate atmosphere surrounding an incandescent filament is very nearly stationary. Heat losses through this gas sheath, known as the 'Langmuir sheath', are almost entirely by conduction, and convection losses take place effectively from the surface of this sheath. This conception is extremely important in many design aspects of incandescent lamps.

In the design of linear iodine lamps it is desirable that the Langmuir sheath extends substantially to the bulb wall of the tubular envelope. This almost eliminates heat losses by convection and improves the overall efficiency. Furthermore, since the density of the filling gas and the tungsten vapour concentration adjacent to the incandescent filament are higher than in a conventional lamp, these combine to suppress the rate of filament evaporation and to extend the lamp life.

From this it can be seen that whilst the iodine regenerative cycle does little directly to improve lamp life, or efficiency, it makes possible radical reductions in lamp volume which result in improvements to lamp life and luminous efficiency.

One of the disadvantages that has been experienced with the longer mains voltage floodlight ratings, has been that they cannot be run at angles greater than 4° from the horizontal; at steeper angles the iodine vapour migrates to the lower end, leaving the upper end starved and the regenerative cycle ceases to function. This can be overcome by filling the lamps to a high pressure, preferably with xenon. This practice in addition to overcoming the disadvantage of iodine migration gives rise to substantial increases in efficiency but at higher lamp cost. Such lamps are likely shortly to be commercially available, enclosed in an outer jacket.

The other halogens. There is very little published information available on reactions of bromine, chlorine and fluorine with tungsten at the temperatures attained in incandescent filament lamps and there is at present considerable research activity to establish facts and collect information. Tungsten bromide and tungsten chloride each dissociate at temperatures well below the normal operating temperatures of a tungsten filament and the regenerative cycle is very similar to that of an iodine lamp but with different boundary temperatures for various zones of activity. In the case of iodine, bromine and chlorine, the tungsten halide formed by the association of evaporated tungsten and halogen will dissociate in the high-temperature zone around the filament, augmenting the tungsten vapour concentration. The deposition of tungsten is preferential on the cooler parts of the filament, and failure occurs quite normally due to thinning of the hot spots.

Practical bromine lamp designs have been established and whilst both floodlight and projector types are possible, at the present time short un-supported filament lamps are the most practical. The main advantage of bromine in place of iodine is that there is practically no absorption of light by the bromine vapour and the integrated lumens from any particular design is slightly increased, for the equivalent life.

Practical difficulties associated with bromine are that the quantity in the filling gas must be fairly exact; there should be sufficient to regenerate the tungsten vapour diffusing to the bulb wall but an excess attacks the cooler parts of the filament causing early failure.

Tungsten-chloride lamps have not yet been marketed although active in the development and research stages. One of the main advantages with chlorine is that its introduction into a lamp is easier in the gas form and the manufacturing process may thereby be simplified.

Of all halogens, fluorine extends the greatest promise for the future. The significant fact about a fluorine addition into a tungsten lamp, is that the dissociation temperatures of tungsten fluoride is in the region of 3300 °K. This means that unlike the other tungsten halides, which dissociate and re-lease tungsten in the zone surrounding the filament, tungsten fluoride will dissociate at the points on the filament that are above 3300 °K, and deposit tungsten on these 'hot spots'. Incandescent filament lamps normally fail due to the development of 'hot spots' and this regeneration would tend to prevent them forming, giving a theoretically infinite filament life. The technical difficulties of achieving this ideal regenerative cycle are considerable and while carefully controlled laboratory tests confirm the existence of the regeneration, investigation is still in the research stages. The prospects are fascinating—filament temperatures at near melting point with long life operation.

Summarising, the now well-established, tungsten-iodine regenerative lamp gives increases in both life and lumens above its conventional counterpart, with considerable reduction in size. These gains are indirectly derived, by permitting changes in physical characteristics in lamp designs. Further development of a high-pressure universal burning lamp is well advanced, and should be commercially available shortly.

Practical bromine lamps have been made and the regenerative cycle is very similar to the iodine lamp. The small quantity of bromine vapour required to support a regenerative cycle is virtually colourless and integrated efficiency is slightly higher than with equivalent iodine types. Present designs are mainly applicable to compact projector-type lamps.

Chlorine and fluorine additions are still in the research and early develop-ment stages. The tungsten-fluoride regenerative lamp is technically very attractive and if it can be developed into a practical lamp design the life and efficiency of the tungsten filament lamp will be extended very considerably.

CHAPTER 16

Discharge Lamps—General Principles

Introduction. A discharge lamp consists of a transparent arc tube, or envelope filled with a rare gas, possibly with the addition of a metallic vapour, or halogen and containing a pair of electrodes between which an arc discharge occurs. The nature of the gas or vapours, the pressure developed and the current density determine the characteristic radiation of the discharge source.

The spectral composition of the light from a discharge lamp differs greatly from that of an incandescent filament lamp, which emits radiation as a continuous spectrum. The discharge source emits radiation mainly in discrete wavelengths and only a small proportion is continuous. In low-pressure mercury vapour lamps or sodium lamps the spectrum consists of 'line spectra' but as the gas pressure is increased the lines broaden, giving rise to 'band spectra'. At very high gas pressures a more continuous spectrum will develop, made up of a series of wide spectral bands but which is still very different and less continuous in form than the radiation from an incandescent body. A more detailed insight into the physics of the discharge has been given in Chapter 4.

Of the many types of discharge lamp which have been developed, differing considerably in the type of envelope, its shape, the electrodes used and gas filling—almost all have one characteristic in common, that the lamps cannot be operated direct from an electrical supply.

The discharge is maintained by collision of the electrons emitted by the cathode with the surrounding atoms and molecules of gas, or metal vapour. With increase in current, ionisation increases still more rapidly so that the potential required to maintain a discharge must be reduced, or alternatively the current will escalate rapidly until the lamp is destroyed. Such an arc is described as having a 'negative' characteristic requiring a current-limiting device for stable operation, commonly known as a ballast, or choke for a.c. supply. For a d.c. supply a resistance ballast is usually employed.

In order to start a discharge lamp a high-energy photon, of a higher voltage than the normal supply mains, is usually required to establish ionisation. Cathode preheating, an earth starting-conductor, or an auxiliary electrode placed close to one of the main electrodes thereby producing ions from field emission, are some of the aids used.

It may only be possible to start the discharge by the application of a very high voltage pulse sufficient to produce a high concentration of ions across the arc gap.

Materials used in discharge lamp designs. Discharge lamps make use of a complex combination of materials many of which are subjected to severe electrical and thermal stresses, pressure gradients, intense radiation and chemical attack by substances in an ionised state.

Their design often embodies an arc tube supported mechanically within an outer glass envelope in a manner which will withstand handling and the transporting to the point of use. When installed it must operate for many thousands of hours, which may be for several years, in an environment subject to vibration, humidity or chemical corrosion.

The arc tube of the discharge lamp must be transparent to the required radiation, e.g. visible, infrared or ultraviolet. It must withstand operation at the highest permissible temperature, which may be in the region of 1000 °C, or more.

Suitable metals must be used to carry the lead-wires through the arc tube wall, via hermetic seals, to support the electrodes and supply current to them.

Arc-tube envelope. The choice of envelope material is generally determined by the required operating temperature. Where resonance radiation is generated in the discharge, mercury at 253·7 nm as in the instance of a tubular fluorescent lamp, or sodium at 589/589·6 nm, the required respective arc-tube temperatures are 40 °C and 275 °C. A lime-soda glass is therefore used because of its low cost and ease in flame-working during the assembly processes. Sodium will quickly react chemically with most glasses, or quartz, to give a very dark brown discoloration, and hence a special flashing or thin coating of a sodium-resistant glass is applied to the inner wall of a lime-soda glass tube for the arc tube of sodium lamps. This sodium-resistant glass has a high barium oxide content mixed with other glass-forming oxides to give an expansion very close to that of the encasing lime-soda glass tube. Such tubing is generally known as 'sodium ply-tubing'.

Where light generation is proportional to vapour pressure the arc-tube envelope is required to operate at the highest practical temperature. The high-pressure mercury vapour lamp has for many years been made with an alumino-silicate glass having a softening point of about 950 °C compared with approximately 710 °C for a soda-lime glass. Today quartz or fused silica is almost completely replacing the hard glass. Research and development in the drawing of quartz tubing and its fabrication into lamps have made this economically possible. It can be operated at higher temperatures (having a softening point at about 1000 °C) which results in a 25% increase in lumen output. Lamps of higher pressure (10 to 50 atmospheres) such as the compact-source mercury and xenon lamps also make use of fused silica envelopes. For these lamps the envelope wall must be several millimetres thick to withstand the high internal pressures and at the same time be of good optical quality. The envelope is generally made spherical in form to assist in meeting these arduous requirements.

More recently a sintered-alumina material has been developed which has high strength at temperatures up to 1900 °C. It has little or no viscous range, being either a liquid or a solid. This creates new problems in lamp design and assembly techniques. The material is chemically inert, poly-crystalline in structure, at least 90% light transmissive, and, with its high temperature operation, offers a new challenge to the lamp engineer. Experimental lamps are being produced with sodium vapour at pressures around one quarter atmosphere to combine high efficiency (100 lm/w) with acceptable colour rendition.

Electrodes. Electrode structures differ markedly from one type of discharge lamp to another. The main functions are to provide a copious supply of electrons to maintain the discharge and to carry the lamp current. Electrode design has a profound influence on the performance of a lamp, in particular on its life.

The efficiency of a cathode depends upon its work function and this can be improved by emitter coatings of barium, strontium, or calcium oxides. Such coated cathodes operate at much lower temperatures than plain metal ones, with a volt drop of about 10 V to 15 V in argon. They are chemically very reactive and are quickly 'poisoned' or destroyed by water vapour, hydrogen, oxygen, halogen, etc.

With fluorescent tubes a tungsten-helix, or a coiled-braid of fine wire is coated with emitter to form an electrode of low thermal mass. On switching on the lamp, it is pre-heated by passing current through it, thereby producing sufficient ionisation to start the arc discharge.

The low-pressure sodium lamp also makes use of a helical coil of tungsten with an emitter coating but there is no pre-heating, sufficient voltage being applied to the lamp to start it with the cathode 'cold'. The cathode is designed to 'cold' start.

With the higher pressure lamps, characterised by a more concentrated arc discharge, such as high-pressure mercury lamps, the electrodes are generally built up from a rod of tungsten with a helical tungsten wire overwind. This helix either encloses a pellet of emissive material, or cavities which are filled with emitter paste. Starting takes place with the electrodes 'cold', usually aided by an auxiliary electrode adjacent to one of the main electrodes and connected through a resistor to the other main electrode. Intense ionisation occurs across the short gap between adjacent and main electrode thus promoting the main arc to start.

The electrodes for the compact-source mercury and xenon lamps, which have to carry currents of up to 100 A or more, are usually of 3% to 5% thoriated tungsten. As the power of a lamp increases with currents above 15 A the electrodes depart from simple rod design. Blocks of tungsten are shaped to provide a sufficient surface area to radiate energy arising from positive-ion bombardment. The electrode tips are also made conical, or wedge-shaped to provide controlled convection flow of the gas, or metal vapour, giving stability to the arc. This shaping of the electrode tip also permits a greater angle of light to be collected from the concentrated arc.

While the electrodes in most lamps will permit operation on d.c. it is necessary, with compact-source lamps carrying 15 A or more, to design the cathode and anode as separate structures. The cathode is generally a thin, slender rod of thoriated tungsten and the anode, a much heavier block of pure tungsten supported on a shank. The anode must be of high density and free from cracks to give good heat transfer from where the arc impinges on its conical tip.

Glass-to-metal seals. In order to carry current to an electrode contained within an arc tube an hermetic seal between the vitreous material of the arc tube body and the metal conductors must be made.

A reasonable match between the coefficients of expansion of the metal and glass must be made over the temperature range at which the seal will operate. Most electrode seals through glass make use of a wire, or rod, of tungsten or molybdenum. The shape of the glass forming the seal has a critical bearing on its strength and resistance to cracking.

It is customary in making such seals to encourage the formation of an oxide layer on the metal surface and to cause this to diffuse, or dissolve into the glass to assist bonding strength. The colour of the oxide bond is generally a very good indication of the quality of the bond. A molybdenum rod seal is characterised by a chocolate brown interface while a tungsten seal has one of a red/brown colour. Some seals are specially made to be free from oxide and the metal surface characterised by a silvery appearance. They are used in some instances to prevent reactive lamp metal-vapour fillings from penetrating the metal/glass seal interface which can sometimes occur with an oxide bond.

The fused silica seal makes use of thin foils of molybdenum, the edges of which are feathered by rolling or etching. By this means the stresses arising from the large differences in expansion coefficients of the molybdenum and the quartz are kept within acceptable limits. The seal made is oxide-free and bright silver in colour. The high temperatures used in making the seal are believed to produce an atomic-hydrogen bond at the interface.

Gas fillings. In order to establish a discharge within an arc tube at a sufficiently low applied voltage a carrier gas is necessary. Argon is commonly used in mercury-vapour lamps as this forms a metastable mixture with the mercury vapour of low ionisation potential and assists a low arc-striking voltage. Argon pressure of only a few millimetres of mercury is used for low-pressure fluorescent tubes whilst for high-pressure quartz lamps a few centimetres pressure is required to avoid electrode-sputter which would otherwise arise from the cold-starting conditions.

Ambient temperature affects the starting voltage level of a mercury lamp since, as the temperature falls, the mercury vapour pressure falls reducing the metastable proportion of argon and mercury. It is of serious consequence only at extremely low temperatures, $-30\,°F$ or less, when provision must be made to increase the voltage available for starting.

The sodium lamp makes use of a metastable gas mixture of neon and a small quantity of argon, usually about 1%, to reduce the starting voltage level. The neon provides a high arc-voltage to develop sufficient wattage in the discharge to achieve and maintain the critical vapour pressure of sodium required for optimum light emission. The small quantity of argon present is capable of being readily absorbed on the glass walls, thereby causing a rise in the starting voltage, and glass compositions which avoid or minimise this effect are of critical importance.

The xenon lamp is dependent upon a high gas pressure to give a high concentration of gas molecules for efficient light production. Lamps are usually filled to a pressure of up to 6 atmospheres at room temperature, which is increased by some $2\frac{1}{2}$ times at normal operating temperature. To start the arc discharge across the short arc gap of a few millimetres, voltage pulses of up to 30 kV are required. Ambient temperature does not affect the starting condition.

Outer envelope. Outer envelopes are used when it is necessary to maintain a controlled thermal relationship between the arc tube and its surroundings. This is particularly important with the sodium lamp, where a high degree of vacuum is maintained within the outer envelope to prevent heat losses. In some designs a heat shield in the form of a glass tube surrounds the arc tube, to further reduce heat losses. More recently, thin oxide films which transmit visible light but reflect the infrared back to the arc tube are applied to the inside of the outer envelope.

The mercury arc tube is very sensitive to local draughts, resulting in cold-spot temperatures which in turn control the mercury-vapour pressure. The outer envelope enclosing a mercury arc tube is filled with a mixture of nitrogen and argon to provide a uniform thermal condition, while at the same time the heat transfer by conduction permits high arc-tube powers to be dissipated. The outer glass envelope also serves to absorb the harmful, shorter wavelength ultraviolet radiation transmitted by the quartz arc tube.

In some lamp designs the outer envelope can be used to support an internal phosphor coating which emits red light by the action of the ultraviolet radiation emitted from the arc, thereby improving the colour rendition properties.

With some of the compact-source types of mercury or xenon lamp it is necessary to dispense with an outer envelope to enable the small arc sources to be placed sufficiently close to an optical system for efficient light utilisation. Lamps of this type must be designed to operate in free-air. The seals are made of sufficient length to keep the exposed molybdenum lead-wires below the oxidation temperature. The arc tube is made sufficiently small to operate in free-air with natural convection cooling.

Discharge lamp designations. As an aid to the classification of the various types of discharge lamp the following nomenclature is used (BS 1270: 'Electric Discharge Lamps for General Purposes').

The different classes of electric discharge lamps are designated by symbols consisting of:

9*

(a) Two letters indicating the nature and classification of each lamp. These are sometimes followed by other letters denoting sub-division of the main classification and representing some special features.

(b) In types other than tubular fluorescent, a letter following an oblique stroke to indicate the usual burning position thus:

/V — vertical cap up   /U — any position
/D — vertical cap down   /H — horizontal position

Lamp descriptions

MA	Mercury linear glass arc tube (medium pressure)
MB	,, ,, quartz ,, ,, (high ,,)
MC	,, ,, glass ,, ,, (low ,,)
MD	,, ,, quartz ,, ,, (liquid cooled)
ME	,, compact source quartz arc tube
NE	Neon linear glass arc tube
SO	Sodium U-shaped glass arc tube
SL	,, linear glass arc tube
XB	Xenon linear quartz arc tube
XE	,, compact source quartz arc tube

Commonly used additional letters

F	Internal fluorescent coating
R	,, reflector ,,
T	,, tungsten filament ballast
W	Ultraviolet filter bulb (Woods glass)
* I	Integral as applied to SL and possibly SO

* denotes *integral construction* in which arc tube and outer jacket are combined to form one unit.

Lesser used additional letters: (Not MCF)

C	Partial colour correction (cadmium)
L	Laboratory use
M	For use in mines

Additional letters used occasionally for MCF lamps

A	Instant start external metal stripe connected to both caps
B	,, ,, internal stripe connected to one electrode
C	,, ,, external metal stripe not connected to either cap
D	,, ,, two internal stripes connected to opposite electrodes
E	,, ,, external water repellant (silicone) coating

Example of designation

MBTRW/U   Mercury quartz arc tube with tungsten ballast, Woods glass outer bulb with a reflector coating, universal burning.

CHAPTER 17

Sodium Lamps

LOW-PRESSURE SODIUM-VAPOUR LAMPS

Introduction. The low-pressure sodium vapour lamp is characterised by its monochromatic radiation and high luminous efficiency. It is useful therefore where large quantities of light are required at low cost, without colour discrimination; for example in street lighting, aircraft runway indication and floodlighting.

Lamp types and characteristics. The sodium lamp consists essentially of a discharge tube having an electrode at each end, containing some sodium metal and a low pressure of gas, mainly neon. This is surrounded by a jacket, or outer bulb which enables the discharge tube to operate at its optimum temperature.

There are two basic lamp designs, one in which the arc tube is bent into a U shape and the other in which the arc tube is linear, although generally non-circular in cross-section. Examples of each type are shown in Fig. 17.1.

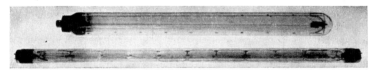

Fig. 17.1   Examples of U-shaped and linear lamps

The essential characteristics are given in Appendix I.

Principles of operation. The basis of operation of all electric discharge lamps is the collision processes between electrons and atoms, or ions, in the discharge tube (cf Chapter 4). These interactions may result in elastic collisions, in which little energy is lost by the electrons; or in the excitation of the atoms, when bound electrons are raised to higher energy levels; or in the ionisation of the atoms with the resultant generation of a further electron, to substantiate the electrical conductivity of the discharge. For each type of atom there are discrete quanta of energy which can be absorbed to excite the bound electrons, their subsequent decline to a lower, or normal, energy state being accompanied by the emission of a photon of radiation of a particular wavelength. In general, there is a particular electron transition between an excitation level and the normal atom state, which gives rise to the so-called *resonance radiation*, which the atom can not only emit but absorb. This process of resonance radiation and absorption plays an important part in sodium lamp operation.

Sodium has a resonance doublet at wavelengths 589·0 nm and 589·6 nm, emitted following electron relaxations from the 2·1 eV energy level. The discharge condition necessary for optimum emission of resonance radiation is evident from a consideration of Fig. 17.2, which shows the relationship between light output and lamp current.

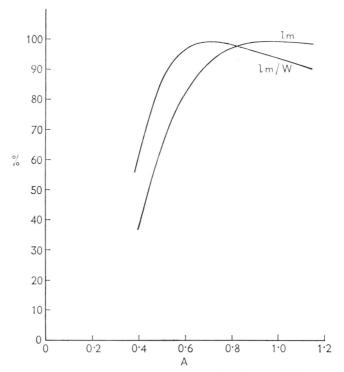

Fig. 17.2   Variation of light output (lm) and luminous efficiency (lm/W) with current in a 100 W SOX lamp

In general, the temperature of the discharge tube is proportional to the power input and it is the temperature which determines the sodium vapour pressure. When this is low, the rate of collision of atoms and electrons and the subsequent emission of light, are also low. As the pressure increases, more collisions are likely and the emission of light increases. An explanation of the fall-off in output at higher pressures and current densities lies in the increased resonance absorption and the higher excitation, or ionisation of sodium ions. These higher excitation levels may result in weak radiations of other wavelengths in the visible, infrared, or ultraviolet regions, but they result in a waste of energy and a reduction of light output. Thus the discharge conditions necessary for good lamp performance are a low vapour pressure (3 to 4 μm) and low current density.

The essential design features of the low-pressure sodium lamp follow from these facts. Sodium has a vapour pressure of 3 to 4 μm at around 270 °C and it is necessary therefore for the discharge tube to operate at this optimum temperature. To achieve a low current density the arc-tube diameter ought to be large but due to resonance absorption only the light generated close to the discharge tube wall is able to leave it, as that generated near the axis of the tube will be absorbed in its passage to the wall. In addition the radial distribution of potential and the diffusion rate of sodium atoms through the neon, cause a concentration of sodium atoms at the wall. Most of the current conduction also takes place in the vicinity of the wall. Consequently the preferred requirement is for a discharge tube of maximum surface area and minimum volume consistent with discharge stability. To achieve this maximal area, a long length of discharge tube can be used which is bent into a 'U' shape in order to reduce the overall lamp length. An alternative approach is to use a large diameter discharge tube but to shape its cross-section to achieve the large surface area, with reduced volume.

Since at room temperature the pressure of sodium is extremely low, a discharge cannot be initiated in sodium vapour alone. A filler gas (neon) is therefore necessary in order to start the lamp. This initial discharge in neon serves to heat the lamp and to raise the sodium-vapour pressure until sufficient sodium ions are available to take part. The function of the filler gas does not, however, cease here for even at the operating temperature of the lamp, the neon atoms outnumber the sodium atoms by about 5000 to 1 and the electrons therefore will collide more frequently with neon atoms. Since these collisions are mainly elastic, little energy is lost by the electrons and the function of the neon atoms is effectively to reduce the mean free path of the electrons, thereby increasing the probability of their ultimately colliding with and exciting, or ionising, sodium atoms.

Construction and design

Discharge tube glasses. At the operating temperature of the lamp the sodium is chemically extremely active. It will rapidly attack and discolour the ordinary glasses used in lamp manufacture; therefore special glasses have had to be developed, specially for sodium lamps. Two basic types are in current use, an alumino-borate glass which is resistent to sodium attack, although it stains slowly during the life of the lamp, and a glass modified by the addition of barium oxide (BaO), which is non-discolouring. Glasses of the latter type are essential in the manufacture of modern high-efficiency, good lumen-maintenance lamps. Unfortunately, either glass is damaged by atmospheric moisture and is expensive and difficult to work. To produce a durable economic material capable of lamp fabrication, a ply-tubing is produced with a thin layer (about 50 μm) of resistant glass on the inside of a tube of standard soda-lime glass.

A further property of the glass used for sodium lamps is its tendency to absorb argon under discharge conditions. A small percentage of argon is added to the neon, as a necessary aid to starting. Its absorption can lead to the lamp failing to start under normal installation conditions and this has, in the past, been a limitation to lamp life. The type of glass also affects the migration of sodium metal within the lamp, as discussed later.

Electrodes and seals. The electrodes of sodium lamps are usually double, or triple coils of fine tungsten wire, impregnated with an electron emissive mixture containing alkaline-earth oxides. They are designed to give a good lamp life and to minimise the electrode energy losses inherent in the supply of electrons to the discharge. The electrodes are clamped or welded to lead wires of dumet, a copper-clad nickel–iron alloy, which matches the thermal expansion characteristics of the discharge tube glass. The seal, an example of which is shown in Fig. 17.3, has to withstand the chemical action of hot ionised sodium, remain gas-tight over wide ranges of temperature (say − 20 °C to 300 °C) and to withstand electrolysis. This electrolysis takes place in the

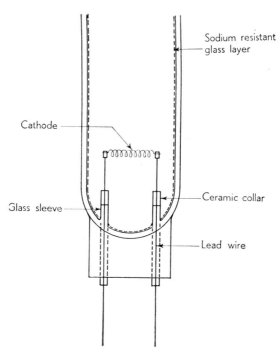

Fig. 17.3   Typical sodium lamp seal design

glass around the lead-wires, due to potential fields in the electrode region and is aggravated by the decrease of electrical resistance of glass with increase in temperature. It can cause an accumulation of decomposition products around the lead wires and subsequently seal cracks. The process can be prevented by sealing a sleeve of glass of high electrical resistance around each lead wire, the end of the sleeve close to the cathode being further protected by a ceramic collar. In some lamps further protection is obtained by coating the sleeve glass with a layer of sodium-resistant glass similar to that used on the inner surface of the discharge tube. Great care is necessary in the choice of materials and processing for these seals and in the control of dimensions, to obtain a good lamp life.

Filler gas. Neon is the gas used in modern sodium lamps, with small additions of argon and/or xenon. Neon has an ionisation voltage of 21·5 eV compared to 5·1 eV for sodium, thus when sodium atoms are made available they are much more easily ionised than neon atoms and carry virtually the whole of the discharge. Since the neon atoms also have a part to play when the lamp is operating, the pressure of gas affects the efficiency of light generation; Fig. 17.4 shows this relationship. The discontinuity in the curve giving a

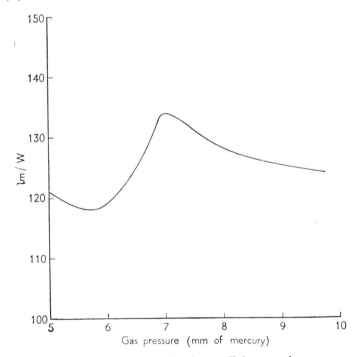

Fig. 17.4   Relationship between luminous efficiency and gas pressure (99% neon, 0·8% argon, 0·2% xenon) for a 200 W SLI lamp

minimum value of efficiency at about 6 mm, results from the existence at this point of optimum conditions for energy losses in the neon gas. The pressure at which it occurs and the degree of the discontinuity varies slightly with the design of the discharge tube. The filler gas is also believed to fulfil a buffering action on ions approaching the emitter-coated electrodes, thus reducing evaporation of the emitter and extending the lamp life. The heavier rare gases, for instance argon and xenon, have higher probabilities of ionisation than neon, so that their use as main filler gases would reduce the efficiency of production of sodium radiation. The lighter rare gas, helium, absorbs energy from the free electrons in elastic collisions and thus reduces their energy; it also allows a greater freedom of diffusion of sodium ions away from the tube wall and thus reduces light output efficiency.

However, a small quantity of argon is added to the filler gas to reduce the striking voltage of the lamp by the Penning effect. The optimum proportion of argon to neon for minimum striking voltage depends on the lamp design but is generally about 0·5% (see Fig. 17.5). Allowance must be made for any

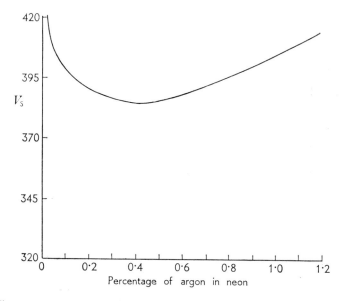

Fig. 17.5   Relationship between starting voltage (V_s) and percentage of argon in neon at 10 mm pressure for 140 W SOI lamp

absorption of argon by the discharge tube glass and a correspondingly higher percentage of argon used; values between 0·8% and 1·4% are customary. Higher ratios add very little to the gas life of the lamp, since the rate of absorption of argon with time appears to be exponential, but they do affect adversely the efficiency and electrical characteristics. The degree of absorption depends on the glass composition; for example the non-discolouring barium alumino-borate glasses absorb argon at a faster rate than the standard alumino-borates and a higher argon to neon ratio is usual. Xenon is added to some designs of lamp since it appears to reduce the argon absorption and also to assist control of the arc voltage of the lamp during its run-up period.

The pressure of gas introduced into the lamp is a compromise between the argon absorption, the luminous efficiency and sodium migration. In general, filling pressures between 6 mm and 15 mm of mercury are chosen, depending on the design of lamp and the materials used.

Sodium location and distribution. We have already seen that there are fewer sodium atoms than neon atoms in the discharge and the range of the sodium ions is therefore limited due to their frequent collision with neon atoms. An even distribution of sodium throughout the discharge tube is necessary if a uniform generation of light is to be achieved. In practice, small differences in temperature occur along a discharge tube, due to dimensional, or thermal insulation differences and the sodium will tend to collect at the cooler spots. The effect can be cumulative, since as a region becomes deficient in sodium, part of the current in that region will have to be carried by the neon which has a higher ionisation voltage; the heat generated in such a region of the discharge will be higher and the migration of sodium will be accelerated. Eventually all the sodium will accumulate in selected areas in the lamp and although these will emit sodium light the remainder will emit mainly red neon radiation—'red burners'—and the luminous efficiency of the whole will be low. At low gas pressures, this effect is reversed due to the voltage wave-form differences in the neon and neon-sodium discharges, for example, in the 200 W linear lamp this occurs below about 6 mm. This is not, however, so beneficial as may initially appear, as the sodium tends to distribute itself evenly along the discharge tube wall. The resultant thin film of sodium absorbs most of the incident sodium radiation and the efficiency of such a lamp will be very low.

In alumino-borate discharge tubes, which discolour due to sodium attack, there is, in effect, a supply of sodium built-up in the wall of the glass through-out the life of the lamp which reduces the effects of migration. In practice, however, and particularly with the barium alumino-borate glasses, it is necessary to control this migration physically. In the U-shaped designs the control generally takes the form of small hemispheres, formed at intervals along the length of the discharge tube, which act as reservoirs for sodium metal. In the linear lamps the 'horns' of the grooves perform a similar function and in the latest designs small reservoirs are formed in each shaped section (see Fig. 17.6). These techniques for locating sodium are also helpful in achieving a high light output since they reduce the area of discharge tube obscured by sodium film.

Thermal insulation. Since it is necessary to maintain the discharge tube at a temperature considerably above ambient in order to achieve the optimum sodium-vapour pressure, the overall efficiency of the lamp will benefit by conserving as much of the generated heat as possible. In the past, U-shaped lamps have been housed in Dewar type jackets, to minimise convection and conduction losses. Since the discharge tube operates in a pocket of air within the jacket, the loss of insulation is significant and the efficiency is corresponding-ly limited. In modern integral lamps, the space between the discharge tube and the outer bulb is evacuated, 'getters' being used to achieve and maintain a

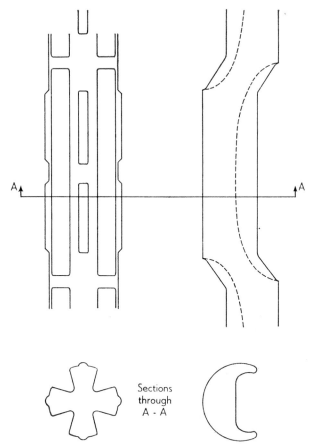

Sections
through
A - A

Fig. 17.6   Comparison of two arc-tube shapes for linear sodium lamps

hard vacuum. In addition, the thermal insulation can be improved by the use of glass tubes which are either concentric with the whole discharge tube, or in the case of some U-shaped lamps with each individual limb. Such a glass heat-insulating member reflects some 10% of the incident infrared radiation and absorbs the majority of the remainder; it is itself thus heated and it re-radiates this heat in approximately equal parts, inwardly and outwardly. A second glass reflecting tube can be added to intercept the outward component from the first but as layers are added the rate of gain in efficiency decreases, while losses due to the absorption of visible light increase. Furthermore, with each added tube, the weight, complexity and fragility of the lamp are adversely affected.

A more advanced technique of thermal insulation is found in the use of infrared reflecting films applied to the inside surface of the outer bulb. The films take the form either of a layer of tin oxide, or of alternate layers of bismuth oxide and gold. Although greater infrared reflectances can be obtained with the latter, the tin oxide coatings can give a greater visible transmission. Reflecting films of tin oxide are now in regular production having infrared reflectances of 75% to 80% combined with 85% to 90% transmission of sodium light. They have the same effect as several layers of glass but with less obscuration of visible light.

Operating characteristics

Starting and run-up. All discharge lamps require a higher voltage to start than to operate and techniques to cope with this requirement are numerous, as will be seen from a study of other lamp types. Sodium lamps in general operate with a stray field transformer, which, in some cases, can be used for more than one lamp rating.

Some of the U-shaped designs have incorporated external probe starting aids, which, in the case of the detachable jacket lamp, also served as a support member.

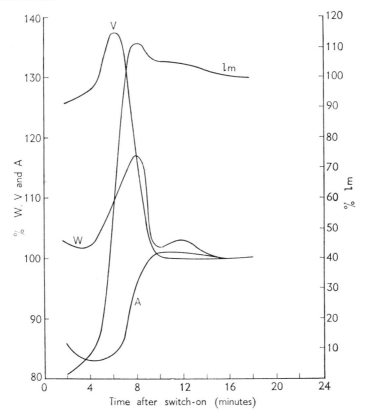

Fig. 17.7 Curves showing changes in light output (lm), watts (W), lamp voltage (V) and current (A) with time after switch-on, compared with stable values. Data derived from 200 W SLI lamp, but other types are similar

The linear lamp was first introduced for operation with a starter-switch circuit but modern designs, although satisfactory in these circuits are intended for switchless operation, on stray field transformer circuits. The infrared reflective coatings referred to earlier depend for their reflective properties on the existence of free electrons in the metallic surface. These also render the coating electrically conductive, having resistivity values of 15 to 40 ohms/cm^2. This property has been utilised to reduce the starting voltage of linear lamps in a manner similar to that adopted in some switchless-start fluorescent lamp circuits, by connecting one end of the coating to one electrode. The effect is to lower the starting voltage by some 200 V to 250 V, and a stray field transformer of open-circuit 475 V adequately allows for the starting voltage rise during life due to argon absorption, and for reasonable fluctuations in supply voltage.

One feature of the sodium lamp is its independence of starting voltage with temperature change which is in marked contrast to the behaviour of the mercury discharge lamp. The vapour pressure of sodium at normal ambient temperatures is insignificant compared to the rare-gas pressure and the starting voltage remains sensibly constant.

Once started the sodium lamp requires between 8 and 15 min, depending upon design, to attain full light output and during this time the electrical characteristics change slightly as shown in Fig. 17.7. To some extent these curves are effected by the gas content. In some lamps a small amount (0.2%) of xenon is added, which controls the tube voltage during run-up.

The effect of mains supply variation on lamp operation. Fig. 17.2 shows the effect on luminous output and efficiency of a sodium lamp due to increasing the current. It will be seen that the efficiency reaches a maximum value at a lower loading than the total output, this follows from the gradual increase in lamp watts with current. From Fig. 17.8, showing the variation in lamp parameters with mains supply, it is evident that the lamp is designed to operate initially between the maximum efficiency and maximum output points and that a slight increase in mains voltage will raise the total light output. Due to sodium distillation, the watts dissipated in a lamp rise somewhat during life, causing a shift towards the maximum light output condition. It is thus possible to control the fall-off in light output during life and to achieve in some linear types, a 100% lumen maintenance characteristic, throughout the rated life of the lamp.

Operating position. The permitted orientation of lamps in operation is limited by the movement of sodium by distillation and gravity. The metal will condense in the coolest region, which generally will be at the lowest point of the lamp. In addition vibration and to some extent gravity, will cause the molten sodium to fall to the lowest point. In U-shaped lamps, cap-down burning can cause lamp failures due to the sodium collecting behind the cathodes and causing short circuits from the cathode to the wall. Cap-up burning can result in sodium collecting in the bend and with all but the shortest lamps will produce 'red burners', due to the upper portion of the

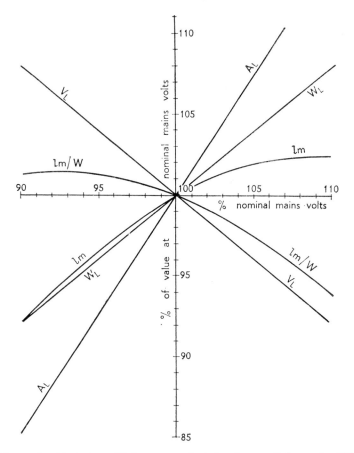

Fig. 17.8 Variation of light output (lm), luminous efficiency (lm/W), lamp watts (W_L), lamp voltage (V_L) and lamp current (A_L), with mains supply volts for 140 W SOI lamps

discharge tube becoming starved of sodium. Dewar and integral lamps with no sodium-retaining facilities, are thus limited to horizontal burning within 5° cap-down and 20° cap-up; apart from the lower wattage ratings which can, with little loss of light, be burned vertically cap-up. Modern integral U-shaped lamps and linear lamps can be operated within 20° of the horizontal.

Size and rating. The performance and efficiency of a discharge tube is dependent upon its surface area, and this in turn depends upon its cross-sectional area and length. In addition, the efficiency increases with discharge tube length since the energy losses at the electrodes, which are proportional to the lamp current, become smaller in proportion to the overall lamp watts.

Thus for a particular current density and temperature, lamp efficiency follows the relationship

$$E \propto \frac{l}{l + c}$$

where E is lamp efficiency, l the discharge length and c a constant.

In these terms the U-shaped discharge tube has an advantage over the linear one, since for a given overall lamp length, almost twice the discharge tube length can be incorporated. The linear lamp however compensates for this by the design of its cross-sectional shape.

Although the efficiency of the lamp can be increased by preserving the heat it generates, by means such as infrared reflecting films, the gain is not a simple one. The first effect of retaining more heat is to raise the vapour pressure above its optimum value with an associated loss of light output. There is also an increase in lamp current. To compensate, the power input must be reduced, or the discharge tube size increased, so that the lamp may operate at its optimum temperature. Therefore for the same physical size of discharge tube the efficiency can be increased, if the energy input is reduced. To achieve a gain in total output, the surface area of the discharge tube has to be increased.

A comparison can be drawn between the original 100 lm/W linear lamp with its tubular glass heat-reflector and two later designs incorporating infrared reflective coatings. The overall size of all the lamps is the same but the discharge tube has been completely changed in shape to give an increased surface area and lower energy losses.

In an outer bulb with an 80% infrared reflective coating the new discharge tube is operated at 0·9 A to give 20,000 lm, at an efficiency of about 150 lm/W. A similar discharge tube is used with a bulb coating of less infrared reflectivity, about, 65% to produce a lamp giving 25,000 lm at 1·6 A (200 W). The cross-sectional shape of the new high-efficiency lamps is shown on the left in Fig. 17.6.

In the case of the newer U-shaped lamp series (SOX type) existing integral lamp sizes have been maintained, the power input reduced and the arc-tube diameter raised slightly, in order to achieve optimum efficiency conditions and compatibility with existing ballasts. Compared to the preceding integral (SOI) type lamps of equivalent size, the design change has raised lamp efficiency by some 40% to 50%, with a slight reduction in total output.

Radiation characteristics. A typical spectral power distribution of low-pressure sodium lamp radiation is shown in Fig. 17.9(a). Although slight neon radiation is evident, 99·5% of the visible radiation is concentrated in the yellow 589·0 nm and 589·6 nm lines of the sodium spectrum. It may at first have been thought that the monochromatic radiation of sodium lamps and their consequent complete lack of colour discrimination would make them unacceptable as light sources. But the wavelength of the light emitted by the lamp is close to that at which the human eye has its maximum sensitivity, thus giving the lamp a very high luminous efficiency. In addition there are applications where colour rendition is unimportant and some instances where the emission of yellow line radiation only is advantageous.

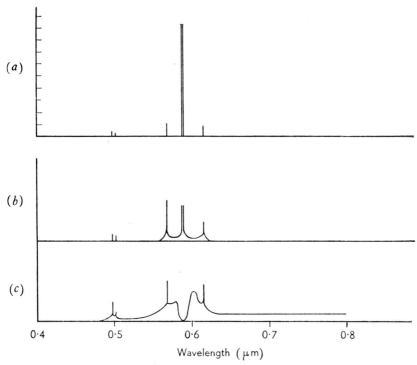

Fig. 17.9   Spectral power distribution of the sodium discharge at
(a) 5 μm, (b) 30 mm and (c) 240 mm

Applications

Street lighting. The chief application for the low-pressure sodium lamp is in the lighting of traffic routes and traffic hazards, where a highly efficient light source is required to provide large areas of good illumination at low cost and where colour rendition is of minor consequence. The British Standard Code of Practice on street lighting indicates the extent of this utilisation (see Appendix). Since it is impracticable for road illumination levels under artificial lighting to be as high as in daylight, the function of seeing in road lighting consists of interpreting contrasts between dimly illuminated vertical surfaces and bright horizontal surfaces. The advantage of the sodium lamp is the tendency towards greater visual contrast between light and dark surfaces lit by yellow light than by any other radiation, due to the Purkinje shift in visual spectral response at low-luminance levels. In addition there can be no confusion of outline due to chromatic aberation using monochromatic light such as can exist with polychromatic radiation, due to the wide pupil aperture of the human eye at low-illumination levels.

Airfield lighting. A novel form of sodium lamp based on the 200 W linear design which can be dimmed as required by current reductions has been developed for airfield approach lighting. A winding of nichrome wire surrounds the discharge tube, acting as a heater coil to maintain the sodium vapour pressure at its optimum value, irrespective of the wattage loading in the arc tube itself. The control circuits use thyratrons, or silicon controlled rectifiers, in the primary of a 550 V open circuit transformer supplying lamps connected in parallel, each with a series choke. At low-illumination levels the cathodes require auxiliary heating, nominally 7·5 V at the lowest level. This is tapped from the heater-coil supply and varies with it. The oven power is also controlled by thermostats exposed to climatic conditions. Lamps may be keyed or flashed as required. Under these conditions and at settings above 30% of maximum rated light output, increased heater inputs are necessary (to compensate for heat lost during the time the lamp is off) to maintain the light output level. This can be achieved by 'backstop' keying of the heater supply. By these techniques light output levels can be achieved and main-tained between 3% and 100% of the rated maximum output (20,000 lm). On changing the level, 60% of the shift is instantaneous and 90% is reached within 2 minutes. The system can be used therefore, within a wide range of visibility conditions.

Floodlighting. There are many floodlighting problems capable of solution by sodium lighting. These include sites where illumination is required irrespec-tive of colour, as a safety measure; and others involving old stone surfaces, or where opportunities exist for dramatic modelling for which the colour of the sodium lamp is eminently suitable.

HIGH-PRESSURE SODIUM VAPOUR LAMPS

Effects of increasing sodium vapour pressure. As the vapour pressure of sodium in a lamp is raised, the efficiency falls to a minimum value and then rises again, with the effect that at a pressure of $\frac{1}{3}$ to $\frac{1}{2}$ of an atmosphere, efficiencies of the order of 100 lm/W can be obtained. Again, as the pressure rises the spectral power distribution from the lamp changes. The line emission at the resonance wavelengths become absorbed, whilst radiation bands develop on either side and particularly toward the longer wavelengths. This change is due to an increasing interaction between excited and normal state sodium atoms. In addition, other individual spectral lines become more marked due to electron relaxations from higher levels of excitation. The spectral energy distribution of sodium discharges at pressures of about 5 μm, 30 mm and 240 mm are shown in Fig. 17.9.

The efficiency and colour of the discharge both depend on vapour pressure, and are interrelated. The colour improves as the pressure rises but the efficiency appears to reach a maximum and then fall away. One aspect of lamp design today is to investigate preferred combinations.

Discharge tube materials. Until recently no suitable material was available which would withstand the extreme chemical activity of sodium at higher pressures and temperatures but a few years ago a form of sintered poly-crystalline alumina was developed in the U.S.A. which would withstand sodium activity up to some 1600 °C. Similar material has been developed in Britain and in Europe with which many experiments have been conducted to determine its application in commercial light sources.

The material is formed from pure alumina powder, together with additives which control crystal growth. These additives are important since they determine the transparency of the final product. The material is moulded into a tubular form from which it can conveniently be reshaped, or further worked. It is subsequently sintered to final form in hydrogen at high temperature for several hours. The result is a translucent, non-porous ceramic which will transmit some 90% of visible light. It is at this time the only material suitable for lamps using high-pressure sodium discharges, although the experimental use of transparent corundum (sapphire) has been reported.

Unlike glasses, alumina has no working range of temperature, therefore fused vitreous seals of a conventional sort cannot be formed and sodium-resistant cements have been developed for sealing end-caps of alumina, or metal, to the alumina body. Some of these cements are based on eutectic mixtures of calcium oxide and aluminium oxide; sometimes with additions of other oxides, such as magnesia.

Since the sintered alumina is a crystalline material with crystal sizes of some 10 μm to 15 μm, interface faults, or dislocations can be incipient causes of lamp failure and considerable work continues not only on lamp-making processes but also on many aspects of material preparation.

Lamp construction and applications. The construction of a typical discharge tube and complete lamp are shown in Fig. 17.10. The discharge

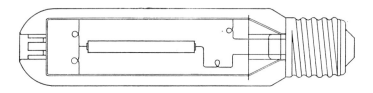

Fig. 17.10 Experimental high-pressure sodium discharge lamp

tube is of 6 mm bore, with a wall thickness of 0·8 mm. The arc length is of some 80 mm. Through each alumina end-cap is cemented a molybdenum shank carrying a tungsten coil electrode impregnated with alkaline-earth oxides, similar to those used in high-pressure mercury lamps.

To achieve a high-pressure of sodium vapour during operation, the discharge tube must be maintained at a high temperature. For example sodium has a vapour pressure of 250 mm at about 760 °C. To enable such conditions to be obtained, similar principles of heat conservation are adopted as in low-pressure lamps, and the discharge tube is mounted in an evacuated bulb containing metallic getters.

A lamp of this type having an argon and sodium filling, dissipates some 400 W at a tube voltage of 60 V to 70 V and has an efficiency approximating to 100 lm/W. The vapour pressure is estimated as approaching half an atmosphere.

The argon filling functions as a starting medium and also as a buffer gas, during lamp operation. The use of xenon, although more expensive, enables higher lamp efficiencies to be attained. With sodium and rare gas alone, the running voltage of 60 V and 70 V would necessitate the use of uneconomic ballasts of high VA rating on normal mains voltage supplies. The addition of a controlled amount of mercury can provide a further buffering medium which contributes very little to the radiation from the lamp but which increases the voltage and reduces the lamp current, for a given wattage loading. The result is a more efficient lamp, compatible with normal-type control gear.

Considerable investigational work is still required in the use of sintered alumina as a lamp-making material to assess the pressure and temperature loadings which it is able to sustain, and further to develop design reliability. Seals and techniques of seal making are the subject of much current activity, as also are the possibilities of inclusions other than sodium, for instance, various metallic halides.

Despite the problems still to be overcome a new design concept has been introduced providing high-efficiency lamps with colour rendering satisfactory for a wide variety of application and of dimensions suited to fittings of small size and accurate light control.

CHAPTER 18

Mercury Lamps

Introduction. Setting aside fluorescent tubes which are dealt with elsewhere, there are three main groups of mercury discharge lamps; namely, the medium-pressure group which have arc tubes made of hard glass and operate at a pressure of approximately one atmosphere, the high-pressure group which have quartz arc tubes and operate at 2 to 10 atmospheres pressure and the extra high-pressure or 'compact-source' group, again with quartz arc tubes, but which operate at about 20 atmospheres pressure.

The designations by which these lamps may be identified can be found in Chapter 16, under the heading 'Discharge lamp designations'.

Principles of operation. Atoms and molecules of the elements of the periodic table are made up of the basic particles of matter. The elements differ from each other in particle content and arrangement of particles in their individual atoms. An atom of an element is the smallest indivisible portion of the element and all atoms of any one element are alike.

Under certain circumstances an atom can store energy by a minor adjustment to the orbit of an electron, one of its basic particles. This process is called *excitation* and is discussed more fully in Chapter 4. Excitation of any atom can only take place at one of a clearly defined set of levels, each different element possessing its own set of levels peculiar to its atomic particle content and arrangement. The energy involved in excitation, measured in electron volts, eV, is given up after a very short time as an electromagnetic radiation, when the atom is said to fall to a lower state of excitation or return to its ground level. The energy given up by the atom equated to a constant determines the wavelength of the radiation emitted. Thus, the higher the energy, the shorter the wavelength of the radiation.

It will be seen therefore that the atoms of any element have their own radiation pattern, or spectrum, which cannot be changed.

To obtain radiation from an element the first requirement is that its atoms be suitably excited. In high-pressure mercury vapour lamps, this is achieved by raising the temperature of the vapour until thermal activity provides the energy. Other elements may also be thermally excited, the operating temperature depending on the value of the excitation levels required. Thus, comparison of mercury and sodium reveals that mercury must be excited by energy in the region of 9 eV in order to emit visible light, while sodium requires excitation only to the 2·1 eV level. A minimum temperature in the order of 4000 °K is required to promote some visible radiation from mercury, while sodium requires substantially lower temperatures.

In the high-pressure mercury lamp of the MB type operating at from 2 to 10 atmospheres pressure of mercury vapour, light is emitted from an axial discharge between the electrodes. The visible discharge in, for example, the 400 W lamp is some 5 mm diameter, while the quartz arc tube has a bore of 18 mm. The temperature at the centre of the discharge will be in the order of 6000 °K, while the maximum temperature of the quartz arc tube will be in the order of 800 °C. From the centre of the discharge, temperature falls fairly rapidly to about 4000 °K at the edge of the visible discharge and from then on less rapidly until very near the quartz wall. The arc discharge is supported between the two electrodes and is stabilised by the presence of the arc-tube walls. The function of the two electrodes when the lamp is operated on a.c. is alternately to supply electrons (this constitutes the main current in the lamp) and to receive electrons from the discharge in the next half-cycle. The electrodes are made of tungsten, the most refractory metal available for the purpose, in the form of a wire helix or rod, or of an assembly combining both. Electron emission is obtained at lower temperatures than for pure tungsten by suitably doping with low work-function materials, such as barium oxide.

The electrodes are self-regulating in providing the correct value of electron emission needed to support the discharge. They operate as follows. During the half-cycle in which the electrode acts as an anode it receives heat from electron bombardment. During the cathode half-cycle, should its electron emission be inadequate, it will be bombarded by positive ions from the discharge and consequently it will rise in temperature. The increased electrode temperature will in turn result in greater electron emission which will cancel some of the ion bombardment and therefore reduce the energy dissipated by the electrode. The converse also is true, in that if the cathode temperature is greater than required, little or no ion bombardment will take place and its temperature will fall.

The maintenance of electrode temperature requires energy which cannot be part of the light emission mechanism of the lamp. It follows that a lamp can be made more efficient by increasing the ratio of power in the arc discharge to power lost in heating the electrodes; hence a high-voltage, low-current lamp would seem desirable.

The question of arc voltage and lamp efficiency is part of the overall economics of providing a practical light source. The arc discharge has a negative current-impedance characteristic such that as arc current is increased arc voltage remains constant, or even falls a little. This characteristic requires a discharge lamp to be operated in series with a current-limiting device, such as an inductance. From an economic point of view it is desirable to use as small an inductance and as high a lamp arc-voltage as possible, for given supply voltage. There is, however, a limit to the arc voltage that may be used for a given supply voltage. The limit is set by the fact that the arc extinguishes at each half-cycle and then has to re-ignite. During the period of zero current the gas in the arc tube is de-ionised, and this results in an increased re-ignition voltage requirement with time. The frequency of the supply will determine the time of voltage rise after arc extinction and with a 50 c/s supply an arc voltage of 130 V is the maximum to be recommended, for 200 V operation.

The arc voltage of high-pressure mercury lamps is controlled to a very large extent by the quantity of mercury introduced during manufacture. With the possible exception of certain special types, all lamps operate under conditions of mercury vapour super-heating, hence the mercury dose controls the pressure within the lamp.

These are the basic design features common to all high-pressure mercury vapour lamps and individual design aspects can now be discussed in more detail.

Medium-pressure lamps

Construction. A medium-pressure lamp has a hard, alumino-silicate glass arc tube which is suspended inside an outer bulb made of soft, soda-lime glass. The arc tubes have electrodes at each end often made of two tungsten coils, one inside the other, the innermost enclosing a pellet of emissive material. The distance between the electrodes is too great for an arc to be directly initiated at normal supply mains voltages. To overcome this an auxiliary electrode of molybdenum wire is positioned close to one of the main electrodes. This is externally connected through a resistor to the main electrode at the other end of the arc tube. A supply voltage of 200/250 V is able to break down the small gap between the auxiliary and adjacent main electrode, ionising the argon filling gas to start the main arc discharge. This form of construction is common to most medium-pressure lamps (Fig. 18.1). An outline drawing typical of a finished lamp is shown in Fig. 18.2.

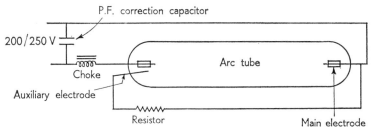

Fig. 18.1   Circuit diagram of a medium-pressure lamp

Mounting of the arc tube inside the outer bulb is by nickel or nickel-plated iron supports held on a glass stem. A low pressure of nitrogen is used in the outer envelope to provide suitable conditions of heat transfer from the arc tube. A fluorescent version of the lamp has a large, isothermal-shaped outer envelope coated on the inside surface with cadmium-zinc sulphide phosphor. This phosphor converts some of the long-wave, ultraviolet radiation of the arc tube into red light, so improving the colour characteristics of the lamp. The phosphor absorbs some of the visible radiation from the mercury discharge however and the efficiency is lower than that of the clear lamp.

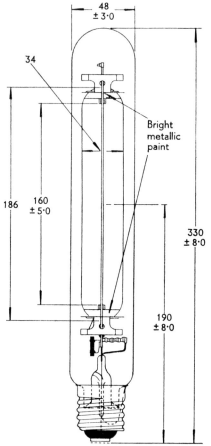

Fig. 18.2   400 W medium-pressure lamp, with glass arc tube

Operation. Medium-pressure lamps are designed to operate vertically, cap uppermost, unless otherwise designated. Lamps of 250 W and 400 W rating may be burnt horizontally, providing that a magnetic arc-control is used. This prevents the arc bowing upwards and coming into contact with the glass.

Uses. Mercury lamps are used for street lighting and to a limited extent in industrial installations. They are now superseded by the high-pressure lamp range which are more efficient, particularly in the case of 'colour corrected' phosphor-coated bulb types. To accommodate existing fittings, high-pressure lamps having the same overall dimensions as 250 W and 400 W medium-pressure designs have been introduced, giving some 20% more light.

High-pressure lamps. Following the introduction of the medium-pressure lamp, it was found that for a number of applications lamps of lower wattage were desirable. A reduction in the wattage input of the lamp from 250 W implies a reduction in all dimensions in order to maintain lamp temperature and hence mercury vapour pressure. When the arc length of the lamp is reduced it is found necessary to increase the mercury vapour pressure in order to maintain arc-voltage drop. The minimum temperature of the lamp therefore has to be raised above the usable limit of a hard-glass envelope. This necessitated the introduction of quartz (fused silica) as an arc-tube material. The early development resulted in lamps of 80 W and 125 W rating, the range having since been extended from 40 W to 2 kW. The 250 W 400 W and 1 kW ratings give higher efficiencies than equivalent ratings of medium-pressure lamps and because they operate on the same control gear they offer a preferable replacement. Further advantages of quartz arc tubes are (a) more ultraviolet transmission, which can be utilised by efficient phosphors to improve colour characteristics, (b) reduced dimensions and (c) they can be operated in any position, without the need for arc-control. High-pressure lamps are normally used for street and industrial lighting; in some cases they are mixed with incandescent lamps for display lighting. In addition, there is a special range of lamps for laboratory use, i.e. spectral radiation sources, etc.

Construction. Quartz has a very low expansion coefficient in the order of one-fifth of that of most metals with melting temperatures sufficiently high to make them suitable for sealing to it. Hermetic seals cannot therefore be made with wires or rods as with glass. It is necessary to choose a ductile metal, such as molybdenum and to use it in the form of very thin foil. The foils are shaped to an elliptical cross-section, and are sufficiently thin to disperse the stresses set up by the expansion mis-match, thereby preventing breakdown of the quartz–metal at the interface bond. The main electrodes are made of tungsten wire in the form of a helix about a solid shank of molybdenum, or tungsten, welded to the seal foil. Emissive material usually consisting primarily of alkaline earth carbonates, is coated on to the helix during the lamp making; the carbonates break down to oxides during the manufacturing process and these provide electron emission throughout the life of the lamp. A calculated dose of mercury and a filling of 20 mm mercury pressure of argon, is introduced into the arc tube. The amount of mercury is such that when a lamp has fully run up, all the mercury is vaporised.

The lamps have outer bulbs of either clear glass, or a pearl finish to give some diffusion. Lamps of the colour-corrected range have their outer bulbs coated on the inside with magnesium fluorogermanate phosphor. This phosphor is able to convert the ultraviolet output of the arc tube into visible red light, which results in the lamp having a whiter colour. Outer bulbs can be somewhat smaller than those needed for cadmium–zinc sulphide phosphor because the fluorogermanate will function at a higher temperature. An elliptical shape is chosen to assist uniformity of phosphor coating and temperature over the surface. Generally lamps of 250 W rating and above have outers made of weather-resistant hard glass, the lower wattages have soft-glass bulbs. In the higher wattage lamps the bulb-neck is moulded at the sealing operation to a screw-thread profile, to match the inside surface of the G.E.S. cap. This is coated with a thin film of thermosetting resin before the cap is screwed on. This form of construction ensures permanent cap attachment throughout the long lives of these lamps. The 80 W and 125 W ratings have either bayonet, or Edison screw-caps, which are cemented on to a moulded seal. A typical design of 400 W MBF/U lamp is shown in Fig. 18.3.

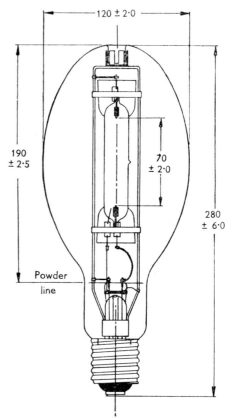

Fig. 18.3   400 W high-pressure lamp, with quartz arc tube

Reflector-type lamps have a specially shaped outer jacket, made of hard glass. The crown of the bulb has a light-diffusing finish, while the remainder has a double coating, first with a reflective material such as titanium dioxide and then with a phosphor such as magnesium fluorogermanate (Fig. 18.4). Such lamps are useful for industrial lighting, where accessibility for cleaning is difficult. Any dirt which collects on the reflective portion of the bulb does not impair the forward light through the crown. When clean however, approximately 20% of the total light output passes through the reflective coating. This can be used if desired for background illumination, or added to the forward light by the use of external reflective fittings.

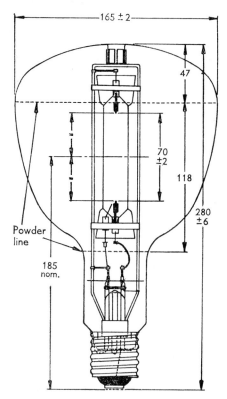

Fig. 18.4   400 W high-pressure lamp, with reflector bulb

The filament-ballasted range of lamps are of a size and shape which make them physically interchangeable with GLS lamps (e.g. the 250 W MBTF/U is interchangeable with a 300 W GLS lamp). An outline drawing of a typical 250 W rating is shown in Fig. 18.5.

Operation.   Designs are normally for operation on a.c. supplies between 200 V and 250 V. There are however 1 kW and 2 kW ratings available for 350/450 V supplies. Modern manufacturing methods no longer demand that lamps are graded for voltages within the range 200/250 V and for each wattage a 'universal' lamp is made. A series-choke ballast is required for current control. To meet national and international test requirements, all lamps are required to start at 180 V at 25 °C but a minimum of 200 V is required to ensure full run-up and stable operation. Run-up time to full light output is up to 5 minutes, by which time the voltage drop of the lamp approximates to 60% of the supply voltage. The exceptions to this method of

10+

operation are the 'blended-light' or filament-ballasted types which have a built-in ballast, comprising a tungsten filament in series with the arc tube. These lamps are graded according to the supply voltage. At starting, the filament carries approximately 90% of the load, the voltage drop of the arc tube being in the order of 20 V. As the mercury in the arc tube vaporises the pressure increases and the volt drop rises. When fully run up the light output is a mixture of that from the mercury discharge and that from the tungsten filament in the approximate ratio of 4 to 1.

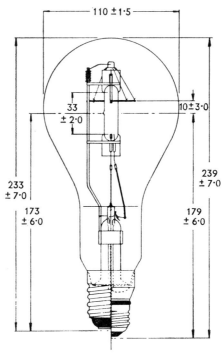

18.5   250 W filament-ballasted, high-pressure lamp

The electrical characteristics of high-pressure lamps can be found included in Appendix 1.

At sub-zero temperatures the striking-voltage level of mercury vapour lamps rises. By careful control of materials and processes, lamps can be made to perform satisfactorily on 200 V supplies, at minus 20 °C. Improved striking can be obtained by the inclusion of a second auxiliary electrode, a gain of between 10 V and 15 V being obtained at minus 20° C, or about 10 V at minus 30 °C. Once the lamp has been lit, the run-up is not seriously affected by low temperatures. Unlike the fluorescent tube, the high-pressure discharge does not depend upon wall temperature for its normal operating condition, and it is protected from draughts by its outer bulb. The lamps are not affected by vibration of the nature experienced on street-lighting columns, or industrial fittings unless this is accompanied by severe supply voltage fluctuations. High-pressure lamps do not give a very good performance on d.c. supplies, as a series resistance is required for current control, and overall efficiency is low. The striking voltage performance of the lamps is also adversely affected since the peak voltage of approximately 1·4 times the r.m.s. value on a.c. mains, is not available on d.c. A series-choke in addition to a resistor is desirable with d.c. operation, to avoid lamp extinction caused by transient changes in the arc, particularly during striking and run-up periods. On d.c. lamps also suffer from electrolytic migration of emissive material from the cathode.

Life. The lives of high-pressure lamps extend over several thousands of hours, but there are economic factors of installation maintenance which may make it worthwhile to replace lamps before they fail (See Chapter 30). The normal end of life is due to loss of emitter from the electrodes, leading to high striking voltage. The lost emitter is to be found in part as sputtered material on the walls of the arc tube. This reduces the light output and so there comes a time when the output may be below an acceptable level. Loss of emitter is accelerated by frequent switching, as the electrodes have most work to do at switch-on and during run-up. Quoted lives are usually based on a minimum of 5 hours continuous burning, per start. Severe under-running of a lamp can cause rapid loss of emitter, whilst severe overloading will raise arc-tube temperature and can cause the quartz arc tube to swell, or break down.

Light-output characteristics. The main lines of radiation from a high-pressure mercury discharge are in the visible green and yellow regions at 496·0 nm, 546·1 nm, 577·0 nm and 579·1 nm and ultraviolet at 365·0 nm and 253·7 nm. This gives a resultant colour which is predominant in yellow/green and deficient in red. Colour-corrected lamps having magnesium fluorogermanate coated bulbs can convert the ultraviolet 365·0 nm energy into visible red between 625·0 nm and 675·0 nm, giving a resultant white colour appearance and fairly good colour rendition. While not as good as fluorescent tubes in colour rendition the more compact size of the colour-corrected mercury lamp is well suited to many installation requirements.

The measurement of colour in 'colour-corrected' mercury vapour lamps is usually expressed in terms of 'red ratio' or 'percentage red' and is defined as the ratio or percentage of the total light output, which is transmitted by a suitably calibrated Wratten 25 filter.

Extra high-pressure lamps ('compact source')

General description. There are several sizes and wattage ratings of 'compact-source' mercury lamps ranging from 100 W upwards. Their design character-istics include (a) short arc length, (b) small spherical, or isothermal quartz arc tubes and (c) very high operating pressures generally above 20 atmo-spheres. Some are available as bare quartz lamps (i.e. they have no outer bulb); others are sealed into glass outer bulbs or are mounted inside metal boxes, with windows. Methods of operation vary, some types have an auxiliary electrode and start on mains voltage in the manner of high-pressure lamps. Others require assistance for starting, either from a voltage pulse, or a high-frequency probe. By inference these lamps have a limited and specialist application and they are mainly used in projection apparatus.

Electrodes of ME/D lamps are made of shaped, thoriated tungsten and may not have any emitter coating. This is necessary because the high-current loading together with the high operating pressure, causes the electrodes to run at a higher working temperature than the electrode of a high-pressure lamp.

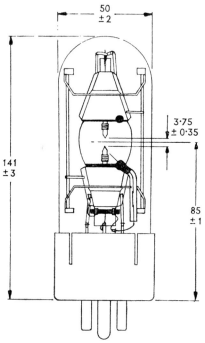

Fig. 18.6   250 W compact source extra high-pressure lamp, with glass outer bulb

A specific example of a popular compact-source design is the 250 W (ME/D) in a hard-glass envelope. This has an isothermal shaped, quartz arc tube with two main and one auxiliary electrodes. The arc gap is 3·75 mm and the arc voltage drop is in the range 60 V to 75 V. A filling gas of neon/argon mixture is introduced into the arc tube, the mixture providing an improvement in striking voltage compared with that obtainable from pure single gases. The neon/argon mixture also gives a quicker run-up time than argon alone, as it provides a higher voltage drop, per unit arc-length when the lamp is cold. The arc tube is supported inside the outer bulb by nickel and nickel-plated iron supports. The outer bulb is filled with nitrogen. A diagram of this lamp is shown in Fig. 18.6.

Operation. 250 W lamps provide a high-brightness source of 20,000 stilb and a horizontal candle-power in the order of 1400 cd. The 1 kW version has a brightness of 40,000 stilb with horizontal candle-power of some 6000 cd. The main spectral line radiations from the arc are at 315·0 nm, 365·0 nm, 404·6 nm, 435·8 nm, 546·1 nm and 579·0 nm but when the lamps have glass outer bulbs, or glass windows in the case of the metal-box types, the radiation below 350·0 nm is filtered out.

The lamps are designed to operate in a vertical position; a tilt of more than 10° from the vertical causes the arc to bow and convected currents of ionised gas can approach the walls of the arc tube with damaging effect. Some 10 to 15 minutes are required for full run-up. Should an interruption in supply cause the arc to extinguish, a delay of up to 15 minutes will occur while the lamp cools, re-strikes and reaches full brightness again. The rated average life of most compact-source lamps is 500 hours on a.c. operation, based on a minimum of 5 hours burning per start. On d.c. a longer life can be achieved for the same frequency of switching but an increased voltage is required for lamp starting.

Metal-iodide discharge lamps. In the high-pressure mercury vapour lamp a considerable portion of the cross-section of the arc tube is not effectively used to emit light. This non-productive space is required to reduce energy dissipation at the wall of the quartz arc tube to a value compatible with the long lamp life. If, however, another element of low excitation-potential can be introduced into the lamp, without interfering too much with the basic mercury discharge, then this element can be excited in the otherwise non-productive space. Its characteristic spectrum will be added to the mercury spectrum so improving colour, while the additional light output should contribute to improved lamp efficiency.

Unfortunately, some of the elements having suitable radiation character-istics also possess excitation levels similar to mercury and hence would make little contribution to better space utilisation in the arc tube. The use of these elements, for example thallium and indium, has to be carefully controlled in order to obtain colour and efficiency benefits, without detriment to the basic mercury discharge.

A further point which must be considered closely when designing for good colour and efficiency, is that one watt of electromagnetic radiation of 555·0 nm (in the yellow–green visible band) will give 680 lm, while one watt of radiation at 712·5 nm in the deep red visible band will give only one lumen of light. The proportioning of the radiation from elemental additions must therefore be designed to give an acceptable combination of colour and efficiency.

Only the excitation and radiation effects of elemental additives to a high-pressure mercury vapour discharge have been considered. When the practical question as to how other elements may be maintained in vapour form in the arc discharge tube is considered, it is found that while the maximum arc temperature of 6000 °K is adequate for the purpose, the minimum wall temperature (behind the electrodes) is inadequate for all desirable elements, except perhaps, the alkali metals. The alkali metals in practice would discolour and destroy the quartz of the arc tube by chemical attack in a very short time.

It has been established that the temperature problems arising from very low vapour pressures of many desirable elements may conveniently be overcome by introducing them in compound form, with iodine. Moreover when the alkali metal iodides are used chemical attack on the quartz can be eliminated. It has been established that in the iodide form large proportions of the elements of the periodic table may be successfully added to the high-pressure mercury discharge. Their visible spectra is thereby included in the light output of the lamp. Iodine itself, in moderate quantities in the arc tube has little or no effect on the characteristics of the basic discharge.

In order to obtain maximum benefit to colour and light-output efficiency, desirable iodides are included in the arc tube filling, in proportions determined by their vapour pressures and desired contribution to the total spectral radiation. During lamp operation the individual iodides exert partial vapour pressures within the arc tube. In regions of moderate temperature between the core of the arc and the walls the iodides will dissociate, liberating iodine and metal atoms. The iodine and metal elements will also have partial vapour pressures and will diffuse through the volume of the arc tube. When however, the metal atoms and iodine atoms meet in regions of the relatively cool walls of the arc tube they will again combine to form iodides and therefore, of particular significance in the case of the chemically active metal elements, there is no chemical attack on the quartz walls.

Design aspects. When iodides operate under saturated vapour conditions, their vapour pressure and hence their contribution to the light output will be a function of the temperature of the coldest spot on the lamp. Also, when iodides operate under super-heated conditions, their quantity inclusion in the arc tube determines their contribution to light output.

The temperature of the coldest region of iodide lamp arc tubes is therefore important and often requires special shaping of the arc tube behind the electrodes, sometimes accompanied by coating these areas to reduce heat loss. Horizontal operation also assists uniformity in temperature distribution over the tube ends.

With these special features mercury-iodide lamp arc-tubes are generally similar to those of the high-pressure mercury lamp from which they have been developed.

For maximum efficiencies it is necessary to choose those iodides which will radiate close to the peak of the visibility curve in the green–yellow region. This requirement can be met by iodides of thallium and sodium. It then becomes necessary to augment the radiation in the blue and red regions to improve colour balance; while there are a number of iodides which will do this, many of them present severe problems in handling, or are very costly. The final choice is therefore more limited; indium will provide ample blue radiation, while many of the rare earths, or others such as lithium, are rich in red radiation.

Operation and performance. As previously discussed, the arc tubes of high-pressure mercury lamps contain a low-pressure filling of argon gas, which forms a metastable mixture with mercury vapour at temperatures in the range -20 °C to $+30$ °C enabling the lamps to start satisfactorily from supply voltage of 200/250 V. In metal-iodide discharge lamps these conditions no longer apply and the necessary striking-voltage level is raised. There are alternative ways by which a suitable starting aid may be provided, by the inclusion of a starter-switch integral with the lamp, a starter-switch positioned across the choke ballast, or by the provision of a transformer winding to provide an adequate peak voltage. Once alight, the lamps run-up to give electrical characteristics interchangeable with those of high-pressure mercury lamps. Dependent on the choice of iodides, efficiencies in the order of 80 lm/W

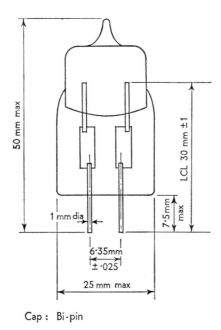

Cap : Bi-pin

Fig. 18.7   An experimental 400 W, compact-source, mercury-iodide lamp

combined with good colour characteristics can be obtained from a 400 W rating. At this time the life potential of the metal-iodide lamp is not fully determined but there seems no reason to expect that it will not achieve the same pattern as conventional high-pressure mercury vapour lamps as production experience increases.

It has been noted that metal-iodide inclusions to high-pressure mercury lamps can enable smaller or more highly-loaded arc tubes to be made. This prospect is of particular value in relation to optical systems used in general lighting fittings and in projection equipments. When considering projection applications the use of iodides now enables discharge lamps of very small dimensions to be used. For example, a design now in advanced development consists of a small, almost spherical quartz arc tube of approximately 16 mm diameter. Two plain tungsten electrodes are sealed parallel to each other, about 9 mm apart, through a conventional pinch assembly to form a single-ended lamp construction, which can be plugged into a simple two-pin holder. The lamp is operated base-downwards so that the arc between the electrodes is in the horizontal plane, with consequent benefit to iodide distribution in uniformity and stability. The lamp has a nominal rating of 400 W, an arc voltage drop of 80/100 V and a running current of 5 A. At rated watts an efficiency of 80 lm/W is achieved with a life of approximately 100 hours. Principal line spectra are at 417·2 nm, 403·3 nm, 535·0 nm, 546·1 nm, 589·0 nm, 589·6 nm and 670·8 nm with a considerable background continuum, due to band broadening at the high operating pressure developed. The design is illustrated in Fig. 18.7.

In common with all other discharge projector lamps a series ballast is required together with a type of high-voltage peak starting aid. Very high screen illumination intensities are obtained, accompanied by good properties of colour rendition.

CHAPTER 19

Compact-Source and Special Discharge Lamps

XENON LAMPS

Introduction. Two types of discharge can be broadly distinguished:

(1) in which the light is derived from excitation of the resonance radiation of the gas filling,
(2) in which the radiation is emitted primarily from a continuum.

Optimum conditions for the production of resonance line radiation are low specific power, low current density and low gas, or vapour pressure. These lead to relatively large sources of low brightness and the need to control operating temperature (and hence vapour pressure), if optimum output is to be maintained.

Optimum conditions for the production of radiation in a continuum are high specific power, high current density and high gas or vapour pressure leading to small, bright, highly loaded sources. The efficiency increases with specific loading and is not sharply dependent on operating temperature. Because of the high specific loading, operating temperatures are high and quartz is normally used in the construction. The rare gas xenon, having few strong lines in the visible region and heavy positive ions of low mobility, is one of the more suitable gases to use as a filling for such a light source.

Characteristics

General. Xenon lamps consist essentially of an arc burning between solid tungsten electrodes, in a pressure of pure xenon gas, contained in a quartz envelope. They may be designed to operate from a.c. or d.c., and be of compact or linear form. The arc of the compact source is a few millimetres in length, is electrode-stabilised, and is located at the centre of a relatively large quartz bulb of approximately spherical shape. The shape of the electrodes has a marked effect on the stability of the arc, and as 'pip-growth', leading to deformation of the electrodes, is more likely to occur with a fluctuating current, the lamps are usually designed to operate from smoothed d.c. supplies. Because of the short arc length the lamp voltage is low and the current is high. Substantial advantages in increased lamp voltage, luminous efficiency and, more particularly, arc brightness accrue from the higher specific power loading as the filling pressure within the bulb

10*

is increased. Cold-filling pressures up to 12 atmospheres are commonly used and as a result there is a potential hazard from explosive failure of the lamp. The arc of the compact-source xenon lamp is extremely bright and it is the only known source from which radiation approximating to sunlight in spectral power distribution, intensity and collimation can be obtained. It is used in projection apparatus.

The linear form of xenon lamp has a wall-stabilised arc contained within a long, tubular, quartz envelope. Electrode shape does not have a serious effect on arc stability and the lamps are usually designed to operate from a.c. supply. The longer arc length gives a higher voltage drop for a given power and the lamp current is correspondingly less. Limitations imposed by the maximum operating temperature of quartz restrict the specific power loading of the wall-stabilised arc and high filling pressures are not used. The lamp is of a simpler design than the compact-source form, assembly can be partially mechanised and hence it is somewhat less costly to produce. The specific power loading is considerably less than in the compact-source lamp and while the higher arc voltages imply a higher ratio of arc watts to electrode losses, similar luminous efficiencies can be achieved only in lamps of very much higher power ratings. The source size is too large for projection purposes but it is compact when compared with other linear sources of similar light output. The very high power ratings in which the lamp can be made can also be an

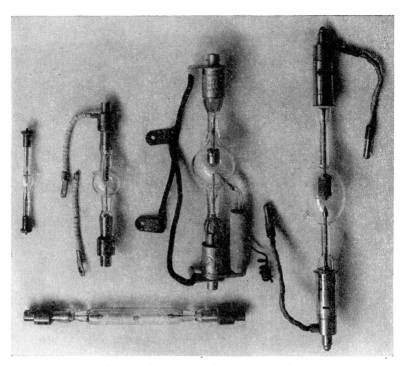

Fig. 19.1 Some xenon lamp constructions

TABLE 19.1

Some xenon lamp characteristics

Lamp description	150 W Compact source	500 W Compact source	2 kW Compact source	1 kW Linear	10 kW Linear
Lamp rating (W)	150	500	2000	1000	10,000
Supply voltage (V)	> 65 DC	> 65 DC	> 65 DC	240 AC	240 AC
Lamp voltage (V)	20	22	25	42	140
Lamp current (A)	7·5	23	80	25	75
Light output (lm)	3200	12,000	70,000	20,000	250,000
Luminous eff. (lm/W)	21	24	35	20	25
H.C.P. (cd)	320	1200	7500	2000	25,000
Centre arc luminance (cd/cm^2)	9000	8000	45,000	100	140
Arc length (mm)	2·5	5	5	100	750
Overall length (mm)	150	215	315	300	1150
Dia. (max) (mm)	20	40	65	25	35
Life (hours)	1000	1000	1000	1000	2000

TABLE 19.2

Spectral distribution data for xenon lamp radiation

Spectral band (nm)	Relative luminous flux in band	Relative radiant flux in band
280–310	0·00	7·9
310–340	0·00	11·5
340–370	0·00	16·3
370–400	0·00	20·8
400–430	0·09	23·8
430–460	0·96	25·9
460–490	4·23	31·2
490–520	12·3	25·0
520–550	24·3	25·4
550–580	27·2	27·4
580–610	19·5	27·5
610–640	8·88	24·4
640–670	2·33	22·3
670–700	0·37	24·7
700–730	0·04	24·8
730–760	0·00	28·5
760–790	0·00	25·5
790–820	0·00	26·6
820–850	0·00	63·3
850–880	0·00	27·0
880–910	0·00	78·0
910–940	0·00	52·5
940–970	0·00	39·4
970–1000	0·00	50·0

advantage and for requirements of area floodlighting with uncollimated light of sunlight quality, the linear lamp in a simple trough reflector has much to recommend it.

In both forms of the lamp, the permanent gas filling ensures that the full light output is available immediately at switch on; there is no 'run up' period as with mercury vapour lamps. A high-voltage high-frequency pulse starter is used to initiate the arc.

A photograph of a group of xenon lamps is given (Fig. 19.1); for convenience only the shortest of the linear range is included. Table 19.1 summarises the characteristics of a typical range of lamps. Spectral luminance distribution and spectral power distribution data are given in Table 19.2. A spectral power distribution graph is shown in Fig. 19.2. An arc brightness distribution map (Fig. 19.3) and candlepower distribution diagram (Fig. 19.4) for a

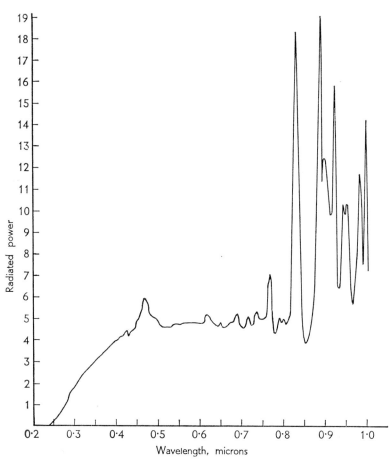

Fig. 19.2   Spectral power distribution of xenon lamp radiation

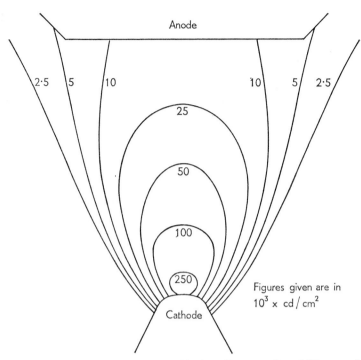

Fig. 19.3   Typical arc brightness distribution diagram of a 2 kW xenon lamp

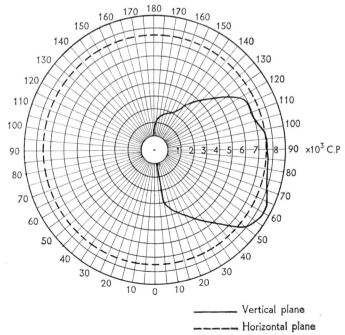

Fig. 19.4   Typical candle-power distribution diagram of a 2 kW xenon lamp

2 kW compact-source xenon lamp, are also illustrated. The information given is intended as a general guide. It should not be interpreted as a specification for any particular commercial design of lamp.

Comparison with other light sources. The xenon lamp is unique among light sources in that it gives radiation which in the visible spectrum is closely akin to sunlight. This is achieved at reasonably high luminous efficiencies (20 lm/W to 50 lm/W depending on the type) and at usefully high brightnesses. In compact-source lamps the usable areas of source are about one-half to one-third the brightness of the sun, and the point brightness of the cathode spot is very much brighter than the sun. It is this combination of good colour appearance and rendition, reasonable luminous efficiency and high brightness which makes the xenon lamp so potentially outstanding. A few comparisons will help to make this clear.

The tubular fluorescent lamp has a reasonable colour and a good efficiency but a very low brightness. Hence the light cannot easily be controlled and used in projection devices.

Incandescent lamps and filter combinations can have good colour and reasonable brightness. The luminous efficiency is poor.

The compact-source mercury lamp has a high brightness and a high luminous efficiency but the colour rendering is poor. In this case the instant availability of full light output is a further practical advantage of xenon lamps over mercury lamps.

In addition the xenon lamp radiates in the ultraviolet and infrared regions. It is the most powerful source of continuous ultraviolet radiation. Powerful, that is, in the sense that both the radiance and the total power radiated are high. Again a few examples may help to make this clear.

Hydrogen discharge lamps are more efficient radiators of ultraviolet continuum but the radiance and power ratings available are low.

The low-pressure mercury vapour lamp is a very efficient radiator of 253·7 nm wavelength radiation but again the radiance and total powers are low.

Medium and high-pressure mercury vapour lamps radiate ultraviolet with the same order of radiance and powers as xenon lamps but it is concentrated in bands rather than in a continuum. (This can be an advantage, of course, if the sole interest is in the band emitted by the mercury lamp.)

With regard to the infrared output, there is a pronounced peak in the near-infrared at about 900 nm. The continuum extends up to 3000 nm. For a given output in the visible region, there is about twice as much infrared in the radiation from a xenon lamp as in sunlight, and much of the excess is at about 900 nm. Here again, the high radiance is a factor very much in favour of xenon lamps when considered as a source of infrared. An electric fire (or a filament lamp) is a good efficient radiator of infrared but the radiance is low, as comparison of the size of a 2 kW bar element with the 5 mm to 6 mm gap of a 2 kW xenon lamp shows.

Serious disadvantages which have materially limited the more widespread use of xenon lamps are largely concerned with the cost and difficulty of operation. The cost per unit lamp is high, although it should be noted that the life is long compared with other projector sources and running costs are competitive. The cost of the control gear is high also, and it is bulky and heavy. Certain suitable precautions are necessary to safeguard against the high-voltage starter pulse, ultraviolet radiation and the explosion hazard* when using compact-source lamps.

Inasmuch as the current for a given power is lower, there is no explosion hazard, and a.c. operation is possible, the cheaper linear form is more convenient for general use. The high-unit powers needed to obtain comparable efficiency and the larger source size restrict its application. The control gear and high-frequency starter needed remain as serious drawbacks.

To summarise, the xenon lamp has some unique features; it is in many ways close to being the ideal light source and it is a powerful source of ultraviolet and infrared. It is however too expensive and inconvenient to use for general lighting applications.

Commercially available designs. Lamps are commercially available in ratings from 150 W to 2 kW in the compact-source form. Ratings up to 500 W can be made to operate from a.c., with a shorter life than the equivalent d.c. form. Above 500 W, a reasonable life can be achieved only on d.c. and the d.c. must be smooth, i.e. the ripple content must be less than 5% r.m.s.

5 kW, 10 kW and 20 kW compact-source xenon lamps have been described in the literature.

Linear xenon lamps have been made in sizes ranging from 1 kW to 300 kW. The higher ratings have been made largely for prestige reasons, 1 kW to 2 kW and 10 kW to 20 kW being the most popular sizes.

Applications

Cinema projectors. The major use of compact-source xenon lamps is in cinema projectors. The 2 kW size is mainly used and is satisfactory for the smaller cinema, seating 300 to 400.

Optical instruments and Colour Printers. The 250 W size is used as a source of continuum in monochromators and projection microscopes. The 500 W and 2 kW sizes are used in colour printers.

Lighthouses. Trinity House have employed a 2 kW compact-source lamp in a 'drum' lens, pulsed to obtain the flashing character and this is at present operating at Dungeness. 500 W and 2 kW continuously burning lamps in rotating optics are being considered. The small, concentrated source enables the enormously large, heavy and expensive lenses previously needed to produce narrow beams of high intensity, to be replaced by designs of a few inches in diameter. This offers the possibility of completely new concepts in

* The explosion hazard should be kept in proper perspective. The lamp is potentially dangerous and sensible precautions have to be taken in view of the damage which could result from an explosion. In practice failures of this nature are very rare.

lighthouse design to supersede the present costly, manned, land-based towers.

Fadeometers and colour-matching units. The close match with sunlight and the constancy of their spectral power distribution are major factors affecting the choice of xenon lamps for these applications. Linear lamps of 1 kW or 1·5 kW rating are usually used and occasionally linear (water-cooled) lamps of 6 kW rating.

Large-area lighting. Installations have been commissioned for the lighting of football fields, sports stadiums, etc., using linear, air-cooled lamps of 10 kW and 20 kW rating. The excellent colour rendering has drawn favourable comment, while the use of lamps of such high ratings reduces the number of lighting points, servicing and maintenance.

Other more specialised uses include solar simulators, arc-imaging furnaces, high-speed photography, infrared beacons and numerous specialised aids to scientific investigations.

ELECTRONIC FLASHTUBES

Introduction. The flashtube is a light source designed to convert stored electrical energy into an intense pulse of light, of comparatively short flash duration. It first gained commercial importance during the Second World War, when its application to aerial photography was appreciated. Subsequent development and experience has led to an enormous number of designs and it is now in widespread use throughout industry and science. Spectral output is similar to daylight in the visible region but the presence of high ultraviolet and infrared components extends the range of applications.

Applications. There are many differing operational requirements for flashtubes and a design of tube is tailored to meet perhaps only one of these modes of operation:

(1) High-energy dissipation applications. For aerial, studio photography or photochemical work.
(2) Medium energy dissipation, with reasonable short flash duration. For amateur and studio photography, general industrial and scientific uses.
(3) Short flash duration, in the microsecond region, for scientific applications.
(4) Short arc, high-loading tubes, for laser applications.
(5) Stroboscopic applications where the tubes work at low energy and high frequencies; used for the inspection of moving parts.

The following list of uses illustrates the diversity of applications:

Aerial photography	Laser stimulation
Studio　　,,	Marine beacons
Amateur　　,,	Airport　　,,
Underwater ,,	Signalling devices

Photochemical processes   Warning lights
Medical research   Stroboscopes
Graphic arts   Ignition timers
Photographic reproduction   Wheel balancers

Construction.   Flashtubes are used in pulse conditions and hence have to be designed with envelopes, electrodes and seals suitable for heavy loads of short duration.

To achieve a high light-output efficiency and a high level of luminous continuum, it is essential that the arc is constricted by the tube. The energy which must be dissipated on the tube wall thus dictates that the general form of flashtube has a long arc length. The tube may be formed into helical, spiral or U shape to give more compact dimensions but most tubes have considerable source size and are unsuited to projection applications. However, one form of tube is a compact-source and is thus very versatile. It may be operated as a continuous burning lamp, as a flashtube at medium energy, or as a high-power stroboscopic tube.

The tube dimensions and gas-filling pressure of a flashtube have considerable effect on the output parameters and consequently large varieties of shapes may be produced dependent on the nature of service involved. Fig. 19.5 gives some indication of the miscellany available.

Generally the lower-power tubes are of hard-glass construction but where source size is of importance, or very high loadings are required, quartz bodies are utilised. Electrodes are usually tungsten rods, or coils; the cathodes and occasionally anodes, having emission coatings. These are generally alkaline earth oxides, or other barium compounds and often getters of either pure barium, tantalum or zirconium are included. High-power tubes, where an emitter coating may be spluttered off, use thoriated-tungsten as electrode material.

The trigger connection usually takes the form of a wire (or a metallised strip) around the body of the tube which, in the based types is connected to a third pin. A third electrode is however, occasionally employed.

The filling gas is usually xenon. This is the rarest and most expensive of the rare gases but it has the highest luminous efficiency. It has also the longest deionisation time and in designs operating in the microsecond region, where flashtube duration is more important than high efficiency, the filling must be modified. This is done either by the addition of another gas to accelerate deionisation, such as hydrogen, or by the use of a different filling gas entirely. For example, one type with a flash duration of approximately 1 microsecond uses a mixture of argon–nitrogen as the filling gas.

Low-voltage tubes designed for the amateur market have fly leads, or integral pins to allow their use in flash heads where space and cost are of prime importance. Higher voltage tubes are often based and covered, to remove any possibility of accidental contact with the lethal voltages employed. Often a fourth pin is used in the base with an internal link, allowing equipment to be wired in such a way that these voltages cannot appear at the holder, until a tube is inserted.

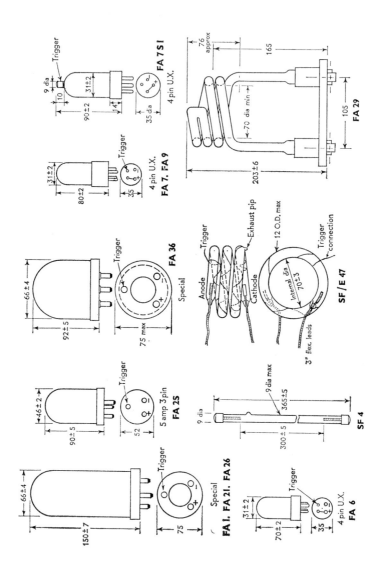

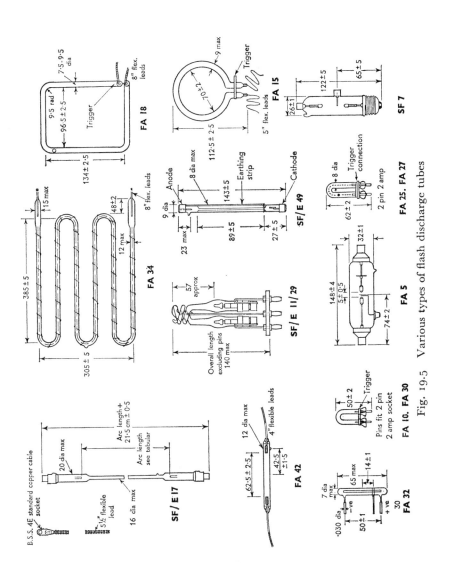

Fig. 19.5 Various types of flash discharge tubes

TABLE 19.3

Characteristics of a Typical Selection of Flashtubes

Type	Length excl. pins	Dia. of glass	Nominal operating voltage	Max. rating (joules)	Max. power (watts)	Min. trigger voltage	Max. flash rate at max. loading	Peak light output (mega-lumens)	Total light output (lumen seconds)	Flash duration (micro-seconds) 1/10 pk	1/2 pk	Base	Application
FA1	150 ± 7	66 ± 4	2500	1000	70	8	1 in 10 sec.	90	40,000	1250	600	3 pin special	Studio
FA2S	90 ± 5	46 ± 2	2000	—	36	8	300 per sec.	—	—	—	—	3 pin 5 amp.	Stroboscopic
FA5	148 ± 4 overall	32 max.	1000–2000	150*	250	12	1 in 10 sec.	2	1500	—	1000*	9 mm ferrules	Compact source
FA6	70 ± 2	31 ± 2	1000	100	7	4	1 in 10 sec.	19·2	4500	410†	180†	4 pin UX	General
FA7	80 ± 2	31 ± 2	2500	200	14	4	1 in 10 sec.	24·8	10,900	800	290	4 pin UX	Studio
FA7S1	90 ± 2	31 ± 2	2000	—	12	4	300 per sec.	—	—	—	—	4 pin UX	Stroboscopic
FA9	80 ± 2	31 ± 2	1000	200	14	4	1 in 10 sec.	10·2	10,500	2000†	770†	4 pin UX	General
FA10	50 ± 2 overall	8 max.	250	100	6	4	1 in 10 sec.	—	4000	2620†	865†	2 pin 2 amp.	Amateur
FA15	70 mm ID circle	—	1000	400	30	4	1 in 10 sec.	3·4	—	—	790†	Flex leads	Scientific
FA18	134 × 96·5 rect.	—	2500	500	40	8	1 in 10 sec.	—	—	—	—	Flex leads	Special
FA21	150 ± 7	66 ± 4	1000	1600	150	4	1 in 10 sec.	20·9	75,000	8000†	2400†	3 pin spec.	Studio
FA25	62 ± 2 overall	8 max.	1000	100	6	8	1 in 10 sec.	—	—	—	—	2 pin 2 amp.	General
FA26	150 ± 7	66 ± 4	2500	4000	300	4	1 in 10 sec.	—	4000	410†	180†	3 pin spec.	Studio
FA27	62 ± 2 overall	8 max.	500	100	6	4	1 in 10 sec.	10·0	—	700†	250†	2 pin 2 amp.	Studio
FA29	203 ± 6	—	2500	15,000*	‡	8	1 in 30 sec.	—	—	—	—	Special flange	Amateur
FA30	50 ± 2 overall	8 max.	500	—	3	8	50 per sec.	6·0	3000	800†	350†	2 pin 2 amp.	Stroboscopic
FA32	65 max.	7 max.	500	65	4	8	1 in 10 sec.	—	—	—	—	Nickel wires	Amateur
FA34	Grid 380 × 305	—	2500	12,000	‡	4	1 in 30 sec.	7·5	12,000	3000†	1100†	Flex leads	Graphic arts
FA36	92 ± 5	66 ± 4	1000	300	20	8	1 in 10 sec.	—	—	2000*	800*	3 pin special	Studio
FA42	62·5 ± 2·5 arc	11	500	500	50	8	1 in 10 sec.	32	16,000	800	350	Flex leads	Laser
SF4	365 ± 5	9 max.	2000	400	40	8	1 in 10 sec.	—	—	—	—	9 mm ferrules	Industrial
SF7	122 ± 5	26 ± 1	7500	56	‡	12	1 in 10 sec.	—	—	3	1	E27/30, 9 mm ferrules	Scientific
SF.E11/29	140 max.	—	8000	125	+	12	1 in 10 sec.	—	—	60	25	3 pin special	Scientific
SF.E17	300 ± 5 arc	14	4000	1200	100	12	1 in 10 sec.	—	—	—	—	End cap and leads	Scientific
SF.E17	1500 ± 5 arc	14	4000	10,000	800	8	1 in 10 sec.	—	—	—	—	End cap and leads	Scientific
SF.E47	70 mm ID spiral	—	2000	2000	150	Series Thyratron	1 in 10 sec.	—	—	—	—	Flex leads	General
SF.E49	143 ± 5	9 ± 0·5	2000	0·5	0·5	—	1 per sec.	—	—	—	—	9 mm ferrules	Stroboscopic

* Using series inductance.   † With electrolytic capacitors   ‡ Single flash only, other types may generally be operated up to 50 c/s at powers up to those stated.

Principle of operation. Fig. 19.6 shows the basic circuit for flashtube operation. The storage capacitor C, is charged through resistance R, to a

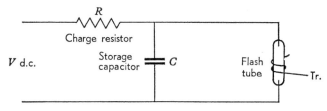

Fig. 19.6 Basic circuit for flashtube operation

d.c. voltage V, which is somewhat below the spontaneous breakdown voltage of the flashtube but above the minimum triggering voltage of the tube. Application of a high voltage pulse to the trigger connection causes the xenon in the tube to ionise, lowering the breakdown voltage. This results in a rapid discharge of the capacitor through the gas and produces an intense flash of light.

Energy dissipation. The amount of energy stored in the capacitor is given by

$$E = \tfrac{1}{2}CV^2$$

where E = energy, in joules (or watt seconds)

C = capacitance, in microfarads

V = operating voltage, in kilovolts.

The remaining energy after extinction of the flash is generally a small percentage only of the initial value and is neglected in loading calculations.

For single-flash operation the tube may be operated at loadings up to the *rated maximum energy per flash* (given in joules). This assumes the intervals between flashes to be of sufficient length to prevent overheating. Slight increases in loading per flash may be used, at the expense of tube life, in some applications. Alternatively the inclusion of a series choke allows higher loadings by reducing peak current. This will lengthen flash duration.

When the flash rate is such that overheating cannot be prevented the tube must be operated within its *mean power* limitations. The maximum allowable energy per flash is given by

$$P = En$$

where P = max. mean power rating (watts)

E = loading per flash (joules)

n = flash frequency (flashes/sec)

Effects of loading on life. The life of a flashtube is generally quoted for operation under single-flash conditions, at rated volts and energy. This is usually of the order of 5000 to 10,000 flashes. End of tube life is determined by either failure to operate, or when the light output falls to an unusable level. Failure to flash may be caused by loss of electrode emission, or contamination of the gas filling by slow leaks through the seal, or outgassing of the tube wall. Low light output may be due to discoloration from spluttering of electrode material or emitter on to the wall; vaporisation of the inner wall of the tube or contamination arising from these causes. Underrunning will give appreciably longer lives, for instance a tube rated at 100 joules operating at full loading may have a life of 5000 flashes, while at 20 joules loading it may exceed 1 million.

In single-flash operation radical overloading may result in the shattering of the tube. Less drastic overloading may lead to crazing, or cracking of arc tube or seals. In addition to weakening the tube, crazing of the inner surface releases absorbed gases from the glass modifying the operating characteristics, perhaps to the extent of making the tube difficult to trigger.

Overloading a tube by operating in excess of the given mean power rating will cause overheating and outgassing of the tube, and result in failure. However, some applications such as in high-speed photography where the total operation time of a burst of high-frequency flashes may only be seconds, take advantage of the thermal inertia to increase the loading, the burst being over before the heat has reached a level high enough to destroy the tube. Forced cooling also allows a degree of overloading.

Use of a high peak current will cause electrode melting. Molten material will be fused to the tube wall causing cracking, contamination, or conducting paths, often resulting in explosion within a few flashes. Seal failure may also occur due to cracking.

Operating Voltage. Flashtubes are generally designed to operate within a range of voltage to allow for fall-off in battery voltage and equipment design etc. BS 3205 specifies a tolerance of $+10\%$ to -20% from the nominal voltage. The flashtube itself gives operational limits somewhat wider than these tolerances, the maximum being the *hold-off voltage*, above which stray photons, or other radiation may trigger off the tube spasmodically. The lower limit is set by the *minimum striking voltage* below which the tube becomes erratic, or fails to fire. In practice this is not a fixed figure and depends on the ionisation produced by the trigger pulse (effectively the voltage and energy of the pulse).

A different method of control, widely used in high-frequency stroboscopes is that of 'overvolting'. Above a voltage called the *self-flashing voltage* the tube will flash spontaneously whenever the voltage is applied. This may be made use of by including a thyratron, or triggered spark-gap, in the discharge circuit and dispensing with the flashtube trigger (see Fig. 19.9). On switching the thyratron the capacitor discharges through valve and flashtube, some of the energy being lost in the valve. The high pulse currents involved often means that the valve is working outside the manufacturer's limits, but experience has proved these circuits and they are invaluable for high-speed stroboscopic work.

Triggering. Triggering is normally accomplished by applying a high-voltage pulse to a wire around the tube, or to a third electrode. It is generally obtained by discharge of a capacitor into the primary of a pulse transformer. Fig. 19.7 gives a typical circuit. The capacitor C_2 is charged from some

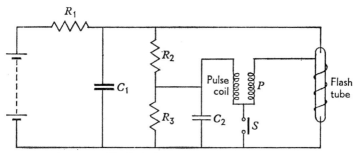

Fig. 19.7   Typical circuit for flashtube operation

convenient d.c. source, in this case derived from the voltage supplying the discharge capacitor, via the resistors R_1, R_2 and R_3. On closing switch S, which may be the camera contacts or a thyratron, this discharges into the pulse coil P. The high-voltage pulse produced is applied to the tube and ionises the gas when C_1 discharges into the tube. For reliable operation, trigger voltages of 4 kV to 16 kV are required, with trigger energy (given by $\frac{1}{2}C_2V^2$) in excess of 5 millijoules for the smaller tubes, increasing with tube size and operating voltage. Rise-time of the pulse is of importance, and coils with natural frequencies greater than 40 kc/s are preferred.

Triggering becomes more difficult in total darkness. Irradiation of the tube, or increase in trigger energy and voltage, ensures positive firing.

Circuit considerations. In Fig. 19.7, the charge resistor R_1 has two important functions. It limits the current drawn from the power supply and where a long recharge period is of no consequence, allows a high power output from a low current rated power supply. Secondly, it must limit this charge current, so that when capacitor C_1 has discharged, the flashtube can deionise and extinguish without 'burn on' occurring. 'Burn on' occurs when the voltage on C_1 rises above a critical value before deionisation takes place. This is of major importance in stroboscopic circuit design and for satisfactory operation the time constant of the circuit should be chosen, so that

$$\frac{1}{fRC} \simeq 4$$

where f = max. frequency (flashes/sec)
  R = charge resistance (ohms)
  C = capacitance (farads)

Some circuits circumvent this limitation by automatically disconnecting the capacitor from the charge circuit, for a short period after each flash.

Electrolytic capacitors are generally used for low voltage ($<$ 1000 V) tubes because of size and weight considerations. Paper capacitors have a lower internal impedance, giving rise to a shorter flash duration and consequently higher luminous efficiency.

The d.c. supply may be from any convenient source, e.g. batteries or rectified a.c. Trigger coils are generally air-cored, Tesla-type transformers, sometimes with isolated primaries. They are of low primary resistance to enable rapid discharge of the trigger capacitor. The coil should be located near to the tube to prevent h.f. losses in long leads. The voltage on the trigger capacitor is derived from any convenient d.c. source. For safety in photographic applications this is generally limited to a maximum of 150 V since this appears on the camera contacts; similarly, to prevent damage at the contacts the continuous current is restricted to 500 μA.

Like other discharge sources, flashtubes cannot be operated in parallel. Each requires its own discharge capacitor, charge resistor, and usually, for reliable operation, a trigger coil. They can be used in series, by a suitable increase in operating voltage and are then triggered by applying the trigger pulse, either to both tubes in the normal way, or to the common point.

For stroboscopic applications the triggering switch is usually a cold cathode valve of the 'Neostron' type, driven from a multi-vibrator circuit. For high-speed repetition rates (> 1000/sec) series control valves are normally used. Basic circuits are shown in Figs. 19.8 and 19.9.

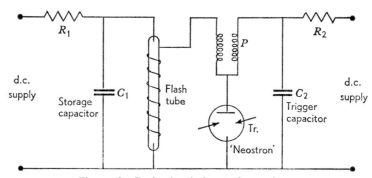

Fig. 19.8   Basic circuit for stroboscopic use

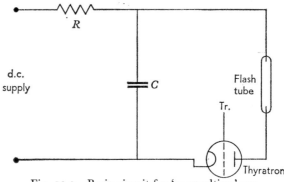

Fig. 19.9   Basic circuit for 'overvolting' use

Long-duration flashes. High-speed cameras of the optically compensated image type, require light pulses of duration from several milliseconds, to a few seconds and of very high intensity.

Two techniques are available. In the first, continuous-burning, compact-source lamps, either xenon or mercury vapour type are used and simmered at a low running current. They are momentarily raised to very high loadings, by shorting out a portion of the ballast

$$10 \text{ times rated max. watts for } 1 \text{ second}$$
$$20 \quad ,, \quad ,, \quad ,, \quad ,, \quad ,, \quad \tfrac{1}{2} \text{ second}$$

are typical figures.

Alternatively, standard flashtubes may be employed, by discharging a transmission line into the tube when a substantially square pulse may be obtained (Fig. 19.10). The energy in the flash is the same as that stored in

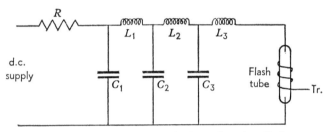

Fig. 19.10 Basic circuit for long duration flash

the individual capacitors and because the peak current is substantially reduced, overloading of the tube by 5 or 10 times its rated maximum may be possible.

Light output. Fig. 19.11 shows a time-intensity plot for a typical flashtube.

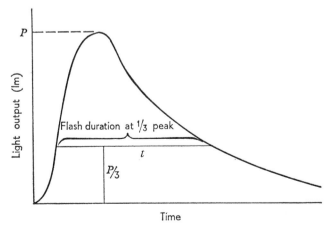

Fig. 19.11 Typical time-intensity curve for a flash discharge

The parameters usually quoted are *total light intensity*, which is the integrated area under the curve, given in lumen seconds (or sometimes HCPS, horizontal candle-power seconds), *peak lumens, P* and *flash duration, t.* Because of the long persistence of low-level illumination, the duration is quoted at some level such as $\frac{1}{2}$, $\frac{1}{3}$ or $\frac{1}{10}$ of the peak value. The approximate relationship between these values is given by:

$$\text{lumen seconds} = \text{peak lumens} \times \text{flash duration } (\tfrac{1}{3}\text{ pk})$$

1 HCPS is equivalent to 10 lumen seconds

The luminous efficiency (lm/W) is given by

$$\frac{\text{Light output (lm sec)}}{\text{energy/flash (W sec)}}$$

and for fully loaded tubes approximates to 40 lm/W.

Flash durations of xenon flash tubes range from 1 microsecond to approximately 10 milliseconds. For short durations in the microsecond region, short arc-gaps are required. The external resistance and the inductance of leads and capacitor must also be minimised. Operation at high voltage contributes to shortening of the flash duration.

Longer flash durations may be obtained by including an inductance in the discharge circuit. The duration is then given approximately by

$$t = \pi\sqrt{LC}$$

where L is in henries and C is in farads.

Since flash duration is roughly proportional to the capacitance for a given loading, small changes in flash duration may be accommodated by variation of operating voltage. However it should be borne in mind that maximum ratings are given for the nominal operating voltage. Shortening the duration will increase the peak current and have an adverse effect on life. This should particularly be remembered in 'overvolting' operations, where the peak current may be several orders higher, thus necessitating either considerable reduction in loading from stated peak values, or artificial lengthening of the flash.

Spectral output. Generally flashtubes have pure xenon as the filling gas, and at the high current densities involved, the characteristic broad continuum is produced giving almost daylight quality (see Fig. 19.12). Higher operating voltages will shift the spectrum towards the blue, and low energy or under-loaded tubes fall off more than usual in the red. At the ultraviolet end, the nature of the envelope, or cover, determines the cut-off, approximately 200 nm for bare quartz and 300 nm for glass tubes. In the infrared there are superimposed peaks in the 850 nm to 1,000 nm region and the radiation falls off at approximately 2000 nm. The colour temperature of a fully loaded tube is 6000 °K to 7500 °K, making it suitable for all photographic work.

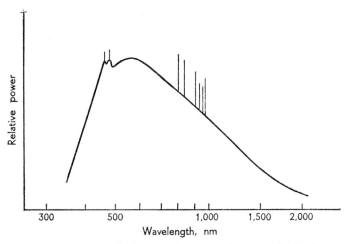

Fig. 19.12   Typical spectral output of a xenon flashtube

MINIATURE LOW-PRESSURE MERCURY DISCHARGE LAMPS

This class of mercury discharge lamp has been developed to meet a need for a small source of ultraviolet and visible radiation. It is generally useful where a mercury discharge source of small physical dimensions is required.

Construction.   Fig. 19.13 shows a typical lamp of this class. The stem and bulb are of soft glass and the arc occurs between two electrodes mounted on the nickel supports. In one design for mains voltage operation the electrodes

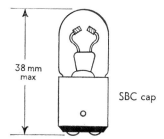

Fig. 19.13   Miniature mercury vapour discharge tube (Type M2)

are tungsten coils coated with an alkaline earth oxide emitter. Another design for low-voltage d.c. operation uses a nickel bar anode, the cathode being an emitter-coated filament, thus providing the extra emission needed in striking the arc at this low voltage. The gas filling consists of a low pressure of argon and excess mercury. The lamp operates at a low pressure of mercury vapour controlled by the bulb size and wattage loading. There is little 'run-up' associated with the lamp, conditions stabilising within a few seconds of initiation.

Operation. Fig. 19.14 shows the operating circuit for the low-voltage d.c. lamp. To initiate the arc switch S is closed, a current limited by R_2 flows

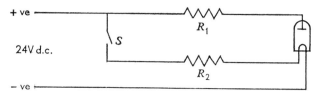

Fig. 19.14   Operating circuit for a low-voltage d.c. lamp

through the filament raising its temperature to about 900 °C. The emission produced strikes the arc between the filament and anode bar, the current flow being limited by R_1. Switch S may then be opened.

Fig. 19.15 shows the circuit for a mains operated lamp. In this case the

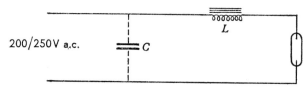

Fig. 19.15   Operating circuit for mains-voltage lamp

lamp current may be conveniently controlled by a choke L whose inductance is given by

$$\frac{1}{2\pi f} \left(\frac{\text{mains voltage}}{\text{arc current}} \right) \text{ henries}$$

where f is the mains frequency. The power factor of the circuit may be improved by including a capacitor C.

Alternatively, resistance control may be used, the value of the series resistance then being given by

$$\left(\frac{\text{mains voltage}}{\text{arc current}} \right) \text{ ohms}$$

Spectral energy distribution.   The spectral output of these sources is typical of a low-pressure mercury discharge and gives appreciable energy at 365 nm. Fig. 19.16 shows an approximate distribution.

Applications.   The original design of lamp was used as a means of exciting fluorescent detail on aircraft instrument panels at low levels of illumination. Subsequently it has found considerable use in technical colleges and other laboratories where a cheap and compact source of ultraviolet, or mercury-green is required. Other applications such as time markers in recording camera equipment, excitation of fluorescent materials, biological and entomological purposes have found favour.

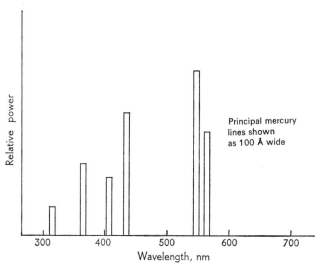

Fig. 19.16 Approximate spectral power distribution of type M lamp

Characteristics

	Type M1	*Type M2*
Arc wattage (at 0·75 A)	4·5	4·5
Operating voltage, V	24 V d.c.	200/250 V a.c.
Operating current, A	0·75	0·5–1·5
Heater current, A	0·8	—
Objective life, hours	200	200
Operation position	Any	Any

NEON LAMPS

Most discharge lamps use the positive column as the source of light. However, if the arc-gap is shortened it is found that the phenomena at the electrodes are unchanged and when the separation is such that the positive column disappears entirely, the light emanates from a glow discharge surrounding the cathode. The neon glow lamps make use of this effect. These lamps are used for many purposes such as indicator lamps and advertising signs. They differ mainly in the electrode form, the bulb shape being chosen to accommodate the dimensions used. For example, the familiar beehive indicator lamp uses the conventional pear-shaped lamp bulb while a sign lamp having a cathode in the form of the letters, say, OPEN would be in a tubular bulb. The electrodes are of pure iron and are unheated. Small quantities of argon are often included to lower the striking voltage. A resistance ballast is used to control the lamp, although the larger lamps tend to have this included inside the lamp cap.

TABLE 19.4

Characteristics of Neon Lamps

Miniature Neon indicators	Low brightness types				High brightness types			
	L1161, L1163 and L1165				L1162, L1164 and L1166			
	100/120 V a.c.	220/250 V a.c.	100/120 V d.c.	220/250 V d.c.	100/120 V a.c.	220/250 V a.c.	100/120 V d.c.	220/250 V d.c.
Nominal current (mA)	0·7	0·65	0·7	0·65	1·8	1·6	1·95	1·6
Striking voltage (min.)	47–55	48–56	68–83	75–87	67–95	67–95	90–130	95–130
Maintaining voltage	42–55	42–55	50–62	50–62	67–95	67–95	67–95	67–95
Extinguishing voltage	44–54	44–54	57–68	63–79	66–94	66–94	74–99	82–115
Min. life expectancy (hours)	10,000	10,000	10,000	10,000	5000	5000	5000	5000
Recommended series resistor (kΩ)	82	270	82	270	20	100	20	100
Max. power dissipated in resistor (W)	0·07	0·18	0·07	0·20	0·15	0·36	0·15	0·40

Beehive Neon

Operating voltage	200/260
Nominal wattage	5 W
Objective operating current	25 mA
Max. operating current	30 mA
Bulb diameter	60 mm
Cap	B.C. or E.S

Neon lamps using the positive column as the light source do exist however, the conventional 'neon lamps' used in advertising displays being of this type. For high efficiency, as high a proportion of the lamp voltage as possible must appear in the positive column. Lamps are therefore of long arc length and require a considerable operating voltage (several thousands of volts). Efficiencies are low (less than 5 lm/W) and this together with inconvenient dimensions and the high operating voltage, restricts the application to advertising signs.

Use of a hot cathode increases electrode emission and the associated decrease in cathode volt drop allows use at normal voltages. It also allows a greater current to be drawn from the cathode and results in a lamp of more reasonable proportions operating on normal electrical supplies and having an efficiency of 10–15 lm/W. One form of this lamp uses similar components to a 200 W linear sodium lamp but having a low pressure filling of neon, and it has found application as a flashing hazard beacon (reference Chapter 14).

CHAPTER 20

Fluorescent Lamps and their Operation

Hot-cathode fluorescent lamp design. A typical hot-cathode fluorescent lamp, shown diagrammatically in Fig. 20.1 consists of a glass tube filled with argon gas at a low pressure, and containing a drop of mercury. Tungsten wire electrodes coated with thermionic emitter are sealed into each end and the inner surface of the glass tube is coated with fluorescent powder.

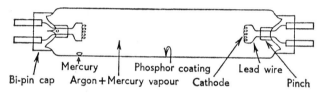

Bi-pin cap   Mercury   Phosphor coating   Lead wire
              Argon + Mercury vapour   Cathode   Pinch

Fig. 20.1   The construction of a fluorescent tube

The lamp is operated in conjunction with control gear which is necessary to heat the cathodes, provide sufficient voltage to start a discharge between them and limit the current through the lamp.

Electrons, emitted by the cathode, are accelerated by the voltage across the lamp and produce ionisation, which sustains the discharge, and excitation of the mercury atoms. Visible light is produced mainly by excitation of the phosphor by ultraviolet radiation from the mercury, but the contribution from the blue and green mercury lines has a significant effect on lamp colour.

The performance of a fluorescent lamp is mainly dependent on the dimensions, the power dissipated, the nature and quality of the fluorescent powder and the cathode design.

Maximum efficiency, i.e. lumens emitted per watt consumed by the lamp, is obtained with a lamp of about $1\frac{1}{2}$ in. diameter operating at a power loading of about 0·16 W per square inch of wall surface. The total lumen output, however, may be increased by raising the loading above the point of maximum efficiency, with a resultant reduction in the number of lamps, and therefore fittings, required for a given lighting level. The efficiency increases with lamp length, owing to the relative reduction in the effect of electrode power consumption, which is dependent only on emitter composition, cathode design and lamp current.

For practical reasons lamps longer than 8 ft are not made and for many purposes shorter lamps are preferred.

In addition to efficiency and total light output, many other factors must be considered in the design of fluorescent lamps and they have produced a large variety of lamps differing in length, diameter, shape, colour appearance, colour rendering, power dissipation and cathode construction. The factors which must be taken into account in lamp design are:

(1) Amount and quality of light required in relation to the purpose for which it is to be used.
(2) Type of electrical supply available.
(3) Convenience (and therefore cost) of manufacture, handling and stocking, including fittings.
(4) Overall cost of installation.
(5) Maintenance.
(6) Customer preference.

These facts often lead to demands which are mutually opposed and the resultant lamp design is a compromise. For obvious reasons, standardisation and considerable stability of design are essential, but both needs and performance are continually changing and therefore frequent re-assessment of design is necessary.

Fluorescent tube type classifications. The influence of the available supply voltage on tube design is considerable and largely accounts for the different trends in Britain and the U.S.A. Although the adoption of the 80 W tube in wartime Britain was influenced by the existence of a choke designed for use with 80 W high-pressure mercury lamps, the fact that nearly all supply voltages were in the range 200/250 V made possible the design of a tube of useful size and running voltage, which could operate with the simplest possible control gear. In the U.S.A., where the common supply voltages are 110/125 (an advantage with incandescent lamps), direct operation using a simple choke ballast is limited to tubes with voltages not exceeding 60, which give inadequate output and efficiency for general purposes. The 40 W tube, with a running voltage of about 108 V and controlled by an autotransformer ballast, giving a step-up to 220 V, was adopted as standard.

Fluorescent tubes may therefore be classified according to their operating voltages, for use on low- or high-voltage supplies. A third class consists of larger lamps requiring a step-up above the range of normal supply voltages.

Tube loading. Another important form of classification divides tubes according to their 'loading', i.e. the power dissipated per unit area of the tube surface, most types falling into either the 'low-loading' group ($0 \cdot 16 \text{W/in}^2$) or the 'high-loading' group ($0 \cdot 25 \text{ W/in}^2$).

The first group includes the 4 ft 40 W, 3 ft × 1½ in. diameter 30 W, the 2 ft 20 W, and the American 8 ft 1½ in. diameter instant-start (Slimline) tubes.

The 5 ft 80 W, 2 ft 40 W, 8 ft 125 W, and the miniature range come into the second group, but the 65 W and the 85 W types, introduced more recently, operate at intermediate loading.

11+

Advantages of low loading are maximum efficiency, lower brightness and better lumen maintenance throughout life, but the greater lumen output per foot of the high-loading types may result in a lower overall cost.

Fig. 20.2 shows how light output varies with current, wattage and length. This diagram is somewhat oversimplified because, in practice, different gas pressures are used for different lamp sizes, and the wattage lines, shown dotted, are slightly curved.

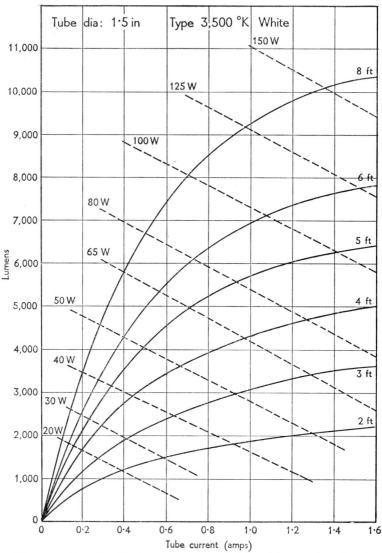

Fig. 20.2   Relationship between tube current and lumens (100 hour) for various tube lengths

Various attempts have been made to increase the loading by controlling the mercury vapour pressure artificially, i.e. by removing its dependence on the 'natural' tube wall temperature. The methods used include heat baffles to keep the ends cool, grooved tubing, external spot-cooling and the use of amalgams with reduced vapour pressure.

All of these methods have been partially successful, particularly for special applications but until lumen maintenance and overall economics compare favourably with standard types, they are unlikely to be more generally used.

Reflector tubes. The usual symmetrical distribution of light from a fluorescent tube can be altered by the inclusion of a reflecting layer between the glass and the phosphor. Finely divided titanium oxide is usually used, covering all except 135° of the circumference, most of the light emerging through this 'window'. These tubes are about 10% less efficient, but have a downward component which is about 1·6 times that of standard tubes.

A special form of reflector tube, has a 'window' of only 30°, from which the phosphor has also been removed and which has a luminance many times higher than any other fluorescent tube. This tube may be used with a special reflector to produce a narrow beam.

Factors affecting performance

Effect of temperature on light output. The performance of fluorescent lamps is strongly influenced by the mercury vapour pressure, which is normally determined by the temperature of the coolest part of the wall. Over the range of temperature usually encountered, the lamp voltage decreases with increasing temperature, and in a lagging circuit, the current increases, the lamp watts remaining fairly constant. In a leading circuit, changes in current are limited and the lamp watts therefore increase.

The light output and efficiency are critically dependent on mercury vapour pressure, reaching a maximum when the wall temperature is between 35°C and 40°C as shown in Fig. 20.3.

The wall temperature of a standard type of fluorescent lamp is determined

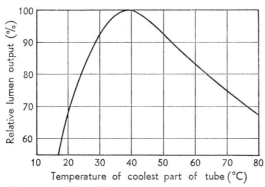

Fig. 20.3   Effect of temperature on lumen output

by its 'loading' or power dissipation per unit area of wall surface and the extent to which the heat generated by the lamp is removed. With a loading of 0·16 W/in² a lamp operating in draught free conditions, with ambient air temperature 25°C, will operate at maximum efficiency. If the lamp is placed in a slight wind or the temperature lowered, the light output will fall rapidly. If the lamp is enclosed or the temperature raised by other means the light output will fall off by about 1% per degree Centigrade. Lamps of 'low loading' fall off more rapidly with decreasing temperature and 'high-loaded' lamps with increasing temperature. It is therefore advantageous to use high-loaded lamps, totally enclosed, for low-temperature use. Where enclosed diffusers are used in normal or higher ambient temperatures, lamps of intermediate or of low loading usually give the best overall performance.

Light output and colour. Of the electrical energy used by a fluorescent lamp, between 10% and 30% is converted into visible light and the remainder into heat. The ratio of light to heat depends on the lamp loading, wall temperature, lamp current waveform, phosphor quality and electrode losses.

Of these factors, the first three are largely fixed by conditions outside the lamp, e.g. ballast and fittings design, and ambient temperature. The other two factors are within the lamp and are mainly responsible for any decline in light output occurring during the life of the lamp, although bad ballast design and high ambient temperature can accelerate the decline.

Lamp efficiency, expressed in lumens per watt, is determined by both the energy conversion efficiency of the lamp and the visual effectiveness of the emitted light, which is dependent on the eye sensitivity.

Thus, two lamps of equal energy conversion efficiencies may have very different efficiencies in lumens per watt. High efficiency types are relatively poor in red emission and this deficiency can be corrected at the expense of light output.

Colour appearance and colour rendering. By the use of different phosphors, either singly or mixed, and pigment filters, a very wide range of colours can be produced. This gives the fluorescent lamp an advantage over other types of light source, but by providing users with a choice of lamps, makes it necessary for them to understand more about colour and colour rendering.

Because all lamp manufacturers use the same type of phosphor for the high efficiency types of lamp (white, warm white, daylight) differences in colour are usually negligible. The eye, however, is very sensitive to small differences in colour, particularly when large areas are viewed, and to obtain the maximum uniformity, installations should be made of lamps from one manufacturer.

With 'de-luxe' lamp types, different makers use different mixtures of phosphors and lamps may have similar colour appearance but very different colour rendering properties. Reference should be made to the spectral power distributions, typical examples of which are shown in Figs. 20.4 and 20.5.

Lumen maintenance and life. The light output of an average fluorescent lamp falls by up to 5% during the first 100 hours of use and thereafter more slowly,

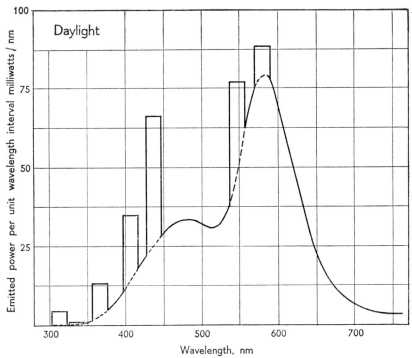

Fig. 20.4   Spectral power distribution—Daylight tube

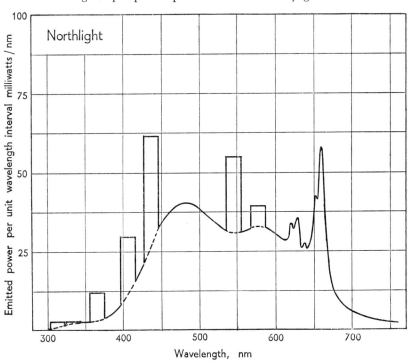

Fig. 20.5   Spectral power distribution—Northlight tube

as shown in Fig. 20.6 (typical lumen maintenance curve). The term 'lighting design lumens' has now been adopted, together with average factors relating the light output throughout life to this value, which corresponds closely to the average through the first 5000 hours of use. Lumen maintenance improves slightly as the lamp loading decreases and as the length increases. In general 'de-luxe' colours have somewhat worse lumen maintenance than 'standard' colours.

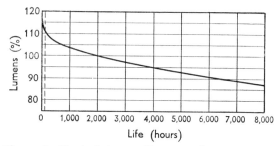

Fig. 20.6   Typical shape of lumen maintenance curve

The life of fluorescent lamps is affected by the conditions of use, particularly the type of ballast and the number of times the lamps are started. Standard conditions are defined in BS 1853 and are based on a 3-hour operating cycle on switch-start ballasts. More frequent switching shortens life and less frequent lengthens it, so that a lamp operating continuously will have a life 3 or 4 times longer than standard conditions allow.

Starting conditions, in particular those which make the lamp start before the cathodes become hot, e.g. inadequate preheat current, will shorten life. In addition to adverse starting conditions lamp life is reduced if the lamp current crest factor is increased by the ballast design above the usual value of 1·45 to 1·5. A crest factor (the ratio of peak to r.m.s. lamp current) of 2·0 reduces life to about half the normal value.

Cathode design.   A fluorescent lamp cathode consists of tungsten wire, coiled or braided, holding a quantity of emissive material. In a finished lamp, this 'emitter' consists of a mixture of barium, strontium, calcium and other oxides held in the tungsten coil or braid. The design must be such that the cathode temperature, under both starting and running conditions, is high enough to produce copious election emission but not so high that the rate of evaporation of barium is excessive. These conditions must be met for a variety of circuits and, in addition, the quantity of emitter must be kept as high as possible in order to obtain a long life.

Three types of coil are used, viz. 'coiled-coil', 'triple-coil' and 'braided', the two latter being developed to obtain longer life and to meet new circuit conditions (Fig. 207).

The coiled-coil consists of a single wire wound into a helix which is then wound again into a helix of larger diameter. The triple coil consists of two wires, one very fine which is wound loosely round the other and this composite 'wire' is coiled twice in the same way as a 'coiled-coil'. The braided cathode consists of eight wires, braided to form a tube which is then coiled once.

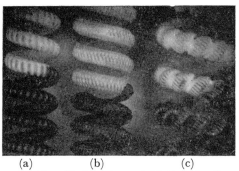

(a)   (b)   (c)
Fig. 20.7   Magnified sections of (a) Coiled-coil cathode
(b) Braided cathode (c) Triple-coil cathode

High- and low-resistance cathodes.   Fluorescent lamps were originally designed for use in 'switch-start' circuits, in which the preheat current through the cathodes was controlled by the choke. The cathodes were therefore made long with 'high resistance', in order to obtain long life. When circuits (quick-start, etc.) using transformers to 'preheat' the cathodes, were introduced in England, the transformers were designed to match the cathode, and connected across the lamp, so that the cathode voltage was reduced when the lamp struck. In the U.S.A. the standard voltage of 118 V necessitated the use of step-up transformers and it was convenient to put the cathode-heating windings on the same core, with the result that the cathode voltage was not reduced when the lamp struck. The 'low resistance' or $3\frac{1}{2}$ V cathode was introduced using the triple-coil construction to maintain adequate lamp life.

The present position is that in some countries, both high- and low-resistance cathodes are available in some sizes of lamp. These lamps are only interchangeable in circuits (e.g. switch-start and semi-resonant start) in which the cathode-heating current and not the voltage is controlled. In Britain, very few lamps with low-resistance cathodes are used, and the possibility of confusion exists only with 5 ft 65 W lamps. The position with this type can be summarised as follows:

5 ft 80 W tubes, with coiled-coil 10 volt cathodes
Can be used in all 80 W circuits (starter-switch and quick-start) and in 65 W circuits (starter-switch and resonant-start) but with slight loss of starting performance and reduced tube life on 65 W circuits.

5 ft 65/80 W tubes with braided 10 V cathodes
Can be used in all 65 W and 80 W circuits (starter-switch, quick-start and resonant-start) without loss of starting performance. Tube life may vary slightly according to the type of circuit but minimum life will be at least as good as with 80 W tubes operating in 80 W circuits.

5 ft 65 W tubes with triple- or coiled-coil 3½ V cathodes

Can be used in 65 W circuits (starter-switch and resonant-start) or 80 W starter-switch circuits without loss of starting performance and with normal tube life. Performance and life of gear and tube will suffer, however, in circuits designed with 10 volt cathode-heating windings (quick-start or instant-start circuits).

Starting and operating circuits. To obtain the best overall performance, the lamp and circuit should be designed so that the lamp is as large as possible and the control gear as small as possible. This result is usually obtained when the lamp operating voltage is roughly half the supply voltage on lagging circuits and two-thirds on leading circuits. Under these conditions the supply voltage is insufficient, by itself, to start the lamp. Additional assistance is required to initiate ionisation and a variety of circuits have been devised for this purpose.

Starter-switch circuits. The circuit in Fig. 20.8 is the simplest possible, containing only the lamp, choke and starter contacts, closure of which allows a current (of about 1·5 times the tube running current) to pass through the tube cathodes, heating them in about one second to thermionic emission temperature. When the starter contacts open, the energy stored in the choke

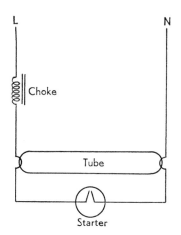

Fig. 20.8   Glow-starter circuit

causes a voltage pulse to be produced across the tube which then starts. Operation of the starter may be manual or automatic.

Manual Starters

These are normally of the push button type, often combined with the mains switch, and their usefulness is limited to hand lamps, desk lamps, lights on machines, etc., where the lamp is close at hand.

Automatic Starters

Glow starter. This consists of two electrodes sealed into a small glass bulb containing an inert gas or a mixture of inert gases. One, or in most cases both, of the electrodes are bimetallic (i.e. are made of two strips of metal, bonded together, which have different rates of expansion). The electrode dimensions and the gas pressure must be carefully controlled so that when the appropriate voltage is applied to the electrodes, which are separated by a fraction of a millimetre, the inert gas glows, generating heat at the electrodes which bend each toward the other. When they touch, 'preheat' current passes through the tube cathodes, the starter electrodes cool off and open and the tube receives its voltage pulse. If the tube fails to start, the process is repeated very rapidly until the tube starts, normally within 2 to 3 seconds from closure of the mains switch.

Glow starters are normally housed in a cylindrical metal canister, together with a small capacitor, which assists starting by increasing the duration of the voltage pulse and reduces the radio interference sometimes generated by fluorescent tubes.

With very few exceptions, glow starters are available for use with all types of tube on all normal supply voltages and, owing to their simplicity, low cost, versatility and robustness have practically ousted all other types.

Thermal starter. This type also depends for its action on the movement of bimetallic electrodes the heat being supplied by a small coil of wire located close to the electrode and connected as in Fig. 20.9. When the supply is

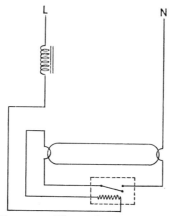

Fig. 20.9   Thermal-starter circuit

switched on the starter contacts are closed, current passes through the tube cathodes and heater, causing the contacts to open after a few seconds and the tube starts. The tube current passing through the heater holds open the starter contacts. The starter may be enclosed in a glass bulb containing a low pressure of hydrogen, or more usually now, just mounted in air within the metal canister.

11*

Disadvantages of the thermal type are that it is more complicated and therefore more costly than the glow type, it requires four connections instead of two and has resetting times of up to 20 or 30 seconds.

Being current-controlled, it cannot be used for tubes having different currents. One small advantage is that it can be used on a.c. or d.c. with the same type of tube.

Cut-out starter. In an installation where the fittings are not individually switched or are inaccessible, the continued blinking on-and-off by a failed tube can be very annoying and for this type of installation the use of cut-out starters is advocated. The thermal cut-out is contained with the glow starter in a normal canister and therefore standard glow starters can be replaced by the cut-out type without alteration to wiring, or holders. The internal connections are shown in Fig. 20.10, the cut-out disconnecting the glow bottle after about half a minute by means of a spring latch, which can be reset by a push-button after replacement of the tube.

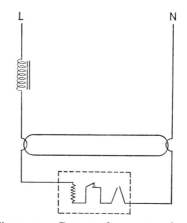

Fig. 20.10   Cut-out glow-starter circuit

Starterless circuits. Starter-switch circuits, for all their simplicity, have the disadvantage that they contain a replaceable component other than the tube. This complicates maintenance and fault finding where no skilled person is available to decide whether tube or starter is at fault. Consequently ways of eliminating the starter have been found.

Whatever method of starting is used, the tube cathodes have still to be heated to emission temperature and a sufficient voltage applied to the tube to initiate the discharge, the various circuits differing only in the way these essentials are produced. Treatment of the tube surface, to avoid the increase of starting voltage due to humidity, is essential with all these circuits. Coating with a water-repellent silicone is the usual method, but a conducting strip bonded to the tube is also effective.

The presence of a conductor connected to earth (or to the 'neutral end' of the tube through a suitable high impedance) considerably assists starting. It may be the fitting itself or a metal or metallised strip on the tube.

Quick-start circuit. This is shown in Fig. 20.11. The transformer has a much higher impedance than the choke (C) and thus almost all of the supply voltage is applied to it, across the tube. This may be sufficient to start the tube when the cathodes (heated by H_1 and H_2) reach emission temperature, but on voltages below 230 V, connection as in Fig. 20.12 is necessary and a further step-up is sometimes provided as in Fig. 20.13.

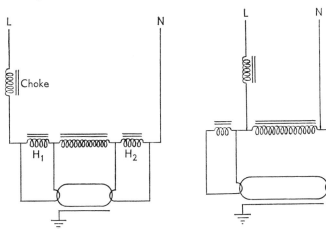

Fig. 20.11   Quick-start circuit for use on 230 V to 250 V a.c.

Fig. 20.12   Quick-start circuit, with step-up connections, for use on 200 V to 220 V a.c.

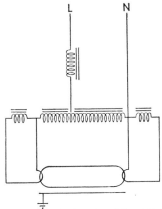

Fig. 20.13   Quick-start type of circuit, with additional step-up winding

When the tube starts, the cathode-heating voltage remains (at about one-half of the 'prestart' value) and helps to reduce the cathode fall. This, combined with the absence of high voltage pulses during starting, results in tube life being extended.

Resonant-start circuit. The 5 ft 65 W circuit is shown in Fig. 20.14 and the vector diagrams during starting and running are shown in Fig. 20.15. In operation, mains voltage is applied to the circuit and the 'prestart' current flows from the 'line' terminal through the primary winding (terminals 1 and

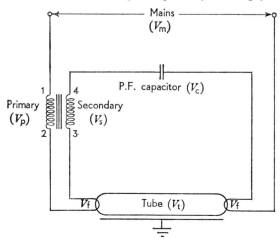

Fig. 20.14   Semi-resonant-start circuit

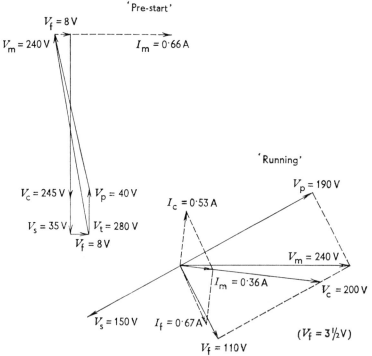

Fig. 20.15   Vector diagram for 65 W semi-resonant-start circuit

2) the left-hand tube cathode (2 to 3), the secondary winding (3 to 4), the power factor capacitor, and finally through the right-hand tube cathode back to the 'neutral' terminal.

The 'prestart' current (I_m) of 0·66 A quickly heats the cathode to emissive temperature and as the circuit is predominantly capacitive, the vector diagram shows that the prestart current is leading the mains voltage. Since the primary and secondary windings are connected in opposition, the primary voltage (V_p) is 180° out of phase with secondary voltage (V_s) so that the mains voltage (V_m) of 240 V is increased to about 280 V across the tube (V_t) by resonance effect, i.e. (V_s) becomes added to the capacitor voltage (V_c).

Once the tube arc is struck the primary winding behaves like a choke to stabilise the lamp current at 0·67 A. The secondary winding then increases the capacitor voltage to a value above the tube voltage, and the capacitor runs at almost normal mains voltage. Since the power factor capacitor and secondary winding are connected in parallel with the tube, the main current in the primary winding consists of two components, i.e. $I_m = I_c + I_t$.

The circuit is arranged so that during normal operation the current (I_m) is almost in phase with the mains voltage (V_m). Because the current (I_m) is non-sinusoidal, the overall power factor is about 0·92 lagging.

The robust braided cathode used in the 65/80 W tube has now enabled good tube life to be obtained with resonant-start circuits. This type of circuit was devised 20 years ago and has the following features:

(1) Starting voltage across a 5 ft tube can be increased to 270 V to 280 V giving reliable starting at temperatures down to −5°C, provided earthed metalwork is adjacent to the tube.

(2) A high power factor of at least 0·9 lagging is obtained with 5 ft tube circuits.

Current transformer circuit. Fig. 20.16 shows a circuit with a different type of cathode-heating transformer, which is particularly useful in two tube fittings.

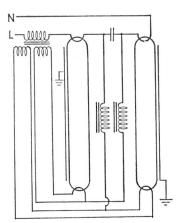

Fig. 20.16 A twin-tube current transformer circuit

A current transformer, connected in series with the power-factor correction capacitor, passes full preheat current, which is reduced when one tube starts. Even under difficult conditions, at least one tube starts very rapidly, and the other within a few seconds, but this type of transformer used in single tube circuits results in slow tube starting because only the reduced level of cathode heating can be provided.

'*Pulse-start*' *circuit.* This differs from the types already listed in that it uses the charging current of the power-factor correction capacitor to produce a high voltage pulse on closure of the mains switch. This produces a glow discharge in the tube, which changes to an arc discharge when the cathode-fall reached a sufficiently low value as the cathode temperature rises.

The usefulness of the circuit, shown in Fig. 20.17 is limited by the reduction of tube life caused by the application of the voltage pulse when the cathodes are cold and by the dependence of the size of the voltage pulse on the moment of switching.

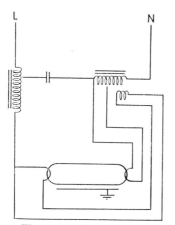
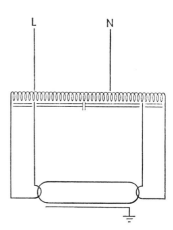

Fig. 20.17   Pulse-start circuit   Fig. 20.18   Rapid-start circuit

'*Rapid-start*' *circuit.* This circuit, shown in Fig. 20.18 is similar in principle to the 'quick-start' circuit, except that the cathode-heating windings are combined with a leaky-field autotransformer which provides ballasting for the tube and a step-up of the supply voltage for starting. No reduction of cathode heating occurs when the tube starts and special tubes with 3·5 V cathodes are used. No 'local arc' develops across the cathode during preheating and starting requires a higher voltage across the tube.

The use of this circuit is most appropriate where stepping-up of the supply voltage is already necessary, and it is widely used in the U.S.A. where the normal supply voltages are 110 V to 125 V.

American instant-start circuit. A leaky-field autotransformer provides a voltage which is sufficient to start the tube without cathode heating (Fig. 20.19), good tube life being obtained by the use of special triple-coil cathodes. The tubes, usually termed 'Slimline', have either single-pin caps, or the pins connected together.

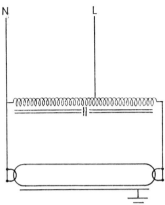

Fig. 20.19   American instant-start circuit for use with slimline lamps

Resistance-ballast circuits.   In either starter-switch, or quick-start type circuits it is possible to use a resistor, or an incandescent lamp instead of the choke. This gives a considerable reduction in weight at the expense of 150% increase in power consumption together with some reduction in life and light-output efficiency.

Starting is made much more difficult by the omission of the choke from a starter-switch circuit and starting aids must be provided as in startlerless circuits.

Capacitor ballasts.   At mains frequencies, capacitors alone are not suitable for ballasting discharge lamps owing to the very high peak current which causes noticeable flicker and short lamp life but in series with a choke they are satisfactory. Fig. 20.20 shows such a circuit which includes a starting compensator in series with the starter. It is now common practice to omit the compensator, which increases the preheat current to the normal (choke

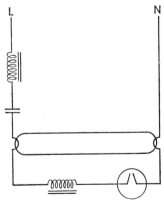

Fig. 20.20   Glow-starter circuit, with capacitor ballast and starting compensator

circuit) value. This omission may cause some reduction in tube life, owing to lower preheat current, but it avoids an undesirable complication.

'Lead-lag' circuits. In two tube fittings, the use of one choke-controlled circuit (in which the current lags the voltage by 60°) with one circuit of the type described in the previous section (current leads by 60°) results in a reduction of flicker and a power factor approaching unity.

A series capacitor may not be used in a simple quick-start circuit without risk of damage to the cathode-heating transformer. Failure of one tube cathode frequently results in the tube acting as a rectifier and the d.c. produced is blocked by the capacitor instead of being harmlessly fed back into the mains.

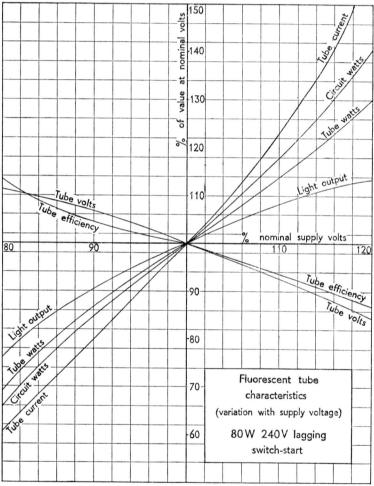

Fig. 20.21   Variation with supply voltage of 80 W fluorescent tube characteristics (240 V lagging switch-start circuit)

Lead-lag quick-start circuits which avoid this difficulty are however complicated and are not in general use.

Variation of tube characteristics with supply voltage. Figs. 20.21–24 show the way in which tube current, volts, watts, light output and efficiency vary with fluctuations in the supply voltage. It will be seen that the quick-start circuit has a greater range of stable operation than the switch-start circuit, and that the variations are smaller in the leading circuit owing to the presence of the capacitor. The latter effect allows the 8 ft 125 W tube to be operated from 230 V supplies in a series capacitor circuit, using a specially designed glow switch.

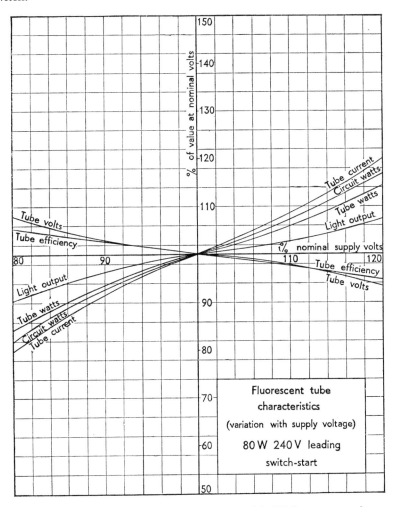

Fig. 20.22   Variation with supply voltage of 80 W fluorescent tube
characteristics (240 V leading switch-start circuit)

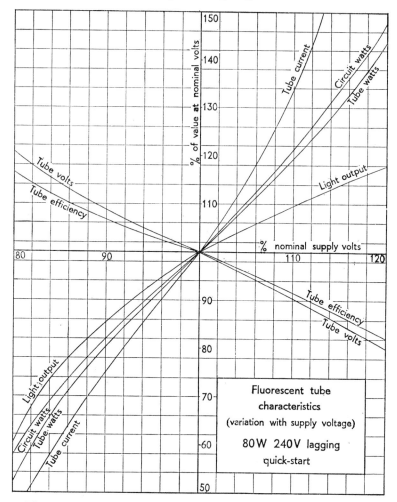

Fig. 20.23 Variation with supply voltage of 80 W fluorescent tube
characteristics (240 V lagging quick-start circuit)

Series operation of fluorescent tubes. Fluorescent tubes of the same rated current
may be run in series provided that the sum of the tube voltages does not exceed about 60% of the supply voltage. Fig. 20.25 shows the circuit for two
2 ft 20 W tubes, using one low voltage glow-starter across each tube. To
ensure rapid starting the glow-starters must be of symmetrical construction,
i.e. must have two electrodes of approximately equal area.

  The only modification required to the quick-start circuit is the provision
of two extra cathode-heating windings, as in Fig. 20.26.

  In both of these circuits the starting and running voltages are roughly
double those required for a single tube, but in the 'sequence-start' circuit

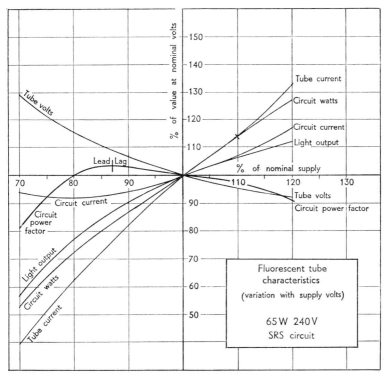

Fig. 20.24   Variation with supply voltage of 65 W fluorescent tube
characteristics (240 V SRS circuit)

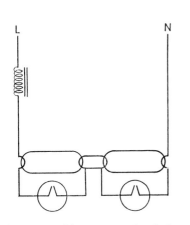

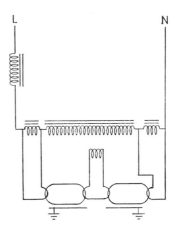

Fig. 20.25   Glow-starter circuit for   Fig. 20.26   Quick-start circuit for two
two tubes in series   tubes in series

(shown in a rapid-start version in Fig. 20.27), considerable reduction is made possible by making the tubes start one after the other.

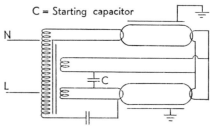

Fig. 20.27   Rapid-start circuit for two tubes starting in sequence

Operation on d.c. supplies.   Fluorescent tubes, although best suited for use on a.c. supplies, may be operated on d.c. in the circuit shown in Fig. 20.28. The choke is necessary, in addition to the resistance ballast, to provide the starting voltage pulse, and a glow switch designed for d.c. operation or a thermal switch must be used. Reversal of the supply polarity every eight hours, or so,

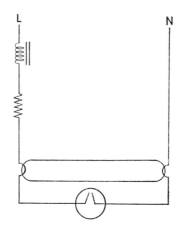

Fig. 20.28   Glow-starter circuit for d.c. operation

is necessary because the positively charged mercury ions drift towards the negative electrode, except with short tubes running hot in high ambients or enclosed fittings; or when the tubes are positioned vertically, with the negative electrode at the top. Special tubes with extra mercury added may also be used to increase the time before reversal of the supply polarity becomes necessary.

Operation on high-frequency supplies.   Considerable advantages in the performance of fluorescent lamps can be obtained by operation on frequencies higher than the normal 50 c/s or 60 c/s. Lamp efficiency gains of up to 20% can be obtained at frequencies of 10 Kc or higher. Ballast heating and noise can virtually be eliminated. Flicker, which at normal frequencies is sometimes noticeable at the tube ends under critical conditions of viewing, is completely eliminated.

The use of high frequency supplies has so far been limited to experimental installations and to transistor invertors operated from low voltage d.c. in trains, buses and caravans. With the further development of solid-state devices, the cost of generating power for fluorescent lighting is likely to come down to a level which will lead to a considerable extension of its use.

Dimming and flashing of fluorescent tubes. For ten years after the introduction of fluorescent tubes it was asserted that they could be dimmed only over a very limited range but soon after the introduction in 1947 of the quick-start circuit, efforts to extend the range of smooth dimming were successful.

The main requirement is that the cathode emission must be maintained whatever the discharge current and this is achieved by connecting the cathode heating transformer direct to the supply and controlling the discharge current independently.

Perfectly smooth dimming down to a current of a few microamperes is possible with a continuously variable impedance in series with the tube but this is neither necessary nor economically possible.

In practice, fixed resistors arranged on a stud-type selector are used for a small installation of one or two tubes and thyratron or SCR control for larger groups.

Dimming by reduction of the supply voltage is not possible, instability developing as the lamp voltage increases with decreasing current, shown in Fig. 20.29. The supply voltage must therefore be maintained at a value allowing an adequate margin over the tube voltage maximum.

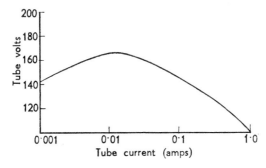

Fig. 20.29   Variation of 80 W tube voltage with tube current

In resistance-dimming circuits the tube current remains approximately sinusoidal throughout the range, but dimming by means of thyratrons results in the tube extinguishing for part of each half-cycle, the light output depending on the fraction of time for which current passes. Restriking of the tube may be ensured by the injection of voltage pulses.

Flashing of fluorescent tubes may readily be accomplished with the type of cathode-heating transformer used for dimming, flashing being produced by interruption of the discharge current circuit only. The substitution of an interruptor for the starter in a switch-start circuit will also cause flashing but the transformer operated circuit gives a better life (several million flashes).

CHAPTER 21

Electroluminescent Devices

The general principle of electroluminescence has been mentioned in an earlier chapter and many uses for this type of illuminant have been proposed. Electroluminescent lamps can be divided into two main groups depending on their mode of construction and called 'organic' and 'inorganic'. The former employ a layer of an organic material in which a zinc sulphide phosphor is embedded, while in the latter the same phosphor is held in a layer of vitreous enamel; in both cases the layer is sandwiched between two electrodes. These groups can be further sub-divided; the 'organic' construction into those in which the transparent front electrode is a piece of electrically conducting glass—the 'organic-on-glass' type—and those in which this glass is replaced by a transparent conducting plastic layer, the 'plastic lamp'. The 'inorganic' construction can be sub-divided into those employing a metal base plate to which the vitreous enamel layer adheres, and those in which the phosphor is embedded in a vitreous enamel layer applied to transparent conducting glass. Each of these four types of construction has its own particular merits under certain conditions and cannot necessarily be regarded as interchangeable with the other forms. The vitreous enamelled form fabricated on a metal base is the type which most readily lends itself to mass production techniques and so will be described first.

Preparation of 'ceramic' electroluminescent lamps. A diagrammatic representation of the coatings involved in the preparation of a 'ceramic' electroluminescent lamp is shown in Fig. 21.1.

After suitable surface preparation, a thin sheet of enamelling iron is coated with a layer of an enamel frit which is then fused to the plate. The function of this is three-fold; it must form a perfectly adherent layer to the iron plate and act as the grip coat for succeeding layers, it must have a high dielectric constant but a low electrical conductivity and it must be white and so act as a light reflector. This layer is only a few thousandths of an inch thick and must be uniform over the plate because any irregularities in thickness can cause differences in field strength and this in turn causes local irregularities in the appearance of the finished lamp.

The phosphor layer—about half as thick as the ground coat—is now applied to the coated plate. This layer consists of a mixture of the finely divided phosphor and enamel particles so that after heating it forms a

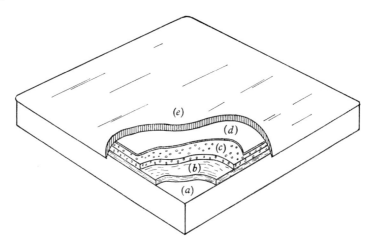

Fig. 21.1   Diagrammatic representation of the construction of a
'ceramic' electroluminescent lamp

(a) Metal plate   (d) Transparent conducting
(b) Ground coat   film
(c) Phosphor in ceramic layer   (e) Transparent overglaze

perfectly adherent layer to the ground coat. The properties of this film are
somewhat different from those of the ground coat. For example, the fusion
point should be lower so that during heating there will be no appreciable
tendency for the ground coat to soften and the uniformity of coating to alter.
Even more important, the phosphor bearing enamel must be free from any
harmful impurities which might affect the phosphor characteristics; in addition, this enamel must be non-conducting and transparent after firing. As
with the ground coat, this phosphor-enamel layer must be uniform in thickness, otherwise irregularities appear in the finished lamp as areas of different
brightness. The upper surface of this layer is made electrically conducting by
spraying while hot with a solution of a suitable metal salt. This forms a
conducting film with a resistance of not more than a few thousand ohms and
at the same time has a high degree of transparency. A narrow region of this
conducting film is removed from around all the edges of the plate in order to
insulate this film from the metal base. At this stage the plate will show electroluminescence, if an electric field is applied.

Finally, the plate is coated with another vitreous enamel which forms a
clear, protective glaze. This overglaze is fused at a lower temperature than
that used for any of the preceding treatments and must adhere uniformly
without affecting the conducting film. It must have highly insulating properties so that at least the front surface of the lamp is electrically safe, and its
application must not materially reduce the electroluminescent brightness. If
necessary, a further white, or tinted overglaze may be added to give an
improved appearance to the surface of the plate in daytime, but such an
additional overglaze will reduce the electroluminescent brightness.

A small area of the conducting film is not overglazed and is used for making one of the electrical contacts. Because this contact has to be made to the front surface of the lamp, it is usually at an edge where it is not obvious, or can be hidden by a frame or surround; otherwise some method of camouflage is necessary. A typical means of making electrical contact to a ceramic electroluminescent lamp, so that both leads are brought to the back of the panel, is shown in Fig. 21.2.

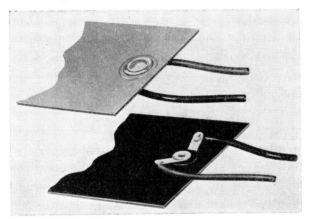

Fig. 21.2   Front and back view of the contact assembly on a 'ceramic' electroluminescent lamp

The 'ceramic' electroluminescent lamp can be made in a great variety of planar shapes, including circular and angular forms. The panel can have holes and slots in it but provision for these has to be made in the metal plate before processing and cannot be made in the finished lamp. However, as the cost of the panel is largely dependent upon its shape and the number of holes, it is advisable from the point of view of economy to use simple rectangular shapes wherever possible and standard sizes of rectangular 'Panelume' lamps are available, up to 10 in. × 8 in. The electroluminescent surface can be made to extend up to about 0·05 in. from any edge or hole, but if holes or slots are used for accommodating fixing bolts it is often unnecessary to have the luminous surface so close to the edge. As these factors influence the ultimate cost of the electroluminescent panel they have to be taken into consideration from the outset.

As a result of the multiple heating processes used in the construction of this type of panel, the metal back plate is subjected to various stresses, and consequently the finished lamp may be slightly bowed. For most applications this bowing is negligible but where a very flat illuminated surface is required, this can often be achieved by providing suitably positioned fixing holes in the panel, which enable it to be fastened on to another flat surface.

Preparation of 'organic' electroluminescent lamps.   In the construction of electroluminescent lamps using organic dielectric materials the phosphor and a light reflecting powder are held in organic resins on a glass sheet which has a conducting transparent film on one surface. This conducting surface is first coated with the phosphor layer, followed by a layer of barium titanate which serves to scatter light forward and to increase the overall dielectric constant, so that more power can be applied to the lamp. Finally, an electrode of either evaporated metal or conducting paint is applied to the back. This type of lamp requires careful sealing to prevent the entry of moisture as this can cause dielectric breakdown, hence the back is usually coated with paraffin wax and aluminium foil, or other moisture barriers. A comparison of this type of construction with a 'ceramic-on-glass' type of lamp (see later) is shown in Fig. 21.3.

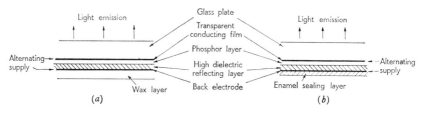

Fig. 21.3   Sections through (a) an 'organic on glass' and
(b) a 'ceramic on glass' electroluminescent lamp

Light is only emitted from those areas of an electroluminescent layer where the phosphor is subjected to an alternating electric field, i.e. where actually sandwiched between two electrodes. Consequently, the back electrode can be shaped so that light is only emitted over this area when the panel is switched on. In this way panels can be made which display an illuminated legend, or pattern, when operated, but the legend is completely invisible when the supply is off and the whole panel then appears blank. This property of the 'organic-on-glass' construction is difficult to achieve with the 'ceramic-on-metal' type of lamp, because in the latter case any limitations of the luminous area have to be achieved by restricting the area of the transparent front electrode.

Other types of electroluminescent lamps. The 'ceramic-on-glass' lamp is similar to the 'organic-on-glass' construction, except that the component layers are vitreous enamels instead of organic resins and so this type of panel has a higher resistance to moisture than the 'organic-on-glass' lamp. However, because the front conducting glass sheet is used as the structural member on which to fabricate the subsequent layers of the sandwich and the phosphor layer is therefore subjected to several heating processes before the construction is completed, this form of lamp is often less bright than either of the other forms described.

The most recently developed electroluminescent lamp is of a plastic construction. In this, the component layers are held in organic resins and the front conducting electrode is a transparent, flexible layer of a conducting plastics material, or a very thin conducting glass tissue strengthened by heat-sealing to a piece of transparent plastic. The back electrode is usually a thin aluminium foil and the whole construction after encapsulation in another transparent plastic envelope, gives a semi-flexible construction of light weight. A section through a plastic lamp to show the component layers is represented diagrammatically in Fig. 21.4. These 'plastic' lamps are available in strips about $1\frac{1}{2}$ in. wide in lengths up to about 100 ft, under the name of 'Tapelite'. Plastic lamps of this type can also be prepared in other shapes and sizes.

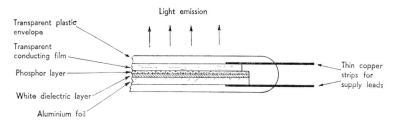

Transparent plastic envelope

Transparent conducting film

Phosphor layer

White dielectric layer

Aluminium foil

Light emission

Thin copper strips for supply leads

Fig. 21.4   Diagrammatic representation of a section through a plastic electroluminescent lamp (not to scale; thickness normally about 0·03 in.)

Electroluminescent materials.   A number of substances such as gallium phosphide, boron nitride, and certain forms of silicon carbide, show electroluminescence, but only the zinc sulphide phosphors are of any present importance. Electroluminescent zinc sulphides are prepared by heating a mixture of pure precipitated zinc sulphide with copper compounds and suitable fluxes, to temperatures of the order of 1000°C in a non-oxidising atmosphere. When the product is cool, it is washed, for example with solutions of acetic acid to remove zinc oxide and with sodium cyanide to remove excess of copper compounds; after drying it is a soft buff-coloured powder. The electroluminescent properties depend on the proportions of copper and halide ions incorporated in the zinc sulphide matrix; phosphors which emit in the green contain slightly more copper and appreciably more halide ions than those which emit in the blue, under similar conditions of excitation. If about 1% of a manganese compound is present in the mixture during the phosphor preparation, a yellow electroluminescent material results. The copper concentrations used in electroluminescent sulphides are several times greater than in zinc sulphides prepared for excitation by ultraviolet, or cathode rays. As in the preparation of other phosphors, very pure starting materials are necessary and careful control of the heating process is essential in order to obtain the brightest phosphors.

The colour of the emission from an electroluminescent source depends to some extent on the frequency at a given voltage. For example, green lamps usually show a shift in emission towards the blue at high frequencies. The spectral power distribution curves for 'ceramic' lamps operating at 1000 c/s are shown in Fig. 21.5.

A few electroluminescent materials emitting in the red have been found, but these materials are not of comparable brightness under the same conditions of excitation as the conventional blue, green and yellow materials. Consequently the only phosphors which have sufficient brightness for commercial applications are these three; intermediate colours including a near-white, result from mixtures. A more satisfactory manner by which other colours, including whites and reds can be obtained, is by using the cascade excitation of certain

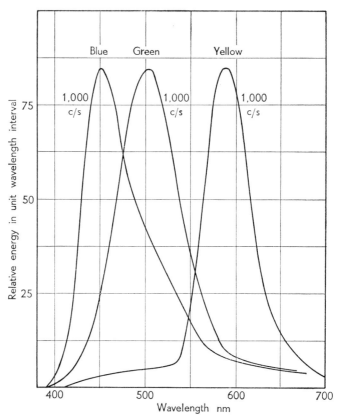

Fig. 21.5   Spectral distribution curves of 'ceramic' lamps operating at 1000 c/s

organic fluorescent paints, applied to the surface of a green electroluminescent plate.

The same phosphors are used in all types of electroluminescent lamps and the designation—'ceramic', 'organic', 'plastic', etc.—refers only to the medium in which the phosphor is held and not to the nature of the phosphor itself.

General characteristics of electroluminescent lamps. The brightness as well as the colour, of an electroluminescent light source is dependent on both the applied voltage and frequency. At a given voltage, the brightness increases with rising frequency up to several thousand cycles per second before decreasing, due to electrical losses which occur in the plate at higher frequencies. The effects of both applied voltage and frequency on the light output from a 'ceramic' lamp are shown in the curves of Fig. 21.6.

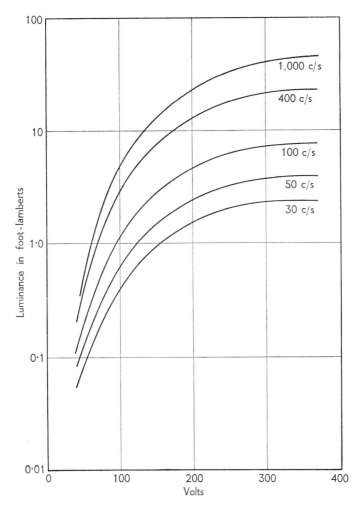

Fig. 21.6   Effect of frequency and voltage on the light output of a
green 'ceramic' lamp

The light output from these lamps usually increases during the early hours of operation and then slowly decreases in intensity over many thousands of hours. The initial surface brightness of a green ceramic lamp, operating from a 240 V 50 c/s supply is about 3 ft L and the panel takes about 0·6 mA/in², while the 'organic-on-glass' type of lamp operating at 350 V 400 c/s has a surface brightness of about 25 ft L and the panel takes about 1 mA/in². Each type of lamp may be easily and smoothly dimmed to extinction by varying the applied voltage with a small variable resistance. They each operate instantly upon application of the required potential.

Uses of 'ceramic' electroluminescent lamps. Ceramic electroluminescent lamps provide a means of illuminating a surface at a low uniform brightness and are especially suited to those circumstances where the spatial requirements of the lighting system must be kept to a minimum. In addition, their long life and robust nature make them eminently suitable for installations where little, or no maintenance is necessary; as, for example, in illuminated electric clock faces, light switch surrounds, self-luminous instrument dials and so on. In such applications, the power consumption is negligible and the thin planar nature of the light source does not involve any outward changes in the shape of the article.

Among the many other applications are cine-projector control panels, map readers (especially for aircraft navigational devices), radio tuning-scales, exit signs, markers for stair risers, dark room safe-lights, printing aids and so on. Electroluminescent lighting of the instruments and controls of motor vehicles is made possible by using a relatively cheap transistor-oscillator to provide an alternating supply from a car battery and car dashboards of this type have been used for some years in the U.S.A.

Another interesting application of electroluminescence is for lighting the instrument panels in aircraft and a diagrammatic indication of how this is achieved is shown in Fig. 21.7. The light from the electroluminescent panels is virtually 'piped' through a clear transparent plastic, the external surface of which is opaque; light emerges only where the exterior of the panel has been

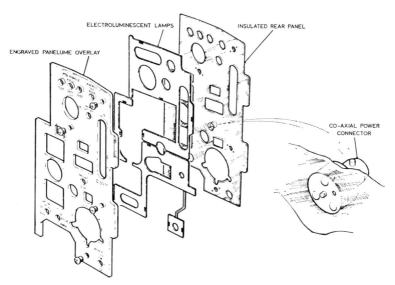

ELECTROLUMINESCENT LAMPS

INSULATED REAR PANEL

ENGRAVED PANELUME OVERLAY

CO-AXIAL POWER CONNECTOR

Fig. 21.7   Exploded view of a section of an aircraft instrument panel
illuminated by electroluminescent lamps by the 'Plasteck' system

engraved through the opaque layer into the transparent layer and so markings on the control panel become illuminated. In constructions of this type the long life and reliability requirements can only satisfactorily be met by using the ceramic type of lamp.

All these applications, although involving potentially large numbers of lamps, are for relatively small sized panels. Larger electroluminescent lamps have been used for road signs in the U.S.A. and signs of the blue and white variety for the new British motorways are a possible development. Similarly, as the brightness and weather resistance of the panels is improved so it becomes increasingly likely that there will be a demand for large decorative panels for architectural features and even buildings clad with exterior panels which are luminous at night become feasible.

Uses of 'organic' electroluminescent lamps. Although 'ceramic' electroluminescent lamps can be made in a great variety of different shapes, with the 'organic-on-glass' structure it is obviously desirable to keep to simple shapes such as rectangles, or discs, in order to avoid complicated glass cutting. However, as described earlier, by shaping the back electrode into letters or symbols, almost any legend can be displayed by the organic type of lamp. Outstanding features of signs of this type are that they have a low power consumption, the legend is invisible when the lamp is off, they are light in weight and occupy little space. Consequently, such panels find wide use in aircraft for the 'No Smoking' and 'Fasten Seat Belts' type of sign, especially as the available supply frequency of 400 c/s gives adequate brightness even for daytime viewing.

Electroluminescent indicator panels can be constructed to replace assemblies of indicator lamps for switchboards. A typical unit is a 3 in. square plate less than 0·25 in. thick and providing over 100 quarter-inch squares, each of which can be individually illuminated. Each individual quarter-inch square lamp, consumes only about 50 μA and can have a superimposed marking to indicate a letter, or number.

Another device is a modified type of panel in which the front electrode is divided into strips and the back electrode is similarly divided but at right angles to the front. When a voltage is applied between one of the front and one of the back strips, the area of intersection lights up, with the two cross-arms less luminous. Such a panel has inherent stability of co-ordinates and so has applications for long-persistence displays. Resolution is limited by the width of the electrode strips and although 100 lines per inch can be achieved there are difficulties in making the individual contacts.

Many instruments use digital read-out systems and electroluminescent digital indicators can be constructed which have the advantage, over some other types of similar device, of a wider viewing angle. The lamp itself is made of a number of separate strips and various combinations of these are illuminated to give the digits 0 to 9, in a slightly stylised but quite readable form, Fig. 21.8.

Since the 'organic' type of electroluminescent lamp does not lend itself so readily to mass production techniques as the 'ceramic' type it is usually more

342 *Lamps and Lighting*

expensive, especially as any shaping, or lettering of the back electrode which may be required is usually a skilled hand operation. The applications for which the 'organic' lamps are most suitable—legends, indicators, etc., often need to be of high brightness, so that they are usually operated at a frequency of 400 c/s and this must be considered when their use is contemplated.

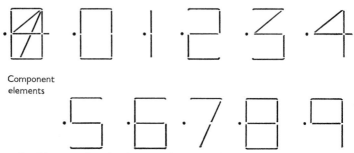

Component elements

Fig. 21.8   Elements involved in an electroluminescent digital indicator and the slightly stylised digits 0 to 9 which result

The plastic 'Tape-lite' is still a relatively recent development in electro-luminescence and consequently its applications are as yet largely unexplored. Various suggested uses are for mimic diagrams, and because of its availability in long lengths (100 ft or more), for luminous markings of both a permanent and temporary nature. For example, as an emergency light source along the passenger gangway of aircraft and also as a temporary diversion sign for motorway use. Another application is for luminous markings for personnel engaged in hazardous situations, such as police on traffic control duty at night. This latter type of use is possible because of the light weight and flexible character of Tape-lite and because it can be operated from a transistor driven by small, rechargeable batteries.

Photoconductive electroluminescent devices. An electroluminescent lamp is particularly suited to control by photoconductive cells of, say, cadmium sulphide and devices of this type fabricated on conducting glass, are of considerable interest. The simplest form of such a device consists of an electroluminescent plate and a photoconductive cell electrically in series one with the other. When radiation falls on the photoconductive cell, it becomes conducting so that voltage is applied to the lamp, causing it to emit light. Cadmium sulphide photoconductive cells are mainly responsive to the red end of the visible spectrum, infrared, X and γ rays and corpuscular energy such as α and β rays. The photoconductive cell can be remote from the electro-luminescent lamp and so the system can be used as a radiation detector, or warning device.

When an electroluminescent lamp, in series with a photoconductive cell, is arranged so that any light from the lamp will fall on the photoconductor and volts are applied in the dark, no light is emitted because the photocon-ductor is in a non-conducting state. If now the photoconductor is irradiated with light it becomes conducting, the electroluminescent lamp emits light and this will keep the photoconductor in a conducting state; the lamp will stay luminous until the supply voltage is interrupted, when it will return to the dark state. Such a device has been termed an *optron*, and is a type of information-storage device. The triggering pulses and decay times of an optron are of the order of a tenth of a second.

Another application of photoconductor-electroluminescent devices is for image conversion and intensification. In an intensifier, a weak light image is projected on to the back of the panel and a much brighter image is seen on the front, the extra energy required being drawn from the electrical supply to the plate. In a converter, the incident image may be formed, for example, by infrared, or X-rays and a typical construction may consist of a conventional electroluminescent lamp but with a layer of photoconductor between the reflecting layer and the back electrode (Fig. 21.9). X-ray image converters

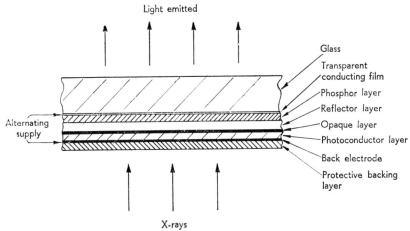

Fig. 21.9   Diagrammatic representation of the construction of an
X-ray image converter

of this type show a brightness gain over a conventional fluorescent screen at X-ray dose rates of about 0·5 roentgen per minute. The use of these panels is limited to stationary objects but, even so, is of potential interest to the medical profession.

Image-retaining panels. A recent development is the *image retaining panel*. This resembles a conventional, ceramic-on-metal electroluminescent panel in construction and finished appearance, but operates from a d.c. potential of about 100 V. When energised in this way in the dark, no luminescence occurs until the panel is exposed to some form of radiant energy. Then, provided the d.c. potential is maintained, the panel emits a yellow glow over that region of its surface which was irradiated. However, if the d.c. potential is removed, the glow on the surface disappears and after a few seconds, if the d.c. is re-applied, the panel is again available for exposure to radiant energy.

12 +

When a panel of this type is irradiated with light, an image of any opaque object placed between the panel and the light source remains as a glowing negative on the surface after the light source has been removed. This image will remain on the panel for upwards of 30 minutes, or until the d.c. potential is switched off. An interesting application for panels of this type is for the detection of the red and near infrared emission from lasers. During the setting up of a laser, panels can be used immediately to locate the emission from such a laser without recourse to photography. These panels have integrating properties for low-intensity electron beams and in certain cases can be used in electron microscopy where the panel functions as the screen on which appears the image of the specimen under examination.

Perhaps the most interesting possibility for panels of this type is for use with X-rays. As the image formed by X-rays can be controlled by the applied d.c. potential, the image can be studied after the source of X-rays has been removed. These panels perform many of the functions of a photographic plate without the need for a photographic development process and can be reused many thousands of times. In the field of industrial non-destructive testing by X-rays a very high resolution (about 1000 lines per inch) is required and the present picture quality of the image retaining panel is not yet up to this standard. However, it is already adequate for a number of diagnostic applications in the medical X-ray field, although here the X-ray dose required is still too high for approval by the medical authorities. An example of the application of an image retaining panel is shown in Fig. 21.10. With further development either, or both the picture quality and sensitivity may be improved.

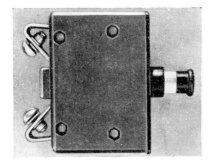 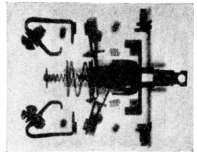

Fig. 21.10 Photographs of a contact breaker (suspected faulty); left, under normal light and, right, the image produced on an I.R.P. by X-rays

Conclusion. Although electroluminescence at its present level of brightness is in no way a competitor with established general lighting techniques, it has great versatility and already provides a convenient means of illumination for certain applications. It is not a substitute for conventional forms of lighting such as filament and discharge lamps but provides a means of illuminating a surface at a low, uniform brightness in circumstances where the spatial requirements of the lighting system must be kept to a minimum. Just as electroluminescence is a relatively new means of providing light, so also the applications for which it seems most suited are new. It is inappropriate to try to achieve by its use results which can more easily be obtained by light sources of other kinds.

CHAPTER 22

Lamps as Sources of Electromagnetic Power (ultraviolet to infrared)

Introduction. Lamps are now used for heating, photochemical and photobiological processes; for the simple understanding of the potentialities of lamps for these purposes it is helpful to consider them as sources of radiated power. The practical potentialities of radiations akin to light, mentioned at the beginning of Chapter 1, need to be studied in more detail.

The electromagnetic radiation spectrum, Fig. 22.1, includes general comments on the effects of each band of radiation: with practical emphasis in an extended diagram of the main ultraviolet, visible and infrared radiation emitted both by the sun and artificial light sources.

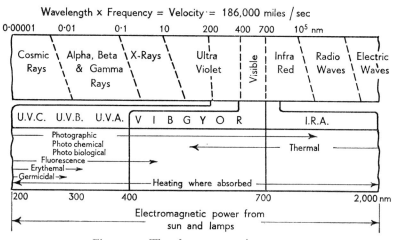

Fig. 22.1   The electromagnetic spectrum

The efficacy of power radiated in any waveband within this region depends on the mechanism producing the required result.

The relative efficacies, with which various effects are produced by equal amounts of power radiated between 200 nm and 2000 nm units, are shown in Fig. 22.2. From this it can be seen that there is a region of maximum efficacy for each specific requirement, while any particular waveband may be capable of producing a number of results, although with different relative efficacies. While such curves give a good pictorial representation of the wavebands

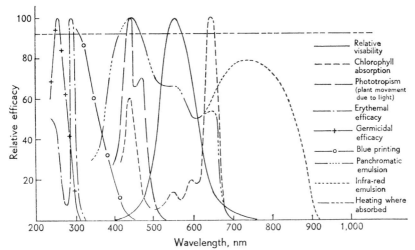

Fig. 22.2 Some effects of radiated power

required for any application, a further step forward can be made if quantitative values can be applied to them. This can perhaps best be illustrated by referring to the effect most important to illuminating engineers, the visibility function described in Chapter 1.

By expressing light flux in lumens and power in watts, it is possible to convert relative visibility into the much more definite curve of the luminous efficacy of radiated power, histogram Fig. 22.3. To define the wavebands over which

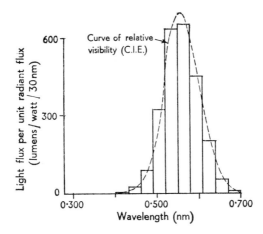

Fig. 22.3 Luminous efficacy of radiated power

Lamps and Lighting

averages have been taken, it is helpful to use blocks for such wavebands, particularly if they relate to light sources which have a mixture of line and continuous radiation, such as high-pressure electric discharge and fluorescent lamps. From this quantitative luminous efficacy of radiated power it can be seen that the maximum efficacy with which green light can ever be obtained from any source is 680 lm/W; while if all colours of the spectrum are required, the theoretical limit is the mean of the values over all the visible wavebands, corresponding to approximately 240 lm/W. Owing to its great importance more quantitative information is available about the eye than for many of the other photochemical, or photobiological effects. However, since with modern radiation measuring equipment, the radiant power from lamps can be given in watts, this in turn will enable quantitative units to be developed for the uses of electromagnetic power to which lamps can be applied. *Evitons* are sometimes used as units of erythemal (sunburning) effectiveness.

Radiated power from lamps is often used to reproduce many of the photo-biological effects of natural radiation from the sun. Astronomers and physicists have provided quantitative data of the intensity of solar radiation in outer space (Fig. 22.4). Modification, mainly by water vapour and ozone in the atmosphere, determines the radiation received at the earth's surface, which promotes our life processes (Fig. 22.4(e)). The irradiance in each waveband, in watts per unit area, forms the basis for calculating the practical possibilities of performing similar functions by radiation from lamps. The irradiance in selected wavebands at the earth's surface in Britain is shown in

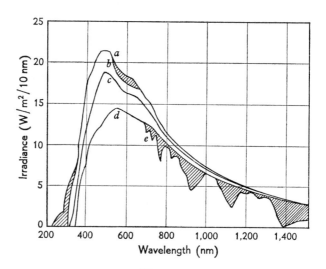

Fig. 22.4
(a) extra-terrestrial solar radiation
(b) after passing through ozone layer
(c) after Rayleigh-scattering
(d) after aerosol absorption and scattering
(e) after water vapour and oxygen absorption

Fig. 22.5. Irradiance in Fig. 22.4 is expressed in $W/m^2/10$ nm, to emphasise the international effort behind such data; in Fig. 22.5 it is given in $W/ft^2/30$ nm, to enable data to be associated with the British luminance measurements of lm/ft^2.

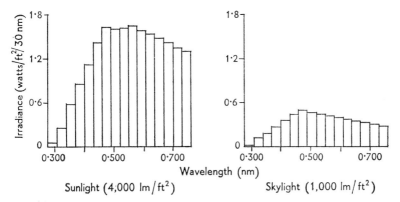

Fig. 22.5 Spectral power distribution histograms of sunlight and skylight

Radiant power from lamps. Space exploration has intensified the need for precise knowledge of the radiated power outside the earth's atmosphere; since satellites are subjected to this radiated power on the side facing the sun, in an environment, which, excepting for reflections of this power from the earth, or other planets, corresponds almost to perfect darkness. As the whole satellite is virtually in a vacuum, it attains temperature stability only by re-radiating power into space. It is obviously desirable to check the many calculations which are made to predict such conditions, by submitting the unit to simulated solar radiation in evacuated low-temperature test chambers, on earth. Since light has to be beamed towards the satellite, high-brightness lamps of great power in accurate optical systems, are needed. Suitable radiation has been provided by the use of high-power carbon arc-lamps

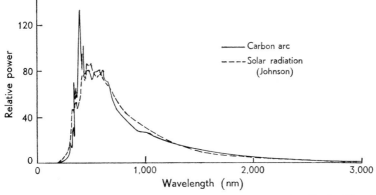

Fig. 22.6 Spectral power distribution, 13·6 mm carbon arc (A. D. Le Vantine)

(Fig. 22.6) or compact-source xenon lamps (Fig. 22.7), which may have some of the excessive near infrared radiation filtered (Fig. 22.8).

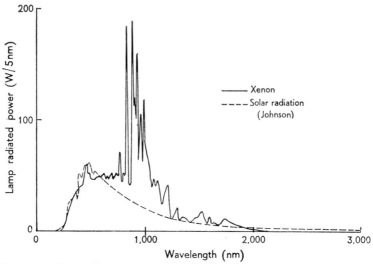

Fig. 22.7   Spectral power distribution, 2 kW compact-source xenon lamp
(test lamp lumens 64,000)

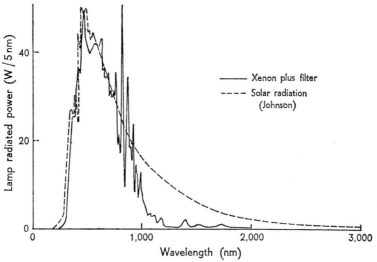

Fig. 22.8   Spectral power distribution, 2 kW compact-source xenon lamp
(test lamp lumens 64,000) plus typical infra-red filter—on 22

For studies of photochemical deterioration, much more attention has to be paid to the detailed spectral power distribution histograms of the visible and ultraviolet regions (Fig. 22.9). The large, square diagram shows that 15% of the input power to the 2 kW xenon lamp is radiated in the visible region, 2% as ultraviolet and 58% as infrared. The close approximation of xenon arc radiation to sunlight, in the ultraviolet and visible regions makes them particularly effective for such studies. Their constancy and the non-consumable nature of their electrodes, makes them convenient for thermal tests.

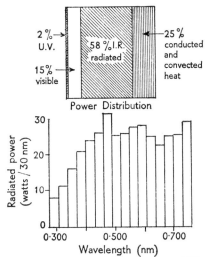

Fig. 22.9   Power distribution histogram of 2 kW xenon lamp
(test lamp lumens 64,000)

While Fig. 22.10 shows that the radiated power from incandescent filament lamps differs greatly from that of sunlight, it will be seen from the square block diagram that such filaments are extremely efficient convertors of electrical power into radiated power. While only some 6% of the input power

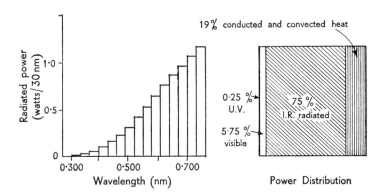

Fig. 22.10   Power distribution diagrams of 100 W incandescent
tungsten filament lamp (test lamp lumens 1260)

12*

provides light, 75% is in the near infrared region—hence the use of incandescent lamps to provide radiated power at more than 80% efficiency, for industrial heating purposes.

Electric discharge lamps can provide radiated power in specific wavebands; an outstanding example of this is the low-pressure sodium lamp (Fig. 22.11); some 22% of the input power is radiated in the sodium resonance radiation doublet. Conversion of electrical power to a single waveband with

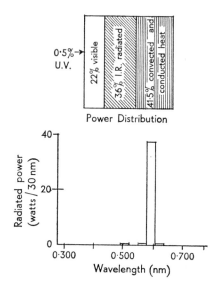

Fig. 22.11   Power distribution histogram for 200 W linear low-pressure sodium lamp (test lamp lumens 20,000)

even greater efficiency is provided by electric discharges through low pressures of mercury vapour (Fig. 22.12(a)); 56% of the input power is concentrated in the 253·7 nm short ultraviolet region. This radiation is effective for killing bacteria.

The dependence of the radiant power distribution on gas, or vapour pressure is emphasised by the corresponding histogram (Fig. 22.12b), for high-pressure mercury vapour lamps. The power radiated in the short ultraviolet is greatly reduced, and that in the near ultraviolet and visible regions is increased; by controlling this mercury vapour pressure by temperature, a range of spectral distributions can be obtained to suit specific applications. Where more red and less ultraviolet radiation is required, this can be provided by high-pressure mercury fluorescent (MBF) lamps (Fig. 22.13).

The flexibility of the spectral distribution of radiated power from tubular fluorescent lamps is shown in Fig. 22.14. Mercury resonance radiation 253.7 nm (Fig. 22.12) is converted with near quantum efficiency to radiation throughout the visible, or even long ultraviolet, or infrared region. Quantum efficiency, the radiation of one photon of light, per incident ultraviolet quantum, gives a power conversion efficiency of approximately 50%, so 22% of the input power is radiated in the visible region. Only 30% is radiated in the infrared which makes fluorescent lamps first choice for much plant growth work.

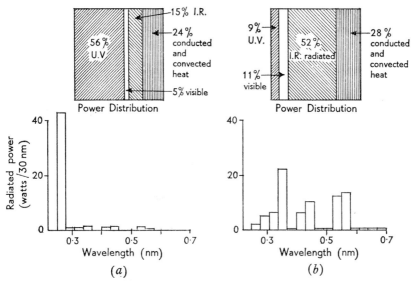

Fig. 22.12   Power distribution histograms for (*a*) 80 W low-pressure mercury lamp (test lamp lumens 510), and (*b*) 400 W high-pressure mercury lamp (test lamp lumens 18,800)

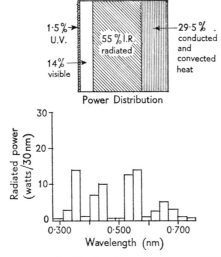

Fig. 22.13   Power distribution histogram of 400 W fluorescent high-pressure mercury lamp (test lamp lumens 19,200)

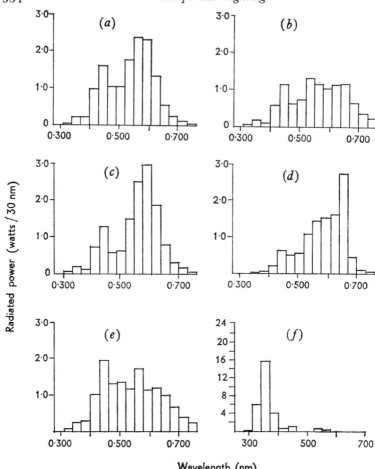

Radiated power (watts / 30 nm)

Wavelength (nm)

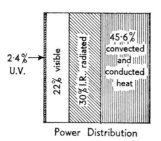

2·4% → U.V.

22% visible   30% I.R., radiated   45·6% convected and conducted heat

Power Distribution

Fig. 22.14   Spectral band diagrams of tubular fluorescent lamps
(a) daylight   (b) Kolorite
(c) warm white
(d) de-luxe warm white
(e) artificial daylight   (f) ultraviolet

Effects of radiant power. Radiated power must be absorbed to be effective. A body receiving radiation from a lamp may use the power absorbed in various ways. It may simply convert the absorbed power into heat. It may re-radiate the power in the form of electrons, as resonance radiation, by fluorescence or phosphorescence. The power may initiate atomic and molecular reactions resulting in an increase of energy, which can excite complex photochemical or photobiological changes.

Reflection, or transmission of radiation, does not absorb power. To assess the effectiveness of radiation for any particular purpose it is necessary to know the extent to which it is absorbed and also the efficiency with which any reflecting, or transmitting, materials direct the wavebands required. Fig. 22.15 (a, b) gives reflection and transmission characteristics of some common materials. It must be realised that whiteness, indicative of high reflection of visible light, may, or may not, be accompanied by high-reflectance in the invisible ultraviolet, or infrared regions. Zinc oxide and magnesium oxide with similar reflectances in the visible region, differ totally in the shorter

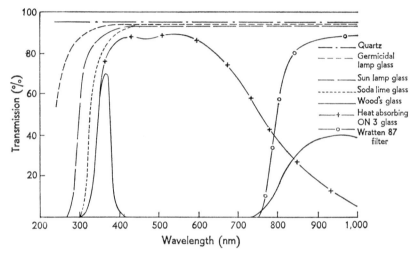

Fig. 22.15(a)   Some spectral transmission data

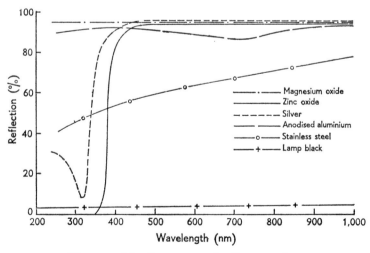

Fig. 22.15(b)   Some spectral reflectance data

ultraviolet regions, zinc oxide absorbing and magnesium oxide continuing to reflect, shorter wavelength radiated power.

Heating. The most easily appreciated effect of radiant power is the heating which it produces. Provided the material will absorb radiant energy, it can be heated preferentially above a surrounding atmosphere, or heated even inside a vacuum. In vacuum the temperatures will be raised until the body being heated re-radiates power at longer wavelengths and eventually reaches an equilibrium temperature. In air, additional cooling by convection results in a lower temperature.

It should be realised that an absorption curve may be the resultant of absorptions giving thermal, luminescent, or photochemical effects, and for heating the data should relate to heating only.

Photo-emission. The concept that radiant power, in units of quanta, acts according to the energy in each quantum, is illustrated by the photoelectric efficacy of radiated power. Photoemission can occur when this quantum energy is sufficient to release an electron from the atomic system of a material. The shorter the wavelength the greater the energy, so that photoemission is most easily produced by ultraviolet radiation; with the development of special photoemissive surfaces, photoemission can be generated by radiant power throughout the visible and even infrared region. Representative photoemission data is summarised in Fig. 22.16. It is possible to determine the most effective photocell/lamp combination for light-beam control applications, by combining this data with radiated power lamp characteris-

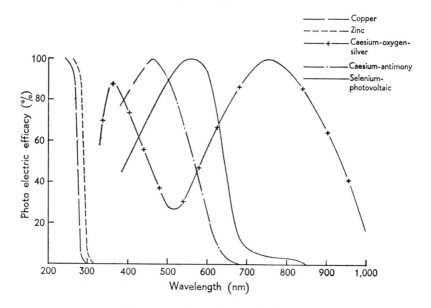

Fig. 22.16 Some photoemission data

tics. Where light beams are objectionable, or secrecy is required, use is made of the infrared region.

An experiment can be carried out with simple equipment, to illustrate the basic excitation of photoemission from simple metals by ultraviolet, using a germicidal lamp, two sheets of glass and an electroscope, upon which is mounted a small sheet of zinc arranged as shown in Fig. 22.17. The germicidal

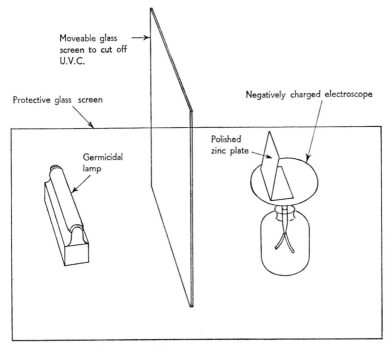

Fig. 22.17   Photoemission experiment

lamp, for reasons of safety, is screened from the user by a sheet of window glass and faces the zinc plate on the electroscope. It will be seen that with the electroscope charged negatively, rapid discharge will occur when the lamp is switched on; this will cease if the second glass sheet is placed in front of the zinc plate. If the electroscope is charged positively, no discharge will occur.

Photoemission is of great use for simplifying the practical measurement of radiated power. Measurement of radiated power by thermal devices is subject to enormous problems, due to the radiation of heat and temperature variations from the surroundings. By using photoemission excited only by the wavelengths to be used, measurements can be made easily with simple meters; lightmeters are typical examples. Care needs to be taken to correct the photoemission curve to provide either, radiant power units, or units of a particular required function.

Since lamps are rated in luminous efficacy and lightmeters are readily available, it is helpful to make use of the radiation measurements carried out in lamp laboratories to determine approximately the radiant power in a selected waveband, associated with the light from the particular lamp. If the illumination at any point on a surface is measured in lm/ft^2, then the radiant power in any waveband, expressed in W/ft^2 can be calculated, using the histograms of radiant power for the appropriate lamp (Figs. 22.6 to 26.14), by the expression:

$$\text{Irradiance per band } (W/ft^2)$$

$$= \frac{\text{Illumination } (lm/ft^2)}{\text{Test lamp lumens}} \times \text{Watts per band (from histogram)}$$

Such values of irradiance can be compared directly with those in sunlight and skylight (Fig. 22.5), where lamps are required to promote photochemical, or photobiological processes produced naturally.

Fluorescence and phosphorescence. The basis of fluorescence and phosphorescence, described in Chapter 5, is the conversion of incident power radiated at one wavelength, to a required band of light. Each material has excitation and radiation characteristics (Fig. 22.18). In addition to the phosphors used for

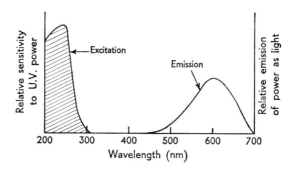

Fig. 22.18   Fluorescence characteristics

lamps, fluorescent materials are used to provide brighter colours by converting short-wavelength light and ultraviolet to blue, green, orange or red light. Modern bleaches provide 'whiter-than-white' whiteness by additional blue light excited by the violet and ultraviolet radiation. To be effective for these materials lamps must contain the exciting wavebands; this has been particularly carefully studied in providing the correct spectral power for artificial daylight lamps (Chapter 5). Fluorescence, excited particularly by long ultraviolet, is used for the critical examination of gems, or forgeries and with fluorescent dyes, for the detection of minute cracks, or the tracking of underground rivers. Examination of this fluorescence requires ultraviolet sources without visible light and high-pressure mercury discharge (Fig. 22.12(b)) or fluorescent lamps with special phosphors (Fig. 22.14(f)) are used with integral or separate Woods-glass filters (Fig. 22.15(b)).

Lamps as Sources of Electromagnetic Power   359

Photochemical. For many photochemical and photobiological uses there is a basic law (Fig. 22.19) which must be understood to achieve predictable results. There is a threshold value below which the radiation has virtually no

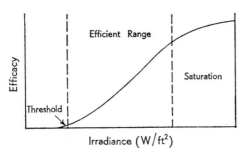

Fig. 22.19   Efficacy/radiated power characteristic

effect. This is followed by the useful range of the material, in which the effect produced is dependent upon the product of irradiance and time. Finally, saturation occurs and the application of intensities in this region becomes progressively inefficient.

Most users of photographic materials are familiar with this characteristic. From representative spectral sensitivity data for photographic, or photo-reproduction materials (Fig. 22.2), with lamp histogram data, the relative photoprinting speeds of lamps can be assessed. To give uniform exposure for photoprinting a special range of high-pressure mercury vapour lamps has been developed, for mounting axially in a cylinder the full length of the tracing to be copied. For xerography, special green fluorescent lamps are provided.

Accurate colour reproduction is critically dependent upon the spectral sensitivity of the photographic materials used. While a comparison between the radiation from sunlight and lamps can provide guidance concerning lamps which should be avoided the critical nature of the work requires experimental confirmation by checks with lamps selected. Colour films are balanced for specific light sources, usually daylight, or incandescent filament lamp light. Special photographic lamps (Chapter 13) are made accurately to a colour temperature of 3250 °K, for professional work.

The fading of materials, or the deterioration of finishes are generally checked with light sources approximating to natural daylight, which have already been described (BS 1006: 1955 classifies the 'Fastness to Daylight of Coloured Textiles'). Light is often mistakenly blamed for fading, for example, light may actually inhibit deterioration of pictures by preventing the growth of mould spores and care must be taken to examine every case on its merits. With modern lighting levels the fading is generally proportional to the product of intensity by time and has often been referred to in terms of foot-candle hours: 50,000 foot-candle hours giving minimum perceptible fading, with average materials. Some general factors due to differences in spectral distribution are given in Table 22.1 below.

TABLE 22.1

Comparative Fading Effects of Light Sources

Light source	Relative lm/ft² equal fading	Average intensity lm/ft²	Time for perceptible fading, hours
Mid-summer sunlight plus skylight	1	5000	10
North skylight	0·5	500	50
Incandescent filament GLS lamps (500 W)	1·8	25	3600
Fluorescent colour-matching lamps	1·5	50	1500

Both short and long wavelength ultraviolet lamps are used to excite catalysts for various chemical manufacturing processes.

Photobiological. While natural light controls a number of plant processes, the most important of these are photosynthesis (the synthesis by green plants of carbohydrates from water and oxygen, aided by light absorbed by the chlorophyll) and photoperiodism (the phenomenon whereby the length of day controls the onset of flowering, or other stage of plant development). In general both effects require from lamps light of similar intensity, spectral quality and exposure time, as provided in their natural habitat.

The threshold for photosynthesis is around 200 lm/ft², so that additional lighting in glasshouses during the winter can produce marked improvement. High-pressure mercury discharge lamps, which are small and obstruct little daylight, are favoured for this. Where growth rooms without daylight are used, fluorescent lamps are preferred.

The relative efficacy with which radiated power produces plant growth effects can be seen from Fig. 22.2. Light of different colours can produce growth distortion; red light produces elongated frail growth, blue light produces stunted growth, and short-wave ultraviolet is catastrophic. For many processes a balanced light source is usually necessary but for photosynthesis, lamps radiating in the blue and red regions corresponding to the peak absorption of chlorophyll, are most effective. Special purplish fluorescent lamps are made for this purpose but owing to the concentrated attention to halophosphate phosphors the performance of standard warm-white lamps through-life is comparable.

Much practical use is now made of lamps to control the flowering of short day plants, such as chrysanthemums. This is attractive, since light intensities between 5 and 20 lm/ft² are adequate for extending the day length from 10 to 16 hours, or for breaking up the 14 hour winter night into two equal dark periods, using lighting for one or two hours only. Reddish light is preferred and with the short burning hours incandescent lamps are generally used. For plant-growth rooms, single or double tiers of closely spaced fluorescent lamps can produce intensities of the order of 4000 lm/ft² and provide an artificially complete and controllable substitute for daylight.

The use of light for animal husbandry is increasing. The most intensive studies have been concerned with poultry keeping and some conclusions are given below.

(1) White light of approximately 1 to 3 lm/ft^2 can extend the day length during the winter and promote egg production over the whole year.

(2) Very low intensities of red light produce restful conditions, during which the birds convert food rapidly into weight.

(3) Birds cannot see blue light and can be caught easily in this way.

Infrared lamps, sometimes with red filters, are used in pig farming; by providing warmth away from the sow, accidental crushing is virtually eliminated.

Violet and ultraviolet light is used to attract insects into traps.

Attention concerning the photobiological effects of light on man has been mainly focused on the sometimes unexpected effects of ultraviolet radiation. The main visual effect, sunburning, is produced by only 0·1 % of the radiated power from the sun, contained in the waveband 290 nm to 310 nm. Intensities of 40 mW/ft^2 of this radiation in sunlight, will produce minimum perceptible erythema with about ten minutes exposure. It is important to realise that there is a latent period of some four hours between the time of irradiation and the reddening of the skin; this accounts for much of the overdosage during the summer holidays. High-pressure mercury vapour lamps with special outer bulbs to limit the short ultraviolet to 280 nm, are the best substitute for sunlight. A known effect of this radiation is the conversion of cholesterol oil in the skin, into vitamin D. This waveband also produces conjunctivitis (inflammation of the surface of the eye) so that for considerable exposures sun-glasses are advisable, both in sunlight on mountains and for artificial treatment.

Infrared radiation from incandescent lamps, generally most conveniently reflector lamps, provides comfortable heating since much of the radiation is absorbed in the body tissues. It can relieve pain from muscular and nervous tension.

Short ultraviolet has attractive germicidal properties. It can inactivate, or kill bacteria and moulds, but will also damage simple plant and animal life. It is efficiently produced by low-pressure mercury vapour lamps, using special ultraviolet transmitting glass. These germicidal lamps can be used in fittings to irradiate airborne bacteria in rooms, or air-ducts; for killing bacteria on surfaces, or for sterilising transmitting materials such as water or sugar crystals.

For use in rooms, lamps are disposed so as to irradiate the upper atmosphere killing bacteria as warm air circulates into this region. Care must be taken to limit back-scattered radiation to safe values. The threshold permits intensities of one tenth of a mW/ft^2 to be acceptable for continuous irradiation. This very low intensity of radiation can be measured easily by making use of a photoemissive material, such as copper or zinc (Fig. 22.16). This is insensitive to any radiation in natural daylight, so that accurate measurements are possible in natural radiant intensities of 100 W/ft^2.

Choice of lamp for radiated power applications. While each use of radiant power should be considered on its merits it is helpful to summarise the effectiveness of lamps for uses that have been proved.

Table 22.2 shows the main ultraviolet, visible and infrared wavebands in which power from electric lamps is radiated. To help visualise these lamps, reference is made to the chapter describing each main lighting type or to the photographs in Fig. 22.20, which relate to lamps made primarily for non-lighting purposes.

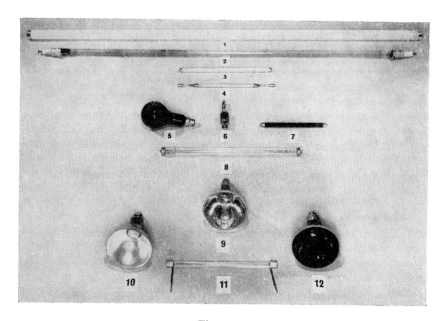

Fig. 22.20

1. Fluorescent lamp, with ultraviolet or blue phosphor: MCF
2. Blue-printing mercury lamp
3. Green fluorescent xerography lamp: MCF
4. Industrial photochemical lamp: MB
5. Black lamp: MBW
6. Laboratory ultraviolet lamp: MBL
7. Fluorescent black lamp: MCFW
8. Germicidal lamp
9. Sun lamp: MBT
10. Infrared heat lamp
11. Quartz heat lamp
12. Red stained, infrared heat lamp

Table 22.3 summarises the lamps which are suitable as sources of electromagnetic power for a range of applications.

TABLE 22.2

Electromagnetic Power From Lamps

Lamp	References	Radiation								
		UVC	UVB	UVA	VA	VB	VC	IRA	IRB	IRC
1. Germicidal (low-pressure mercury)	Fig. 22.20 No. 8	X								
2. High-pressure mercury										
Photoprinting	Fig. 22.20 No. 2		X	X	X	X		X		X
Sun lamp	Fig. 22.20 No. 9		X	X	X	X		X	X	X
Type MB quartz	Fig. 22.20 Nos. 4 & 6	X		X	X	X	X			X
Type MB glass	Chapter 18				X	X	X			X
Type MBF	Chapter 18			X	X	X	X	X		X
3. Black lamp—MBW	Fig. 22.20 No. 5	X	X					X		X
4. Xenon	Chapter 19	X	X	X	X	X	X	X	X	X
5. Fluorescent xerography green	Chapter 20			X	X	X	X			
	Fig. 22.20 No. 3			X	X	X	X			
6. Ultraviolet fluorescent + Woods glass	Fig. 22.20 No. 1			X	X					
	Fig. 22.20 No. 7			X	X	X				
7. Sodium	Chapter 17					X		X		X
8. Carbon arc	Chapter 22		X	X	X	X	X	X	X	X
9. Incandescent	Chapter 12				X	X	X	X	X	
10. Incandescent infrared	Fig. 22.20 Nos. 10, 11, 12				X	X	X	X		X

TABLE 22.3

Electromagnetic Power Applications

Application	Effect	Suitable Lamps
1. Visual aids using fluorescence	Reveal invisible faults	Black lamp—Type MBW or Type MCFW Lamps rich in UVA and VA
2. Photochemical (general)	Photographic	High-pressure mercury lamps. Arcs. Blue and ultraviolet fluorescent lamps
Blue printing		Green fluorescent lamps
Xerography	Photographic	3250°K tungsten lamps. Flash bulbs. Flash tubes
Photography (colour)	Photographic	Tungsten lamps and Wratten No. 87 filter
Photography (infrared)	Photographic	Arcs. Xenon lamps. Banks of artificial daylight fluorescent lamps
Fading of materials or deterioration	Simulate sunlight	Carbon arcs. Xenon lamps. High-pressure mercury
Satellite testing	Heating or photochemical deterioration	
3. Photobiological Plant growth		
Photosynthesis	CO_2 + Light (Chlorophyll) Plant sugars + H_2O	Fluorescent lamps particularly warm white with blue and red bands. MB and MBFR for supplementing daylight in winter glasshouses
Photoperiodism	Daylight control of flowering	Incandescent lamps. Red fluorescent lamps
Potato sprouting		Fluorescent lamps, preferably daylight
Animal husbandry		
Photoperiodic	Egg stimulation	Incandescent
Heating	Warming pigs and chickens, and human comfort	Red incandescent
Vitamin D	With suntanning (erythema)	Sun lamps
Germicidal	Sterilising air, water and some solids	Germicidal lamps
4. Insect trapping		MB, MBW and MCFW lamps

CHAPTER 23

Control Gear

Control gear components. It has been explained in previous chapters that the electron-atom collisions which occur in all sodium, mercury and fluorescent lamps are cumulative and that some form of resistance or impedance must be placed in series with the lamp to restrict or control the current to the designed value. Such resistance or impedance is often called a stabiliser or ballast, and forms part of the control gear necessary to operate lamps.

The performance and operation of discharge lamps depends very much upon the characteristics and design of the ballast and other circuit components. For example, lamp starting, light output, lamp wattage and lamp life all depend upon the control gear, and unsatisfactory control gear will give unsatisfactory lamp performance.

In addition to the ballast it may be necessary to provide other control gear components such as a starting device and capacitors, which correct the power factor or reduce radio interference. These components may be supplied separately or they may be combined in a single box or unit.

Ballasts

Resistor ballasts. A simple wire-wound resistor can be used as a ballast for a fluorescent tube, but the disadvantage is that considerable power is wasted in the form of heat in the resistance, and thus overall efficiency is low. An incandescent filament lamp can be used as a resistor ballast, providing some additional light, and thereby limiting this reduction in efficiency.

For operation on d.c. supply a resistor ballast is essential, together with a small choke to provide a voltage pulse to assist lamp starting. A polarity reversing switch is also necessary to reduce the effect of mercury migration.

Choke ballasts. The choke (or inductor) ballast is almost always used for stabilising mercury lamps and fluorescent tubes since it is the most efficient means of control. Power loss in a choke is relatively low and overall circuit efficiency is usually 80% to 90%. A choke has two main functions; it must deliver correct current and power to the lamp, and it must also allow correct pre-heat current to pass through the lamp electrodes if a starter-switch circuit is used. In addition, a choke should be relatively quiet, have long life, absorb minimum power losses, withstand supply voltage variations and have no adverse effect upon lamp life.

Choke design is a compromise between conflicting requirements but the aim of the designer is to obtain maximum performance with minimum of cost. The size of a choke is roughly determined by its volt-ampere rating, and large lamps operating at high currents require large chokes. Chokes for fluorescent lighting are often made long and slim in shape so that they can be easily fitted into narrow channels or fittings, but such elongation necessarily results in higher choke losses (Fig. 23.1).

Fig. 23.1 Construction of a fluorescent lamp choke

The two coils are connected in series and wound with enamelled copper wire upon rectangular pressboard tubes. Each layer of winding is interleaved with paper. The magnetic core is formed from U-shaped stampings of silicon-iron. The air gaps between the ends of the stampings are cemented and adjusted to give the correct inductance. The connecting wires are soldered to two terminal blocks and the choke is placed in a deep-drawn steel case and pressure filled with 'Permaset' thermosetting compound

A simple choke consists of coils of enamelled copper wire insulated with Class A (105 °C) materials complying with BS 2757 and assembled on to a high permeability core of silicon-iron laminations. An air gap is provided in the iron core to obtain satisfactory electrical characteristics and to reduce magnetic flux saturation. To improve insulation, electrical strength, heat conductivity and to reduce noise level it is necessary to impregnate the choke assembly with varnish compounds, or alternatively fill the choke with resin or bitumen mixtures. *Permaset* or *Polyester* compounds provide first class thermosetting fillings which cannot drip or melt. Chokes are enclosed in sheet steel cases or boxes and fitted with terminals or connecting wires. The steel case screens any stray magnetic field from the choke and prevents vibration and noise being induced into adjacent steel parts of a lighting fitting.

Capacitor Ballasts. Capacitors cannot be used by themselves as ballasts on a.c. power supplies of normal 50 c/s to 60 c/s frequency. The rapid charge and discharge which would take place during each a.c. cycle would damage the lamp and produce a very noticeable flicker. Capacitors are sometimes used in series combination with chokes to provide ballasts which give leading power-factor circuits. Such circuits tend to have a constant current characteristic and give stable operation even when lamp voltage approaches the value of the supply voltage. Capacitor-choke ballasts are used for long lamps, and for the leading power-factor branch of lead-lag twin circuits.

Capacitors are also used for power-factor correction and this application is discussed later.

Leakage reactance transformer ballasts. Mercury, sodium and fluorescent lamps require a certain minimum voltage for starting and operation, and it may be necessary to step up the available supply voltage to a higher value. Some sodium lamps, for example, require 460 V for reliable starting and this voltage is obtained from normal 240 V supply by using a transformer. The ballast impedance also required to stabilise the lamp can be incorporated in the transformer design by deliberately introducing leakage reactance.

Such a transformer is known as a *stray-field* or *leakage-reactance* transformer. The primary and secondary windings are loosely coupled so that the mutual magnetic flux linking the coils is reduced when a load is taken from the transformer. In this way the lamp current is limited to the correct value by the inductive-leakage reactance. Some leakage reactance transformers also include cathode heating windings for the preheating of lamp electrodes.

Ballast performance and tests. The performance and construction of ballasts is specified in standard specifications. As a guide, ballasts complying with BS 2818 (Auxiliaries for Operation of Fluorescent Lamps) meet the following test requirements:

(1) Correct impedance to ensure correct lamp watts, full light output and long lamp life.
(2) Correct starting current and voltage to the lamp to ensure reliable and satisfactory starting.
(3) Freedom from unduly 'peaky' lamp current waveshape to prevent short lamp life and end blackening.
(4) Freedom from external magnetic stray-field effects.
(5) Noise level below 30 dB to ensure quiet operation.
(6) Satisfactory insulation resistance above 2 megohms and insulation strength above 2000 V.
(7) Winding temperature rise below 70 °C under normal operation conditions to ensure long ballast life.
(8) Winding temperature rise below 105 °C under starting conditions to prevent overheating.

(9) Endurance test cycle at a surrounding temperature of 85 °C to ensure freedom from leakage of filling material.

Power factor and its correction. In a lamp circuit controlled by choke or transformer the power factor may have a value near 0·5 lagging. Thus there is a need for power-factor correction, a low value of power factor being undesirable for the following reasons:

(1) It unnecessarily increases the current and kVA demand from the supply.
(2) The useful load that can be carried by cables and accessories is reduced.
(3) Special tariffs and penalties may be imposed on the consumer taking a load with a low lagging power factor.

Lagging power factor can be corrected quite simply by connecting a suitable capacitor in shunt across the a.c. supply. The capacitor takes a current which is leading in phase and this partly cancels the lagging current taken by the chokes.

Fig. 23.2 shows a simplified vector diagram for an 80 W fluorescent lamp circuit in which the shunt capacitor improves the power factor from 0·5 to 0·85 lagging and reduces the supply current by 40%. Power factor can be improved to a higher value but the size of the capacitor then required is not usually justified on economic grounds. A corrected power factor of 0·85 lagging is usually accepted in Britain.

An alternative way of correcting the power factor in a fluorescent lamp circuit is to connect a suitable capacitor in series with the choke ballast. For satisfactory operation with this type of circuit the reactance of the capacitor must be about twice the reactance of the choke and this means that the over-all power factor will be 0·5 to 0·7 leading, depending upon the lamp voltage and length. If a choke-controlled circuit with a lagging power factor of 0·5 is combined with a circuit having a series capacitor operating at a leading power factor of 0·5 the overall power factor of the two circuits will be nearly unity. The arrangement of the two circuits is called a lead-lag circuit and is also shown in Fig. 23.2.

Capacitors may be placed inside the lighting fitting, together with other equipment such as chokes and starters, or they may be mounted separately, e.g. in the base of a street-lighting column. Most modern capacitors have aluminium foil electrodes separated by 2 or 3 Kraft paper tissues impregnated with a liquid or solid dielectric medium. The chief impregnants used are shown in Table 23.1. The maximum and minimum operating temperatures are usually marked on the capacitor, together with the working voltage and the capacity in microfarads.

Capacitors are sealed into metal containers and fitted with two terminals or connecting wires. A discharge resistor is fitted across the terminals so that the voltage will be reduced to less than 50 V one minute after switching off. Some capacitors are fitted with internal fuses to give protection against internal failure. If a fuse is fitted, the capacitor container is marked 'F' or 'fuse fitted'.

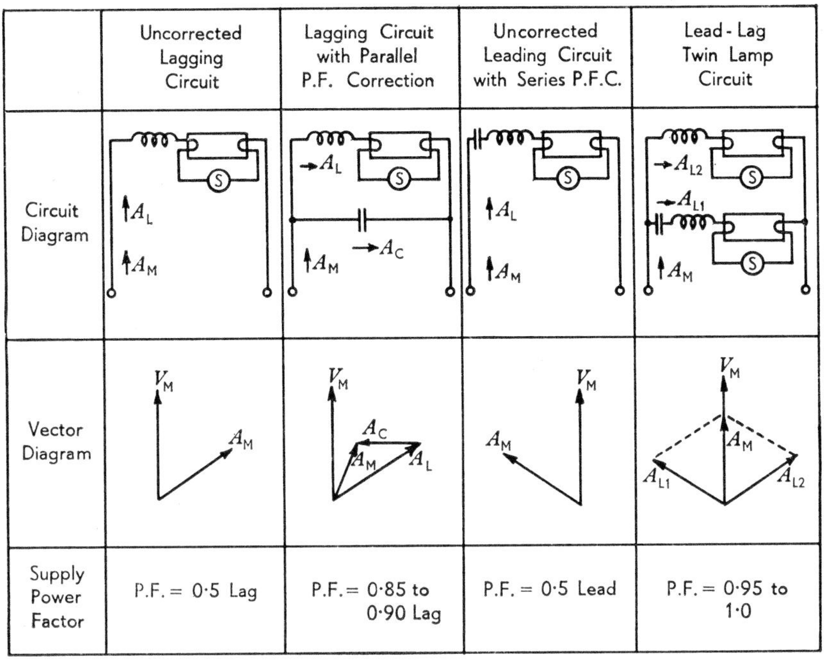

	Uncorrected Lagging Circuit	Lagging Circuit with Parallel P.F. Correction	Uncorrected Leading Circuit with Series P.F.C.	Lead-Lag Twin Lamp Circuit
Circuit Diagram				
Vector Diagram				
Supply Power Factor	P.F. = 0·5 Lag	P.F.= 0·85 to 0·90 Lag	P.F. = 0·5 Lead	P.F. = 0·95 to 1·0

Fig. 23.2   Power factor correction for switch-start circuits on
200 V to 250 V 50 c/s a.c. supply
V_M = supply voltage
A_M = supply current
A_L = lamp current
A_C = capacitor current
S = starter switch

TABLE 23.1

Temperature Limits for Capacitor Impregnants

Capacitor impregnant	Permitted temperature limits
Stabilised chlorinated wax impregnated paper with petroleum jelly filling	$-25\ °C$ to $+50\ °C$ max. (or $+70\ °C$ max. according to dielectric thickness)
Mineral oil	$-40\ °C$ to $+60\ °C$ max.
Pentachlorodiphenyl	$-5\ °C$ to $+70\ °C$ max.
Trichlorodiphenyl	$-25\ °C$ to $+70\ °C$ max.

Capacitor performance and tests. The performance and construction of capacitors is specified in standard specifications. As a guide, capacitors to BS 2818 comply with the following tests and requirements:

(1) Heat test at high temperature to ensure there is no leakage of filling.
(2) High-voltage test a.c. or d.c. between terminals to check dielectric.
(3) Extra high voltage test a.c. between container and terminals.
(4) Test of discharge resistor.
(5) Measurement of capacity and tolerance.
(6) Dielectric insulation resistance test to check insulation leakage.
(7) Thermal stability test at excess voltage and excess temperature.
(8) Discharge inception test at excess voltage.
(9) Humidity test at 95% humidity for 28 days.
(10) Endurance or life test.

Starting components

Starter switches—glow type. The action of the two main types of starter switch has already been described in Chapter 20. The glow-type switch is cheap, simple and reliable and is used for most fluorescent tube switch-start circuits. It consists of a small glass bulb together with a small radio interference suppressor capacitor (usually 0·006 μF) housed in a small metal canister which has two contact pins. The starter switch is fitted into a plastic starter socket and can be easily removed by a simple anti-clockwise twisting action. The glass bulb contains two symmetrical bimetal contacts together with a low pressure filling of gas (see Fig. 23.3). The correct type and rating of starter switch should be selected according to tube size and supply voltage.

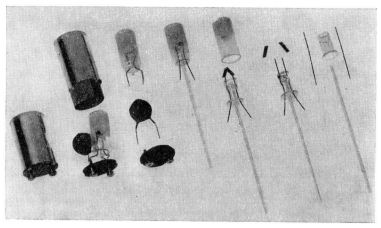

Fig. 23.3   Construction of a glow-starter switch

The two bimetallic contacts are welded to the electrodes of a stem which is then sealed into a glass bulb. The inside of the glass bulb is coated with radioactive material to assist ionisation. The bulb is pumped and filled with low pressure gas and the exhaust tube is then sealed off. The bulb is fitted to a 2-pin base together with a small disc-type radio interference suppression capacitor. The assembly is then fitted into a metal can which has an insulating lining

Starter switches—thermal type. The thermal type switch is used for applications where longer cathode preheating is required. It consists of a glass bulb containing bimetal contacts and a small heater coil or filament. Current flowing through the heater coil causes the contacts to bend and open. The switch is essentially a current-operated device and must be used in conjunction with the correct ballast and tube type. Thermal starters are housed in large metal canisters having four contact pins. The switch contacts are connected to the two large pins while the heater coil is connected to the two small pins.

Starting transformers. Circuits which use transformers for preheating fluorescent tube cathodes prior to starting have been described in Chapter 20. Starting transformers can be divided into two main types—'voltage-fed' and 'current-fed'.

Voltage-fed transformers are generally called quick-start transformers and consist of a primary winding connected across the ends of the tube and two secondary windings which are connected to the two cathodes (see Fig. 20.11). This type of transformer is constructed in the conventional way and usually has a single coil of copper wire assembled on to a stack of silicon-iron laminations. The transformer may be fitted into a metal case which is filled with Permaset compound and has a four-way terminal block at one end for lampholder connections. To reduce radio interference from the tube a small ceramic suppression capacitor is fitted inside the quick-start transformer to by-pass much of the interference across the ends of the tube. During normal lamp operation quick-start transformers have low power loss and generate very little heat.

Some lamp-starting circuits (see Fig. 20.16) use a small current transformer connected in series with the P.F. capacitor to provide cathode heating for one or two tube cathodes. This is the 'current-fed' transformer. The preheating current supplied from the secondary windings depends upon the current flowing through the primary winding and by suitable design of the circuit the cathode heating can be reduced after the tube has started.

Starter performance and tests. Starter switches which comply with BS 3772 are tested as follows to ensure satisfactory life and operation:

(1) Check on dimensions and torsion test on pin terminals.
(2) 1·5 kV high-voltage test between pins and casing.
(3) Test of speed of operation at reduced voltage.
(4) Check on 'contact closed' time to ensure adequate tube cathode preheating.
(5) Check on minimum reclosure voltage to prevent 'blinking'.
(6) Peak voltage pulse test to ensure that the starter switch gives sufficient voltage to start the lamp.
(7) Endurance test with an on–off cycle for 6000 operations or lamp starts.
(8) Failed (deactivated) lamp test to ensure that the starter remains serviceable if fault conditions occur.
(9) Insulation resistance check at high relative humidity.

Control gear life and temperature. The power losses in control gear, together with heat from lamps, will cause equipment to run warm. The insulating materials such as enamel and paper used in the coils and windings of ballasts and transformers will slowly deteriorate at an increasing rate as the temperature rises above 105 °C and this will in time lead to burn-out and destruction of the equipment. Assuming correct application and operation at correct voltage with correct lamps, however, average continuous ballast life will be 10 to 20 years. In order to keep winding temperatures within the prescribed limit of 105 °C it is essential that chokes and ballasts should be mounted in such a way as to provide maximum heat transfer to the surrounding air. Ballast heat will then be effectively dissipated.

It should be noted that enclosure of fluorescent tubes inside plastics or glass diffusers will considerably increase lamp temperature, and this in turn will reduce light output and increase lamp and ballast current. Unfortunately this aggravates the heating problem still further, and fittings designers must use care and ingenuity in arranging the control gear mounting to ensure proper ballast temperatures. Fittings should be tested to ensure that the temperature rise of ballast and transformer windings does not exceed 80 °C under normal operating conditions (refer to BS 3820).

Capacitors generate very little heat since their losses are low, but if they are mounted in a ballast or in a fitting they will receive heat from lamps and other components, and it should be noted that capacitors are liable to suffer damage if they are subjected to excessive temperature.

Above the rated maximum temperature of a capacitor the losses in it may rise very rapidly and cause a 'run-away' temperature rise in the interior of the capacitor, which will lead to rapid destruction. Every care is therefore necessary in locating the capacitors with respect to the ballast and lamps so as to ensure that the rated maximum temperature of the capacitors as marked on their containers is never exceeded, even under the worst operating conditions, e.g. high supply voltage and/or high ambient temperature in the vicinity of the fitting.

Capacitor life should be at least ten years provided rated temperature or voltage is not exceeded, although a small proportion may fail before this time due to inevitable variations in manufacture. The relationship between life and temperature for capacitors and ballasts is shown in Fig. 23.4.

Ballast noise. Any electromagnetic device such as a transformer or ballast operating on alternating current is inherently liable to be noisy, to a degree dependent upon the power it handles and upon its design. Electric discharge lamp circuits give rise to harmonics ranging from 100 c/s up to 3000 c/s or more, so that ballast noise may vary from a low pitched hum to a high pitched 'rustle'.

Noise can be generated in several ways, by magnetostrictive changes in the dimensions of the core, by vibration of the core and, at the worst, by stray magnetic field causing vibration of the ballast case or even of the fitting in which the ballast is mounted.

Vibration of the ballast core can be almost eliminated by suitable design, good clamping and by cementing air gaps. Magnetostriction noise cannot

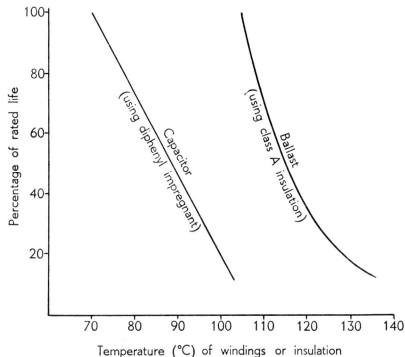

Fig. 23.4   The life of capacitors and ballasts

entirely be eliminated but it can be kept to a minimum by using short magnetic circuits and by avoiding high flux densities and uneven distribution of flux in the core. It follows, therefore, that units such as leakage-reactance transformers and some kinds of ballasts which rely upon special core configurations and flux distributions must be more noisy than simple chokes.

In general, ballast noise tends to be amplified by the fitting. To minimise this effect, control gear should be securely fastened and fittings well constructed to eliminate parts which might vibrate. Thin panels or boards upon which fittings are sometimes mounted can also act as sounding boards. Such mounting should be avoided.

The ambient noise level of the location in which the lighting fitting is used dictates the level of noise which can be tolerated from the fitting and in very quiet situations it may be necessary to mount the control gear in a remote position.

The present British Standard test requires the choke or ballast to be suspended in an echo-free enclosure and readings to be taken at various positions at a distance of 1 in. from the surface of the ballast. The r.m.s. summation of the noise levels measured must not exceed 30 dB. The measurements are made with a noise level meter as specified in BS 3489.

Work is being done by control gear makers and other interested bodies with the object of devising another method of noise testing to approximate more closely to the conditions which obtain when the ballast is mounted in a fitting. As different types of ballast have different noise levels, consideration is also being given to a system of noise grading for ballasts and/or fittings according to the environment for which they will be suitable.

Transistor and thyristor ballasts and invertors.　The high efficiency, long life and even illumination provided by fluorescent lamps makes this form of lighting attractive for the interiors of vehicles and aircraft. On transport vehicles it is necessary to convert the low-voltage d.c. from the battery to a.c. at higher voltage, and preferably at a high frequency, to operate fluorescent lamps. This is now done by static invertor equipment using semi-conductor devices. Battery drain is an important consideration; a heavy loading may be tolerated on vehicles covering long distances without stopping, but local delivery vans and city buses have a heavy drain because of regular starter motor use and because suitable engine speeds for peak recharging are rarely attained.

The light output per unit current drain from the battery (lm/A) is 3 to 4 times higher for invertor driven fluorescent lamps than for filament lamps. Invertors can be divided into two groups:

Group or bulk invertors.　In this system the low-voltage d.c. from the battery is converted into 200 V to 250 V a.c. at a frequency of 400 c/s to 3000 c/s or more by a large central thyristor invertor. This a.c. is then fed to individual fluorescent lamp circuits and fittings, which are provided with starterless ballasts usually of the semi-resonant type but adapted to high-frequency operation.

Individual invertors.　In this sytem the d.c. battery voltage is fed to each fluorescent lamp fitting containing a small transistor invertor to provide 5 kc/s to 20 kc/s a.c. which is then fed to a built-in ballast operating each lamp.

CHAPTER 24

Lighting Fittings and their Installation

The basic principles underlying the control and redistribution of light from a lamp have been dealt with in Chapter 6. The practical application of these principles to the design of lighting fittings will now be considered, together with other aspects which must be allowed for by the fittings designer, e.g. aesthetic appeal, mechanical construction, heating effects, electrical circuitry and installation conditions.

LIGHTING FITTINGS

Fundamental considerations. A lighting fitting has to fulfil several functions and satisfy a number of requirements.

By means of *optical control*, a fitting modifies the distribution of light emitted from a bare lamp so creating a more suitable distribution for a specific purpose. For example, the horizontally emitted light, which can cause glare, may be shielded from view, or diffused, or redirected to the working plane. Alternatively the upward lighting component may, if required, be redirected downwards.

Lamp protection. The fitting must be designed to support the lamp and also to afford it some protection from damage. Limited protection may be provided, as in open type fittings where only the electrical connections are enclosed, but more effective protection is provided in a totally enclosed fitting, e.g. one designed for use in 'hostile' atmospheres. Special protection may also be necessary to safeguard the lamp against vibration and shock, and also against the ingress of corrosive fumes and moisture. Design of protective enclosures must, however, allow for dissipation of the heat generated by the lamp (and sometimes auxiliary control gear) to avoid deterioration and inefficient operation of the fitting. The internal wiring of the fitting must also be protected against the effect of excess heat.

Mechanical design details. It is important to note that the design shape can affect the robustness of a fitting, e.g. a properly formed chassis or back-channel for a fluorescent tube can be made from 22 gauge sheet steel and yet have the strength of another fitting made from 20 gauge metal which does not have lengthwise forming to brace the section. Gauge of metal is not,

13+

therefore, the sole criterion of mechanical strength. Further strengthening can be obtained by the use of cross-brackets which have the combined effect of bracing the main chassis section and also acting as support platforms for reflector cover plates. These brackets and end diaphragms are normally spot-welded in position, although some invisible joints and corners may be gas welded.

Electrical safety. All electrical connections and cables must be adequately insulated and mechanically protected, allowing for the operating conditions in which the fitting is intended to be used, e.g. excess heat and humidity. The general conditions for meeting the normal requirements of electrical safety are laid down in the wiring regulations issued by the Institution of Electrical Engineers. British Standards also give guidance on detailed requirements for fittings design and a list of relevant specifications is given in the Bibliography.

Installation and maintenance features. The design must allow simplicity of access and assembly during installation, and the fitting must have ample capacity for incoming cables. Facilities must be provided for secure fixing, either by suspension or direct to the ceiling, and additional jointing accessories may be necessary when continuous end-to-end mounting of fluorescent fittings is required. Provision must be made for routine maintenance to be carried out quickly and simply, so as to allow the use of semi-skilled personnel with the minimum labour cost. Maintenance features should be such as to facilitate lamp replacement and the removal of attachments for cleaning, as well as routine electrical maintenance of internal wiring and any auxiliary control gear.

Economic justification. The lowest initial cost of fittings and lamps does not necessarily result in minimum overall lighting cost. Design features which may increase the cost of a fitting can result in a saving on maintenance or installation cost which is several times greater. Also, it is often found that a larger and, therefore, more expensive diffuser or reflector will have a higher light-output efficiency, as the lamp itself is less obstructive and, in the case of fittings for fluorescent tubes, the lower operating temperature in the larger fitting may give increased tube efficiency. In some circumstances a more expensive fitting with greater aesthetic appeal may be justified because of its prestige value in creating a more attractive or imposing installation.

Distribution classification. The basic efficiency of a lighting fitting is measured in terms of the *light-output ratio*, i.e. ratio of light emitted from the fitting to the total lumen output of the lamp(s) enclosed within the fitting. A lamp suspended on a cord-grip lampholder on a length of flexible cable would have a 100% light-output ratio, with virtually no fitting at all. It can be shown however, that by using, say, an effective reflector as part of the lighting fitting more flux can be redirected on to the working plane than is gained by comparatively inefficient reflection from the walls and ceiling of the room. In order to estimate true lighting efficiency, therefore, including the effect of wall and ceiling reflection, it is necessary to classify the performance of lighting fittings to take account of the directions in which proportions of the light flux are distributed. The *utilisation factor* indicates the performance of the fitting in specific interiors.

Gradings for light distribution for general lighting fittings are given in I.E.S. Technical Report No. 2, 'The Calculation of Coefficients of Utilisation', The British Zonal Method, which groups fittings into ten main distribution classes. Fittings are designed to give a distribution which approximates to one or other of these distribution classes (BZ1 to BZ10).

Choice of materials and finishes

Reflector materials. Sheet steel is the most commonly used material for the manufacture of industrial metal reflectors, owing to its mechanical strength. It cannot, however, be used in its natural state because of its tendency to rust and its lack of good reflecting properties. The metal must therefore be protected against corrosion and rusting by means of stoved or vitreous enamel finishes, which have partly diffuse reflecting properties (see later).

In designing reflectors it is desirable to avoid sharp edges and corners since the paint film would thin out at the edges, due to surface tension, and thus be more liable to damage. Reflectors for stove enamel finishing are normally constructed from sheet steel with a thickness of between 0·02 in. and 0·032 in., whilst reflectors for vitreous enamelling are normally made from material of about 0·036 in. thickness. Metalwork for vitreous enamelling must be specially constructed to avoid buckling at the very high temperatures to which it is subjected during the process, and the sheet steel must have a low carbon content and an open grain.

Aluminium is used for lightweight reflectors for fluorescent fittings, and can be spun into conical, spherical or other shapes for use with filament lamps. Although stove enamel finishes can be used also with aluminium, it is possible to get a good optical performance by polishing the metal and subsequently anodising the surface to protect it against corrosion by the formation of a relatively hard oxide film which may be transparent, thus preserving the appearance of the pretreated surface. It should be noted that corrosion due to electrochemical reaction will occur if aluminium is in contact with a dissimilar metal, such as brass, nickel, copper or phosphor bronze. This means that all non-aluminium accessories, such as support brackets, should be plated with a metal of intermediate potential, e.g. cadmium-plated steel (see Table 24.1).

Commercial grade aluminium has a reflection factor of 70% to 80% when polished and anodised. For even better optical performance, super purity grade (99·99%) aluminium is used in low-voltage spotlight fittings, and this gives nearly 90% reflection factor when polished, electrolytically brightened and anodised. However, new methods have been evolved for electrolytically and chemically polishing aluminium alloys to give a specular reflection factor approaching that of super-purity grade but without the extra cost or softness.

Plastics such as PVC or glass fibre are sometimes used in place of metal for reflectors and other parts of fluorescent fittings. These materials are non-

TABLE 24.1

Electrolytic Action

Materials should be selected to avoid a potential difference greater than 0·25 V. The potential difference between any pair is equal to the difference between the values given for each. The material having the higher potential will tend to corrode in contact with that of the lower potential.

Material	Potential against calomel electrode volts
Dural heat-treated and aged	0·65
Aluminium silicon	0·81
Aluminium	0·62
Brass	0·27
Aluminium bronze	0·26
Phosphor bronze	0·22
Copper	0·22
Monel	0·20
Nickel	0·22
Steels—stainless, austenitic	0·20
Chromium 12%	0·45
Steels—non-stainless, mild, semi-silver, etc.	0·79
Elekton (chromated)	1·59
Miscellaneous	
Cadmium plating	0·82
Zinc plating	1·13
Tin (tinned steel)	0·50
Tinmans solder	0·51
Nickel plating	0·22

corrosive and light in weight, but PVC is limited to operating temperatures below 70 °C and is also less rigid than metal reflectors. Translucent plastics are referred to in the section on diffusers.

Silvered glass has the best properties for accurate specular reflection, but glass reflectors are very vulnerable to mechanical and thermal shock and therefore have a limited application. A reflection factor of 80% to 90% is normally obtained, the usual method of manufacture being to coat the glass surface with silver or aluminium, which is then backed with a protective coating of copper and/or lead. A further protective coating of varnish or paint may also be applied.

Plated metal gives good specular reflection for spotlight fittings, and plated metal reflectors are also mechanically strong. Silver plating has an initial reflection factor of about 90% but is subject to tarnishing. Chromium plating has a lower reflection factor of 60% to 65% but does not tarnish. For highly corrosive atmospheres, polished stainless steel with a reflection factor of about 60% can be used, but this material is rather expensive.

Sheet-steel finishes. Standard stove enamel finish (based on alkyd resin) is used on most fittings for use indoors where the atmosphere is relatively dry (up to 80% relative humidity), free from chemical corrosion, and where heavy condensation is not likely to occur. The enamel is normally applied over a lightweight iron phosphate pretreatment of the steel surface, which ensures cleanliness and improves adhesion of the enamel.

In conditions of high humidity or heavy condensation water can penetrate the enamel at edges or other weak spots and outcrops of rust will result; similarly rusting will occur at the point of any mechanical damage where paint has been removed. The severity of the rusting and extent of spread from the outbreak will depend on the prevailing atmospheric conditions.

Acrylic stove enamel finish is a comparatively recent development and is generally used on all luxury range fittings. Here again the enamel is applied over a lightweight iron phosphate pretreatment but, due to the more impervious nature of the enamel, short term exposure to conditions of high humidity and condensation is withstood better than with standard finish. Being harder than standard finish, acrylic withstands abrasion better and therefore maintains gloss and colour longer; resistance to attack from chemicals is also superior.

The spread of rust from damaged areas in similar atmospheres will be slightly slower than with standard finish owing to the harder film, but this depends to a large extent on the type of pretreatment used.

Vitreous enamel is highly corrosion resistant and, since it is suitable for use in temperatures up to 200 °C, it is used extensively for filament lamp reflectors and in most other situations where resistance to high temperature is required. Vitreous enamel comprises a thin layer of glass which is fused into the metal surface at high temperature. A porous ground coat is first applied at a temperature of about 800 °C and a white finishing coat is then added. The resultant finish has a total thickness of about ·012 in.

Table 24.2 shows a typical test programme and representative results when tests are carried out on acrylic and standard stove enamel.

There are various acid-dip or electro-plating methods in use today, primarily for the protection of the base metal, but in some instances also serving as a decorative finish. Plating is used extensively to protect nuts, screws, brackets and other small parts, and is usually either cadmium or zinc. In normal atmospheres this protection is quite adequate, but in hostile atmospheres there is likely to be corrosion of the plated coating; however, since the protection of zinc and cadmium is by sacrificial action, no rusting of the steel will occur until the plating has been removed.

Plastics materials are used for finishes in very moist conditions (up to 100% humidity) and in corrosive areas. One of the most suitable materials is PVC. It is usually applied to form an envelope over the part to be protected, thus preventing the ingress of moisture or corrosive fumes and dust. The reaction of this material to various corrosive agents is shown in Table 24.3 and from this it can be seen that the material is unaffected by all agents except strong acids, thus making it ideally suited to most chemically contaminated atmospheres.

Plastics materials in lighting fittings. Opal translucent plastics are now used extensively for the manufacture of diffusers for fluorescent tubes as

TABLE 24.2

The Testing of Protective Finishes

	Minimum requirements	Probable result	
		Standard stove enamel	Acrylic stove enamel
1. Hardness tests. Special pencils of increasing hardness grade are pushed across the enamel surface until a hardness grade is reached which cuts through the enamel before the pencil breaks due to excessive pressure.	F	2H	5H
2. Scratch resistance. Enamel subject to 'strokes' with a point load of 1000 g until the paint finish is broken.	35 strokes	40 strokes	200 strokes
3. Stain resistance. Not specified, but ink, mustard and lipstick are good test samples.	No test	Slightly stained	Unstained
4. Heat and humidity resistance. The test calls for four 12-hour test cycles at 35 °C and 100% humidity on a sample where the finish has been cut with a razor blade. Corrosion shall not have penetrated more than $\frac{1}{32}$ in. from the cut and reflection factor shall not be less than 75%.		Passes	Passes

Note: BS 3820: Electric Light Fittings gives no details for testing of paint finishes, but the above tests indicate an acceptable standard.

Additional tests are carried out at 100% humidity with a cyclic variation between 42 °C and 48 °C every half hour. This produces heavy condensation on the test sample, as the 'dew point' is passed on both the rise and the fall stages. Although both standard and acrylic finishes meet the test limits, the acrylic sample gives better resistance to corrosion penetration and maintains a high gloss and reflection factor.

the operating temperature is fairly low, and long diffuser sections can be handled with less risk of breaking and injury than with glass. Various types of translucent plastics are now in use, and these include such materials as acrylic, PVC, polystyrene and glass fibre. Clear plastics material is also used but mainly for mechanical screening or enclosure of fluorescent tubes without diffusion of the light.

Acrylic material is supplied in sheet or granule form and is available in clear, opal or coloured grades. This material can be shaped by applying pressure whilst softened by heat, or extruded through a ring die and thus formed into the required diffuser shape. Injection moulding of the material is also frequently used for small items or diffusers. Since standard grade acrylics will 'support combustion' they may not be suitable for use in cinemas and public halls where special fire regulations are applicable.

Polystyrene is often used as an alternative to acrylics, as it has similar optical properties, but it is unsuitable for exterior use. Ordinary grades of polystyrene tend to become yellow with age owing to the effect of ultraviolet, but special light-stabilised grades of polystyrene are available.

It should be noted that diffusers designed to give close optical control can be either extruded or injection moulded, but the latter process usually gives more consistent results. Injection moulding of long diffusers, i.e. 4 ft and above, is usually uneconomical and the extrusion process is normally used.

Glass fibre is a material consisting of filaments of glass woven into mats and impregnated with various resins. These resins can either offer resistance to chemicals, heat and burning or provide great mechanical strength (properties vary widely with different types). Glass fibre has good weathering properties without the need for paint finishes. Hand lay-up mouldings (moulded detail one side only) require only a low tool cost but production rate is slow and moulding cost high. Matched metal mouldings (moulded detail both sides) permit faster production with lower unit cost but expensive tools are required.

Opal vinyl is supplied in thin sheets which can be formed into moulded dishes or corrugated sheets to give added strength for use with suspended luminous ceiling systems. Flexible vinyl, which is available in clear, opal and a range of colours, is also used. This material is available in a self-extinguishing grade, which does not support combustion.

Urea formaldehyde is a thermo-setting material used primarily for compression moulding of small accessories where its electrical and self-extinguishing characteristics are important. Lampholders are often made from this material. For conditions in which even better heat stability is required, a phenolic material can be used.

Table 24.3 shows how some of the plastics materials react to climatic, chemical and other conditions.

TABLE 24.3

Properties of some Plastics Materials

Effect	Glass fibre	Urea	Acrylic	PVC	Polystyrene
Burning rate	Slow	Self-extinguishing	Slow	Self-extinguishing	Slow
Of sunlight	Slight	Slight	Very slight	Slight	Slight
Of weak acid	Slight	Slight	None	None	None
Of strong acid	Attacked	Attacked	Attacked	Slight	Attacked
Of weak alkalis	Slight	Slight	None	None	None
Of strong alkalis	Strong attack	Strong attack	Attacked	None	None
Of organic solvents	None	None	*	*	None

* These materials are attacked by some solvents, particularly those used in cellulose lacquers and some stoving enamels. It is unlikely that enough solvent vapour would be present in the atmosphere to attack acrylic.

Glass in lighting fittings. In making incandescent filament lamp diffusers, opal glass is often used because of the relatively high operating temperatures (above 80 °C), though some modern fittings have been designed which permit the use of plastics by keeping the lamp well away from the diffuser. Clear glass (with 85% to 90% transmission factor) is used for the mechanical screening or enclosure of filament lamps without diffusion, but where diffusion is required, the following kinds of glass are used:

Acid etched clear glass is available with fine or coarse texture, the various grades having reflection factors of 10% to 25% and transmission factors of 70% to 85%. This material gives only partial diffusion of light.

Pot opal glass is the most dense diffusing material since it consists entirely of particles of calcium fluoride which have different refractive indices, and thus the individual light rays are completely inter-mixed. Pot opal has a reflection factor of 50% to 70% and a transmission factor of 20% to 40%.

Two- or three-ply opal glass consists of a layer of pot opal glass with a layer of clear glass on one or both sides. This arrangement has the advantage that the layer of pot opal gives the necessary diffusion whilst the clear glass layers give added strength and allow the use of thin opal layers. Opal ply glass has an average reflection factor of 45% and a transmission factor of 50%. This type of glass may be given a satin finish by applying a light acid etch to both inner and outer surfaces, and this prevents specular surface reflections.

Clear patterned glass can also be used to give a degree of diffusion, the more commonly used finishes being pinhead, reeded and hammered patterns.

Fabrics and miscellaneous materials. Plastics-coated fabrics, plain fabrics and plastics films are used as diffusing screens in the design of some domestic lighting fittings, but the operating temperature must be fairly low.

In addition to materials chosen for their optical properties, others are required to form the lamp support or general enclosure sections. Non-ferrous metals such as brass, bronze, copper and gunmetal are sometimes used for decorative filament lamp fittings. Castings in aluminium, iron or zinc alloy are also used for certain industrial fittings such as bulkhead and wellglass units, as well as for specialised lighting units designed for exterior or flame-proof use. Opaque plastics materials are often used in place of wood or metal in domestic lighting fittings, owing to their smooth finish and the fact that they can be moulded into attractive shapes fairly cheaply.

Fittings for various operating conditions. All fittings should be designed to comply with British Standards and to meet specified variations in operating conditions and should comply with one or more of the following definitions of protection against moisture, dust and corrosion.

Ordinary fittings. These fittings are constructed to operate continuously in normal dry indoor locations such as shops, offices and general industrial premises where no atmospheric contamination is present, as well as for most domestic interiors except kitchens and bathrooms.

Drip-proof fittings. These fittings are designed to operate continuously and satisfactorily in locations where drops of water may fall on the fitting when

it is mounted in its normal position, e.g. under a surface from which condensation may drip, such as cinema entrance canopies, loading bays and
covered forecourts.

Rainproof fittings. Fittings under this classification are constructed to operate
in all weather conditions for normal exterior use, e.g. a lantern mounted on a
column or to the exterior of a building, for street-lighting or floodlighting
purposes. Fittings designed for these applications need very special consideration to combat not only the ingress of water but also the probability of
corrosive effects.

Jetproof fittings. Designed for use in car washing bays and non-immersed
fountain illumination, these fittings must withstand a direct jet of water from
any direction without affecting their satisfactory operation.

Dustproof fittings. Fittings so constructed that dust of a specified nature and
fineness cannot enter in an amount sufficient to interfere with the satisfactory
operation of the fitting. During the design procedure it is necessary to simulate
dusty conditions of various degrees of severity, and Fig. 24.1 shows the test
chamber in use.

Fig. 24.1   Apparatus for dustproof testing

In very dusty atmospheres special attention must be paid to the cleaning
and maintenance of the exterior of the fittings. When selecting fittings for use
in heavily laden atmospheres, such as cement works, corn chandlers, etc., it
may be necessary to choose fittings with clear plastics enclosures so that
maximum light output is obtained.

Various other 'clean' installations, such as food factories, may require
dustproof fittings for an entirely different reason, e.g. to prevent any small
amounts of dust in the atmosphere from entering the fitting and so eliminate
the possibility of food being contaminated when lighting maintenance is

carried out. A very important feature which is normally required in these installations is enclosure of the tube and the facility for replacing lamps at ground level, thus eliminating the possibility of broken tubes falling into the food vats.

Flameproof fittings. Filament lamp and fluorescent fittings are available to satisfy flameproof requirements in certain groups of gases detailed in the following list:

Group I	Methane
Group II	Petroleum vapours and a variety of industrial vapours and gases
Group IIIA	Ethylene and similar gases
Group IIIB	Town gas and coke oven gas
Group IV	Hydrogen and acetylene

BS 889 and BS 229 state that flameproof lighting fittings must be designed to withstand an explosion of the gas group concerned within the fitting without igniting an explosive atmosphere of the same gas group outside the fitting.

Flameproof lighting fittings are certified for use with particular gas groups as indicated below:

Fluorescent and incandescent fittings are available for all except Group IV. No fittings have been certified for use in Group IV, so lighting must be provided through sealed armour plate-glass windows, or by using pressurised fittings with automatic cut-out relays to disconnect the supply in the event of the pressure falling. Of necessity, flameproof fittings are bulky and are also expensive. In some situations, therefore, such as cellulose paint spraying booths, it may be cheaper to use standard fittings outside the flameproof area and to direct the light into the room through glass or plastics windows.

Division 2 fittings. Certain hazardous industrial units such as petrol-storage depots, oil refineries, flour mills and some chemical works, have a limited explosion or fire risk which can be catered for by 'Division 2' fittings. In designing fittings for these locations various precautions need to be taken, including:

(1) Ensuring that an adequate seal between separable parts is obtained. To determine this, a test has been devised (using again the apparatus shown in Fig. 24.1) which entails building up the pressure within the fitting to 12 in. water gauge above atmospheric, and allowing this to fall to 6 in. water gauge above atmospheric in not less than 30 seconds.

(2) Ensuring that no external part exceeds a temperature of 200 °C (391 °F).

(3) Ensuring that the possibility of sparking within the fitting is eliminated. This means that the standard pinch type of terminal is not permitted and special methods must be used such as clamping plates, soldered ferrules, friction-fit tags, etc.

Operation at high temperatures. The limitation of temperature is one of the most important factors in lighting fitting design, as heat can affect the life and performance of the lamps as well as any associated control gear, and even the protective finish of the fitting wiring. Undue heat can cause plastics materials to soften or lose their shape. Heated ceilings also present special problems. The following section deals with these problems, and suggests how they can be overcome.

Incandescent lamp fittings. The operating temperature of the tungsten filament in these lamps is in the region of 3000 °C and therefore a small increase of 10 °C or 20 °C in the ambient temperature will have very little effect on light output or life. It is important, however, that the capping cement joint between brass lamp cap and glass bulb does not exceed 210 °C. Careful consideration must therefore be given to the design of the fitting and lampholder to achieve this.

Because of conduction and convection currents, a considerable heat build-up will be maintained in the area just above the lamp. It is essential therefore that the mains cable connected to the lampholder should have insulation capable of withstanding temperatures of 100 °C or even more in certain cases, e.g. decorative fittings with a tightly fitting shade surrounding the lamp. The temperature limitations of conventional rubber and thermoplastic cables are detailed in Table 24.4. These limiting temperatures are those found to be appropriate in lighting fittings, but they are not necessarily those recommended by the cable manufacturer.

TABLE 24.4

Maximum Temperature Rating of Cables

Type of Insulation	°C	(°F)
Vulcanised rubber insulated cable	60	(140)
PVC general purpose	70	(158)
Polythene	70	(158)
Butyl rubber	85	(185)
PVC high temperature	105	(221)
Varnished terylene	110	(230)
Silicon rubber	150	(302)
Impregnated glass fibre	130	(266)*
,, ,, ,,	180	(356)*

* According to type of impregnating resin.

Extreme care must be taken when relamping fittings of an early design, since it may now be physically possible to relamp these fittings with the new small type 100 W lamps although originally they may have been designed to accept 40 W or 60 W lamps only.

Fluorescent lamps and fittings. Fig. 20.3 in Chapter 20 shows the effect of variations in the operating temperature of a fluorescent tube on its efficiency. When a fluorescent tube is first switched on, the tube surface has the same temperature as the room, i.e. about 20 °C to 25 °C (68 °F to 77 °F). The diagram shows that the initial light output obtained from the tube is about 75% of its peak output. Within 3 or 4 minutes of switching on, the tube warms up and when the temperature at the coolest part of the tube surface reaches about 38 °C the tube will be found to give 100% light output. In practice, the coolest part of a fluorescent tube is usually at the bottom centre of the tube, as the additional heating of the cathode filaments increases the temperature at the tube ends.

If the temperature of the glass tube is allowed to rise above 38 °C then the light-output efficiency falls steadily, and the diagram shows that a drop of approximately 1% in light output is produced for every 1 °C rise in tube temperature. In practice it is not always possible to make tubes operate at exactly 38 °C but efficiencies of over 90% of peak value can be achieved when the tube temperature is between 30 °C and 50 °C.

Control gear and accessories. High tube temperatures also cause the circuit current to increase, which in turn can cause overheating of the choke unit. Under normal operating conditions, fluorescent lighting control gear runs hotter when mounted inside a fitting than it does in free air. This is particularly so when the fitting has more than one tube mounted below the control gear chassis and where the tubes are enclosed within a diffuser. It has been found that a good quality choke with class A insulation will give an average life of about 10 to 20 years under ordinary operating conditions, assuming that its winding temperature does not exceed 105 °C (see Fig. 23.4). When this temperature is exceeded, insulating materials such as enamel and paper used to insulate the coil winding from the metal core of a choke will gradually deteriorate at an increasing rate and will eventually lead to failure of the choke. A similar effect will be experienced with power-factor correction capacitors.

With Permaset filled control gear the temperature difference between the internal winding and the metal case can be as small as 15 °C and this means that a surface temperature on the choke of up to 90 °C can be experienced without any serious effect on the life of the choke. Because of this, care should be taken to avoid contact between the choke surface and any materials with a low melting point. Particular consideration should be given to cables which, through necessity, must pass near the choke and the correct type as detailed in Table 24.4 should be used, e.g. high temperature grade PVC cable or equivalent.

If standard grade cable of 60° C (140 °F) to 70 °C (158 °F) rating is used for incoming mains connections, then each core should be suitably sheathed with glass insulated sleeves where it is likely to touch the surface of a choke unit or, alternatively, a heat insulating barrier should be inserted between the cable and choke surface to ensure satisfactory cooling.

Power-factor correction capacitors do not generate any appreciable heat within themselves, but care should be taken not to locate these components near to choke units or other 'hot spots' within the chassis enclosure. The maximum operating temperature of capacitors is discussed in Chapter 23.

In certain situations in which it is not convenient or desirable to mount control gear in the direct vicinity of the fluorescent tube, the gear may be accommodated by mounting it on a convenient wall area. Where a large number of control gear components are to be mounted close together in this way, care must be taken to avoid overheating. As a standard practice, it is recommended that individual control gear components (choke, capacitor and starting device) should be mounted on metal-base trays and these trays should be spaced away from the wall by means of brackets to allow free air flow on all sides of the components. Because the choke unit develops the most heat, it is desirable to mount the gear trays so that the choke units are upper-most and the starting device and capacitor are below. Should the banks of control gear subsequently be enclosed in some form of protective cupboard, then arrangements must be made for the top and bottom sections of the cupboard to be left open (perforated metal mesh can be used) to allow ventilation.

Heated ceilings. Heated ceilings are usually designed to give a comfortable working temperature at desk level of about 20 °C (68 °F). This means that the air temperature at ceiling level is considerably higher and usually varies between 25 °C (77 °F) immediately beneath the ceiling to 45 °C (113 °F) in the void above the fittings. In addition, the heated ceiling or hot-water pipes can vary between 65 °C (149 °F) and 80 °C (176 °F). If standard fluorescent fittings are specified for use in these situations they must be suspended at least 6 in. beneath the ceiling to enable cool air to circulate and thus reduce the surrounding air temperature to not more than 25 °C (77 °F). If it is essential that fittings be close mounted against or within a heated ceiling then special consideration must be given to the control gear if a satisfactory life is to be expected.

If standard fittings must be used in hot situations then reference should be made to Fig. 23.1 to determine the expected control gear life. For example, if the continuous operating temperature of the air at fitting level is as high as 40 °C (104 °F), i.e. 15 °C (57 °F) above the maximum specified, then choke life may be reduced to approximately 30% of its rated life, about 3 to 6 years.

Operation at low temperatures. For exterior operation of fluorescent tubes in ambient temperatures near freezing point, it is likely that quick-start type circuits will prove less satisfactory than starter-switch or resonant-start circuits. Where it is necessary to operate 5 ft tubes on quick-start circuits at temperatures between 0 °C and +5 °C it is recommended that metal strip grade 'White' 5 ft 65/80 W tubes be used, as these have a lower argon gas pressure than normal tubes, and this assists starting.

A special lighting problem which has become increasingly more important is the lighting of refrigerated cold stores, which can be sub-divided into the following categories:

(1) *Chill stores*
    These are buildings in which products such as milk and butter are

kept in a temperature just above freezing, i.e. between 0 °C (32 °F) and 5 °C (40 °F).

(2) *Cold stores*

These are buildings in which the temperature is constantly maintained below freezing point. These buildings can be sub-divided into the following two groups:

Those cold stores ranging from above −15 °C (5 °F) to 0 °C (32 °F) and where products such as meat and some frozen foods are being stored.

Other cold stores for ice cream and deep-frozen foods, operating at sub-zero temperatures below 0 °F, i.e. −30 °C (−22 °F) to −15 °C (5 °F).

There are three main problems which have had to be solved in designing satisfactory cold-store fluorescent lighting:

(1) Starting of a fluorescent lamp becomes more difficult as the temperature becomes lower and at the extreme value of −30 °C (−22 °F it is necessary to use a special switch-start control gear circuit.

(2) The light output from a fluorescent tube falls rapidly if the temperature of the tube surface is very much below the optimum value of 38 °C at which peak light output is obtained.

(3) The fitting should not overheat when operating at normal room temperature during shut-down periods.

For cold stores between 0 °C (32 °F) and −10 °C (+14 °F) the light output of an orthodox fitting would drop appreciably, but a fitting can be used which has a 2 in. diameter clear plastics sleeve enclosing the fluorescent tube over its entire length. Heat is retained within this sleeve and the fitting is suitable for cold stores operating just below freezing point. For deep-freeze cold stores below −10° C (+14 °F), particularly where strong air blast cooling is applied, the insulation effect of a single plastics sleeve may not be adequate and further protection is required, consisting of a 2½ in. diameter sleeve fitted over the standard 2 in. diameter sleeve. This arrangement has been found to be satisfactory for cold stores where the ambient temperature ranges from −15 °C (+5 °F) to −30 °C (−22 °F). The fitting with a double sleeve can be used without risk of overheating of the control gear or tube when in a normal room temperature of 20 °C (68 °F) as may be experienced during periods when the cold store is shut down for renovation or repairs, though at this higher ambient temperature the light output of the tube will, of course, be reduced.

Operating temperature in enclosed fluorescent fittings. The need to restrict glare has encouraged the use of diffuser types of fluorescent fittings, and where these are totally enclosed the operating temperature of the tube can rise appreciably. The light output can therefore be significantly reduced unless the fitting is carefully designed, taking full account of the electrical and thermal conditions.

Efficient operation of a diffuser type fitting can be promoted in one or more of the following ways:

(1) By correct choice of tube loading, e.g. 65 W instead of 80 W for a 5 ft tube.
(2) By providing ventilation of the diffuser.
(3) By the use of measures which cool a small area of the tube surface. One method is to fit a mechanical cooler in the form of a solid metal block which conducts heat from a small area of the top surface of the tube to the cooler region within the metal chassis of the fitting. Alternatively, the diffuser can be designed to produce a jet of cool air directed on to the bottom centre of the tube.
(4) By increasing the size of the diffuser enclosure.

To illustrate the importance of these four factors, Table 24.5 shows the effect on alternative designs of a twin tube 5 ft diffuser fitting, and that the light-output ratio of the fitting can vary from 70% to 53% according to its design.

TABLE 24.5

Comparative Efficiencies of Enclosed Fluorescent Fittings

Type of fitting and tubes				Light-output ratio
Twin 5 ft 65 W	Ventilated	No coolers	Large diffuser	70%
,, 5 ft 80 W	,,	,,	,,	66%
,, 5 ft 80 W	Unventilated	,,	,,	60%
,, ,,	,,	,,	Small diffuser	53%
,, ,,	,,	With coolers	,,	62%
,, ,,	,,	,,	Large diffuser	67%

The effectiveness of a mechanical cooler is dependent on the difference in temperature between the top surface of the tube and the air in the metal chassis of the fitting, so a bigger advantage is obtained by adding coolers to a small unventilated diffuser with 80 W tubes than to a large ventilated diffuser with 65 W tubes. In practice it is found that by using 5 ft 65 W tubes in a large ventilated type diffuser fitting, the light output is only a little lower than that obtained from an equivalent 5 ft 80 W diffuser fitting, because the 5 ft tube operating at 65 W has an efficiency 6 lm/W higher than the same tube operating at 80 W. On the other hand, the lower loaded tube offers a considerable saving in current consumed.

THE INSTALLATION OF FLUORESCENT FITTINGS

Special factors apply to the installation of fluorescent lighting fittings which do not apply to incandescent filament lamps. A brief summary of the more important factors is given below.

Switching transients. A fluorescent lighting circuit normally incorporates an inductive iron-cored ballast with a capacitor which is directly connected across the mains input terminals. Thus when an a.c. supply is connected to the circuit, a momentary surge (or transient) occurs due to the storage of energy by the capacitor. Oscillograph measurements have shown that the transient charging current taken by the capacitor can be 10 or 20 times greater than the steady circuit current, e.g. more than 10 A in the case of a single 5 ft 80 W tube circuit. It is also found that when the circuit is switched off, the sudden collapse of the magnetic field in the iron-cored choke also causes a transient surge, which can result in a high voltage pulse of several thousand volts.

The exact pulse value created by transient switching surges depends on the following factors:

(1) The instantaneous value of the alternating supply.
(2) The impedance of the mains distribution system back to the generator.
(3) The nature of the switch mechanism that breaks the circuit.
(4) The type of fluorescent lighting circuit.

It will be found that much higher switching transients will be measured on a circuit which is connected close to a main sub-station than on a circuit which is at the end of a fairly long low-voltage feeder cable. The type of switch used will also vary the transient peak value, so as to cause surges of over 3000 V (this maximum voltage pulse is normally caused when a 'quick-break' switch is used to interrupt the current flow through an inductive circuit).

Of the standard lighting switches in common use, the 'quick-make' and 'quick-break' type of switch adequately deals with the initial charging surge of the capacitor but causes excessively high voltage surges when breaking the circuit. With the 'a.c. only' type of switch (slow-make and slow-break) there is a greater tendency for the contacts to weld together when making the circuit, but the transient voltage pulse when the circuit is opened is substantially reduced. For these reasons, the ideal switching arrangement for fluorescent tube circuits would be one comprising a 'quick-make' and 'slow-break' mechanism.

Experience has shown that 'all-insulated' switches are normally preferable for fluorescent circuits. Care should be taken when selecting switches which have a quick-break action, or switches with an earthed metal action or cover plate, since these may not withstand the switching transients produced by fluorescent lighting between "line" and "earth".

Fuse ratings. Because of the previously mentioned switching surges, it is necessary to use a higher fuse rating than that of the steady running current taken by the circuit. Although satisfactory operation may be obtained with 'rewireable type' fuses (without premature failure of the fuse element) when the fuse rating is only $1\frac{1}{4}$ times the steady circuit current, it may be necessary to use a higher fuse rating when high rupturing capacity (H.R.C.) cartridge fuses are employed. For example, a single 5 ft 80 W tube circuit will have a steady running current of approximately $\frac{1}{2}$ A, but because of the quick response of the fuse element in clearing an excess current load it is necessary to use a 2 A rated fuse in order to ensure that the element will not fail under transient conditions. Similarly, a 5 A cartridge fuse is only suitable for loads of up to four 80 W tubes (2 A steady load current).

This 'down rating' requirement with H.R.C. cartridge fuses must be carefully considered when planning the wiring installation, since if larger fuses are needed to overcome switching transients, then it may be necessary to increase the size of cables and accessories in order to meet the requirements of I.E.E. Wiring Regulations which state that all wiring must be at least equal to the rating of the fuse which protects the circuit.

Three-phase lighting circuits. Because voltages in excess of 400 V exist between the phase or line conductors of a 3-phase supply, it is normally recommended that all lighting equipment in a given room should be connected to the same phase conductor thus limiting the maximum voltage present to 250 V. I.E.E. Wiring Regulations also state that where medium voltage (in excess of 250 V) is present, then all conductors must be enclosed in earthed metalwork and not be readily accessible. Also, where it is necessary or desirable to install lighting fittings on different phases, then the fittings must be at least 6 ft apart.

It is often desirable to use more than one phase in a given workshop or building since it is then possible to run adjoining rows of fittings on different phases, thus helping to balance out the load on 3-phase fuse-boards and reducing stroboscopic flicker. Improved after-glow with modern tubes now makes single-phase lighting acceptable without the need for lead-lag circuits.

Earthed neutral supplies. In the standard 3-phase 4-wire a.c. distribution system which is used in Britain, the neutral conductor is bonded to earth throughout the distribution network. This means that the neutral conductor is at earth potential, i.e. if a voltage of 240 V exists between line and neutral then there will also be a potential difference of 240 V between line and earth. In the case of fluorescent fittings with quick-start control gear, the best starting performance is obtained when the metalwork adjacent to the exterior glass tube surface is at the same potential as one of the internal end electrodes. This can be achieved, in the case of an 'earthed-neutral' supply, by bonding the metalwork to earth, which is virtually the same as connecting it to the neutral electrode. Note that this bonding of the metalwork to earth will not provide efficient quick-start operation in the case of special supply systems where the normal 200/250 V input is obtained between phases, since 'earth' potential is then midway between the phase (and electrode) voltages.

Harmonics and neutral current in a.c. circuits. A standard 50 c/s alternating voltage is normally produced by the power station alternators as a pure sine wave-shape, but it is possible for the voltage wave-shape to become slightly distorted by the time it reaches the final user. This distortion is due to a small percentage of 'harmonics', i.e. ripples on the pure sine wave-shape which represent higher frequencies than the basic 50 c/s alternating voltage. For example, it is possible to pick up harmonic distortion from the local distribution load and it may be found that the wave-shape of the supply voltage being received on the premises is not a perfect sine wave but contains about 1% or 2% harmonics. This variation in harmonics in the supply voltage will normally affect the larger and more important harmonic percentage in the load current, i.e. it is not possible to quote just one precise value of percentage harmonics in the load current per phase, since this may vary with the percentage harmonics in the supply voltage.

In some circuits, a capacitor is connected directly across the main supply terminals of a lighting fitting, so as to correct the lagging power factor created by inductive choke ballasts. These capacitors have the effect of reducing the mains current but do not normally reduce the 'harmonic current' caused by the distorted wave-shape. Therefore, as a general rule, the mains current is reduced as the power factor of the circuit is improved but the 'per cent harmonics' will increase. For example, if a single tube circuit has a power factor of say 0·8 then it may have a mains current of 0·5 A whilst the 'harmonic current' included in this total may be about 0·1 A, i.e. 20% harmonics per phase. If the power factor is now improved to unity, then the mains current will be reduced from 0·5 A to 0·4 A but the harmonic content will still be 0·1 A. This means that the 'per cent harmonics per phase' is now 25%. It is also possible that the 'harmonic current' produced in the mains can be further increased by the power factor correction capacitors, because these capacitors will have a lower impedance to the higher frequency harmonics. Allowing for all the factors above, the values of 'per cent harmonics' applicable to standard fluorescent tube circuits are shown in Table 24.6.

TABLE 24.6

Effect of Harmonics from Standard Circuits (240/415 V supply)

Tube size	Type of circuit	% Harmonics per phase	Value per phase		Value in neutral	
			Mains current (amps)	Harmonic current (amps)	Minimum current (amps)	Maximum current (amps)
8 ft 125 W	Switchstart (Leading P.F.)	14/15	0·94	0·135	0·405	0·97
8 ft 125 W	Quickstart (special H.P.F.)	8/9	0·66	0·055	0·165	0·67
8 ft 85 W	Twinstart (series pair ballast)	13/14	(2) 0·90	(2) 0·12	(2) 0·36	(2) 0·93
8 ft 85 W	Quickstart (single tube unit)	7/8	0·42	0·03	0·09	0·43
5 ft 80 W	Switchstart (no PFC capacitor)	6/7	0·85	0·055	0·165	0·86
5 ft 80 W	Switchstart (leading P.F.)	14/15	0·85	0·12	0·36	0·88
5 ft 80 W	Switchstart (twin lead-lag)	21/22	(2) 0·80	(2) 0·175	(2) 0·525	(2) 0·86
5 ft 80 W	Switchstart (@ 0·85 lagging)	15/18	0·46	0·075	0·225	0·48
5 ft 80 W	Switchstart (@ 0·90 lagging)	17/20	0·43	0·08	0·24	0·46
5 ft 80 W	Switchstart (@ 0·95 lagging)	19/22	0·41	0·085	0·255	0·44
5 ft 80 W	Quickstart (@ 0·85 lagging)	15/18	0·48	0·075	0·225	0·50
5 ft 65 W	Switchstart (@ 0·85 lagging)	15/18	0·37	0·06	0·18	0·39
5 ft 65 W	Resonant start (@ 0·92 lagging)	24/25	0·36	0·085	0·255	0·39
(100 W)	(Standard filament lamp example)	(1/2)	(0·42)	(0·01)	(0·03)	(0·42)

The table shows the range of '% harmonics per phase' and the average third harmonic current which will be produced in each phase, when allowing for about 1% to 2% harmonics in the supply voltage which is feeding the circuits.

Note: Minimum neutral current flows when the load is perfectly balanced in all three phases, whilst maximum neutral current occurs when there is full load on only two phases (no load on third phase).

CHAPTER 25

Lighting for Industry

This chapter discusses suitable lamps and fittings for the general and local lighting of industrial interiors, with information on lighting design. The closely linked subjects of lighting for inspection and the maintenance of lighting installations are dealt with in Chapters 26 and 30 respectively.

Good lighting in industrial interiors is recognised as one of the most important ways of ensuring increased efficiency and quality of the manufactured product; it tends to reduce accidents and generally assists in the well-being of personnel.

Care of the operator's sight and provision of the best seeing conditions for manufacturing operations is the concern of specialists such as the architect, lighting engineer, works engineer and safety officer. Thus in designing the building the architect ensures that windows are suitably positioned so as to provide a sufficient quantity, quality and direction of daylight on the working area, and that suitable visual rest centres are provided for operators when not critically viewing the task. The lighting engineer should arrange for adequate lighting and design of the visual field. The works engineer arranges suitable layout of factory machinery and equipment, including visual aids. The works safety officer ensures the enforcement of Government regulations such as the wearing of goggles as a protection from glare and invisible radiations from arc-welding equipment. Though the 1941 Factories (Standards of Lighting) Regulations specified a minimum general level of 6 lm/ft² at 3 ft above the floor, present-day minimum recommended amenity lighting in most work areas is 15 lm/ft².

The visual task. Discussion under the general heading of *Visual inspection analysis* (Chapter 26), including illumination levels, the use of natural and artificial light and inspection booths, is equally applicable to the more general visual tasks where lighting is required for manufacture of the product. The Illuminating Engineering Society's Code gives tables of recommended minimum illumination and limiting values of glare index for many specific industrial tasks; where illumination values are not listed a nomogram can be used which takes account of the reflection factor of the lightest part of the critical detail of the visual task and its apparent size. This nomogram is given in the I.E.S. Code.

As in all visual tasks, correct design of the visual field is most important and includes such techniques as outward grading of the brightness from the task to the intermediate background and surround.

The operator performing the visual task sees the work against its immediate background which should preferably contrast with it either in colour, or brightness, or both. The intermediate background and surround should in general be less bright than the task or immediate background. This assists the operator's concentration on the work in hand, reduces the danger of undue brightness contrasts, and provides visual rest areas when he is not critically viewing the product.

Many visual tasks involve the critical examination of objects which are moving relative to the observer, as on conveyor belts. Good contrast and adequate illumination are important, but the time available to recognise and classify possible defects which are outside the tolerance limits is usually relatively short. This throws more nervous strain on the operator so that it is even more important to maintain good seeing conditions.

Choice of light source. Choice of light source depends mainly on efficiency, lumen maintenance, life and cost, but also on the quality of the light, the degree of diffusion required, whether the amount of heat generated with the light reaching the workplane is important, the ease of light control, and the physical size of the source. Table 25.1 compares some of the more important aspects of lamps commonly used for general and local lighting in industrial areas. Additional information on the various types of lamps is

TABLE 25.1

Major Characteristics of Light Sources for Industrial Lighting

Light source	Wattage range	Gear losses (if any)	Rated life (hours)	Luminous efficiency (exclud. gear losses) lm/W	Colour rendering
GLS incandescent (100 V to 130 V and 200 V to 250 V)	25–1500	Nil	1000	10–20	Acceptable
Tungsten-halogen incandescent (burning position horizontal ±4°) (110 V to 120 V and 240 V)	500–1500	Nil	2000	22	Whiter than GLS sources
Low-voltage incandescent (12 V to 24 V)	50–150	10%	1000	15–18	Whiter than GLS sources
Tubular fluorescent high efficiency	20–125	20%	7500	68–(5 ft 80 W) 72–(8 ft 125 W)	Acceptable
Tubular fluorescent good colour rendering	20–125	20%	7500	35	Good
Miniature tubular fluorescent	4–13	80%	5000	35	Acceptable
Colour-corrected high-pressure mercury vapour	80–1000	15%	5000	31–39	Fair
Sodium	45–200	25%	6000	69–125	Poor

given in earlier chapters. Other salient points of these lamps when used for industrial lighting are:

Incandescent filament lamps. The small filament size allows close optical control for directional and local lighting. Where the absence of heat with the light is desirable special integral reflector lamps using dichroic coatings can reflect the light in the desired direction but allow transmission of the infrared through the reflector away from the workplane.

Tubular fluorescent lamps. Compared with GLS incandescent filament lamps the fluorescent lamp, with its high efficiency, results in energy economy and lower wiring costs, since fewer lighting points are required for a given illumination. Its comparatively large source area and low brightness, though still requiring some screening, minimise glare and shadows.

Colour-corrected mercury vapour lamps. Colour-corrected mercury vapour lamps in external reflectors and the similar type of lamp with integral internal reflector (usually with some additional screening to reduce glare) are being extensively used for industrial lighting, both inside buildings and for flood-lighting marshalling yards and factory approach roads.

Sodium lamps. Sodium vapour lamps are little used in industrial lighting of interiors due to their monochromatic spectrum and their resultant poor colour rendering. They are sometimes used for roads and some loading bays.

Light source suitability and factory size. The extent to which present ranges and types of light sources are suitable for particular factory sizes and proportions has been examined theoretically, some of the results being indicated in Figs. 25.1, 25.2 and 25.3. Fig. 25.1 gives a family of curves indicating the

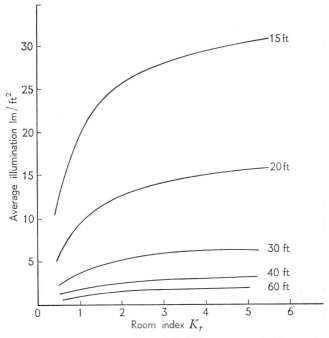

Fig. 25.1   Variations in illumination with different room indices and mounting heights for an array of fittings of 10,000 lumens per point

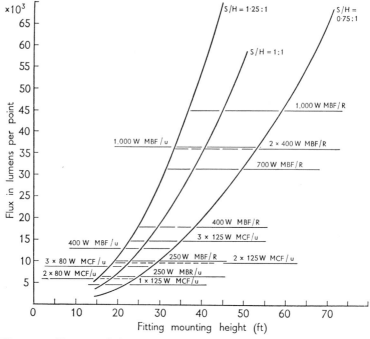

Fig. 25.2   Types and sizes of lamps/fittings at various mounting heights
to give 15 lm/ft²

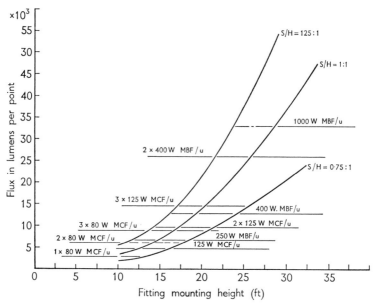

Fig. 25.3   Types and sizes of lamps/fittings at various mounting heights
to give 30 lm/ft²

average illumination on the workplane for a formation of lighting units of 10,000 lm per point, when at mounting heights of 15 ft to 60 ft, for factories of room index, $K_r = 0.5$ to 5.0. Figs. 25.2 and 25.3 relate lm per point against mounting height for three spacing/height ratios for workplane illumination of 15 and 30 lm/ft² respectively. The ranges of usefulness of various source types and wattages are indicated, allowance having been made in the calculations for variations in source luminous efficiency, fitting light-output ratio, fitting intensity distribution and average fitting and room surface reflectivities. The data apply strictly only to factories of average room index, $K_r = 2$ to $K_r = 3$, and therefore the data should be used only as a guide to the number of fittings of any given type for a particular installation. For values of K_r less than 2, the number of fittings should be increased by 10%, i.e. spacing/mounting-height ratio should be decreased. For values of K_r greater than 3 the spacing/mounting-height ratio should be increased slightly.

Choice of lighting fittings. Selection of lighting fittings depends on such factors as the type of light source, the required light distribution, screening angle to control glare, method of fixing and whether the fittings will satisfactorily withstand local conditions of temperature, dust and corrosion.

In the past, the light distributions of fittings were classified by such terms as dispersive or concentrating and later by the words broad, narrow and extra narrow; light distributions are now classified by their British Zonal (BZ) classification as given in the I.E.S. Technical Report No. 2.

General lighting fittings. Fig. 25.4 shows two typical general lighting fittings used in industrial locations. The tubular fluorescent fitting and spun-metal reflector fitting (for either incandescent or mercury vapour lamps) are slotted in their upper surfaces to give some upward light and promote convected air currents which help to maintain lamps and fittings clean.

Screening of fluorescent lamp reflector fittings, particularly in the plane of the minor axis, is possible by using louvers but these tend to reduce the light-output ratio, are difficult to keep clean and are comparatively expensive. Alternatively, a reflector fitting with closed ends can be fitted with various types of plastics prismatic plates which give light control in the plane of the minor and major axes of the fitting. Where some degree of sideways diffused lighting is required, prismatic diffusers can be extruded in one piece with opal plastics side panels.

An example of a directional fitting for fluorescent lamps, sometimes for the lighting of vertical surfaces or to give additional lighting near the walls of buildings is shown in Chapter 29 (see Fig. 29.2). A fitting using an incandescent lamp, but also designed for the lighting of the vertical plane is shown in Fig. 25.5.

Local lighting fittings. Local lighting should supplement general lighting and should not be a substitute for it. Adequate screening of local lighting fittings is important and in some cases limitation of movement in adjustable fittings may be necessary to prevent glaring conditions for other room occupants.

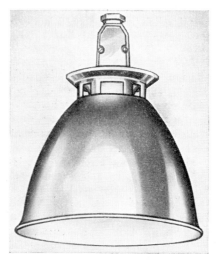

Fig. 25.4   Typical fittings for general lighting in industry

Fig. 25.5   Angle reflector for the lighting of vertical surfaces

Use of screened low-voltage lamps mounted on factory machines assists safety, and their comparatively robust filaments tend to resist vibration and rough usage.

Fittings for hazardous areas. Care must be exercised in choosing lighting fittings used in situations where hazardous conditions prevail. Fig. 25.6 indicates the various types of hazard met with in industrial areas and the types of lighting fittings to meet these conditions. (See also Chapter 24.)

For detailes of explosion-proof (i.e., flame-proof) fittings reference should be made to BS 889: 1965, and I.E.S. Technical Report No. 1 (1965). Non-explosive hazards include wet conditions ranging from the effects of condensation to actual submersion of the lighting fitting. Some types of dust particles which gain access to fittings may be an explosive hazard; or the ingress of larger quantities of ordinary dust affects the light output of the fitting. Corrosion includes the effects of salt-laden atmosphere and severe contamination by the corrosive atmosphere in chemical plants.

Temperature modifies or accelerates the effects of moisture and corrosion. In some cases lamps or lighting fittings are used to view the inside surfaces of atomic reactors by means of periscopes or television cameras and such fittings must be made of 'compatible' materials (i.e. materials which will not affect, nor be affected by, the fission process) and usually require special construction.

Lighting fittings have been developed for use in most of these hazardous areas except Division O where lighting is remote, e.g. the lighting of such areas may be by fittings behind wall-mounted windows. Lighting equipment for Groups I to III must be certified by the Ministry of Fuel and Power as suitable for use in Division 1 areas.

Lighting techniques. In most industrial buildings there are usually at least two conditions for which lighting is required:

(1) For personnel moving about, operation of fork lift trucks and cranes, etc.

(2) More specific visual tasks where operators are working at benches or machines, checking components on conveyors or such very severe tasks as stitching black thread on black material.

Lighting for (1) is usually by general lighting; for (2) it may also be feasible to use general lighting if the level, quality and direction of this is sufficient for the most difficult task and does not interfere with performance of less exacting general tasks. Such general lighting might be provided by an overall louvered or trans-illuminated ceiling lit by fittings in the cavity above. Alternatively specific tasks may require supplementary local lighting.

The use of local direct lighting alone without general lighting is not recommended, due to too great a difference in task and surround brightness, tending to produce glare and 'tunnel-effect'. In certain cases some alleviation of these conditions is possible by providing some upward light from the local lighting fittings to the ceiling and upper parts of the walls.

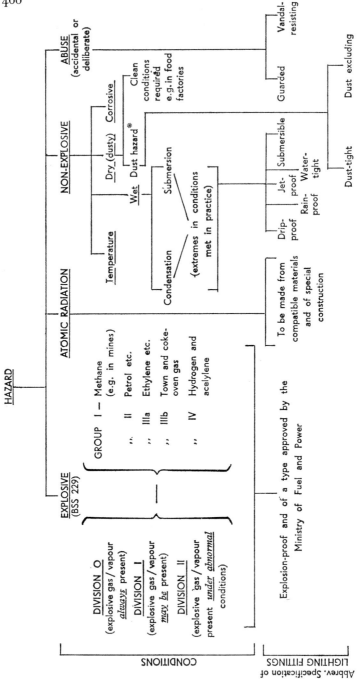

Fig. 25.6 Range of hazards to which lighting fittings may be subjected and relevant abbreviated fitting specification

Lighting installations. Industrial lighting installations generally consist of either (a) general lighting, (b) localised general lighting or (c) general plus local lighting.

General lighting. Depending on the lighting level required, general lighting usually consists of symmetrical rows of fittings, either ceiling or surface-mounted, suspended, or mounted on trunking. The fittings are usually arranged with a spacing/mounting-height ratio of not more than 1·5:1 so as to produce lighting with a diversity factor of not less than 0·7. The fittings usually have upward light slots.

Alternatively the fittings may be built into the structure of the building, e.g. in the form of artificial 'skylights' or as modules in a suspended ceiling.

The advantages of the symmetrical arrangement of general lighting fittings are:

(1) Since the illumination is relatively uniform, the plant within the area can be repositioned without the necessity of relighting the area; and

(2) Since the illumination is fairly uniform the eyes are adapted for the range of brightness of both the visual scene and visual task.

Localised general lighting. In this system rows of fittings are placed near to, and parallel with, the major axes of the assembly benches, conveyors or machines. Usually relatively higher intensities are produced with fewer fittings than are required for general lighting. Careful screening is required to prevent glare to operators; spill-over light from upward light slots on the ceiling and directly on the floor (some of which may be reflected to the walls and ceiling) provides some background lighting. A disadvantage of this system is that plant layout cannot easily be changed without altering the lighting.

General plus local lighting. In this system general lighting is supplemented by local lighting of the individual tasks. This lends itself to systems where the tasks requiring more intense lighting are relatively far apart and do not warrant a higher illumination intensity throughout the whole area.

Trunking systems. Where there are long lines of tubular fluorescent fittings, some savings in suspension and wiring costs are possible by using metal trunking, while the general appearance of the installation is often improved and the housing of other services, e.g. telephone lines, signal circuits, etc., is facilitated. Earlier forms of trunking consisted of an inverted steel trough containing the control gear, the lamp tray being mounted beneath. As present-day fluorescent fittings are relatively smaller in cross-section and lighter in weight they can be mounted directly to much shallower steel trunking.

Catwalks. In very high industrial interiors where fittings are likely to be inaccessible, servicing is facilitated by placing railed catwalks alongside the rows of fittings, or mounting pivoted fittings beneath trap doors in the catwalk.

Lighting design and calculations. Lighting calculations are fully discussed in Chapter 9, but notes on the procedure of lighting design are given here for the sake of continuity.

With most industrial fittings it is usual to arrange them so that the spacing between fittings is not greater than $1\frac{1}{2}$ times the mounting height above the working plane. Because of the fall-off in illumination towards the walls, it is usual practice to make the distance of the first row from the wall half the spacing between the remaining rows in the room.

Attention must also be paid to the orientation of linear sources such as fluorescent fittings. Correctly designed reflector fittings are usually less glaring if viewed side on, and this is particularly important where there is a predominant sight line. It will be found that when reflector fittings of good design are used in a well-planned installation, the degree of glare will not exceed the glare index limits proposed in the I.E.S. Code for most industrial installations.

In designing an industrial lighting installation it may be found convenient to record the results of analysis of the general and specific visual tasks and other information on a work sheet as set out in Table 25.2.

Additional points to note are as follows:

(1) Analysis of the lighting problem: What is the precise nature of the general and specific visual tasks performed? Is the lighting of vertical surfaces important?

(2) Select the needed lighting level(s) and treat the calculation for general and local lighting separately.

(3) Determine the designed lighting quality.

(4) Select the suitable light source.

(5) Select the appropriate lighting system, e.g. general lighting only, localised, general plus local lighting, and the method of applying it to the building.

(6) Make a trial lighting calculation to find the approximate number of fittings required and their spacing and mounting height above work-plane (see Chapter 9).

(7) Check that the BZ glare index for the installation does not exceed the recommended value.

(8) Prepare the lighting layout, indicating the position of the fittings relative to the machinery, benches, etc., so as to minimise direct and reflected glare and the production of high brightness images in polished flat or cylindrical surfaces.

(9) Prepare a flexible control of the system, e.g. consider advisability of switching lamps by bays, or individually by pull or toggle switches; use of single or balanced 3-phase systems.

(10) Analyse available system of electrical circuits.

(11) Check proposed lighting system for feasibility. In certain cases, e.g. particularly where discharge type lamps are used or where there might be danger to life on failure of the main supply, it may be advisable to consider the installation of emergency lighting, preferably fed from an alternative supply.

TABLE 25.2

Suggested Form of Worksheet for Planning Industrial Lighting Installation

General work carried on and/or product made........

Building structural features............

....

Floor area......... ft²   Height of ceiling......... ft

Decoration: Floor   Ceiling   Walls
Colour   ....
Reflection factor ....
Factory situation: Dirty/Average/Clean.
Special lighting difficulties............

Visual tasks	Colour rendering Important/ Not important	Visual task contrast Good/Medium/Poor	From I.E.S. code Required illum. (lm/ft^2)	Task lit by Gen./loc. ltg.	Visual aid required
(1) General task in building	....	....	....	....	....
(2) Other specific tasks	....	....	....	....	....
(3) do.	....	....	....	....	....

Special ltg. (e.g. for emergency)
....

	General ltg.	Local ltg.
Choice of light source.........	....	....
Choice of lighting fittings.........	....	....

Required light distribution:
    Very Broad   Broad   Narrow
BZ No.   10, 9, 8   7, 6, 5, 4, 3   2, 1.
Required spacing/mounting height.
Calculated number of fittings.
Recommended I.E.S. glare index =
Calculated glare index =
Method of fixing fittings
Maintenance facilities—Good/Average/Poor
Economic considerations

CHAPTER 26

Lighting for Inspection

Industrial inspection entails the critical examination of components or of the finished product to reveal possible flaws, and usually requires the use of sight and light. Depending upon the nature of the product and the type of flaws required to be revealed inspection may be performed by using one or a combination of the five senses—touch, hearing, taste, smell and sight.

Inspection of a product may include various mechanical or electromechanical methods of proving the quality and fitness of the product for its purpose. The way in which these aids are related is shown in Fig. 26.1; some of these techniques are outside the scope of this survey.

This chapter describes the broad principles of using light to reveal faults during product inspection and indicates the most suitable light sources for each purpose. Table 26.3 summarises lighting techniques used in visual inspection and this may be of particular help to inspectors, plant engineers and production and quality-control engineers.

Visual inspection analysis. In scanning the product the inspector mentally compares successive visual images of this with the equivalent views of a real or memorised image of a standard product. To prevent rapid visual fatigue it is of paramount importance that the object being examined should be illuminated with light of suitable quality, intensity and direction so that the inspector has a clear visual image of the object and its possible faults. This entails a careful analysis of the precise nature of the visual task by questioning the Chief Inspector and the person carrying out the inspection, followed by personal observation of the relevant conditions. Any tentative solution to the problem should be tried out under mock-up conditions. The inspection area should preferably be quiet and free from distraction, and such matters as ventilation and temperature are of particular importance owing to the critical nature of the task.

A careful check should be made that the lighting in the main manufacturing area is adequate, to minimise faults in the product.

Individual faults may usually be classified in one of the following groups:

(1) Discrepancy in physical shape or dimensions.
(2) Discontinuity in a material—mechanical breakage, cracks or embedded foreign bodies.

(3) Change in surface texture—differences in depth of pile in carpet, abrasions, dents and tool marks.

(4) Colour differences.

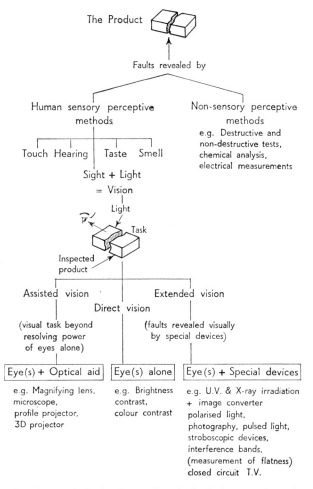

Fig. 26.1   Methods of revealing faults in inspected products

The visual performance attainable depends upon the nature of the visual task, the size of the detail to be seen, the adequacy of the lighting, the technique of brightness grading, the periods of time devoted to continuous inspection and to resting the eyes, and, to some extent, the physical condition of the inspector.

Usually, faults in physical shape and dimensions which are within the resolving power of the eyes, and mechanical faults, are best revealed by a sufficient level of diffuse white light. Surface texture and faults which are comparatively small depressions or projections of the surface material (which therefore tend to be of similar brightness to that of their immediate background in diffuse lighting), should be examined with light falling at grazing inclination.

Slight colour differences may be made more evident by using high uniform levels of illumination of diffuse light with a suitable spectral distribution. In specific cases, coloured lighting can be used with advantage to increase the contrast between adjacent areas. The types of lighting distribution required for various visual inspection problems are summarised in Table 26.1

TABLE 26.1

Types of Lighting for Visual Inspection

Type of faults revealed by inspection	Type of lighting distribution				
	Vertical direct diffuse	Side diffuse	Transmitted diffuse	Projected beam	Edge lighting
Shape and dimensions	×	×			
Mechanical discontinuity	×	×	×		
Surface texture (opaque materials)		×		×	
Surface texture (transparent materials)					×
Colour differences	×				

Natural and artificial lighting and illumination values. A comparatively high level of diffused natural lighting has usually been preferred wherever possible for both manufacturing and inspection purposes due to general availability and good colour rendering properties, although these alter with different building aspects, the presence of cloud and sunshine, and the time of the day and year.

Because man's earliest attempts at imitating natural light from the sun and sky were so dissimilar in both intensity and quality, artificial sources were rightly looked on as inferior substitutes. With modern light sources, such as xenon discharge lamps and good colour rendering fluorescent lamps, it is possible to match approximately all phases of natural light. Also the intensity and quality of such artificial sources can be maintained 24 hours per day. Natural and artificial light may therefore in most cases be looked upon as equivalents.

Often inspection in day-time is done for long periods near factory windows giving access to direct sunlight. Such high intensity lighting is often objectionable as it may cause direct and reflected glare from the surfaces within the field of view, sometimes producing unwanted harsh shadows and frequently too much heat.

In certain inspection tasks, such as the grading of raw cotton, artificial light is used to imitate the technique adopted when using natural light. In other cases, such as the inspection of tinplate, artificial light can be used with advantage in ways which are difficult to repeat with the same revealing effect and degree of visual comfort using natural lighting.

The value of illumination needed for any particular task is dependent on the size of the smallest detail to be perceived, the reflection factors of the materials being worked, the degree of contrast in the task insofar as this affects the clarity with which the details can be seen under a given illumination, and anything which reduces the viewer's concentration such as movement of the object or an unavoidable cause of distraction.

Diffuse-lighting techniques

Light sources. Tubular fluorescent lamps and other mercury vapour discharge lamps have largely replaced tungsten filament lamps for providing general lighting economically in factory buildings. Tubular fluorescent lamps, having comparatively low brightness and generally superior colour-rendering properties, are particularly suitable for producing diffuse and shadow-free lighting, for both general and (at increased illumination levels), for local lighting over inspection benches. These lamps are also suitable for mounting either below a white reflector or above some form of translucent material, such as opal 'Perspex', to provide a comparatively large area diffuse source. Miniature fluorescent lamps, such as the 8 W 12 in. fluorescent tube, are useful for lighting small local areas. Closely spaced silica-coated tungsten filament lamps may be used in smaller local lighting units where a uniform source of light of comparatively high brightness is required.

In general, where the luminance of the lamp or lighted surface exceeds 1 cd/in² (452 ft-L) it will be necessary to screen it from the eyes of the inspector. It should be noted that the luminance of tubular fluorescent lamps usually exceeds this value. As a general guide to prevent excessive brightness, Sections C and D of Table 26.2 show respectively the nominal luminance of typical incandescent filament and tubular fluorescent lamps particularly suitable as diffuse light sources.

TABLE 26.2

Luminance of Typical Natural and Artificial Light Sources

Section and class	Light source	Nominal luminance in convenient units		
		stilbs (cd/cm²)	cd/in²	ft-L
A Natural	Sun Clear blue sky Overcast sky (Average conditions)	160,000		1000 1500
B High brightness	Carbon arc Xenon arc (2 kW) High-pressure mercury vapour (250 W ME Box) Mercury iodide (400 W) Experimental	60,000 60,000 20,000 12,500		
C Incandescent	Gas-filled tungsten projector, 230 V/250 W Clear GLS 100 W Pearl GLS 100 W Silica coated 100 W	2000 650 13 2·5	4200 85 16	19 × 10⁵ 38,500 7250
D Tubular fluorescent	Warm white 80 W/5 ft (2000 hours) 65 W/5 ft (2000 hours) 6 W/9 in. (2000 hours)		5·8 5·3 4·0	2620 2400 1800

14+

Application. Where the general lighting is used for the dual purpose of ordinary manufacturing processes and bench inspection, and the inspection point is not screened off from the rest of the room, rows of standard industrial type single-lamp fluorescent fittings may be adequate if the illumination level required for the inspection process does not exceed about 30 lm/ft²; but frequently much higher values than this are required, and it then becomes necessary to use multi-lamp fittings, or single-lamp fittings at close spacing. Local illumination over the inspection area may be increased usefully to approximately 1000 lm/ft² depending upon the nature of the work involved.

When a number of individual reflector fittings are used to light inspection areas, surfaces of polished metal objects (such as scales and measuring blocks) will reflect the images of bare lamps, the reflector surfaces of lower brightness, and the darker areas between fittings. These will form a pattern in the polished surfaces which can easily cause disability glare, hindering rather than assisting the visual task.

Increased brightness contrasts. Fig. 26.2 illustrates a useful technique, in which a translucent sheet of material with a black line regular grid pattern and lit from above is being used to show up dents in a sheet of polished material.

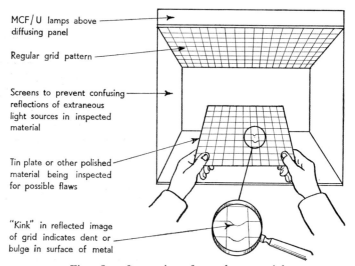

MCF/U lamps above diffusing panel

Regular grid pattern

Screens to prevent confusing reflections of extraneous light sources in inspected material

Tin plate or other polished material being inspected for possible flaws

"Kink" in reflected image of grid indicates dent or bulge in surface of metal

Fig. 26.2   Inspection of specular materials

Fig. 26.3 shows the arrangement of a vertically mounted diffusely lit grid used for showing up flaws in jars, bottles, bulbs, etc., by refraction. Grids or vertical bars in front of larger illuminated panels are used for checking plate glass for flaws. By edge lighting glass or clear acrylic plastics sheets it is possible to show up defects such as scratches as bright lines against a darker background. Care must be observed in this method of lighting translucent material, as it also tends to illuminate surface dust which may be confused with the scratch marks.

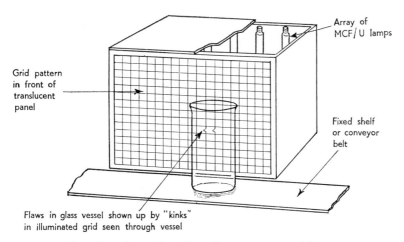

Array of
MCF/U lamps

Grid pattern
in front of
translucent
panel

Fixed shelf
or conveyor
belt

Flaws in glass vessel shown up by "kinks"
in illuminated grid seen through vessel

Fig. 26.3   Inspection of regular transparent objects

Discrimination by colour.   In general, discrimination of objects or materials of very slightly differing colour may best be carried out in diffuse natural or artificial daylight, as long as precautions are taken to avoid direct and reflected glare.

Colourists prefer natural total skylight, excluding direct sunlight but including some long-wave ultraviolet, for colour-matching purposes. Approximate daylight is obtained from tungsten filament lamps run at 2848 °K with a blue liquid filter to give standard illuminant A. A better approximation to daylight is obtained from xenon lamps in sizes ranging from 150 W to 2000 W, as it is possible to vary the light output from the lamp over a wide range by adjusting the power input without appreciably altering the lamp's colour and spectral power.

Two types of fluorescent lamp are currently available, one having a colour appearance of diffused sunlight with excellent colour rendering for general purposes. The other type, known as Artificial Daylight, also has excellent colour-rendering properties, has an ultraviolet spectral content to brighten fluorescent dyes, and is favoured by colourists for accurate colour matching purposes at comparatively high intensities.

For adequate discrimination of colours the illumination should be at least 70 lm/ft^2 and in general 100 lm/ft^2 is satisfactory as long as the spectral quality of the source is not modified by the decoration of the viewing area. A light neutral grey is desirable. The use of dark rooms with small brightly lit areas is deprecated because of the high contrast and consequent visual fatigue.

Directional lighting techniques.   Where light has to be projected by reflectors or used in an optical system, the luminance and area of the source are of more importance than its efficiency or directive candle-power. Though electric arc lamps have been greatly improved in efficiency and luminance during recent years, and have many uses in projection, they suffer from the disadvantage of requiring skilled attention to provide consistently uniform light intensities.

High-brightness sources such as xenon lamps or mercury vapour type ME box lamps having non-consumable electrodes overcome this trouble and when fitted with lenses or reflectors provide a useful means of inspection. The nominal luminance of these and other high-brightness sources is given in Section B of Table 26.2.

A visual aid in the spinning industry for showing the position of broken threads directs a parallel beam of light from an ME Box lamp across the plane containing the threads on the spinning frame. Even comparatively thin dark-coloured vertical threads are seen by the operator as glinting filaments; any spaces in the otherwise regular pattern indicate the position of broken threads.

Integral-mirror spot and floodlamps, with either blown- or pressed-glass bulbs and integral plain, frosted or prismatic spreader cover-glasses, have been considerably improved in recent years. Special dichroic coatings on pressed-glass reflector lamps permit most of the light to be reflected forwards while the infrared is transmitted through the reflector, thus producing a relatively cool light beam.

Amongst many inspection uses of spotlamps are those of inspecting the inside of tubes, barrels and similar vessels.

A specially designed internal reflector lamp has been used to throw a narrow beam of light on to vertical warp threads in a loom, the reduction in reflected light on a photomultiplier cell due to a broken thread causing a relay to operate and stop the machine.

Though tubular fluorescent lamps are usually considered as being diffuse light sources, they can be used with reflectors to give fan-shaped beams of light which when applied at grazing angles to the surface of products such as polished leather, piled carpets or dents in metal plate, reveal possible flaws as variations in the general brightness of the material. If specular materials are used it is important that the reflected light is directed away from the eyes of the observer.

Assisted vision. Most of the applications considered below are examples of assisted vision in that some form of optical system or other device is used to enable the eyes to see what would otherwise be difficult or impossible to see.

Lighting for magnification. Magnifying lenses, either with or without local lighting, are necessary to reveal fine detail beyond the resolving power of the eyes. The objective area of industrial microscopes, as used for instance in an incandescent lamp factory for examining coiled filaments, should be efficiently lit to reduce eye strain and glare. Class F tungsten filament lamps have been specially developed for this kind of work.

Profile projectors facilitate visual tasks which are beyond the resolving power of the eye; they are used for the examination of screw gauges and contours, gear-wheel profiles, components for clocks and watches and, as shown in Fig. 26.4, for checking the electrodes in making discharge lamps. Since the enlarged image is many times that of the real object, any irregular shapes, contours or spacings are more easily detected.

In normal profile projectors the viewed object appears as an enlarged shadow. Certain types of optical projectors present two superimposed enlarged images of the same brightly lit object on the screen in such a manner that the observer sees them as a three-dimensional solid.

Fig. 26.4   Typical profile projector for checking electrodes in making discharge lamps

Closed-circuit television.   Closed-circuit television, in black and white or colour, as shown on a monitor tube as an apparently three-dimensional image, can be used in situations where it would be difficult or impossible to have human observers, as in the inspection of the inside of atomic reactors or jet engines running under test conditions. Inspection with television devices can in some cases reduce operator fatigue, concentrating attention by means of lighting techniques and magnification, and also by modifications of the electrical signal from the camera.

Minimum intensities and quality of lighting when operating television cameras depend on the type and sensitivity of the camera and whether pictures are to be reproduced in black and white or in colour. Quite often normal illumination values and quality of natural or artificial lighting are sufficient.

Inspection booths. Most products consist of an assembly of many parts, and each of these may have been made by machine in a number of complex operations. Each part must reach an accepted standard of quality, as the failure of one part involves the failure of the whole. It is therefore usual to carry out inspection on each part near to the position of the last operation. General room lighting may be suitable for these intermediate stage inspections, but frequently additional local lighting is necessary at each open inspection area. Such a system, however, has many disadvantages:

(1) Unless local lighting is carefully screened it may interfere with other tasks in the workshop.

(2) The general workshop lighting may produce confusing reflections in the inspected articles.

(3) The unscreened background may be distracting to the inspector, or cause undue contrast owing to its lower brightness compared with that of the locally lit visual task in the open inspection area.

Where inspection is carried out at definite stages in the process of manufacture, individually lit inspection booths or other screened areas, such as inspection pits, may overcome the disadvantages of the open inspection area. Booths are usually arranged to fulfil one or more of the following functions:

(1) Screen the area of the visual task, immediate surround and inspectors' eyes from the light of extraneous sources; this is particularly important where the articles viewed have polished surfaces,

(2) Provide light of the correct quality, level and distribution on the visual task, intermediate surround and background areas, to provide good visibility without glare; this can be assisted by grading the brightness from the task outward as recommended in the I.E.S. Code.

(3) Provide visual rest centres for the inspector when not engaged on critical viewing.

(4) Provide optical aids such as lenses or grid patterns where required.

Fig. 26.5 (a, b, c and d) indicate typical forms of inspection booths and suggested methods of lighting them depending on the nature of the inspection task, the number and position of inspectors, and the quality and direction of light which best reveals the particular faults expected in the materials or objects being examined.

Extended vision. Extended vision is provided by techniques and devices which make visible various types of faults which could not be seen in ordinary white light. Some of these techniques are considered below.

Increased colour contrast. Where there is little or no colour contrast in the visual task, parts are sometimes dyed different colours to improve contrast, e.g. specular surfaces of metal may be stained so that scribe marks show up more

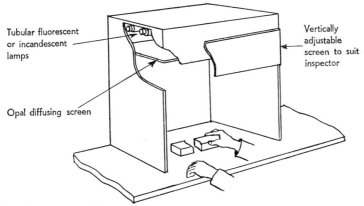

Tubular fluorescent
or incandescent
lamps

Vertically
adjustable
screen to suit
inspector

Opal diffusing screen

(a) Downward diffuse lighting

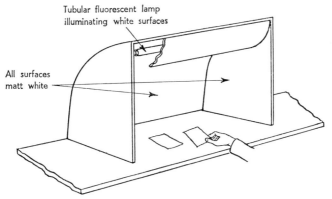

Tubular fluorescent lamp
illuminating white surfaces

All surfaces
matt white

(b) Omni-directional lighting

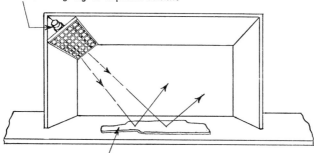

Tubular fluorescent lamp with louvres giving
directional lighting of inspected material

Material: e.g. polished leather

(c) Directional lighting for semi-polished materials

Fig. 26.5 Typical artificially lit inspection booths   [*see over*

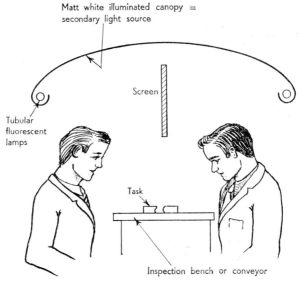

Matt white illuminated canopy =
secondary light source

Screen

Tubular
fluorescent
lamps

Task

Inspection bench or conveyor

Fig. 26.5 *(cont.)*

(d) Diffusely lit canopy over conveyor for continuous inspection of moving products

clearly. Likewise the background against which the visual task is viewed can be made to assist in producing contrast and thus facilitate the visual task. An example of this latter kind in the lamp making industry is the inspection, grading and counting of complete filaments; the filaments are seen on a background formed by translucent panels of 'Perspex' which are illuminated from below with 6 W green fluorescent lamps.

Monochromatic light. When details of the visual task are so small as to approach the limit of size which the eye can detect, monochromatic light may improve acuity of vision. Such monochromatic light may be obtained by using the sodium vapour lamp where fairly low intrinsic brightnesses are required, while for higher brightness mercury vapour lamps, with or without filters, can be used.

The method of measuring errors in flatness of gauges or precision-finished surfaces using optical flats is a measurement of light wavelength. Using monochromatic light, the reflections from the surface being tested interfere with the light reflected from the optical flat, and set up bands or fringes which are observed through the optical flats; the number and contour of these fringes indicate the error and curvature of the surface.

Polarised light. The detection of internal strain in glass, mounted lenses, transparent plastics, etc., can be facilitated by transmitted polarised light. The non-uniform spectral transmission of a strained part causes the formation of colour fringes that are visible to an observer. Another use of polarised light is in the examination of crystal structure of metals. Polarised monochromatic light from a sodium lamp is directed on to the crystals which are viewed through a microscope, the orientation being indicated by the brightness of the light reflected from the crystals.

Ultraviolet radiation. Ultraviolet radiation may be used under certain conditions to make things visible by its effect on fluorescent and phosphorescent substances.

Precautions must be taken when using short-wave ultraviolet to ensure that operatives are protected against the harmful effects of this radiation on the skin and eyes, and where long-wave ultraviolet is used protection must be given to limit eye fatigue due to fluorescence of the eye lens. High-pressure mercury vapour discharge lamps, with or without Wood's glass filters to reduce unwanted visible light, produce this radiation efficiently. Tubular fluorescent lamps using special phosphors for long-wave ultraviolet radiation, again with or without an integral Wood's glass filter, may also be used.

Short-wave ultraviolet radiation is produced by low-pressure mercury vapour lamps made with either quartz envelopes or with special ultraviolet transmitting glass tubes, e.g. 'germicidal lamps' (see Chapter 22).

Materials which in ordinary light look alike may show marked differences when irradiated with ultraviolet radiation in darkness. Some stains on fabrics become clearly visible under ultraviolet radiation. By adding fluorescing tracer materials to fluids in tanks, transformers and water-tube boilers, it is possible to detect leaks when they are irradiated by ultraviolet.

Photography. Photography has been used for many years as a means of recording the instantaneous position of a moving object. Shutters are used to limit the time exposure, and consequently the movement as recorded on the film is also limited. Great savings in energy are possible by illuminating the moving object by a relatively short-time pulse of high-intensity light synchronised with the shutter operation. Besides the well-known flashbulb, pulsed electric discharge arcs or flashtubes can be used to give single or repetitive intense flashes of short duration (see Chapter 13).

For inspection work, photography using ordinary cameras and developing procedures tends to be rather slow and costly, but the use of recently developed cameras such as the 'Polaroid-Land' allows shots to be printed in either black and white or in colour in 10 or 60 seconds respectively.

High-speed photography may be used to record fast-moving intricate mechanisms; the resulting film can then be projected at slower speeds to reveal movement which before was faster than the unaided eye could perceive.

Stroboscopic devices. Where repetitive motions (particularly in rotating machinery) have to be examined, approximate synchronising of the flashtube's flashes with the mechanism motion can apparently slow up the mechanism so that detailed operation of each part can be examined.

Some of the uses to which stroboscopes have been applied are in the

14*

inspection and study of fuel-injection systems, balancing of armatures, the examination of rotors of high-speed turbines, and electric lamp filaments under conditions of vibration.

Miscellaneous devices and techniques. Amongst various other devices and techniques using light for inspection purposes may be mentioned the use of Schlieren effects, whereby light beams may be used to reveal the movements of hot gases by the change in their refractive indices; this system is also used for examining aerofoil shapes in the aircraft industry.

Visual counting of components as they come off a conveyor may be replaced by a counting device employing a beam of light and a photoelectric cell. Many other ingenious photoelectric devices are used for checking dimensions, measurements of reflectivity of neutral and coloured surfaces, etc.

Although methods of production are changing rapidly and processes are increasingly being controlled by machines, product inspection will remain a vital necessity. Undoubtedly changes in methods of production will bring new inspection problems for lighting engineers; a full understanding of the basic principles of lighting and design of the visual field are essential to solving both present and future problems.

Inspection is always an arduous task; the aim of the lighting engineer is to ease the work of the inspector as much as possible, and to shorten the time spent on inspection. Each industry has problems peculiar to itself; the purpose of this survey has been to indicate general principles which can be applied to many problems, and to stimulate consideration of suitable lighting aids when inspection problems arise. A summary of lighting techniques and suggestions for guidance are given in Table 26.3.

TABLE 26.3

Summary of Visual Inspection Techniques

Technique	Type of light	Class of lighting	Typical sources	Type of fitting and general arrangement	Comments
Inspection of comparatively large objects, e.g. wooden furniture		General room lighting	GLS, MCF, MBF, MBFR/U, MBT/U, etc.	Dispersive fitting with cut-off, in rows	May be fitted in angled reflectors to give directional bias. See Chapter 25
Increased illumination locally for open areas where booths not considered necessary		Local lighting on benches	GLS mains and low voltage incand. fil. lamps. Incandescent internal reflector, PAR, MCF —long and miniature lamps	Aluminium or enamelled steel concentrating reflector or protective housing. Individual fittings on fixed or adjustable brackets	Carefully screened from view of inspectors and others in vicinity
Inspection of small parts, particularly those with specular surfaces	'White' diffused lighting	Small inspection booths	Up to 5 ft 80 W MCF/U and MCFR/U	Indirect fitting on white ceiling and walls or above glass or opal 'Perspex'—diffusing screen	Ditto. Fig. 26.5(b) Fig. 26.5(a)
Inspection by more than one person of stationary objects or on conveyors		Larger inspection booths	8 ft × 1½ in. MCF or MCFR/U	Direct or indirect, single lamp or continuous rows	Fig. 26.5(d)
Inspection in garages, loco-sheds, docks, etc.		Inspection pits Graving docks etc.	GLS, MCF and MCFR/U incandescent internal reflector	Dispersive bulkhead plus protective guards—fixed, swivel or portable fittings. Submersible fittings.	Screening usually difficult. Use louvers or prismatic control if possible

Table 26.0 (*cont.*)

Lighting in hazardous areas	'White' diffused lighting	Depends on specific hazards	GLS, MCF and MCFR/U	Fixed flame-proof, dust-tight and water-tight fittings etc.	See Chapter 25
Revealing texture	Directional	Directional lighting in rooms and booths and on benches	Incandescent filament internal reflector MCF/U and PAR, MCFR/U	Protective reflectors and/or louvers Fixed or swivel lampholders	See comments for general room lighting above and Fig. 26.5(c)
Colour matching of samples, e.g. textiles, tiles	Lighting of good colour rendering	Colour matching and discrimination	Incandescent filament lamps plus filters. MCF/U having good colour-rendering properties	Special cabinets and booths. Normal illumination levels 75 to 100 lm/ft² for accurate colour discrimination	De-luxe daylight lamps of warmer colour appearance may be used for general purposes. MCF/U 'Artificial Daylight' lamps are for colourists and others requiring accurate colour discrimination
Checking shape and dimensions of small parts	Assisted vision	Profile projectors, microscopes, lenses	Incandescent filament projection (Class F). Miniature MCF	Special optical system Lamps built into surround	(E.g. Fig. 26.4) See also Chapter 13
Increasing colour contrast, e.g. in colour printing	Extended vision	Coloured light	Incandescent filament lamps plus filters; pigmented and non-pigmented coloured MCF/U lamps	Use white stoved enamel reflectors or other white surfaces	Exaggeration of colour differences in samples of slightly different colour by viewing them under coloured light

Application		Method	Source	Special optical system	Remarks
Exam. of strains in transparent substances		Polarised light	Incand. filament lamps, ME box lamp	Special optical system	For example, strain viewers
Measurement of flatness etc. Improvement in visual acuity		Monochromatic light	Sodium or mercury discharge lamps plus filters	Ditto	For example, for interference patterns
Flaws in castings revealed after dipping in phosphor fluid, surplus removed and irradiated. Addition of, e.g., fluorocine to water in water tube boilers reveals leaks on irradiation with ultraviolet	Extended vision	Long-wave ultra-violet	MBW/U, MCF/U (U.V. non-filter tube) 5 ft 80 W (MCFW/U Integ. Wood's glass filter) 4 W and 6 W	Flat or cylindrical Wood's glass filters may be used with non-filter tube long-wave ultraviolet emitting lamps, or lamps with integ. filter may be used	Fluorescence of phosphors. See Chapter 22
		Short-wave ultraviolet	Mercury discharge in quartz tubes, or 30 W, 15 W germicidal lamps	Anodised aluminium effective as reflector.	Fluorescence of phosphors. Ozone given off; protect eyes.
Study of moving parts		Stroboscopic sources	Xenon flashtubes	Special reflectors with electronic or cam-driven device to produce repetitive flashes	See Chapter 13
Ditto		Photographic	Ditto high-ouput lamps and flashtubes	Ditto or single flashes. Battery operated.	See Chapter 13

CHAPTER 27

Lighting for Offices and Schools

The provision of adequate lighting in offices and schools is based upon the well-accepted principles of good general lighting, a sufficient illumination level and freedom from glare. There are, however, special conditions in both classes of interior which make lighting requirements different from those of industrial premises.

In offices it has become the practice to install fittings whose appearance is more attractive than that of industrial fittings; in fact, fittings are often selected primarily on grounds of appearance and only secondarily on grounds of performance. Yet there is little justification for this, as the visual tasks in some offices are more exacting than those involved in many industrial processes and lighting equipment in offices should be just as functional as lighting equipment in industry. If, however, better appearance can go hand-in-hand with good performance, then the additional expenditure is justifiable.

In schools, again, the accepted principles of the general lighting installation also apply, but three factors must be taken into special consideration; the regular and rather unusual 'sightline' in classrooms, the age of the occupants, and (in the case of schools used for day-time classes only) the relatively short operating hours of the installation.

OFFICE LIGHTING

Visual tasks. Office work contains a wide variety of visual tasks. Some are, of their nature, exacting, whilst others are easy. Some are continuous and others only occasional; and the age of office workers varies from the adolescent to the elderly. It may be, therefore, that a young person capable of good visual performance may only be called upon for casual seeing, whilst a much older person is performing a severe visual task almost continuously for long periods. In recent years, therefore, a great deal of emphasis has been placed on the role of lighting (both natural and artificial) in the life of the office worker, and the Offices, Shops and Railways Premises Act 1963 requires 'the provision of sufficient and suitable lighting in every part of the premises in which persons are working or passing'.

Many office occupations involve the reading of type, either printed or type-written, and the severity of the visual task (assuming a normal reading distance) depends upon the type size and its clarity, the reflection factor of the typed or printed character and the reflection factor of the paper on which the message appears. The management can, therefore, ease the visual tasks of their employees by paying attention to the choice of type and typewriter, by ensuring that people are not regularly required to read poor carbon copies, and by choosing papers with appropriate reflection factors; this applies in particular to the choice of papers for 'office systems', which often require continuous manual entries and checking.

In many office tasks, the *ergorama* contains several areas of interest. For instance, the typist is concerned with her notebook, the keys of the typewriter, and with the typescript in the machine. In the case of the experienced typist, her notebook engages her interest almost exclusively, and this should be remembered in planning lighting installations. Nevertheless, attention should be paid to the inscriptions on the keys of typewriters and other office machines, and also to the material from which they are constructed. Often the operator is hindered visually by quite unnecessary specular reflections from the keys of such machines.

Those who choose office furniture and equipment can help also in another way, namely, in choosing appropriate materials and colours for desk tops. Assuming that papers are likely to be white or near-white, undue brightness contrast can be produced if desk tops are very dark in colour. Moreover, shiny desk tops are likely to cause reflections of lighting units, which could also be distressing.

Perhaps the most exacting visual tasks are in the drawing office where critical details must be seen with great precision and where contrasts are often poor, e.g. pencil lines when seen through tracing paper or cloth. There is also the danger of reflected glare since the 'board' often occupies a large proportion of the visual field and is usually of high reflectance.

LIGHTING RECOMMENDATIONS

General offices. The I.E.S. Code recommends that the illumination levels provided in general offices should be as follows:

General offices (reading, writing, filing, indexing, mail sorting, stenographic work, typing, accounting)	30 lm/ft²
Business machine operation	45 lm/ft²

These illumination levels represent the values to be maintained in service on the work being performed. The levels are, of course, much higher than those obtaining before the Second World War and this reflects both the increased visual efficiency now expected, and the relative decrease in the total cost of providing artificial light. Much office accommodation is denied good daylighting, and in many cases some artificial light is required throughout the working day. To provide the recommended levels of illumination it is obvious, therefore, that a source of high luminous efficiency is required, and it is easy to understand why the fluorescent tube is now so widely used for office lighting.

As in other fields of lighting, however, the *quantity* of light cannot be divorced from the *quality* of light, and here again the fluorescent tube, as a light source of considerable area, helps to provide uniform illumination without hard shadows. The prevention of glare is another important consideration when planning a general lighting scheme for a large room in which the occupants may be orientated in various directions, and where desk layout is varied from time to time. The I.E.S. Code emphasises this by proposing a glare limit of 19 in general offices.

Although the luminance of the fluorescent tube is low, the tube is too bright to be used unshielded at the mounting heights generally available in offices, and fittings which either mask or diffuse the direct light are commonly employed. The planning of economical lighting installations often requires the use of multi-tube fittings, usually with a fairly wide distribution and providing some upward light to reduce brightness contrasts between fittings and ceilings. Where decorations are light in colour, and where there is a light-coloured floor, the need for upward light from the fitting is not vital, as the ceiling receives sufficient light by inter-reflection. An installation of this type is shown in Fig. 27.1 where modular fittings are used to light an accounting-machine room.

Fig. 27.1   Accounting machine room lit by recessed modular fittings

Considered functionally, the colour of the tube does not matter a great deal, and high efficiency tubes have been extremely successful in office lighting. If, however, there are psychological reasons for better colour-rendering, then tubes of improved colour quality but lower light output could be considered.

General offices usually require a reasonably uniform distribution of light, but local difficulties can arise in the positioning of lighting units in relation to typewriters and other machines. Here a certain amount of ingenuity is required, and an interesting installation is shown in Fig. 27.2 where supplementary lighting from *behind* the operator at a low angle is provided by reflection from a wall.

Fig. 27.2   Functional supplementary wall lighting in an office

The lighting of general offices is not, therefore, a complicated procedure if fittings are available which will provide the required illumination level efficiently without causing glare. These fittings are usually of a diffusing or louvered type, employing fluorescent tubes, and a few further examples of fittings used in offices are given in Fig. 27.3.

These examples show a number of methods of controlling brightness in a lighting fitting. Fitting (1) is the normal totally enclosed diffuser which is effective in reducing the observed brightness of the source. It is obvious, however, that the sideways distribution of a fitting is an important factor in limiting glare, and fitting (2) uses a 'twin-tone' diffuser in which the side area is of a more dense material than the bottom area. It is found, however, that glare in an installation is perhaps most effectively reduced by the employment of the louver principle and fitting (3) combines the principles of louvering and diffusion. If, however, it is required to reduce possible glare to

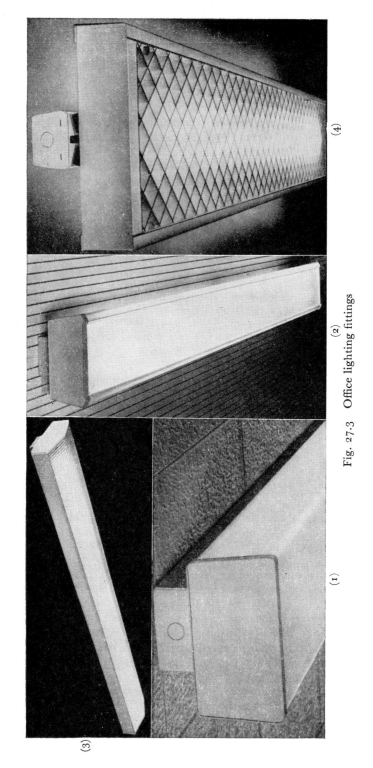

Fig. 27·3　Office lighting fittings

(1)　(2)　(3)　(4)

very low levels the sideways distribution from a fitting should be at a minimum and the louvered fitting (4) has virtually opaque sides, though these areas are pierced to provide some sparkle and liveliness.

The operation of the I.E.S. Glare Code shows that the possible glare in an installation is determined to a large extent by the area of the office, and a fitting of the type (4) is shown to be particularly appropriate for the large office where glare restrictions must be particularly stringent. It will be recognised, however, that the use of fittings which have a severe cut-off and a predominantly downward distribution, whilst effectively reducing glare, can also result in dark ceilings, and the whole problem has called for new ingenuity from the fittings designer and the lighting engineer.

In many new office buildings—and sometimes in reconditioned buildings—a suspended ceiling system is adopted. In such cases it is possible to incorporate the lighting with the ceiling. It is even possible to integrate partitions also and one such system is shown in Fig. 27.4. The suspended ceiling is an

Fig. 27.4   Integrated lighting, ceiling and partitioning system

ingenious combination of acoustic ceiling, electrical distribution, lighting and support for partitioning. Basically the ceiling consists of extruded aluminium support channels running on every grid line across the 50 ft width of the building, these supporting steel frames carrying an expanded metal panel upon which rests acoustically absorbent material. To the channels, anywhere along their length, may be fixed lighting equipment and in the case of fluorescent fittings these can be either parallel, or at right angles, to the support channel. Either arrangement results in lighting fittings being on the surface of the suspended ceiling, but recessed lighting, flush to the ceiling, can also be arranged virtually anywhere over the whole ceiling area. This total integration of ceiling, partitioning and telephone floor ducts provides a high degree of flexibility in the use of office space.

Of course, it is also possible to consider a completely luminous ceiling for a general office, but such an installation should be planned with great care. The demand for uniform lighting—an understandable demand—in the general office brings with it the danger of visual monotony, and this danger is apt to increase as the illumination level increases and especially when the decoration is uniformly light in colour. This monotony can be relieved by changes in decoration or by adding variety to the lighting. With the luminous ceiling this can be done by using occasional unlighted panels, panels equipped with incandescent lighting, or by adding coloured vertical baffles, which can also assist the acoustic properties of the room.

Private offices and conference rooms. Whilst occupants of a general office are usually engaged for long periods in such activities as reading, writing, calculating and typing, the occupant of the private office spends much of his time in discussion and dictation. Uniformity in the lighting is not called for, therefore, and in fact it may prove to be undesirable. It is necessary to light the desk area to an illumination level of 30 lm/ft² (in accordance with the current I.E.S. Code) but this element of the lighting should be separately controlled, so that 'basic lighting' only can be used when appropriate. This basic lighting may be provided by orthodox lighting units, either suspended or ceiling mounted, but it could also be provided by lighting certain wall areas. The aim should be to provide a comfortable but stimulating environment. Glare must be avoided, and in this connection it should be remembered that the predominant sight-line is likely to be nearer the horizontal than is the usual sight-line of a worker in a general office.

To a great degree the same principles apply in the lighting of the conference room. Whilst it is often necessary to make notes at the conference table, much

Fig. 27.5   Combined tungsten filament and fluorescent lighting
in a conference room

of the time is taken up with discussion, and an evenly lit room rarely helps to create an appropriate atmosphere. Fig. 27.5 shows a conference room in which the functional light on the table is provided by incandescent spotlights, recessed into a suspended ceiling, whilst fluorescent tubes concealed behind the leading edge of the ceiling light the wall area.

Drawing offices. The most exacting of office tasks are carried out in the drawing office, where, for instance, the intersection of fine lines constitutes a critical detail which demands good lighting conditions. The contrast contained within the task is also poor, e.g. when hard pencil lines are to be seen on ordinary drawing paper. Still poorer contrast exists when these lines are to be seen through tracing paper and tracing cloth. Further difficulties arise through the possibility of shadows thrown by drawing instruments and also of specular reflection from such instruments. Finally, as the drawing board can at times fill a large part of the visual field of the draughtsman, the possibility of reflected glare from this large area of high reflectance is considerable.

It is not surprising, therefore, that drawing-office lighting has always been a controversial topic, and during recent years the choice in most offices has been between a relatively modest general lighting installation supplemented by local lighting, and a more ambitious and carefully designed general lighting scheme, usually employing fluorescent tubes.

For the former approach it can be claimed that the draughtsman appreciates the local control at his disposal, allowing him the means to re-orientate the direction of light at will. Psychologically also, he may claim that the localised element in the lighting gives a degree of privacy which helps concentration.

On the other hand, the use of localised lighting can cause brightness differences throughout the office which may be distracting and even uncomfortable, especially when the local light used by one draughtsman becomes a source of glare to another. It appears therefore, that the careful design of general lighting systems is likely to be the line of future development, particularly when it is remembered that the average draughtsman spends by no means all his working day at the drawing board. Much time is spent at the adjoining work table and also in general discussions which often involve reference to drawings in other parts of the office.

Whilst the drawing board is of the greatest importance, therefore, adequate lighting over the whole area of the office is a real necessity. The I.E.S. Code recommends an illumination level of 45 lm/ft² for drawing and tracing, and 30 lm/ft² generally throughout the room with a glare limit of 16. This can usually be achieved by the correct positioning of fluorescent fittings, but the distribution characteristics of these fittings must be such that there is a severe restriction on direct glare, and yet that the brightness pattern in the whole interior is pleasant. The choice of fitting must be determined to some extent by the ceiling structure and in some cases it is possible to integrate the lighting system with the ceiling. An example of this is shown in Fig. 27.6 where troffer fittings employing four 65 W fluorescent tubes are inset behind ½ in. acrylic plastics louvers, the latter providing a good cut-off angle to prevent any direct sight of the tubes from usual working positions.

Fig. 27.6　Drawing office installation with permanent supplementary
artificial lighting

For tracing, there is much to be said for the provision of a back-illuminated
panel, comprising a sheet of acrylic material lit by a careful arrangement of
fluorescent tubes to give even diffusion over its surface. A panel luminance of
about 200 ft-L is desirable for this purpose.

The relationship between artificial lighting and daylight.　In many
buildings it is necessary to use a certain amount of artificial lighting even in
daytime because the daylight factor at certain working positions is not
sufficient. This often happens in offices, and whilst the problems that are
created also arise in the lighting of factories, schools and many other buildings, the subject will be dealt with in this section.

When artificial lighting is used solely as an occasional supplementary
measure, two considerations are of importance:

(1) The switching of the installation should be so arranged that the
lighting units furthest from the window are under separate control.
Sometimes this supplementary lighting is automatically controlled
(by photoelectric methods) so that it is switched on when the daylight
level falls to a predetermined value.

(2) The quality of the light should match reasonably well with daylight.
When fluorescent tubes are used, the choice of tube colour depends
to a large extent on the function of interior. For instance if a school
classroom used only in day-time requires some supplementary artificial
lighting, then the 'Daylight' tube can be used. If, however, there is
extensive use of the installation after dark, then tubes of a slightly
warmer colour may be preferred.

Although the question has been argued many times, it is still generally held that most people prefer natural light when it can be made available. In office buildings of considerable depth, however, useful space exists which must often depend upon artificial light, and if this light can be made permanent then offices can be made deeper and economic benefits arise because a greater floor area is efficiently employed.

This is one of the arguments in favour of 'permanent supplementary artificial lighting'. Another argument in its favour is concerned with the relative brightnesses seen within the view of the worker seated at some distance from the window. When daylight is good, the aspect of the sky (particularly on upper floors of high buildings) can constitute a source of glare of relatively large area. One solution to this problem is to raise the 'adaptation level' by means of supplementary artificial lighting, which must be of a permanent nature since it may perform a more useful function before dark than after dark. In fact, the illumination level in this area may need to be higher than in the window area. Because of this the installation must be carefully planned in relation to the visual requirements, the dimensions of the room and its fenestration. The drawing office, already shown in Fig. 27.6, has a permanent supplementary artificial lighting installation (P.S.A.L.I.). An illumination level of 45 lm/ft² is provided generally throughout the area, but additional fluorescent tubes under separate control at the side remote from the windows increase this to 60 lm/ft² under conditions of high sky brightness.

SCHOOL LIGHTING

Legislation. The Standards for School Premises Regulations 1959 contain certain requirements in connection with artificial lighting which can be summarised as follows:

(1) In all teaching accommodation (and also in all school kitchens) the maintained illumination level *on the appropriate plane* in the area of normal use shall be 10 lm/ft².

(2) In all such areas no luminous part of any lighting unit having a maximum luminance greater than 1500 ft-L or an average luminance greater than 1000 ft-L shall be visible to any occupant in a normal position within an angle at the eye of 135 degrees to the perpendicular.

(3) Sufficient light shall fall upon the ceiling and upper wall areas to prevent excessive contrast between the fittings and their background.

It will be seen from the above that equal emphasis is placed upon qualitative factors and quantitative factors, and this has led to the design of special lighting units for use in schools.

It should be pointed out that the illumination level recommended in (1) is the *minimum* level on the *appropriate* plane. If a really adequate average level is to be provided on the vertical plane (e.g. a chalkboard) then the illumination level on the horizontal plane must exceed 10 lm/ft². It is in the light of these facts that one should consider the recommendations of the I.E.S. Code, which proposes the following maintained values for school lighting.

Assembly hall
general	15	lm/ft^2
when used for examinations	30	,,
platform	30	,,

Classrooms and lecture theatres · · · · · · ,,
desks		30	,,
on chalkboards	20 to 30		,, on the vertical surface

Laboratories · · · · · · 30 ,,

Libraries
shelves	5 to 10		,, on the vertical surface
reading tables		30	,,

Art rooms	45	,,
Embroidery and sewing rooms	70	,,
Offices	30	,,
Staff rooms, common rooms	15	,,
Corridors	7	,,
Stairs	10	,,

Lamps for school lighting. The incandescent lamp is still the most generally used light source in schools. Until recent years the fluorescent tube had been adopted on only a limited scale, chiefly because the annual lighting hours in primary schools are very limited and the additional capital expenditure for fluorescent equipment was not justified by the economy in current. With the greater emphasis on the control of glare, however, fluorescent lighting has been received with greater favour, particularly for schools and colleges which are used both day and evening.

Visual tasks. There are some visual tasks in schools which have their counterparts in other spheres. For instance, woodwork and metalwork rooms have tasks similar to those in industry, whilst domestic science rooms have tasks similar to those in the home. These interiors are not dealt with, therefore, in this chapter.

In the classroom or lecture theatre, however, the visual task is quite distinctive. Whilst pupils must, of course, be concerned with the desk area when reading or writing, they are often looking at the teacher or at the chalkboard, and this is the reason for the rather exacting limits on glare referred to above, since the sight line is approximately horizontal or a little above the horizontal.

In judging the visual capacity of classroom students, account must be taken of rather unusual factors. For instance, a young child may not achieve the same standard as an adult partly because he has not yet acquired the experience to 'guess' the identity of indistinct writing or other characters. Again, it is possible that the most 'critical' detail to be seen by a student is not something which occurs in his own desk work, but an index in an algebraic expression written on the chalkboard some distance away.

The lighting of classrooms. As has been indicated above, the choice of light source is determined chiefly by economics, whilst the design of fitting is

Fig. 27.7   Fitting for tungsten filament lamp

Fig. 27.8   Tungsten filament lighting in a classroom

chiefly governed by the necessity to limit glare in classrooms. When annual lighting hours are not considerable, e.g. in schools used for day classes only, the incandescent lamp is often employed, and the fitting associated with this lamp must not only limit its luminance at the significant angles, but also ensure that the upper walls and ceiling receive a reasonable proportion of light to provide a good brightness pattern. The most usual type of fitting is therefore constructed from a glass or plastics diffusing material, carefully chosen to meet luminance requirements, but the fitting is often open at both top and bottom to achieve good efficiency and correct light distribution. A typical fitting is shown in Fig. 27.7, whilst Fig. 27.8 shows a classroom installation.

Although the fluorescent tube has a luminance considerably lower than that of the incandescent lamp, the unshielded tube would not meet the requirements referred to above. It would be possible to use reflector fittings, but these would need to be equipped with louvers to shield the tubes and the distribution of light above the horizontal would be restricted. Diffusing fittings are more suitable for classroom lighting and an example is shown in Fig. 27.9. This is a batten fitting with the addition of 'Clipluve', a supplementary diffusing device which was specifically designed to meet the school regulations.

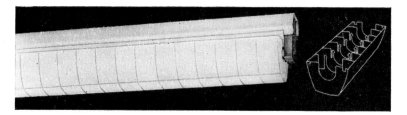

Fig. 27.9   Batten fitting with 'Clipluve'

Where, as in most orthodox classrooms, the chalkboard is permanently fixed, it is best lit by a fluorescent angled reflector fitting, the tube being completely shielded from the eyes of the pupils and an even distribution of light on the vertical plane being achieved. Such a fitting is seen in Fig. 27.10.

A fixed chalkboard implies also a fixed arrangement of desks, and the layout of the general lighting of the classroom should be designed appropriately.

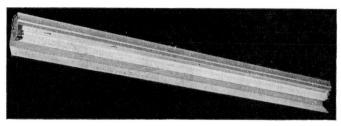

Fig. 27.10   Fluorescent angle reflector fitting for chalkboard lighting

It should be remembered that the desk area may extend to positions quite close to the walls and it is particularly important (especially in the case of incandescent lighting) that the back row of fittings should not be too far forward. Fittings at the side of the room also should not be too far from the wall and this is specially important to the left hand side of the pupils, as light coming from the left generally helps to avoid shadows when writing and reduces the risk of reflected glare from glossy papers and desk tops.

The larger area and lower luminance of fluorescent fittings make their exact positioning less important, but it is always desirable that pupils should look along the major axis of fluorescent fittings so that the projected area at the eye is at a minimum, and the possibility of glare is therefore further reduced.

Assembly hall, gymnasia, etc. A brief mention should be made of the special problems which often arise in the lighting of assembly halls in schools as these halls sometimes serve many purposes. They are, of course, used regularly for school assembly, when the required standard of artificial lighting is not high—though even in such circumstances the illumination level in the platform or stage area should be higher than that in the body of the hall.

At other times, however, the assembly hall may be used for examination purposes, when students require a high standard of lighting during long periods of concentration, and the initial installation should take account of these conditions. On other occasions, the hall may be used for stage performances, and it would be well to consider dimming arrangements for the general lighting, together with some provision for special stage lighting effects.

Finally, there are assembly halls which are also used as gymnasia; these situations may demand special considerations, both in the choice of 'protected' fittings and in the integration of lighting into the ceiling structure to eliminate unnecessary obstructions.

CHAPTER 28

Lighting for Hospitals

Hospitals are complex structures both because of their physical form and because of the diverse procedures which take place within them. These combined factors complicate the lighting requirements. Though there are many areas which have specialised functions, there are some which have the same purpose as similar areas found in industry or commerce, and may be lighted in the same way. This chapter makes recommendations for the satisfactory lighting of those interiors of hospitals which are distinctive in their nature and function.

The lighting of a hospital must satisfy the often exacting visual requirements of the medical staff, yet create a reassuring and pleasing atmosphere to the patient; this applies particularly to ward lighting. The lighting throughout the medical and nursing areas of a hospital must be fully integrated, particularly in the case of 'wheel' or 'race-track' ward units where there are corridors and service rooms which receive little or no natural light.

Ward lighting needs. The general lighting of a ward must be satisfactory for both the nursing staff and the patients. For the former it must be adequate for the efficient care of patients, and for the latter it must enable reading and other bed occupations, or alternatively rest and sleep as required.

In a ward for recumbent patients the general lighting must be sufficient and suitable for circulation and amenity over the whole area. At the bedside and in the centre of the ward it must be adequate for the usual nursing procedures, such as marking charts and reading thermometers. The direct illumination on the patient's face should be at a low level to minimise discomfort glare and to enable him to rest or sleep. It is therefore recommended that the illumination on a patient's face should be provided by the indirect component of the general lighting and should be between 3 lm/ft^2 and 5 lm/ft^2. The general lighting should also contribute to the decor and help to produce a pleasing interior, which is so important to the patients' morale.

Bedhead lighting. The patient's bedhead lighting fixture is required to give a good light for reading and bed-occupation and should be under the patient's own control. The staff may use this lamp for everyday nursing tasks such as reading thermometers but it should not be required to act as an examination lamp as well. If it is adjustable, to permit its convenient arrangement relative to the patient's bed-posture, its range of movement should be limited so that it cannot cause glare to other ward users, but the lamp should be capable of being swung back to the wall when beds and apparatus are being moved.

It is assumed that reading lights will usually be provided for all beds in hospitals, but there are occasions when it is undesirable to have such fittings within easy reach of some children and some types of mental cases. In these circumstances it is suggested that such fittings should be removable, or that high level wall or ceiling mounted fittings be used.

A 'watch light' or dimming circuit may be provided with the bedhead light if low level night lighting is to be used.

Night lighting. Ward night lighting must provide the minimum illumination which will permit safe movement about the ward without requiring too lengthy a time for dark adaptation on entering, but it is important that the night lighting should not disturb a lightly sleeping patient. It is not necessary for the night lighting to illuminate the patient unless he is out of bed.

The Ministry of Health recommends that the night-lighting level of illumination for children's wards should be 0·1 lm/ft² and that for adult wards 0·01 lm/ft². These levels are adequate and should not be exceeded where practically possible. The night lighting in the corridor may well contribute towards the night lighting of the ward and could in certain cases be sufficient, such as in open plan ward layouts.

Physicians have found that nightmares or phantasmagoria are more likely to be experienced when the ceiling is slightly illuminated, and a totally darkened ceiling seems less disturbing to feverish patients and especially to children. Therefore neither the bedhead nor the ceiling should be illuminated by the night-time lighting, which should be confined to the floor or the lower half of the beds.

It is recommended that blinds or curtains be drawn over the ward windows at night to prevent stray light entering; the shadows of trees cast by motor-car headlights are particularly disturbing, as also is the light from adjacent windows.

Watch lighting. The purpose of watch lighting is to enable continuous observation of a very ill patient after the main lighting has been switched off; he must be observed without disturbing him, and quite low illumination levels are suitable for this purpose. A level of less than 0·5 lm/ft² is adequate if the night lighting level is low. A convenient arrangement is the provision of a low wattage lamp in the bedhead light, or the use of a dimming circuit for the bedhead lamp itself; but the dimming of tungsten lamps produces a noticeable change in colour of the light emitted.

Lighting for examination. A bedhead fitting of a design suitable to act both as a patient's reading lamp and also as an examination lamp would by necessity be of a complicated design, particularly if it were constructed so as not to cause serious glare to other ward users. Also it would be of little use for the examination of the lower half of the body.

Fittings which are detachable from the wall or locker introduce dangers of electric shock and accidents due to the lamp failing. It is suggested that the general use of a free standing wheeled examination lamp in the ward would enable simplification and standardisation of bedhead lighting equipment, as well as providing greatly improved local illumination for diagnosis and treatment. Such examination lamps (BS 3541) should be hygienically constructed, silent in movement and available in sufficient numbers at all times.

There is no objection to the nursing staff using the bedhead fitting for cursory examination of a patient or for the administration of minor treatments.

Nurses' stations. Nurses' stations are generally located at strategic positions in relation to the wards. Often they have little or no daylighting, and during the day they should be illuminated to about 30 lm/ft². This lighting may well be used during the evening. If so, the lighting fittings should have no bright parts, and the luminance of any part of the fitting visible to recumbent patients should be no greater than 300 ft-L.

At night it is necessary to provide a low level of illumination of about 3 lm/ft², to enable a nurse to do her work. However, the source of illumination must be sufficiently well screened to prevent distraction or glare to sleeping patients. Care must be taken to obviate distorted shadow effects, but if the local lighting just reveals a nurse at the desk this can be reassuring.

Ward lighting recommendations

Illumination levels. Recommended illumination levels for wards are given in Table 28.1.

TABLE 28.1

Recommended Average Horizontal Illumination Levels in Wards

General lighting	Patient's reading lighting	Night lighting at bedhead (3 ft from floor)

At bedhead
  Minimum 3 lm/ft²
  Maximum 5 lm/ft²
Circulation space*
  10 to 20 lm/ft²
	Minimum 15 lm/ft²	0·01 lm/ft²
		(0·1 lm/ft² in children's wards)

* The area between the bed foot rails and the end walls of the ward at a height of 2 ft 9 in from floor level.

Discomfort glare. The recumbent patient is less affected by the illumination provided on the horizontal plane and is much more affected by the brightness of the ceiling, walls and lighting equipment which are in his field of view. The limiting glare indices as usually computed on the basis of the I.E.S. Code are not easily applied to the case of the reclining patient. The usual criteria for determining the degree of discomfort still apply, but as the installation does not consist of a regular array of fittings and as the observer's line of sight is not horizontal but may centre on a lighting fitting suspended almost over the foot of his bed, the normal methods of calculation cannot be applied. Discomfort glare may be present and distressing to a patient while not being at all noticeable to the staff, for the patient's eye level and direction of view are never shared by his medical attendants. Prolonged exposure to even moderate glare may cause headaches and nervous tension in sensitive patients or those who are prone to ocular discomfort because of disease or the effects of medication, and recovery from any type of malady might be retarded by such conditions. Reflected glare from any surface should also be avoided.

Design requirements for ward lighting fittings

Limitation of glare. The I.E.S. Code recommends that the glare index for hospital wards should not be greater than 13 as calculated from the position of a patient in any usual or necessary posture, or from the position of any person standing anywhere in a ward—in each case the calculation should take account of light sources appearing within an angle of 45° from the primary line of sight.

The Ministry of Health indicates that providing the luminance of any part of the fitting does not exceed certain limits the required limitation of glare will be met. These limits are as follows:

Pendant fittings (semi-indirect)	300 ft-L.
Surface mounted and recessed fittings	200 ft-L if total light emitted above horizontal is less than 20% of the total. 300 ft-L if the total light emitted above horizontal is greater than 20% of the total.
Wall mounted indirect fittings	(*a*) Ceiling not brighter than 50 ft-L at any point.
	(*b*) Luminance of wall not higher than that of ceiling.
	(*c*) Diversity of luminance over wall above the fitting should not be greater than 10 to 1.

Bedhead lighting. The minimum acceptable level of illumination for bed occupations is 15 lm/ft². This level should be so provided as to enable a patient to read or write in any position in bed, whether sitting or lying down. Any possible adjustment or switching on or off of the fitting should be easily done by the patient.

Night lighting. The Ministry of Health recommends that any lighting fitting which is in use during the night and which can be seen from the bedhead should not have a luminance in excess of 1 ft-L.

There are two systems of night lighting—high and low level. The latter system readily reveals obstructions in the ward, but the nursing staff may not easily see a sleeping patient against a comparatively brightly lit floor. Low-level wall mounted fittings must be located so that recumbent patients cannot see bright reflections in the floor.

Lighting fittings and hygiene. Lighting fittings for use in hospitals, as compared with other interiors, must satisfy stringent medical requirements for hygiene and safety. Airborne dust particles can transport harmful bacteria. Lighting fittings, in common with other items of ward equipment, can be the medium of transfer of infection by surface contact or by the dust particles they may harbour.

Lighting fittings for hospital use should have the minimum area of horizontal or near-horizontal surface on which dust can settle, and such dust must be easily removable by simple cleaning methods. Although through-draught fittings may be used, they must be so constructed that settled dust is unlikely to be reconvected into the air. The interior of enclosed fittings should be inaccessible except by the use of a tool or key to open the unit.

Lighting fittings may require sterilisation and physical cleansing to restore hygienic conditions in addition to the routine cleansing necessary to maintain light output. To aid efficient cleaning, no porous or spongy material should be used for sealing or insulation.

The external surfaces of fittings must be smooth and devoid of apertures or crevices which cannot easily be wiped clean. All finishes, particularly paint finishes, must withstand frequent application of cleaning agents.

Noise. The mounting of control gear for fluorescent tubes must be such as to ensure that any hum is not amplified by resonance of the fitting on the structure to which it is attached, or by any other such resonance where the control gear is located remotely from the tubes. It is particularly important that recognition should be given to this problem when considering fluorescent bedhead lighting. At night the ambient noise level drops considerably, especially in country districts, and even a hum which is only just perceptible can be very irritating to sensitive patients.

No part of any fitting should rattle when in a draught of air, or when subject to normal building vibrations.

Electrical safety. Electrical safety of a very high order must be achieved. This is especially important in the case of bedhead fittings and low-level night-lights which are accessible to patients. Adequate earthing must be provided, the construction must be robust, and the fitting must be capable of being securely fixed to wall, partition or locker. 'Pear' and 'torpedo' switches at mains voltage are dangerous in wards, and the use of low-voltage relay switching at 4 V to 24 V is recommended. Relay-actuating control switches for bedhead lights may be incorporated in the patient's nurse-call apparatus. If a mains-operated switch has to be incorporated in a bedhead light for the patient's use, it is advisable that it should be operated by a nylon pull-cord (which is easily sterilised) or by a disposable manilla string, as this arrangement makes for hygiene and electrical safety. Electrical connections should be inaccessible except by the use of tools. Provision must be made for easy cleaning of the inside of enclosed fittings without risk of electric shock to the cleaner.

Mechanical safety. Removable portions of fittings should, if possible, be so made that gravity assists their retention in position and locking devices should be positive and not dependent on a spring. Sick people are often unpredictable in their behaviour, so fittings should be capable of withstanding a fair degree of tampering and rough usage. A child of five years of age can reach to a height of about 8 ft when standing in a hospital cot, and any bedhead light provided in juvenile wards must be regarded, therefore, as being freely accessible to the children.

Light sources. The artificial light sources for the general lighting of all nursing and clinical departments should have acceptable colour-rendering properties. The judgment of colour of a patient's skin and tissue is a critical task, and the artificial light sources must enable the medical staff to perform this task wherever a patient might be within the hospital. Many laboratory tests depend on accurate assessment of colour or colour changes.

It has been shown that an appropriate colour of fluorescent lamp can provide good colour rendering for medical purposes. This light source can be loosely described as having properties akin to a 'sunlight' phase of daylight.

In order to ensure that the correct colour rendering light sources are used at all times it is recommended that the same colour of fluorescent lamp is used throughout a hospital. This will obviate heterogeneous re-lamping and will also prevent medical staff having to attune themselves to varying colour-rendering characteristics in different places. At present lighting varies over a wide range, from daylight to incandescent lamps, whereby objects of medical interest may assume very varied appearances. As in ordinary life, a process of adaptation allows us to discount these differences to some extent, but it would evidently be an advantage if uniform lighting made this unnecessary.

In addition to the light sources being medically acceptable, which is the prime consideration, they should not cause the decor, particularly in the wards, to appear gloomy or cold. Also, where permanent supplementary artificial lighting is employed, the spectral quality of the lamps should be such that it blends with daylight. Another consideration, which may conflict with the one just mentioned, is that lighting levels in wards are much reduced in the evening. In these conditions lighting that is warm in colour is particularly acceptable, and it is therefore desirable to choose a colour as warm as possible consistent with a reasonable blending with daylight.

Lighting design for deep plan (race-track) ward units. The lighting of race-track units (see Fig. 28.1) requires to be related to the needs of the diverse rooms and duties and the varying conditions which occur during the day, evening (and early morning) and night time. Where possible daylight is preferred, but in the core area, where there is no natural light, during the daytime it will be necessary to provide illumination to a higher level than

15+

would otherwise be needed at night-time. This course prevents the constant re-adaptation of the eye when going to and from well and poorly lit areas. The lighting system for these areas should be so designed as to allow the use of

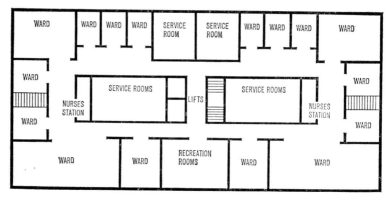

Fig. 28.1   Typical compact ward unit layout

the upper or lower level of illumination according to the time of day. The two levels of lighting may be provided by the individual switching of lamps in multi-lamp fittings, which is preferred to the switching of complete fittings. The locations concerned are:

All naturally lit rooms—wards and dayrooms. These rooms will have levels of illumination as discussed earlier, though during the day the levels will be dependent upon the fenestration design and will range from 5 lm/ft^2 at the rear of the room on a dull day to 300 lm/ft^2 near the window on a bright day.

Corridors open or partially open to naturally lit areas. To obtain an acceptable balance of illumination during the day, a permanent supplementary lighting installation may have to be adopted, giving approximately 30 lm/ft^2 in the corridor area. For evening lighting 10 lm/ft^2 to 12 lm/ft^2 would be adequate, whilst at night 0·5 lm/ft^2 would be satisfactory and may provide indirectly the necessary level of night-lighting in the ward. The lighting fittings should be so designed and located as not to cause glare to any patient.

Corridors without natural light. These should be illuminated to a minimum of 20 lm/ft^2 to compensate for the lack of daylight. During the evening and night these levels can be reduced as in the corridors referred to above. During the evening the appearance of the corridor wall as seen from the bed position is of psychological importance. If the illumination level in the corridor at this time is not below 10 lm/ft^2 the wall will be sufficiently bright to give the impression that the ward is not isolated from the rest of the building.

Internal rooms. These can be classified into two groups, treatment, utility, etc., and ablutions. In daytime the level of illumination for the former should be about 30 to 40 lm/ft² and for the latter 20 to 30 lm/ft². These levels will reduce the apparent contrast of brightness when passing from these rooms to those which are naturally lit. During the evening and at night, the levels may be reduced to 20 lm/ft² and 15 lm/ft² respectively. Experiments have shown that it is not difficult to view a patient in bed under conditions of night-lighting when having just come from an internal room lit to 25 lm/ft². The appropriate lighting levels at different times of the day and night are indicated in Fig. 28.2.

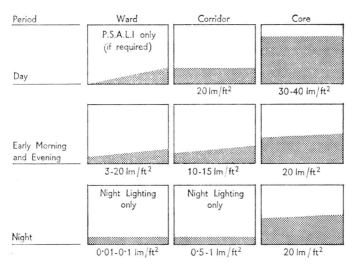

Fig. 28.2 Typical artificial lighting levels required in 'compact' ward blocks

Operating theatre suites. The layouts of theatre suites do not conform to any definite pattern. The nature of the ancillary rooms may depend on the type of surgery carried out. For general surgery the following rooms would form the basis of the suite; theatre(s), anaesthetic, sterilising, sink and scrub-up rooms, recovery, sister's office, nurses' preparation room, storage area, dark room, cleaner's room and engineering plant. Other rooms which might be necessary include a minor theatre, laboratory, plaster, endoscopy, X-ray and autoclave rooms. The main rooms are considered to be the theatre(s), anaesthetic, sterilising, sink and scrub-up rooms.

General lighting of operating theatres. Essentially there are two lighting systems in an operating theatre. Of foremost importance is the illumination of the operating table, and of secondary importance the general lighting. Because the lighting of the theatre table is a specialised subject it is not discussed here.

The visual tasks in the theatre are the detailed examination of the patient on the table, the colour appearance of skin and tissue and the viewing of small detail in ancillary equipment. The theatre table lighting equipment will provide the necessary illumination in the relatively small areas of the operation; this may have an illumination level in excess of 1000 lm/ft².

The surgeon and (even more so) his assistants will, by necessity, be repeatedly looking at and away from the area of operation. Therefore, it is necessary to have background illumination of a complementary level to ensure the ideal visual conditions, and the general lighting should be from 1/10th to 1/25th of that in the area of operation. Thus, the level of illumination should be between 40 and 150 lm/ft².

The ideal lighting system allows a high illumination level in the area of the table—60 to 100 lm/ft²—falling off towards the periphery to about 40 lm/ft². The I.E.S. Code recommends that the general lighting should have a limiting glare index of 10. However, the problem is eased if the lighting units are concentrated over the operating table. It is important that no light source is seen even by peripheral vision from the vicinity of the table.

Depending on the surgical requirements of the theatre, consideration may have to be given to the general lighting from the patient's viewpoint. If this is of importance, then indirect lighting might be required to prevent visual discomfort to the patient.

In the interests of safety all lamps installed in the theatre must be in totally enclosed fittings so that should a lamp break the remnants remain in the fitting. The fittings should be designed to provide protection against mechanical damage and hosing down, yet, at the same time, facilitate speedy relamping.

Light sources. Usually the operating table lighting equipment employs one or more tungsten filament lamps giving high levels of illumination and good colour rendering. The light sources for the general lighting should have equally good spectral qualities to obviate the need for the surgeon, anaesthetist and their assistants to repeatedly re-adapt to both colour and brightness when they look away from the area of operation. Since high levels of illumination are required in the theatre, it is not expedient to use tungsten lighting owing to its high heat output which makes undue demands on the ventilating system. As fluorescent light sources have good colour rendering properties and low heat output, their use is often demanded.

Other rooms. The general lighting throughout the suites should be at the same level as that in the theatres, employing the same light sources. These areas include anaesthetic, sterilising, sink and scrub-up rooms, recovery, plaster rooms and laboratories. Similarly, the lighting fittings should have the same mechanical properties as those used in the theatre.

Emergency lighting. The provision of emergency arrangements are essential to obviate the serious circumstances which could arise due to the failure of the main electrical supply. Emergency lighting should be permanently installed not only in the theatre but in at least the anaesthetic, sterilising, sink and recovery rooms. The lighting for the operating table itself usually has a secondary system for such an occurrence, which automatically comes into operation on the failure of the primary circuit. A similar system may be used in the case of the general lighting, and the illumination level it provides under emergency conditions should be equivalent to that of normal operation.

Maternity departments. The lighting requirements for maternity units should be to the normal hospital standard. However, there are a number of aspects which need special consideration.

Wards. The general lighting of the wards should follow the practice described earlier, but it may be justifiable to introduce some feature lighting in an effort to create a more congenial atmosphere. Some maternity wards are so designed that the child is in a cot beside the mother's bed. In such cases, it may be advisable to mount the adjustable bedhead fitting so that it can be used to illuminate both the bedhead and the cot, thus facilitating cursory examination of the baby.

Examination, delivery and treatment rooms. The form of lighting in these rooms will be dictated by the medical requirements. The general lighting may be required to be indirect, and adjustable examination lamps should also be provided. In the delivery room an adjustable overhead high intensity spot-lamp is necessary.

Nurseries. Care must be taken in the lighting of these rooms to prevent the babies being subjected to glare. The cots are usually too close together to permit the use of standard ward lighting fittings. Since the required levels of illumination for general lighting are the same as for general wards, a semi-indirect lighting system may be preferred, having independent control of the upward and downward components. The spectral quality of the lighting must be medically acceptable, particularly for the observation of jaundiced babies.

The hot, warm, cool and observation rooms of the Special Baby Care Suite may have similar lighting to the nurseries. The temperatures of these rooms, which are designed to be interchangeable, are as follows:

Hot room or incubator room	75/80 °F
Warm humidified room	70/75 °F
Cool room	65 °F

Intensive care units. These are specialised medical units which are designed to aid the recovery of the chronically sick, who are often comatose or semi-comatose. Therefore, the lighting must enable close medical attention over the full extent of the bed and the level of illumination should be in the region of 20 lm/ft^2. The lighting fittings should afford the minimum of glare to the recumbent patient. However, the lighting of these units must be considered in relation to their special requirements.

Laboratories. The visual tasks in hospital laboratories not only demand high levels of illumination but also accurate colour discrimination. However, there are many tasks which require no higher illumination than that required for general office lighting. The layout of the laboratory should be such that those tasks which require good lighting are located near the windows, and the general artificial lighting can be associated with those areas which require high illumination.

At night the minimum level of illumination should be 30 lm/ft², and for laboratories with no natural light during the day an illumination level of 50 lm/ft² should be provided. The limiting glare index for laboratories is 19.

Exterior lighting. It is to be expected that all roads and paths in the hospital grounds will be well illuminated. However, the lighting equipment should not only be considered from the aesthetic and utilitarian viewpoints, but as a possible source of distraction to sleeping patients. Unshielded road lights can cause grotesque patterns to be formed on walls and ceilings. These sources of irritation could be reduced by careful design of the access road lighting, and by minimising the necessity for cars to use their headlights whilst in the hospital grounds.

Design procedures for hospital lighting

Traditional wards. Wards are generally as shown in Fig. 28.3 and 28.4, the dimensions being from 90 ft to 120 ft long, 12 ft to 16 ft high and 28 ft to 32 ft wide. The layout of the service rooms will vary.

To determine the mounting height of pendant fluorescent fittings consider the cross-section of the ward (see Fig. 28.4) with the bed position and its height indicated. From a point at the foot of the bed strike an angle of 40° to

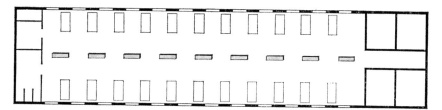

Fig. 28.3   Plan of traditional ward

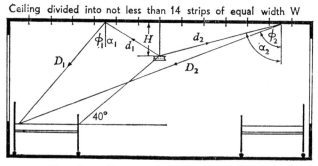

Fig. 28.4   Cross-section of traditional ward

the horizontal, and produce this line until it cuts the vertical centre line of the ward. This intersection indicates the suspension length (H).

To determine the level of illumination at the bedhead in a traditional ward using pendant fluorescent fittings:

The illumination at the bedhead is due to the diffused indirect component of the pendant fitting. To assess the illumination it is necessary to evaluate the contribution made by each part of the ceiling. A convenient method is as follows:

(1) Divide the ceiling into not less than 14 strips of equal width (see Fig. 28.4).

(2) Calculate the illumination, E, each panel gives at the bedhead where

$$E = \frac{\rho W \pi}{4} \frac{I\alpha \cos^2 \phi \cos \alpha}{D_1 d_1}$$

W = width of strip

ρ = reflection factor of the ceiling having a diffuse finish

$I\alpha$ = the intensity in candelas per unit length from the indirect component of the fitting to the centre of each panel.

The total illumination at the bedhead is the sum of the contributions from each strip, assuming the lighting fittings to be continuous.

Lighting of four-bed wards. Fig. 28.5 shows the room and bed dimensions for a typical four-bed ward. Figs. 28.6 and 28.7 indicate the lighting requirements and possible installations for four-bed wards having ceiling heights above and below 9 ft 6 in.

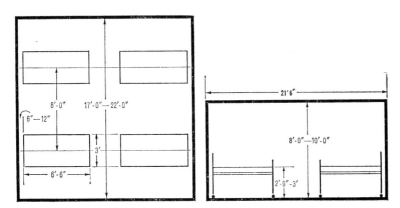

Fig. 28.5 Plan and cross-section of four-bed ward

In wards having ceiling heights at, or above 9 ft 6 in., suspended fluorescent fittings having a semi-indirect distribution will give the required levels of illumination. (The minimum recommended suspension length is 18 in.)

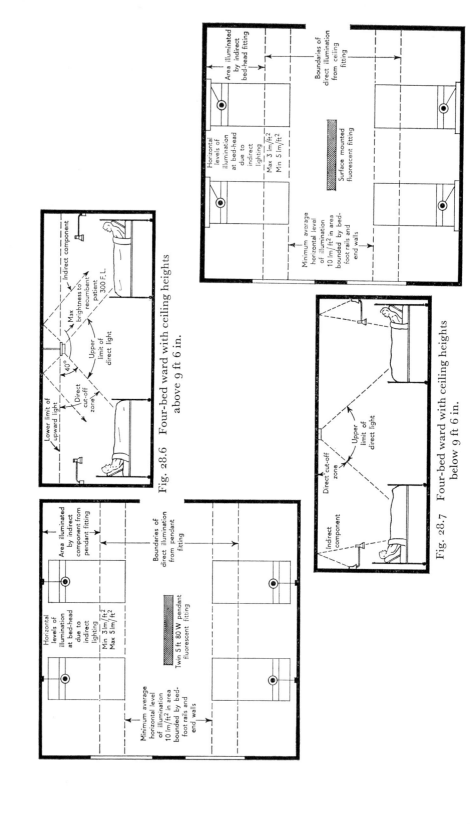

Fig. 28.6 Four-bed ward with ceiling heights above 9 ft 6 in.

Fig. 28.7 Four-bed ward with ceiling heights below 9 ft 6 in.

For wards which have low ceilings, i.e. below 9 ft 6 in., it is necessary to provide the indirect component from wall-mounted fittings mounted at about 6 ft above each bed. Such a unit can incorporate the bedhead lighting. The direct component is provided by a surface or recessed unit, the recommended luminances of which are:

Upward Flux Fraction less than 20%—maximum luminance 200 ft-L.
Upward Flux Fraction greater than 20%—maximum luminance 300 ft-L.

Lighting of single and two-bed wards. Single and two-bed wards cannot be satisfactorily illuminated with standard fittings since the layout is asymmetric, and a complementary lighting system has to be employed. Figs. 28.8 and 28.9 indicate suggested lighting arrangements for these wards.

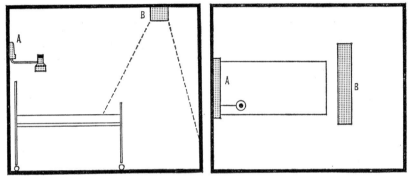

Fig. 28.8   Cross-section and plan of a single-bed ward

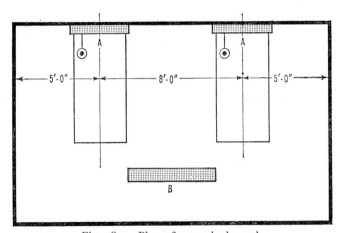

Fig. 28.9   Plan of a two-bed ward

Fitting A is a suggested design of combined bedhead unit, having a single 3 ft or 4 ft fluorescent lamp for ceiling and indirect illumination at the bedhead, and an adjustable 40/60 W tungsten reading light with an optional 15 W pigmy watch light.

15*

Fitting B is a suggested direct lighting unit, having louvers giving a transverse cut-off of 50°. The acceptable brightness of the fitting, from the patient's viewpoint, is governed by the Upward Flux Fraction, and the luminance limits given above should be observed. A twin 5 ft fluorescent fitting would be suitable for a two-bed ward and a single 5 ft unit for a single bed ward.

Bedhead lighting. The requirements of a bedhead lighting unit are as follows:

(1) The minimum acceptable level of illumination on the bed is 15 lm/ft².

(2) Restricted adjustability to prevent annoyance to adjacent patients and to those opposite.

(3) The fitting must be positioned so that it can be adjusted by a sitting patient, yet not interfere with bed apparatus, such as balkam beams. It should be capable of being swung back to the wall but with stops to prevent actual contact.

(4) The switching facilities must suit an incapacitated patient.

Fig. 28.10 indicates how these requirements can be met. Watch lighting can be provided by means of a separately switched 15 W lamp in the reflector of the bedhead unit.

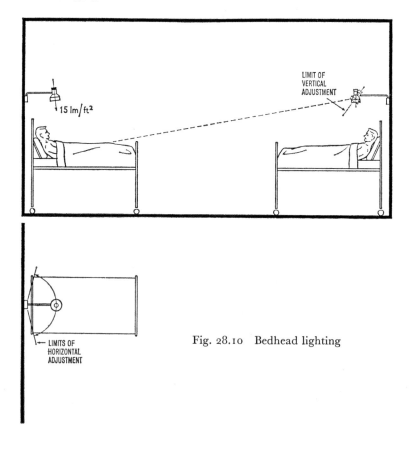

Fig. 28.10   Bedhead lighting

Lighting of corridors. By mounting a continuous line of recessed fluorescent fittings at position A in a closed corridor having architectural features similar to those shown in Fig. 28.11, neither bedded patients nor those on a trolley would be subjected to glare from the corridor lighting.

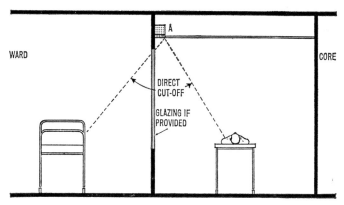

Fig. 28.11   Lighting for a closed corridor

The mounting at position A enables the adjacent corridor wall to have an acceptable brightness in comparison with the daylighted wards which may be seen from the internal rooms.

Providing the illumination at floor level in the centre of the corridor during the evening is not less than 10 lm/ft^2, the corridor wall adjacent to the core will have an acceptable apparent brightness when seen from within the ward. (This is dependent on the floor having a 25% to 30% reflection factor.)

In the open type of corridor (Fig. 28.12) it is preferable to have fittings at position B rather than A, since a bedded patient is less likely to be subjected to glare, and it also helps to give a more acceptable brightness to the corridor wall, which in effect is a part of the environment of patients in the ward.

The luminance of fittings as seen by a recumbent patient in the ward is kept

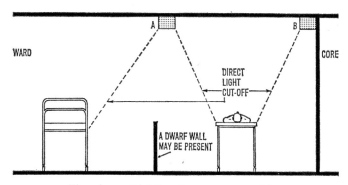

Fig. 28.12   Lighting for an open corridor

to a minimum, if possible not greater than 200 ft-L. At night, low-level corridor lighting must be employed, so designed as not to be disturbing to patients.

Depending on the design of the ward corridor wall, the level of illumination of 1 lm/ft² in the corridor may be sufficient to provide adequate night lighting in the ward by inter-reflection, assuming that the corridor floor has a high reflection factor.

CHAPTER 29

Lighting for Shops

Lighting is always essential for selling; it is now so closely related to the technique of merchandising that it is a major selling tool, with a function that ranges well beyond the everyday task of providing lighting merely for seeing. Provision of emphasis, atmosphere, circulation, colour, scale and many other aspects of modern retailing can be helped, or even created, by suitable forms of lighting.

Although the avoidance of glare is an important consideration in both window and shop interior lighting, small areas of relatively high brightness are often deliberately introduced, providing 'sparkle' or liveliness. Large differences between maximum and minimum illumination are sometimes permissible in order to create variety; in fact, the lighting of display areas depends more upon attracting attention by variation than by uniform lighting. Illumination values are therefore decided in a less technical way and approximations can be allowed which would not be permissible when planning office or factory lighting.

THE SHOP WINDOW

The lighting of a shop window can be considered in terms of the following factors:

Quantity of light
Quality of light
Types of lamp and
    lighting equipment

Type of window
Type of merchandise
Colour
Special effects

There is, of course, no single formula for all shop-window lighting, and the relative importance of these factors varies considerably with the type of shop. Thus, within the scope of this review, each aspect is discussed broadly, to show how the choice of a particular lighting arrangement is determined by local conditions and specific requirements.

Quantity of light. *Illumination level* is a useful yardstick by which to assess the broad category into which a particular standard of window lighting would fall. The level of illumination is usually indicated as an 'average' value although this may be implied rather than stated. Also, unless otherwise indicated, illumination values are assumed to be in the horizontal plane at window-bed level; this is of somewhat academic interest, for the illumination on the vertical surfaces of a display is usually of greater importance.

It is generally more practical and convenient to think of window lighting as falling within broad groups covering a range of levels, the choice of lighting level group being mainly influenced by the district. The following is an indication of how the grouping of the illumination levels can be related to types of districts.

Class A 200 lm/ft² and over—central shopping areas of larger cities; prestige shops in towns and cities.

Class B 100 to 200 lm/ft²—high density areas in larger towns; major shopping streets in important suburbs of cities.

Class C 50 to 100 lm/ft²—typical for moderately sized centres.

Class D 30 to 50 lm/ft²—smaller shopping centres; isolated or relatively isolated shops in moderately sized centres.

The heating effect of lighting equipment must also be taken into account, for it is directly related to lighting quantity. The fluorescent lamp, although more efficient than its incandescent counterpart, producing about a quarter of the heat for the same light, is, on the other hand, more sensitive to temperature differences (see Chapter 20) and in shop windows the problem is usually one of overheating. Without precautionary measures, overheating is likely in windows with Class A illumination, and quite possible with Classes B and C. Much depends on air volume and the extent of enclosure, together with other local factors, but generally speaking some provision for cross or through ventilation should be allowed (e.g. by window-bed ventilation) and complete enclosure of the window should be avoided.

The life of fluorescent control gear is also adversely affected by over-heating (see Chapter 23) and where possible gear should be mounted at a distance, not greatly exceeding 20 ft, outside the window area; this applies particularly to Class A installations. Voids above suspended ceilings should be used with caution as they can become heat traps, and they should always be ventilated.

The problem of deterioration of certain types of merchandise through heat-ing is well known to retailers and it must be appreciated that a concentration of light is inseparable from a concentration of heat for most types of incandescent lamps, the exception being those using dichroic reflectors (see Chapter 15). This means that care must be taken in the use of directional incandescent lamps and, in particular, low-voltage equipment with strongly directional performance may not be suitable for merchandise which is subject to deterioration through heating.

Quality of light. Whilst the quantity of light can be objectively measured, the quality of lighting is a subjective matter, difficult to define but at least recognisable, though recognition necessitates an understanding of the factors contributing to quality.

Avoidance of glare or distraction. A prime factor is that the source of light shall not compete for attention with the merchandise. Lighting can certainly create initial attention by dramatic emphasis, colour or movement, but having performed this function, lighting of good quality should be complementary to the display rather than a competing distraction. Initial attention can also be created by lamps deliberately arranged to be glaring. This may be acceptable for some seeing techniques and situations—fairgrounds and market stalls are typical examples—and in a carefully modified form the idea can be used in more sophisticated situations. But for normal window displays such methods defeat the main objective, i.e. that of providing the optimum lighting for appreciation of the display.

For example, the completely exposed fluorescent tube, particularly when viewed across its length or vertically, can actually reduce the effectiveness of the illumination due to the eye adapting itself to the brightness of the exposed tube; thus a higher illumination level on the display than would otherwise be necessary has then to be provided.

Modelling. The degree of modelling is governed by the size of the light source, the ability to control the light from the source, and its position relative to the display. Fluorescent tubes, being relatively large, tend to soften shadows, and are generally acceptable for providing the overall lighting using the most efficient light source. Incandescent lamps, on the other hand, being relatively small sources of light, can create sharply defined shadows, sometimes to an unwanted extent, but generally in a useful way, helping to express shape and depth. A particular virtue of the incandescent lamp is that the light from the filament can be simply controlled and a distribution of light chosen to suit the particular requirements of the display.

Thus the modelling quality of the lighting is closely related to the type of light source; the degree of modelling desirable depends upon the merchandise and the type of shop. Usually both fluorescent and incandescent lamps are needed to produce the best results, although the exclusive use of either is sometimes justified.

Colour and spatial effects—particularly background lighting—also make an important contribution to lighting quality, and these are dealt with separately. Table 29.1 shows possible variations on the type of light source for a selection of typical shops, particularly in relation to the colour rendering of merchandise.

Lamps and lighting equipment. Four main types of light source are used for shop-window lighting. They are, tubular fluorescent lamps, colour-corrected mercury vapour lamps, mains-voltage incandescent lamps, and low-voltage incandescent lamps. These, with their associated equipment, will be considered in turn.

Tubular Fluorescent Lamps. Practical sizes of fluorescent tubes for window lighting are 8 ft 125 W and 8 ft 85 W, 5 ft 65 W and 4 ft 40 W. They are available as either standard or reflector tubes.

TABLE 29.1

Light Sources for Shops

Shop type	Fluorescent (good colour)	Fluorescent (high efficiency)	Alternative or supplementary light sources
Baker	De-luxe Natural or De-luxe Warm White		IMV desirable as supplementary
Greengrocer	De-luxe Natural, Natural 3 or Kolorite	Daylight	Alternatively MBF/U with IMV
Fishmonger (wet fish)	De-luxe Natural	Daylight	IMVC necessary as supplementary
Fried-fish shop	De-luxe Warm White	Warm White	
Confectionery	De-luxe Natural or De-luxe Warm White	White	Alternatively MBF/U with IMV
Butcher	De-luxe Natural		
Grocer	De-luxe Natural	White	Alternatively MBF/U with IMV
Jeweller	Natural 3 or Kolorite	Daylight	IMVC necessary. T.H.
Furniture	De-luxe Natural or De-luxe Warm White	Warm White	IMV or ILV desirable as supplementary. T.H.
Shoes	Natural 3, Kolorite or De-luxe Natural	Daylight	Alternatively MBF/U with IMV. IMV or ILV desirable with fluorescent. T.H.
Dress	Natural 3, Kolorite or De-luxe Natural	White or Warm White	Alternatively MBF/U with IMV. IMV or ILV desirable with fluorescent. T.H.
Tailor	As Dress Shop	As Dress Shop	As Dress Shop
Hardware	Natural 3 or Kolorite	Daylight or White	Alternatively MBF/U with IMV. T.H.
Lingerie	De-luxe Natural or De-luxe Warm White	Warm White	IMV or ILV desirable as supplementary. T.H.
Wallpaper	Natural 3, De-luxe Natural or Kolorite	Daylight	Alternatively MBF/U with IMV. IMV or ILV desirable with Daylight fluorescent. T.H.
Soft Furnishings	Kolorite, Natural 3, De-luxe Natural or De-luxe Warm White	Warm White	Alternatively MBF/U with IMV. IMV or ILV desirable with fluorescent. T.H.

Flowers	De-luxe Natural, Natural 3 or Kolorite	Daylight	Alternatively MBF/U with IMV. IMV desirable with Daylight fluorescent.
China	Natural 3 or Kolorite	Daylight or White	Alternatively MBF/U with IMV. IMV or ILV desirable with Daylight or White fluorescent. T.H.
Chemist	De-luxe Natural or De-luxe Warm White	White	
Furrier	Northlight, Natural 3 or Kolorite	Daylight	Alternatively MBF/U with IMV. IMV or ILV desirable with fluorescent.
Toys	De-luxe Natural, Natural 3, or Kolorite	White	Supplementary IMV or ILV desirable. T.H.

	Index	Suggested minimum illumination values
IMV	Incandescent mains voltage general purpose pearl; internally silvered reflector lamp, spot or flood	50 lm/ft² minimum with Northlight fluorescent tubes. 40 lm/ft² minimum with Natural 3 or Kolorite tubes. 30 lm/ft² minimum with De-luxe Natural fluorescent tubes
IMVC	Incandescent mains voltage general purpose clear	Where mains voltage incandescent is indicated with fluorescent, equal wattage is implied
ILV	Incandescent low voltage	
MBF/U	Colour-corrected mercury	
T.H.	Tungsten-halogen interior floodlight	

A commonly used method of window lighting is to locate the equipment as close as possible to the face of the window, and direct light into the body of the window from this position. The question of whether this is the best method for a particular situation depends on such factors as the depth and type of the window, the quantity of light required and, of course, the available budget, for this method is probably the most economical.

For the lower range of Class D installations a convenient reflector is of the type constructed from anodised aluminium contoured to direct the maximum light within a forward 60° zone (Fig. 29.1). A reflector of this type can efficiently employ only one tube. The anodised aluminium reflector exhibits low brightness, and this is particularly advantageous when windows with one or more 'returns' permit a view into the fitting. Also, it is possible to position this type of unit behind an obscured glass transom without the need for a pelmet.

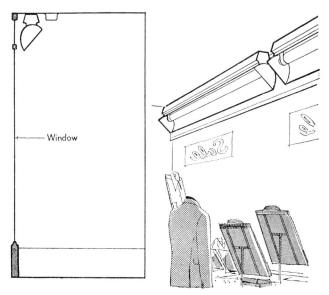

Fig. 29.1   Lighting to lower range Class D illumination standard employing
an anodised aluminium directional reflector for one 65 W fluorescent tube

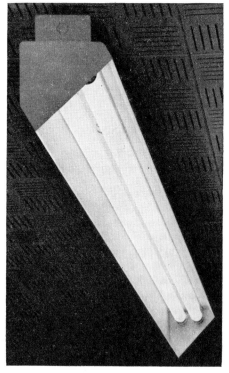

Fig. 29.2   An enamelled directional reflector fitting for two 65 W
fluorescent tubes, suitable for Class D illumination standards

Twin-tube fittings can be used in conjunction with a stove enamelled reflector—Fig. 29.2—providing increased illumination but not in proportion to the wattage, due to the less effective control of light. Table 29.2 gives an indication of the illumination likely from single and twin 65 W aluminium and stove enamel reflectors respectively, on a horizontal plane 6 ft below the fitting using White fluorescent tubes.

TABLE 29.2

Illumination from Directional Fluorescent Fittings

Fitting type	Distance from window		
	2 ft	4 ft	6 ft
Stove enamelled reflector twin 65 W	50	45	35 ⎫
Aluminium reflector single 65 W	35	35	30 ⎭ lm/ft²

As can be seen, this type of equipment is only suitable up to the middle range of Class D, and for levels beyond this it is necessary to use multi-tube fittings which do not provide any high degree of control. Standard tubes can be used, grouped one above the other at an angle of 30° to 40° from the vertical, using either flat or convex reflectors (Fig. 29.3). In most cases, due to space limitations, the 'reflector' is no more than a convenient means of assembling a group of tubes into a reasonably compact form, and it is unlikely that the material or finish of this component will have much effect on the efficiency

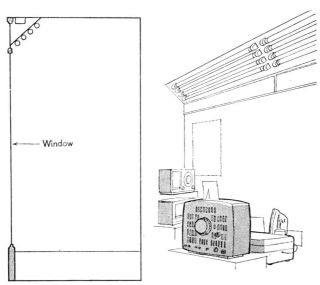

Fig. 29.3   Multi-tube fittings for general lighting to upper range of Class C standards (three 65 W tubes) or lower range of Class B (four 65 W tubes)

of the system. It is important to allow adequate distance between the tubes —an inch minimum for standard tubes—to minimise mutual obstruction of the light, and to avoid reduced efficiency due to overheating. An arrangement of three 65 W tubes should produce general illumination to the upper range of Class C standards for an average depth of window.

When using this system an approximate indication of the illumination level can be calculated by using the lumen method of design with utilisation factors for single-tube batten fittings. For example, if a window is 12 ft long by 6 ft deep with tubes mounted 5 ft to 6 ft above the display, then if eight 5 ft 65 W White tubes are installed (four rows of two tubes) and the average reflection factors are taken as 75% ceiling and 30% walls then for a room ratio of about 0·6 to 0·8 a utilisation factor of 0·22 to 0·3 (say 0·26) can be assumed.

$$\text{Average illumination} = \frac{8 \times 4500 \times 0\cdot26 \times 0\cdot8}{12 \times 6}$$
$$= 104 \text{ lm/ft}^2$$

Allowing for the various approximations made a value of between 90 lm/ft² and 120 lm/ft² would be obtained, i.e. largely the lower range of Class B. For a total of 6 tubes, an illumination of 65 lm/ft² would be obtained, i.e. the upper range of Class C.

The use of reflector tubes for this application is an advantage if the distance between the tubes is not more than one inch. If the distance is appreciably more than this then the overall greater light output of the standard tube will produce better results, particularly if the reflecting surface of the enclosure has a light finish.

For deeper windows a further row of tubes at half the depth is frequently used behind a pelmet, thus overcoming some of the directional disadvantages in limiting lighting to the front of the windows. A logical development of this is to arrange standard fluorescent tubes equally spaced from the front to the back of the window, usually close to the soffit, and to have shallow screens, or baffles, between these tubes to shield them from normal view (Fig. 29.4). This has the advantage of an even diffusion of light over the area, greater efficiency (as the tubes are not in close proximity) and an apparent ceiling that can be attractive without being distracting. These advantages have to be paid for not so much by the increased cost of the lighting equipment, as by shop fitters' costs in providing the baffles, and by some inevitable increase in the wiring costs.

The simplest arrangement uses vertical baffles of plywood, just deep enough to conceal from direct view the tube nearest the window (thus automatically concealing the others) with the tubes centrally between baffles. They should not be deeper than is necessary to shield the nearest tube, and from the lighting point of view there is little virtue in sloping them inwards.

The lighting equipment can be simple batten fittings or merely the tubes clipped to the soffit, with remotely positioned control gear boxes. Illumination values will depend on the spacing of the tubes, and if this is, say, 6 in to 7 in values should be in the middle to upper range of Class B for an area within the length of 5 ft 65 W tubes. Approximate illumination values for this system can also be calculated by the lumen method, using typical batten utilisation factors, and allowing a reduction in efficiency due to the baffles of 15% when painted white, or 30% when black.

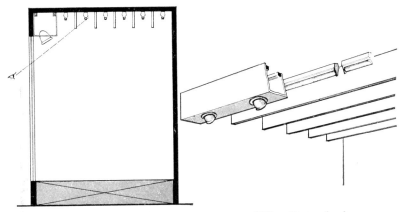

Fig. 29.4   Lighting to upper range of Class B standard
employing a baffle system

Taking the same 12 ft by 6 ft area and allowing for the first foot in depth to be taken up by incandescent spotlamps, it will be practical to install nine rows of 65 W tubes, two per row, the rows being 7 in apart. Assuming the use of batten fittings the same utilisation factor would again apply and the approximate illumination received would be:

$$\text{Average illumination} = \frac{18 \times 4500 \times 0\cdot26 \times 0\cdot85^* \times 0\cdot8}{12 \times 6}$$

$$= 198 \text{ lm/ft}^2$$

* Correction factor for white baffles.

Allowing for approximations made, a value of 170 lm/ft² to 230 lm/ft² would be achieved, that is, the upper range of Class B or the lower range of Class A.

The general lighting arrangement just discussed reflects the most recent development in technique to achieve the maximum efficiency with the minimum maintenance, but earlier devices, and in particular the luminous ceiling, are still popular.

The luminous ceiling is basically a translucent plastics diffuser in the form of a panel above which any practical number of fluorescent tubes can be arranged. The panels can have a small cell formation—$\frac{3}{8}$ in cube being common—injection moulded from opal plastics. Alternatively, flat diffusing sheets or stretched films can be used in a large number of forms but for shop-window lighting the louver principle is preferable owing to the greater concentration of downward light, and the plastics louver is preferred to stove enamelled metal because of better maintenance characteristics, with a more lively appearance. The louver panels are usually supported on metal or plastics inverted T-section at transom level, and frequently a solid soffit at the same level is provided between the panels and the window to carry incandescent fittings for directional lighting. Fig. 29.5 illustrates the luminous ceiling in an open type showroom, the solid portions being introduced partly to overcome the problem of beams and partly as dummies to establish a regular pattern.

Fig. 29.5   The application of a luminous ceiling to a showroom using a stretched vinyl film as the diffusing medium.

The principal advantage of luminous ceilings is that lamps are screened from normal view from any direction, whilst systems using screens are only effective from one principal viewing direction. Disadvantages are lower efficiency, the possibility of the brightness of the panels being distracting for high-illumination levels, and the greater need for maintenance compared with other systems. Continuous rows of fluorescent lamps above a luminous ceiling, say 6 in apart, should produce illumination values in the middle to upper range of Class B. The ceiling above must be painted white and the distance from the tubes to the luminous ceiling should not be less than twice the distance between the tubes.

The calculation of utilisation factors for luminous ceilings has been explained in Chapter 9, and the lumen method of calculation can be applied to check approximate illumination levels.

Considering the previous example of eighteen 65 W tubes the approximate illumination for tubes on 7 in centres and a utilisation factor of 0·19, would be:

$$\text{Average illumination} = \frac{18 \times 4500 \times 0\cdot19 \times 0\cdot8}{12 \times 6}$$

$$= 170 \text{ lm/ft}^2$$

Allowing for approximations made, a value of 145 lm/ft² to 195 lm/ft² will be obtained, that is, the middle to upper range of Class B.

Where a complete luminous ceiling is not called for, but general lighting flush to the suspended ceiling is required, then standard fluorescent lighting fittings can be used. This type of equipment is normally based on a 1 ft module, being 1 ft or 2 ft wide and 2 ft, 4 ft, 6 ft or 8 ft long, the 1 ft wide fittings usually having two tubes and the 2 ft fittings from two to four tubes. This type of equipment is mainly used for general interior lighting and the small plastics louver panel has been largely superseded by either the plastics prismatic panel or the opal sheet diffuser. For shop window application the prismatic panel is suitable, and approximately 140 lm/ft² should be obtained 5 ft below the centre of a four-tube 65 W fitting with White fluorescent tubes.

In shallow shop windows, particularly where a large variety of relatively small objects is displayed (frequently by the use of shelves) lighting from the top of the window alone is not entirely satisfactory and in these circumstances the vertically arranged fluorescent tube can be useful. This is usually mounted at the sides or corners of the window, close to the glass, and it is extremely important that the tube be screened from any direct view from the window front (Fig. 29.6). This technique can be quite effective for shallow windows with small merchandise but should be used with caution for other situations, for the vertical tube can have a slightly disconcerting effect on the modelling of displays in which clear expression of depth is important, e.g. in clothing displays.

Fluorescent tubes used horizontally at the foot of the window have a limited

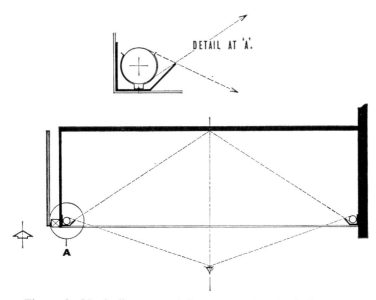

DETAIL AT 'A'.

A

Fig. 29.6   Vertically arranged fluorescent tubes, behind screens, for shallow windows

value for supplementary lighting for the effect is bound to be localised due to the necessity for screening the tubes from the observer's view. They can also have a disconcerting effect on the appearance of the display, for all the shadows and highlights one normally, but subconciously, expects are largely reversed. This arrangement should definitely be avoided for any merchandise having a polished—gloss or semi-gloss—vertical surface, as reflections of the tubes in these surfaces can be most distracting.

Colour-corrected mercury vapour lamps

The use of this type of lamp for shop window lighting is relatively limited, but it is justified by the distinctive appearance it creates, and also by the fact that very high illumination levels can be achieved. In recent years the development of the reflectorised lamp has been an additional advantage.

The mercury vapour lamp is a discharge lamp of high efficiency; like all discharge lamps it requires the use of control gear, which is not always easily accommodated in display-lighting installations. The basic type of mercury lamp emits a blue-white light which is very weak in the red part of the spectrum. The development of colour-corrected lamps with a good red content has considerably widened the field of application and some very effective high-level lighting has been achieved, for at these levels the colour-rendering problem is less acute than it is in the lower groups. Installations to Class A standards can provide satisfactory colour-rendering for many types of merchandise, particularly if some supplementary lighting is provided, but the suitability has to be considered for each situation. For example, quite apart from the question of atmosphere, lounge furniture might create a colour rendering difficulty while kitchen furniture and equipment may not.

An accepted method of using mercury lamps for Class B installations is to improve colour rendering at these lower levels of illumination by using also some incandescent lamps. Earlier installations of this type used an incandescent/mercury wattage ratio of 2 to 1, but satisfactory results can often be achieved with a ratio of 1 to 1.

The reflectorised type of lamp permits a highly efficient lighting system, easily capable of adjustment as to direction, and without the problem of depreciation in efficiency inherent with reflector systems external to the lamp. An installation of 400 W, internally silvered, colour-corrected mercury vapour lamps on 2 ft 6 in. centres at 10 ft mounting height should provide illumination of about 200 lm/ft^2 to 250 lm/ft^2.

Mains-voltage incandescent lamps

The standard GLS incandescent lamp is used for shop-window lighting, but special types of lamp have also been developed. These include the reflector lamp in which part of the internal surface of the bulb is silvered, the crown-silvered lamp with an external reflector, and the tungsten-halogen lamp.

The general purpose lamp is commonly used for supplementing overall fluorescent lighting, the lamp housing incorporating a polished reflector. These housings tend to be decorative and rarely have a functional shape. Fig. 29.7 shows a fitting intended for surface mounting; equipment for recessing into a suspended soffit generally uses reflector or PAR 38 lamps. The main disadvantage of incandescent GLS lamps for display work is the relatively large size of reflector needed to achieve a performance comparable to other lamp types; and, of course, the reflector tends to deteriorate.

Fig. 29.7   An adjustable fitting for an incandescent lamp.
The metal housing has no optical function

Reflector lamps are in turn sub-divided by type into blown-glass and pressed-glass patterns, the convention being to refer to the former as reflector lamps and the latter by their American derivation of PAR 38 (Fig. 29.8). The degree

Fig. 29.8   A 150 W sealed-beam reflector lamp, the PAR 38

of light control is substantially better with PAR 38 lamps, largely due to the greater accuracy of the pressed-glass bulb forming the reflector.

Both the reflector and PAR 38 lamps are available in 150 W rating with either a spotlight or floodlight distribution. There is a 100 W rating of the reflector lamp in spotlight pattern. Although these constitute the major types in use at the moment the range of wattage, light distribution and colour of the PAR type lamp is considerable. These lamps represent a more effective way of achieving supplementary directional lighting than GLS lamps with external reflectors, and have the added advantage that reflector depreciation is virtually eliminated.

The third category of lamp and fitting combination is shown in Fig. 29.9. A crown-silvered lamp is used efficiently with an external reflector. Rated at

Fig. 29.9   An adjustable fitting for the 100 W crown-silvered incandescent lamp, the fitting incorporating adjustable focus

100 W, and with semi-matt finish reflector, this equipment has a peak intensity some 60% greater than the 150 W reflector spotlight, but of course it is not so compact. The arrangement is economic in first costs and in lamp replacement, the limitations being in size, depreciation of reflector finish and lamp wattage. The performance of a typical lamp and fitting combination is given in Table 29.3 which also includes the performance data for the various patterns of blown-glass and pressed-glass reflector lamps. It should be noted from this that the rated life of the PAR 38 lamp is 1500 hours compared with the 1000 hours for reflector lamps.

For the general—as opposed to local—lighting of windows the incandescent

TABLE 29.3

Comparative Performance of Incandescent Display Lamps

Lamp	Peak illumination 3 ft	6 ft	9 ft	Rated life (hours)	Beam spread
Mains Voltage					
150 W reflector flood	140	35	16	1000	110°
150 W reflector spot	400	100	44	1000	60°
100 W reflector spot	240	60	27	1000	60°
150 W PAR 38 reflector flood	330	80	37	1500	35°
150 W PAR 38 reflector spot	820	200	90	1500	20°
*100 W crown silvered	640	160	70	1000	20°
Low Voltage					
50 W 12 V reflector spot	1000	250	110	1000	15°
*50 W 12 V crown silvered	3000	750	330	1000	8°
*50 W 12 V tungsten-halogen	6900	1650	740	2000	6°

* Associated with suitably designed reflector.

lamp has been largely superseded by fluorescent lighting although the development of the tungsten-halogen lamp (see Chapter 15) has opened up new possibilities for incandescent lighting. This compact source has enabled highly efficient asymmetrical reflectors to be produced (Fig. 29.10). Advantages of this unit are simplicity of installation; relatively low capital cost for relatively high intensities; and a marked improvement in modelling, depth and liveliness in comparison with a general fluorescent system. The main disadvantage is the greater consumption for equal illumination; this increase

Fig. 29.10   A general lighting fitting for the 750 W tungsten-halogen lamp, the fitting having an asymmetrical light distribution

can be from 50% to 70% for the complete system, making reasonable allowance for supplementary incandescent lighting. Also the rated lamp life is shorter—2000 hours against 7500 hours for fluorescent tubes. In such an installation, any specialised effect required for emphasis is best provided by very high localised illumination, probably from equipment using low-voltage tungsten-halogen lamps.

In planning general window lighting of this kind conventional calculation methods are either inappropriate or rather complex, and therefore *isophot diagrams* are used to determine direct illumination (Fig. 29.11). For more than

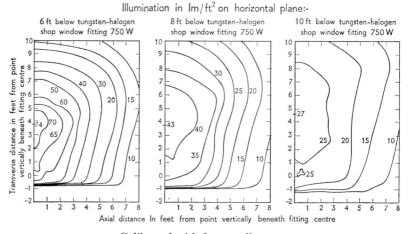

Illumination in lm/ft² on horizontal plane:-

Calibrated with foot-candle meter

Fig. 29.11　Isophot diagrams for the fitting in Fig. 29.10 at various heights

one fitting the curves are summated and a new isophot diagram drawn. It should be appreciated that no allowance is made for light received by inter-reflection and this could add as much as 15% to the calculated values. This type of equipment, when used in shop windows, is intended to be arranged as close as possible to the window face, the asymmetrical distribution giving a cut-off in the vertical downward almost parallel to the window, and a 60° cut-off from the downward vertical towards the back of the window. Surface and recessed type fittings are available, but care has to be taken in achieving adequate ceiling void volume for the latter type.

The rear cut-off type of unit is usually very sharp, and with closed back windows some fluorescent lighting on the backing is therefore desirable.

Low-voltage incandescent lamps

An important factor governing the control of light in a beam is the size of the lamp filament, and low-voltage lamps have more compact filaments than mains-voltage lamps; thus, combined with a correctly designed reflector, a much closer degree of light control is possible.

Three types of lamp are available, all rated at 12 V 50 W, two being conventional, the third using the tungsten-halogen principle. Of the former the spherical crown-silvered lamp is intended to be used with an external reflector (Fig. 29.12) and the 'mushroom'-shaped lamp is one of the internally silvered pattern operating on the same principle as the mains-voltage reflector lamps (Fig. 29.13).

Fig. 29.12   An adjustable incandescent fitting for the 12 V 50 W crown-silvered lamp. An adjustable focus is incorporated and a separate transformer for each fitting is necessary

Fig. 29.13   An adjustable incandescent fitting for the 12 V 50 W reflector lamp. A separate transformer for each fitting is necessary

With low-voltage lamps, those using external reflectors are very substantially more effective in the degree of light control than reflector lamps. Another advantage is the low brightness of the reflector when seen from all angles outside the narrow beam. The development of a low-voltage tungsten-halogen lamp for use with an external reflector is particularly important because the lamp itself is so small; in fact, the peak intensity can be more than twice that produced by conventional lamps of the same rating.

Table 29.3 includes performance data for the three types of low-voltage lamps, and in the case of the crown-silvered and tungsten-halogen this performance relates to lamp and reflector as an integral design. Fig. 29.14 illustrates a type of fitting with integral transformer.

Fig. 29.14   An adjustable incandescent fitting for the 12 V 50 W
tungsten-halogen lamp. The fitting is of fixed focus and the
transformer is integral

Type of window. The shape and structure of the window are the chief factors which determine the choice of lighting system, for it is necessary that there should be adequate screening of the lighting from normal view, whilst the characteristics of the window are used to the best advantage. For front-viewing windows, without glass returns, simple screening by baffles parallel to the window is all that is necessary for general fluorescent lighting; alternatively, lighting limited to the window front presents no difficulties. There is little virtue in the use of louver systems which provide screening of the lamp in all directions.

Windows with one glass return need to be treated with greater care, and the luminous ceiling is a simple and obvious answer. For Class A and Class B levels of illumination, however, screening by baffles for return windows with low soffits can be permitted, though this arrangement allows a view of the exposed tubes down their length (Fig. 29.15).

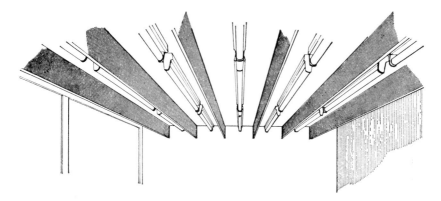

Fig. 29.15   For low soffits baffles permitting a view of the tubes down their length with return windows are acceptable from the glare aspect

Baffles can quite satisfactorily prevent glare, provided that the soffit is relatively low or, more precisely, that the angle between a viewer close to the window and the middle point of the closest tube looking down the length is small—up to about 20°. This technique can be extended logically to 3-sided and island windows, but for higher soffits a luminous ceiling or a similar multi-way screening device is the only satisfactory answer.

Great care must be taken to avoid glare from directional incandescent equipment for 3-sided or island windows and the only satisfactory equipment is the low-voltage type with external reflector.

Open back windows are frequently co-ordinated with the shop interior lighting expressed as extensions of the same lighting techniques, and can be quite satisfactory, although extra light in the window area is usually necessary. The situation is similar to that for 3-sided or island windows, and the lighting can be designed accordingly.

Type of merchandise.   The range of merchandise sold in the shop affects the choice of lighting in two ways, for the lighting can be related to the quality of the market in which the retailer is principally concerned, and also to the nature of the merchandise. Guidance on the latter is given in Table 29.1 but it can be appreciated that it is not possible to generalise on the former, which is often a question of choosing the lighting equipment to meet the specific design requirements for the shop front. The more specialised the shop, the greater the need for the closest integration of the lighting if this is successfully to reflect the nature of the shop, and this integration can only be successful if the lighting is considered as part of the whole design at the instigation of the project.

Colour. A wide range of near-white fluorescent tubes is available and, ideally, the particular colour of tubes should be related to specific groups of merchandise; Table 29.1 gives recommended tube colours.

Quite apart from its basic function in enabling the display itself to be seen, lighting can make a contribution to the equally important job of attracting initial attention. Coloured background lighting is very effective, not only as an attraction, but also as a foil to the display. It is best used at the top and bottom of the window background, especially if the background is textured in some way (Fig. 29.16). Plain Terylene net, with plenty of fullness, is a good material.

Fig. 29.16   Background lighting requires a textured or draped surface
for the most effective results

In its simplest form a single tube, or row of tubes, is used at the foot and head of the background not less than 6 in away (and preferably 12 in) and screened from direct view by a pelmet, or by stopping the window bed and ceiling soffit short of the background. The use of two tubes increases the flexibility considerably; for example, if the tubes were red and blue, then three colour choices—the colours used independently or mixed—are available through switching, and the background colour can, if desired, be varied from day to day. The most effective background lighting is three-colour automatic colour-change by dimming with continuous and automatic mixing of coloured light at a selected speed and sequence. This is a system made possible through the development of compact thyratron valve or silicon-controlled rectifier dimmers.

For this background lighting to be effective, care must be taken to prevent the general lighting from interposing white light; luminous ceilings should certainly be avoided and also general lighting based on the window front.

The baffle system is ideal and it may be worth some loss in efficiency to make the baffles matt black, in order to increase, by contrast, the apparent brightness of the background.

Sometimes a high intensity of coloured light is used on a part of a display, employing low voltage equipment with colour filters—usually 'Cinabex'—or PAR 38 lamps with coloured front glass, or the 100 W mains-voltage crown-silvered lamp with colour anodised reflector, providing a dramatic and possibly a deliberately distorted effect.

THE SHOP INTERIOR

Most of the factors influencing window lighting are also applicable to the shop interior. However, whilst the type of shop and type of merchandise have some influence on the window (particularly with reference to architectural and display design) they have a more profound effect on the interior design, and therefore on the lighting.

Quantity of light. The illumination level inside the shop naturally bears some relation to the chosen window lighting group, but not in direct proportion. Illumination levels should not be much less than 30 lm/ft² as a minimum for general lighting. On the other hand, values of 200 lm/ft² would be difficult to find in shop interiors, though such levels have been adopted in windows. Generally, values are in the range of 30 lm/ft² to 100 lm/ft² but the average may be lower for specialist shops—though with particular displays lighted to much higher standards. The general level may also be higher for large turn-over shops, such as supermarkets in high density neighbourhoods. Table 29.4 gives a guide for the relationships between window and interior lighting.

TABLE 29.4

Suggested Relationship between Window and Interior Illumination

Class of window illumination	Interior illumination (lm/ft²)
A	50–100
B	40–80
C	30–60
D	30 minimum

Quality of light. The points made in connection with the quality of window lighting are equally valid for shop interiors, though there may be differences in emphasis. A shop should, for example, have 'liveliness' almost regardless of the market type, and this is often promoted by lighting. Boundaries should be clearly defined, particularly where the proportions of the interior are difficult, and here lighting can help to provide an easy and effective solution.

Lamps and lighting equipment. *Fluorescent lighting* has become the established basis of interior lighting for the majority of shops, because of its

16+

high efficiency, low running costs and long life. When fluorescent lighting is used intelligently—and often in combination with incandescent lamps—it can provide a lighting system suitable for most interiors. The exposed tube has probably been the cause of much prejudice against fluorescent lighting, but its application can be satisfactory where:

(1) general lighting is to a minimum of 60 lm/ft².
(2) the sales appeal is to a mass market through large shops and stores with a high turnover.
(3) the store has appreciable length in relation to width and the fluorescent tubes are parallel to that length. Widths appreciably over 50 ft with mounting heights below 10 ft can create glare problems.

Exposed fluorescent tubes across the width of the shop parallel to the window should be avoided if possible. If, however, such an arrangement of fluorescent tubes is unavoidable, the tubes should be screened from pavement view by a simple pelmet in the window backing; otherwise distracting glare from the shop lighting will seriously detract from the effectiveness of the display. Exposed tube systems should preferably use the 8 ft 85 W tube because of its low brightness, and also to achieve economy in capital and installation costs. Four-tube fittings are normally the most suitable for the upper range of Class B and over. Ceiling reflectance should be kept as high as possible, and never less than 70%.

Numerous fluorescent lighting fittings incorporating various methods of screening the tube are available for general lighting, and typical examples are shown in Fig. 29.17, summarised as follows:

Type A   General diffusing for surface mounting or suspension. (See also Chapter 27, Fig. 27.3 (1).)

Type B   Prismatic fitting for surface mounting or suspension. The design allows a low BZ classification, which helps to eliminate glare in the installation. The range of possible shapes is, however, rather limited (see also Chapter 27, Fig. 27.3 (2)).

Type C   General diffusing fitting for recessing into a suspended ceiling;
and   this has an exposed metal trim supporting the diffuser,
Type D   whilst in type D the metal support is concealed and the diffuser is completely modular—the so-called 'trimless troffer'.

Fittings of types C and D can house two, three or four tubes, and as fittings are available in lengths of 2 ft, 4 ft, 6 ft and 8 ft there is little difficulty in integrating the lighting into the ceiling design.

Incandescent equipment is also used in suspended ceilings, sometimes to supplement general lighting, but more commonly to provide localised lighting for a specific area where this type of source may be preferred, e.g. the cosmetic counter. Such focal points play an important part in 'impulse buying' and they can also have a circulation function. Emphasis lighting is usually necessary at a focal point, and either the internally silvered lamp or the low-voltage external reflector lamp is suitable for the purpose. Fig. 29.18

illustrates typical fittings, though the fittings shown in Figs. 29.7, 29.12 and 29.13 can also be used for this localised lighting.

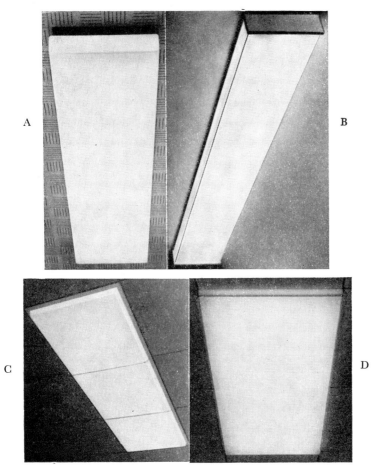

Fig. 29.17   Typical lighting fittings for general interior shop lighting.
For type description see text

Focal interest can also be created by the pattern and brightness of the lighting fittings themselves. Clearly, this must be handled with care to avoid uncomfortable or distracting glare, but such techniques are valuable in influencing circulation to a desired pattern. Fig. 29.19 shows a suitable fitting which can be used as a 'pattern maker'.

Luminous ceilings are sometimes used in shop interiors, and whilst in shop windows luminous ceilings are relatively small in area and lend themselves fairly easily to tailor-made methods, those for the interior are generally much

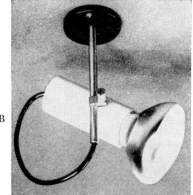

Fig. 29.18   Typical incandescent fittings, mains voltage (type A)
and low voltage (types B and C) for emphasis lighting in the shop interior

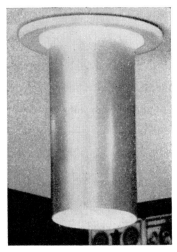

Fig. 29.19   A typical incandescent fitting for a 60 W lamp
used as a pattern maker

larger; the actual components have a larger scale, and a more sophisticated finish is desirable. A large range of luminous ceiling types is available, the majority using either sheet vinyl, vacuum formed into panels for rigidity, or thin vinyl films stretched over a metal frame. Small-cell polystyrene louver panels can also be used, but their application is usually limited to relatively small areas. Stretched vinyl systems can have two membranes separated by the frame thickness, and the inevitable dust and debris which collects on the top surface is not so obvious as with rigid vinyl panels. The double skin system is also easier to clean and is far stronger than rigid vinyl.

Utilisation factors for a double skin stretched vinyl film luminous ceiling, based on a 75% reflectance structural ceiling, panel transmission of 78% and cavity depth of 1 ft are as follows. (For cavity depths of more than 1 ft and up to 3 ft the figures should be reduced by 5%.)

Room ratio	0·6	0·8	1·0	1·25	1·5	2·0
50% Wall R.F.	0·22	0·28	0·34	0·38	0·41	0·46
30% Wall R.F.	0·18	0·24	0·30	0·33	0·37	0·42

It is important to appreciate that the luminous ceiling is essentially for high-illumination levels; 40 lm/ft² is a minimum and 50 lm/ft² or over is preferable. Anything less than the minimum will appear disappointingly dull and dowdy. Also, the luminous ceiling by itself, and particularly in fairly large areas, tends to be monotonous and uninteresting. It is important to relieve the appearance by solid areas, e.g. opaque panels within the luminous ceiling support structure, or by a suitable balance of luminous to solid ceiling. The use of small incandescent fittings within the solid areas to introduce a local pattern of relatively high brightness also helps considerably in the 'liveliness' of the ceiling.

There is a natural tendency to think of the luminous ceiling as a low-brightness source, but it has been shown that discomfort glare can be experienced when the ceiling brightness significantly exceeds 150 ft L, which is likely to be achieved with illumination levels between 100 lm/ft² and 130 lm/ft² for a medium to large-sized shop. Although this study was based on working environments it undoubtedly has some relevance to other more casually used areas, such as shops.

A refinement in luminous-ceiling technique is the introduction of the ultra-low brightness louver, in which the sides of the cells are wedge shaped and are given an aluminised finish. The effect is that the ceiling itself appears hardly luminous from many angles, even with quite high values of illumination, but the use of this type of ceiling requires special skills, and design should only be undertaken by a specialist.

Alternative ceiling lighting systems use either lighting beams or open grids. Lighting beams (Fig. 29.20) consist essentially of two vertical solid members, timber or metal, arranged on each side of a fluorescent tube, generally 3 in to 6 in apart and spanning between walls or an opening in a suspended ceiling. Three types of light distribution are possible; totally indirect, totally direct, and direct/indirect. For the two latter types crosswise shielding of the tube should be between 45° and 60°, for this type of design is most effective

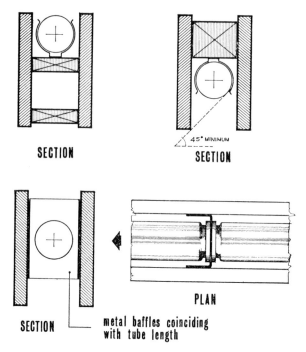

SECTION

SECTION

45° MINIMUM

SECTION

PLAN

SECTION metal baffles coinciding
with tube length

Fig. 29.20 Lighting beams of a totally indirect, totally direct and
indirect/direct type for spanning between walls or openings in ceilings

in its simplest form with no enclosure of the top or bottom of the beam. This
system can be used to give the impression of greater width to a narrow,
relatively long area, or to obtain a change of pattern within a suspended
ceiling, particularly where height necessitates careful planning. It is best used
at fairly low heights, say 8 ft to 10 ft, when perspective can give the illusion
of a solid ceiling and the exposed tube is viewed at the minimum angle when
looking along its length (Fig. 29.21).

Approximate calculations for lighting beams can be based on the normal
lumen method, using utilisation factors for batten fittings, and then applying
the following correction factors:

Totally indirect	0·6 to 0·7
Totally direct	0·75 to 0·8
Direct/indirect	0·85 to 0·9

Showcase lighting can provide emphasis to supplement general lighting.
The most convenient method is to arrange fluorescent tubes at the top front
of a glass showcase, screened from frontal view by silvering a strip of the glass
of adequate width at the front corner of the case, or by using a simple metal
screen. Compactness of the light source is an essential requirement and the
1 in diameter 5 ft 50 W and 3 ft 30 W tubes are very useful for this purpose.

Fig. 29.21 A lighting system using direct/indirect lighting beams. Also included is a black baffle system over the fashion walk and perimeter lighting for stock areas

Control gear is normally housed in the base of the stand. Vertical tubes at the side of the case are not usually successful, owing to the considerable difficulties of providing adequate screening.

With glass-top cases, care must be taken that other lighting is not seen as a reflection in the case, for this can largely distract from seeing the detail of the display within, particularly when incandescent pendant fittings are suspended just above the case.

Perimeter lighting, that is lighting following the boundary walls of the shop, is a well established and effective technique. Normally providing local lighting for the wall fixtures (either counter or self-service) with which it is associated, perimeter lighting can help customer penetration by defining the boundaries of the shop, particularly if it is designed to light also the upper wall surface.

AN EXERCISE IN SHOP LIGHTING DESIGN

Basic information. The plan of the shop is L-shaped, the main area being 50 ft long by 30 ft wide, with a right-angled extension 16 ft by 24 ft, this area having two laylights for daylighting and ventilation. Part of the

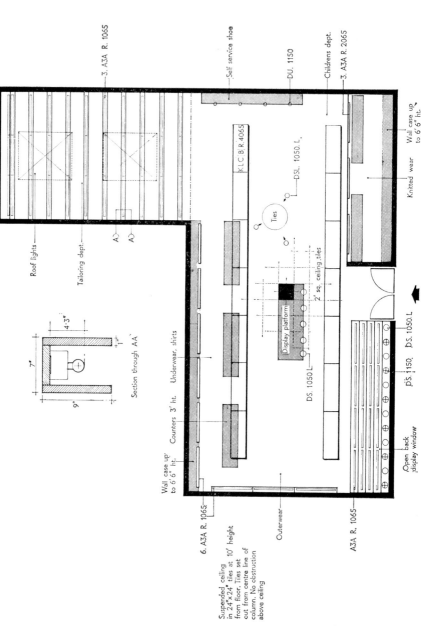

Roof lights

3. A3A. R. 1065

Tailoring dept.

A'

A'

Section through AA'

Self service shoe

KLC B R 4065

DU. 1150

Ties

DSL. 1050. L.

Childrens dept.

3. A3A. R. 2065

Knitted wear

Wall case up
to 6'6' ht.

Wall case up'
to 6'6" ht.

Counters 3' ht.   Underwear, shirts

Display platform

2' sq. ceiling, tiles

DS. 1050 L.

Open back
display window

pS. 1150.   DS. 1050.L

Outerwear

6. A3A. R. 1065

A3A R. 1065

Suspended ceiling
in 24"x24" tiles at 10' height
from floor. Tiles set
out from centre line of
column. No obstruction
above ceiling

Fig. 29.22   Plan of men's wear shop showing lighting and, inset, a detail of the lighting beam in the tailoring department

general area is an open-backed display window to the street, 22 ft long by 5 ft deep (see Fig. 29.22).

A dry construction proprietary suspended ceiling is allowed for, arranged at 10 ft from the floor, and formed from 2 ft square panels. The central column is intended to be faced up to be exactly 2 ft square, and will form the setting-out point for the ceiling tiles in both directions. The ceiling is suspended 12 in below the underside of the structural beams, and there are no obstructions above the ceiling. Reflection factors of 50% for the ceiling and 30% for the walls can be assumed. The shop is situated in the High Street of a medium-sized town and will sell a variety of men's wear. The functions of the various areas are shown on the plan.

Good colour quality in the artificial lighting is essential and accurate colour rendition blending with natural daylight is required in the tailoring department.

This is a speciality shop with a bias towards advanced styling and high-quality merchandise. The decor will be sophisticated, and the lighting is required to provide flexibility in the display areas and functional standards in the main sales areas, supplemented by effects to increase the apparent spaciousness of the interior.

General appraisal. This type of shop in a central location would seem to fall into Class C with window illumination up to 100 lm/ft^2. The open-back window demands a lighting system equally comfortable from both outside and inside the shop.

The standard of the interior illumination is influenced not only by location but also by the type of merchandise and selling methods. For a shop with a normal retail trade, 40 lm/ft^2 to 75 lm/ft^2 for the upper range of Class C windows would be reasonable, but for a speciality shop requiring a consider-able degree of local lighting 45 lm/ft^2 of general lighting should be adequate. The suspended ceiling sets some limitations on lighting layout with regard to tile size, and the use of the column for setting out is a controlling factor. To achieve integration of fluorescent and incandescent lighting for the interior, advantage should be taken of the suspended ceiling for the recessing of fluorescent lighting.

The construction, position and use of the counters is important because of the danger of reflected glare and the need for visual emphasis. It will be assumed that the construction is basically a glass box on a solid base, and that the counter height is 3 ft.

There are some significant points to consider in regard to the 16 ft by 24 ft extension. Firstly, it is necessary to ensure that this area should not become a 'dead-end', and lighting presents the most effective method of preventing this. Secondly, the use of this area for tailoring, with the requirements of good colour rendition, makes an illumination level of about 60 lm/ft^2 desirable.

The requirement for acceptable colour rendering is met for the window and general area by either the Natural 3 or the Kolorite fluorescent tube, whilst the tailoring department, with its higher colour-rendering standards, could best be served by the Northlight tube.

16*

Each area of the shop will be considered, in relation to both illumination level and brightness pattern.

Window area. Approximately 22 ft by 5 ft. The main suspended ceiling continues over the window area, with clear glazing from window bed to ceiling level, the 10 ft height of the latter being inconvenient as a basis for lighting. A level of about 8 ft would be better, for it provides greater concentration with higher illumination, eases source screening problems (particularly from inside the shop) and, by freeing the upper ceiling of equipment, assists in the free-space impression clearly intended by the full-height window.

The most simple and appropriate lighting system for these circumstances would be an arrangement of vertical baffles, parallel to the window, possibly within a frame. Between the baffles would be fluorescent tubes, except for a space for incandescent equipment adjacent to the window. In planning for 100 lm/ft², the most suitable tube size would be 5 ft 65 W, four of these fitting comfortably into the 22 ft length.

Fluorescent tubes at 12 in centres should give about 100 lm/ft², and this can be approximately checked by a lumen method calculation assuming batten fittings, 50% ceiling reflectance, 10% wall reflectance and 85% baffle efficiency.

The *room ratio*, allowing for a 12 in window bed and 3 ft average display height is

$$\frac{22 \times 5}{4(22+5)} = \frac{110}{108} = 1 \text{ approximately}$$

This would give a utilisation factor of about 0·29 for a typical batten fitting and for the reflection factors given. The number of tubes required is given by:

$$N = \frac{100 \times 5 \times 22}{3100^* \times 0\cdot29 \times 0\cdot8 \times 0\cdot85\dagger} = 18 \text{ approximately}$$

* Average design lumens for 5ft 65W Natural 3 tubes
† Correction factor for baffles

Sixteen tubes in four rows will give a reasonable approximation to the target illumination.

Incandescent equipment for emphasis and modelling could usefully include both mains-voltage and low-voltage lamps, and between 75% and 100% of the fluorescent wattage would be a reasonable proportion. Six adjustable angle fittings for the 150 W incandescent internally silvered spotlamp, or PAR 38 lamp, and six 50 W 12 V crown-silvered lamps should provide adequate facilities.

Main sales area—general lighting. With a ceiling height of 10 ft, and taking the 3 ft counter height as the working plane, the theoretical maximum spacing is 7 ft × 1½ = 10½ ft. For the 25 ft width of the main sales area three rows of fittings would normally be considered, but for a shop of this type a greater diversity of illumination than that achieved by strict adherence to the spacing/mounting-height ratios is acceptable, provided that the equipment is reasonably located in the principal selling areas. Also, three rows of fittings would present a rather crowded appearance for this relatively small area. Two rows across the width can therefore be the basis of the design.

$$\text{Room ratio} = \frac{25 \times 50}{7(25+50)} = 2 \cdot 4 \text{ approximately}$$

Recessed fittings using general diffusers would be suitable, and four-tube fittings would be appropriate to provide the required illumination level. A recessed fitting used in a room of this size and shape is likely to have a utilisation factor of, say, 0·43.

It is possible to consider either the 5 ft 65 W tube with average design lumens of 3100 or the 8 ft 85 W tube with average design lumens of 4700. The number of 4-tube fittings, either 65 W or 85 W, will then be given by

For 65 W

$$N = \frac{45 \times 50 \times 25}{4 \times 3100 \times 0 \cdot 43 \times 0 \cdot 8} = 13 \text{ approximately}$$

For 85 W

$$N = \frac{45 \times 50 \times 25}{4 \times 4700 \times 0 \cdot 43 \times 0 \cdot 8} = 9 \text{ approximately}$$

As two rows of fittings are needed, the 65 W system results in seven fittings per row, and as each fitting has a modular length of 6 ft, a minimum length of 42 ft per row is necessary; this is convenient for the 50 ft dimension of the shop.

For the 85 W spacing the minimum number of 8 ft fittings to obtain equal fittings per row would be 10, i.e. two continuous rows of 40 ft length. The alternatives can therefore be considered to be comparable, but the total capital cost of the 85 W fittings is substantially less than that of the 65 W, and the smaller number results in lower installation costs. The arrangement of fittings is shown on the plan.

Tailoring department. The artificial lighting must be related to, but should not appreciably obstruct, the laylights, and the fact that the latter are used for ventilation has to be taken into account. The 10 ft height in relation to the 16 ft width is not an entirely happy proportion, and a ceiling, or apparent ceiling, at about 8 ft height would help the scale of the area. A solid suspended ceiling with recessed fittings would eliminate the natural daylight, but a luminous ceiling would largely overcome this objection, even allowing for transmission losses through the material, and ventilation could be allowed by stopping the ceiling short of the walls. However, with the illumination level envisaged, the brightness of the ceiling at this height could be distracting, and the necessity to fill the space at the front of the department between the luminous ceiling at 8 ft and the suspended ceiling at 10 ft would create a rather heavy appearance. A more satisfactory solution may be to span across the 16 ft width with lighting beams using the totally direct type, for it would be best to reduce the illumination on the upper ceiling; in any case, a substantial area of this has no light-reflecting properties.

A lumen method calculation can be made, assuming 75% efficiency for the lighting beams, and the required number of Northlight tubes can be assessed. Two 8 ft tubes would fit into the 16 ft width, but two 8 ft batten fittings are just too long so the design would most conveniently be based on 5 ft batten fittings within the lighting beams.

$$\text{Room ratio} = \frac{16 \times 24}{5(16+24)} = 1 \cdot 9$$

The utilisation factor for a suitable 5 ft batten fitting is 0·51, and the average design lumens for the Northlight tube are 2550. To provide an illumination of 60 lm/ft² the number of tubes required is

$$N = \frac{16 \times 24 \times 60}{2550 \times 0 \cdot 51 \times 0 \cdot 75 \times 0 \cdot 8} = 30 \text{ approximately}$$

Using three fittings in each lighting beam requires ten beams, on about 2 ft 5 in centres. This general lighting arrangement will give emphasis to the area by a 50% increase in illumination over that in the main shop, by the lower apparent ceiling, and by the brightness pattern formed by the narrow but brighter inner faces of the lighting beams. It is important, however, to have good definition of the end wall in this 'cul de sac', and this can be achieved by arranging additional tubes on the rear face of the lighting beam nearest the wall. Further emphasis could be given by painting the wall a fairly saturated colour, and choosing the tube colour to suit—provided, of course, that this colour dramatisation does not adversely affect the display.

Reverting to the main shop, the knitted wear area requires supplementary lighting, and a simple solution here would be a timber member about 12 in deep, spanning across the front of the recess at a height of 8 ft, behind which could be arranged three twin-tube 65 W batten fittings.

Shoe department. Supplementary incandescent lighting would be useful, both for emphasis and additional red rendition. To retain an uncluttered appearance fittings should be recessed into the suspended ceiling, and to avoid a source colour clash with fluorescent tubes a very low brightness baffle unit for 150 W mains-voltage internally silvered reflector lamps should be used.

Counters. Lighting fittings are so located in relation to counters as to avoid reflection problems in the glass tops from the customers' side. It would be desirable, however, for the counter facing the entrance to have internal fluorescent lighting along the top front edge, appropriately screened from direct view.

Display platform. The display platform should be a focal point for passers-by, as well as for those entering the shop, and a number of low-voltage adjustable spotlight fittings recessed into the suspended ceiling can be used to give very high local lighting with deep modelling, for dramatic effects.

Spatial effects. A sense of spaciousness can be promoted by upper wall lighting, and the wall case behind the counters provides an excellent opportunity for housing fluorescent tubes mounted continuously on top of the case, screened from frontal view. Here again, as in the tailoring department, colour can be used to good effect. The technique could with advantage be continued on the adjacent wall, using a form of pelmet set out about 9 in from the wall, permitting upward and downward lighting. In this case Natural 3 or Kolorite tubes should be used in order that a useful supplement to the outer wear section is obtained in the vicinity of the wall.

CHAPTER 30

Lighting Economics and Planned Maintenance

The subject of 'lighting economics' covers a very wide field, since it includes specialised economic factors associated with applications such as floodlighting, street lighting or cold-store lighting. Secondary cost factors may also be involved, such as the saving on heat losses in windowless factories. In addition, lamp performance and lighting costs are subject to continuous variation and this means that worked examples are quickly out of date.

In this chapter, therefore, it has only been possible to outline the basic principles of lighting economics as applied to interior installations for general lighting in offices or factories. The worked examples of annual cost and planned maintenance are based on the latest available performance and cost data but are mainly intended to illustrate the method used in assessing the total annual lighting cost for any given installation and in planning the most economic maintenance programme. This study is based on fluorescent lighting, because this is now the usual choice for any ordinary industrial or commercial building. A section is included, however, which deals with the effect of voltage variation on the economics of incandescent filament lamps.

LIGHTING ECONOMICS

If a lighting scheme has been designed to give, say, 30 lm/ft² over a given area, and an alternative scheme, perhaps using another lamp type, gives the same lighting level, then a choice must be made between the two schemes. In many cases, the scheme finally chosen may be based on one very simple factor, i.e. which is the scheme with the lowest cost of fittings and lamps? If all other factors are equal, then lowest cost is the right choice, but in lighting, and particularly fluorescent lighting, there may be very sound reasons for paying more in order to get better quality. For example, if a specially protected fitting is used in a corrosive area where it lasts three times as long as a standard stove enamelled fitting, then it would certainly be an economic proposition even if it costs twice as much as the standard unit.

In most cases it will be found that the economic comparison is based on two main factors, i.e. the initial cost of the lamps and fittings plus the running costs due to the electricity consumed. This comparison should, however, be based on the total annual lighting bill for alternative schemes which provide an equal lighting level.

Annual lighting costs. The method used to calculate the total annual lighting cost for a given scheme will be best appreciated by means of the worked example detailed below:

A lighting scheme has been worked out for a typical factory workshop 100 ft long × 70 ft wide with a height of 16 ft from floor to roof trusses. By using four rows of eight twin-tube 8 ft 85 W fittings with slotted metal reflectors an illumination of just over 30 lm/ft² can be obtained, but an alternative scheme could be used with six rows of eight twin-tube 5 ft 65 W reflector fittings suspended from the roof trusses. A comparison of the total annual lighting costs will show which of these two alternative schemes is the more economic proposition.

TABLE 30.1

Comparison of Total Annual Lighting Costs (2500 *hours' use*)

(Based on a factory 100 ft long by 70 ft wide by 16 ft high)

	Twin-tube metal reflector	
Type of fitting .	5 ft 65 W	8 ft 85 W
Tube size		
Number of fittings required	48	32
Nett price per fitting (list less 20%)	£7 13 7	£9 10 5
Total cost of fittings	£368 12 0	£304 13 0
15% annual depreciation (fittings)	£55 5 9	£45 14 0
Installation wiring cost per fitting	£6 0 0	£7 0 0
Total cost of installation and wiring .	£288 0 0	£224 0 0
10% annual depreciation (wiring)	£28 16 0	£22 8 0
Total watts per twin-tube fitting	160 W	205 W
Total kilowatt load	7·68 kW	6·56 kW
Electricity M.D. cost at £10 per kW .	£76 16 0	£65 12 0
Electricity unit cost per 2500 hours (at 1½d. per kilowatt-hour unit)	£120 0 0	£102 10 6
TOTAL COST (excluding tubes and cleaning) .	£280 17 9	£236 14 6
Net price per tube (list less 20%)	£0 8 5 (+ 1/10d. P.T.)	£0 12 10
Total cost of tubes .	£49 4 0	£37 1 4
Average tube life in hours	7500	7500
Tube cost per 2500 hours' use .	£16 8 0	£12 7 1
Replacement labour cost per tube	£0 4 0	£0 4 6
Cost of individual tube replacements	£19 4 0	£14 8 0
Tube labour cost per 2500 hours' use	£6 8 0	£4 16 0
Cleaning cost per twin-tube fitting .	£0 5 0	£0 7 0
Number of cleanings per annum	ONE	ONE
Cleaning cost (fittings and tubes)	£12 0 0	£11 4 0
TOTAL ANNUAL COST (2500 *HOURS*) .	£315 13 9	£265 1 3
*DESIGN ILLUMINATION PROVIDED** .	34 lm/ft²	33 lm/ft²

* Allowing for 5 ft 65 W = 4500 lm, and 8 ft 85 W = 6600 lm at 2000 hours ('White' tubes). Maintenance factor of 0·80 allowed for in calculating the design illumination value.

The 8 ft 85 W and 5 ft 65 W twin-tube schemes give about the same quantity and quality of light. A detailed assessment of lighting costs can therefore be made on the basis of equal lighting performance and the final choice will be directly dependent on the total annual cost of each scheme. These cost details are given in Table 30.1 and the individual factors which have been applied will now be examined in turn.

The comparison table gives cost details for the two schemes being considered. Each scheme provides just over 30 lm/ft^2 and the schemes are compared for an equal period of use, i.e. 50 hours of lighting per week or 2500 hours per annum.

The total annual lighting cost of each scheme will include seven separate items of cost, as detailed below:

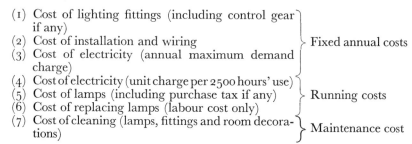

(1) Cost of lighting fittings (including control gear if any)
(2) Cost of installation and wiring — Fixed annual costs
(3) Cost of electricity (annual maximum demand charge)
(4) Cost of electricity (unit charge per 2500 hours' use)
(5) Cost of lamps (including purchase tax if any) — Running costs
(6) Cost of replacing lamps (labour cost only)
(7) Cost of cleaning (lamps, fittings and room decorations) — Maintenance cost

These seven cost items must be assessed as 'annual' costs and the total will then give the annual lighting cost for each scheme. Items (1) to (3) can be considered as 'fixed' annual costs, since they are independent of the actual hours of use, whereas items (4) to (6) are called 'running' costs because they vary in direct proportion to the hours of use. Item (7) is a 'maintenance' cost, to which can be added the extra cost of group lamp replacement, since this only affects the value of wasted light at end-of-life.

Lighting fittings cost. In the cost table, twin-tube fittings of the open-ended slotted-metal reflector type have been allowed for, i.e. 48 twin 5 ft 65 W or 32 twin 8 ft 85 W fittings. The fluorescent fittings have switchless-start type control gear and therefore no cost allowance need be made for expendable items such as starter switches.

The assessment of 'annual' fittings cost depends on the assumption that the user plans for a given life from his plant and equipment and can appreciate the accepted method of allowing a gradual depreciation on the capital value. For example, if he proposes to spend £1000 on lighting fittings and is willing to accept a nominal life of say 10 years, then he can allow one-tenth of his capital cost as an annual depreciation, i.e. 10% of £1000 = £100 depreciation. It is possible that the user may work on the basis of obtaining a loan for the capital expenditure involved and in this case it would be necessary to pay interest on the £1000 loan as well as repay the capital amount. Assuming that the sum of £1000 is to be repaid over a 10-year period, it is probable that the extra interest would amount to about £500. This means that a total of £1500 must be allowed for over a 10-year period and this is shown in the cost table as an annual depreciation of 15%, i.e. 15% of £1000 = £150 annual depreciation for 10 years.

Installation and wiring cost. This second item in the cost table covers the cost of wiring to the lighting fittings and also the cost of installing the fittings. It is difficult to give any average value since this could vary widely according to the type of system used, e.g. conduit or trunking, etc., and also the mounting height of the fittings; for the cost of installation will obviously be increased if expensive scaffolding is necessary to reach the roof trusses. It is also difficult to give an average value to the cost of the main cables feeding the lighting installation which may be included in the installation wiring cost. However, a nominal value of £6 or £7 per outlet has been allowed in the cost table according to the size of fitting involved. These values should only be taken as a very rough guide to the cost of other installations and, if possible, an estimate should be obtained from the electrical contractor involved when carrying out a cost comparison for any given scheme.

As with lighting fittings cost, the cost of installation wiring will also be an item of capital expenditure with an annual depreciation factor applied. It is probable, however, that a longer life will be assumed for the wiring than for the lighting fittings and in the cost table it has been assumed that the normal life will be 20 years. It has also been assumed that the capital sum will be borrowed and that interest will have to be paid as well as capital repayment. Over a period of 20 years, approximately £1000 would have to be paid as interest in addition to the £1000 originally borrowed. This means that a total of £2000 would be required over a period of 20 years and therefore a 10% annual depreciation factor has been allowed in the table, i.e. 10% of £1000 = £100 depreciation, for 20 years.

Electricity cost—maximum demand charges. There are a number of different electricity tariffs in use throughout Britain and in some areas it may be found that a direct unit charge is applied for every kilowatt-hour of electricity consumed. Another tariff may slightly modify this unit charge so that a higher price is paid for, say, the first 100 units of electricity (at about 6d. per kilowatt-hour) and this price gradually reduces as the total number of units increases.

The more common tariffs, however, are those based on a two part payment system and this is the type of tariff allowed for in the cost comparison table. For most smaller commercial and industrial premises, the local electricity board may assess the maximum demand load for the complete installation and make an annual charge for this peak demand. The charge may vary from £5 to £12 per kW p.a. according to the size of the installation and the area involved (in general it will be found that charges tend to be slightly lower in Northern England than in Southern England). In the cost table it has been assumed that the maximum demand charge is based on £10 per kilowatt of peak load. In the case of some very large users, special maximum demand meters are installed which measure the peak load, and the maximum demand charge is then based on the meter reading. It will often be found that this maximum demand meter measures kilovolt-amperes instead of kilowatts, and this means that it would then be in the interest of the customer to maintain a higher power factor. For installations where the M.D. charge is based on kilowatt measurement, there is normally a condition that the power factor shall not be less than a specified value, normally 0·85 lagging P.F., but sometimes 0·9.

Electricity cost—unit charge. The second part of the electricity cost is the charge made for kilowatt-hour units of electricity consumed. If the customer has already paid a maximum demand charge then the additional unit charge will vary between ½d. and 2d. per kilowatt-hour. In the cost table, it has been assumed that a unit charge of 1½d. per kilowatt-hour is applicable. The total unit charge is therefore assessed by multiplying the total kilowatt load by the annual hours of use (2500 hours), which will give the total number of kilowatt-hours consumed. The cost is then obtained by applying the appropriate charge of 1½d. per kilowatt-hour in the worked example.

Total cost (excluding tubes and cleaning). This sub-total in the cost table excludes the cost items which are incurred in routine maintenance, i.e. tube replacement and cleaning. The subject of economic planned maintenance will be discussed in detail later in this chapter, together with the advantages of group replacement of lamps. In the cost table, however, it has been assumed that only modest lighting maintenance is carried out, i.e. that the tubes are used until they fail individually and that the fittings are cleaned only once a year.

Lamp cost. Although the cost of lamps may be considered as an 'initial' cost item, and therefore subject to conditions of capital expenditure, the lamps are also expendable items which need replacing. In the cost comparison table, only the replacement lamps have been considered, the initial batch being included as expendable cost items.

When arriving at the total cost of lamps, it is necessary to allow for any discounts that the user may be entitled to and it is then necessary to add purchase tax in the case of those lamps which are subject to tax.

Once the total cost of a batch of lamps has been assessed, it is then necessary to take into account the different lamp lives, e.g. general purpose filament lamps have a rated life of 1000 hours, whereas fluorescent tubes and most discharge lamps have a rated life of 7500 or 5000 hours. A factor of 7500 hours has been allowed for in the cost table for 8 ft and 5 ft tubes in arriving at the total lamp cost per 2500 hours' use.

Lamp replacement labour cost. This item of annual cost may not always be applicable, for if group replacement of lamps is carried out after a specified period then it may be possible to arrange for this operation to coincide with one of the cleaning periods. If this is possible, then it will cost no more to replace an old lamp with a new lamp than it would to clean the existing lamp. For this reason it is not necessary to make a labour charge where group replacement of lamps is co-ordinated with the cleaning programme. If lamps are not replaced as part of a systematic maintenance programme, but allowed to operate until they fail individually, then the labour cost of carrying out individual replacements can be extremely high and investigations have shown that the labour cost can be more than 15s. per lampway. In the cost table, however, a nominal figure of 4s. or 4s. 6d. has been allowed for each lamp change. It is again necessary, of course, to allow for the difference in lamp life when assessing annual labour costs for different lamp types.

Cleaning cost (lamps and fittings). The annual cost of cleaning the lamps and lighting fittings depends on the accessibility of the fittings, type of fitting involved and also the number of cleanings carried out per annum. If the fittings are mounted at a considerable mounting height and scaffolding is necessary to reach them, then the cost per cleaning can be very high, possibly more than £1 per fitting. It will also be found that if an enclosed diffuser type of fitting is to be cleaned, then the plastics diffuser must normally be cleaned with an anti-static cleaning fluid which prevents the electrostatic attraction of dust. The cost of cleaning a diffuser type fitting is therefore considerably higher than that for a batten fitting. The final factor which determines the frequency of cleaning is largely dependent on the nature of the working area. For example, fittings in an air-conditioned office may only require cleaning once a year, whereas fittings in a dirty industrial atmosphere may economically justify cleaning every month. In practice, it will be found that cleaning is normally carried out either once or twice a year. In the cost comparison table it has been assumed that the reflector fittings will only be cleaned once a year and a cost of 5s. or 7s. per cleaning per fitting has been included. The cleaning cost for room decorations will be dealt with later.

Total annual lighting cost. The cost table shows that by adding together the seven individual cost factors the total annual lighting cost can be assessed for a given period of use, i.e. 2500 hours. A study of the cost comparison table will show how the individual factors vary for the two lighting schemes under consideration. Because of the smaller number of 8 ft fittings required, the 85 W scheme is cheaper than the 5 ft 65 W scheme for all seven individual cost factors and is clearly the better economic proposition. It may be of interest to note that the electricity bill accounts for more than half the total annual lighting bill and is obviously the most important individual cost factor.

The method outlined in this chapter, and given as an example in the cost comparison table, should prove useful in dealing with any other lighting installation where it is desirable to compare two or more schemes of equal lighting performance.

Fig. 30.1 can be used to estimate total annual lighting costs for fluorescent lighting, assuming present-day equipment and electricity costs and average cleaning costs. The two curves given for each of the popular ratings of fluorescent tube differentiate the 'small user' from the 'large user' in terms of lamp discounts and electricity tariffs.

Cleaning cost (room decorations). Although the room decorations are not entirely a lighting cost item, dirt on the walls and ceiling reduces the reflection factors and thereby causes a loss of illumination. This is particularly noticeable in rooms with light decorations, where the reflected light from the walls and ceiling should form a useful part of the total illumination on the working plane.

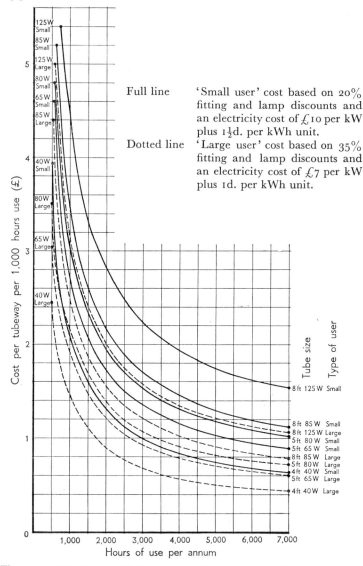

Full line   'Small user' cost based on 20% fitting and lamp discounts and an electricity cost of £10 per kW plus 1½d. per kWh unit.

Dotted line   'Large user' cost based on 35% fitting and lamp discounts and an electricity cost of £7 per kW plus 1d. per kWh unit.

Fig. 30.1   Total annual lighting cost. Cost factors applied to curves*

* The curves are based on single tube fittings. For twin tube fittings, reduce the cost curve value by approximately 10%

Although the exact loss of light due to dirt on the interior room surfaces will vary according to a number of factors (reflection factors, rate of depreciation and the light distribution of the fitting) it is reasonable to assume an average loss of 10% for normal commercial or industrial interiors in which redecorating is carried out at intervals of 4 to 6 years.

ECONOMICS OF PLANNED MAINTENANCE

Basic principles (value of wasted light equals cost of maintenance). The illumination initially provided by a lighting installation will decrease gradually throughout life, owing to a reduction in the lamp lumens and also owing to dirt on the lamps, fittings and decorations. This means that if the illumination falls by, say, 20% after a given period of use, then 20% of the total lighting bill is being wasted. If the rate of lighting depreciation is linear, then the average light output throughout life will be half-way between the 'initial' and 'end-of-life' values, e.g. if the useful lumens drop from 100% initial to 80% end-of-life, then the average illumination throughout this period would be 90% which means that 10% of the total lighting cost has been wasted.

It can be shown that the most economic maintenance programme is one in which the amount spent on maintenance (cleaning or lamp replacement) is equal to the average value of the light wasted as a result of dirt or depreciated lamp lumens respectively.

Maintenance formula for linear rate of depreciation. The most economic maintenance period can be calculated by means of a fairly simple formula in the case of those installations where the illumination depreciates by a fixed amount per month. This formula is derived as follows:

Let T = total cost of lighting per month for 100% light output

L = most economic maintenance period, in months

C = total cost per month, excluding maintenance cost

M = cost of maintenance (per cleaning)

D = fractional depreciation of light output per month.

If maintenance is carried out after L months of use, then the illumination will have fallen by DL at end-of-life and the average drop in illumination throughout this period will be $\frac{1}{2}DL$. This means that the total cost for L months, including the cost of one maintenance operation, will give an average illumination of $1 - \frac{1}{2}DL$.
Then:

$$\text{Total cost for } 100\% \text{ output} = \frac{\text{total cost for } L \text{ months}}{1 - \frac{1}{2}DL} = TL$$

but,

$$\text{Total cost} = (\text{cost per month}) \times L + \text{maintenance cost} = CL + M$$

Therefore   Total cost for 100% output $= TL = \dfrac{CL + M}{1 - \frac{1}{2}DL}$

and   Total monthly cost for 100% output $= T = \dfrac{C + M/L}{1 - \frac{1}{2}DL}$

Now $\left(\dfrac{1}{1 - DL}\right)$ can be expanded into a series

$$(1 + DL + D^2L^2 + D^3L^3 + \cdots),$$

so $T = \left(C + \dfrac{M}{L}\right)(1 + \frac{1}{2}DL + \frac{1}{4}D^2L^2 + \frac{1}{8}D^3L^3 + \cdots)$

When $\frac{1}{2}DL$ is fairly small (less than 10%) then $(\frac{1}{2}DL)^2$ and higher terms in the formula can be ignored, since they would only incur an addition of 1% or less. This approximation simplifies the formula as follows:

$$T = \left(C + \dfrac{M}{L}\right)(1 + \frac{1}{2}DL) = C + \frac{1}{2}CDL + \dfrac{M}{L} + \frac{1}{2}MD$$

so $\dfrac{\mathrm{d}T}{\mathrm{d}L} = \frac{1}{2}CD - \dfrac{M}{L^2} = 0$ (for minimum or maximum cost)

and $\dfrac{\mathrm{d}^2T}{\mathrm{d}L^2} = + \dfrac{2M}{L^3}$ (positive value so $\mathrm{d}T/\mathrm{d}L$ is minimum cost)

Since $\frac{1}{2}CD - \dfrac{M}{L^2} = 0$

then $\frac{1}{2}CDL^2 = M$

i.e. Average value of wasted light $(\frac{1}{2}CDL^2) = $ Cost of maintenance (M)

also $L^2 = \dfrac{2M}{CD}$

so $L = \sqrt{\dfrac{2M}{CD}} = $ Most economic maintenance period

ECONOMICS OF FLUORESCENT TUBULAR LAMPS

Calculation of most economic life. Sufficient life test data have been compiled to enable the average light depreciation of fluorescent tubes to be assessed. The depreciation curve in Fig. 30.2 is the average for the most popular sizes and colours of fluorescent tubular lamps. This curve becomes approximately linear after the first 1000 hours, with a depreciation of about 2% per 1000 hours' use. If this straight line is drawn back to the y axis, then it gives a value of 95% at 0 hours, i.e. the lumen output from a standard fluorescent tube can be assumed to have an initial depreciation of 5% followed by a linear depreciation of 2% per 1000 hours' use. In practice, the 'initial' value of 100% is taken after the normal 100 hour ageing period, i.e. the light depreciation between 0 and 100 hours is ignored.

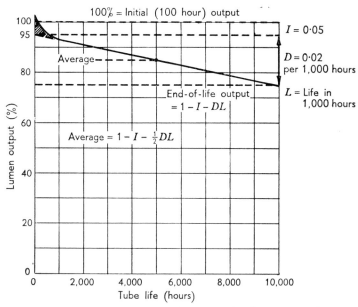

Fig. 30.2 Lumen depreciation curve for fluorescent tubes

When calculating the most economic tube life for group replacement purposes, the maintenance formula can be modified to take into account the initial non-linear depreciation as follows:

Let T = total lighting cost per 1000 hours' use for 100% light output

L = most economic tube life (in 1000 hours).

C = total cost per 1000 hours' use, excluding tubes and labour

M_t = total cost per batch of tubes

D = fractional depreciation of lumen output per 1000 hours' use.

I = initial non-linear depreciation (at 0 hours).

Then $$T = \frac{C + M_t/L}{1 - I - \frac{1}{2}DL} \quad \text{and} \quad L = \sqrt{\frac{2(M_t - IM_t)}{CD}}$$

The above formula only takes into account the effect of depreciated light output and the result is, therefore, only correct in those cases where the labour cost for tube replacement is negligible. In the case of group replacement of fluorescent tubes, labour cost is negligible when the tubes are replaced as part of a cleaning programme but an allowance must be made for the labour cost in replacing any individual life failures prior to the group replacement period. A correction must, therefore, be made to the main formula in those cases where there is a significant number of individual life failures.

Effect of labour costs. Fig. 30.3 shows the normal life depreciation curve for fluorescent tubular lamps having an average life of 7500 hours. The life performance for a batch of fluorescent tubes will normally follow the shape of the curve in Fig. 30.3, in that there will be a negligible number of tube life failures up to approximately two-thirds of the average life of the batch and the rate of failures will be approximately linear from this point onwards. For

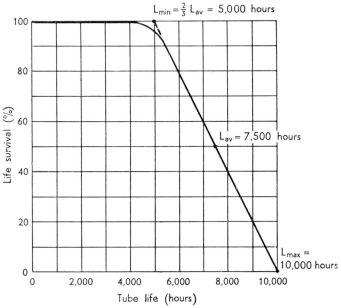

Fig. 30.3   Life depreciation curve for fluorescent tubes
(based on rated 7500 hours' life)

calculation purposes, therefore, the labour cost for individual life failures can be allowed as a correction to the main formula for those cases where the most economic life is greater than two-thirds of the average life, i.e. the labour cost factor can be ignored for any tube life up to 5000 hours but a correction should be applied to any tube life in excess of 5000 hours. Although varying hours of use per switching cycle may cause the average life to vary between 5000 and 10,000 hours, the minimum life can be taken as two-thirds of the average value.

The following relationship has been found to exist which can be applied as a correction factor in those cases where the most economic life calculated by the main formula is in excess of two-thirds of the 'average' batch life:

$$\text{True economic life} = (L - \tfrac{2}{3}L_{\text{ave}})\left(\frac{M_t - M_1}{M_t}\right)^2 + (\tfrac{2}{3}L_{\text{ave}})$$

where L = most economic life as calculated by main formula

L_{ave} = average life for batch of tubes (normally 7500 hours)

M_t = total cost of batch of tubes

M_1 = labour cost for 100% individual life failures.

Note: When the labour cost per individual life failure is greater than the net price per tube, then the most economic tube life has a maximum value of two-thirds of average life, i.e. $(M_t - M_1)$ can be taken as zero.

Worked Example—Calculation of Most Economic Fluorescent Tube Life.

By using the formula given in the previous section it is possible to calculate the most economic period for group replacement of fluorescent tubes, i.e. the tube life which will give mimimum annual cost, for a given quantity of light. The proposed method can be applied as a worked example to the lighting installation used in the cost comparison example, i.e. the 8 ft 85 W scheme detailed in Table 30.1 on p. 485.

The cost factors given in Table 30.1 can be rounded off to give the following values for use in the economic life formula:

Details of 8 ft 85 W scheme:

Total annual cost (2500 hours)   = £265

Total cost, less tubes and labour = £248

Total cost per batch of tubes   = £37

Total labour cost (100% failures) = £14½

Let C = total cost per 1000 hours (excluding tubes and labour)—£100 (approx.)

M_t = total cost per batch of tubes—£37 (approx.)

M_1 = labour cost for 100% individual life failures—£14 (approx.)

Assuming that the initial non-linear depreciation (I) is 0·05 and the linear depreciation per 1000 hours (D) is 0·02, then,

$$\text{Most economic life} = L = \sqrt{\frac{2(37 - 0\cdot05 \times 37)}{0\cdot02 \times 100}}$$

$$= \sqrt{\frac{2(37 - 1\cdot85)}{2}}$$

$$= \sqrt{35\cdot15} = 5\cdot925 = \underline{5925 \text{ hours}}$$

This would be the economic life if there was no labour cost involved for the replacement of individual tube failures. In the worked example, however, the following labour cost correction is applied:

Since 'average' life for batch of tubes = 7500 hours (normal) then,

'Minimum' life = $\frac{2}{3} \times 7500 = 5000$ hours

So: Corrected life $= (5925 - 5000) \times \left(\dfrac{37 - 14}{37}\right)^2 + (5000)$

$$= (925) \times \left(\dfrac{23}{37}\right)^2 + (5000)$$

$$= (925) \times (0{\cdot}62)^2 + (5000)$$

$$= (925) \times (0{\cdot}386) + (5000)$$

$$= (360) + (5000)$$

$$= \underline{5360 \text{ hours}}$$

$$= \text{Most economic tube life.}$$

Practical group replacement programme for fluorescent tubes.   In the case discussed in the worked example, the lighting is used for 2500 hours per annum, and Table 30.1 allows for cleaning of lamps and fittings once per annum. It follows that the most practical group replacement scheme would be at intervals of 2 years, since this would give a tube life of 5000 hours which is very close to the most economic value and the tubes can be group-replaced every second annual cleaning.

When using the 'most economic lamp life' formula, the total cost per tube-way per 1000 hours can be obtained from Fig. 30.1. Because the value of C in the formula is total cost *excluding* tubes and labour, the value obtained from Fig. 30.1 should be reduced by 5% to 10% to give an approximate value for C.

Most economic cleaning period.   If a series of lightmeter readings are taken at monthly intervals, it is possible to determine the average monthly rate of light depreciation due to dirt. When this is an approximately linear rate of depreciation, then the most economic cleaning interval can be calculated using the formula

$$L = \sqrt{\dfrac{2M}{CD}}$$

For an average depreciation of 0·02 per month, and using the cost factors for the worked example of the 8 ft 85 W scheme in Table 30.1, then total annual cost, less cleaning, is £254 and so $C = £21$ per month and $M = £11$ per cleaning.

Therefore:

$$\text{Economic cleaning period} = \sqrt{\dfrac{2 \times 11}{0{\cdot}02 \times 21}} = \sqrt{\dfrac{11}{0{\cdot}21}}$$

$$= \sqrt{52\tfrac{1}{2}} = 7\tfrac{1}{4} \text{ months.}$$

This would give a practical maintenance programme of cleaning every 8 months and group replacement of fluorescent tubes every 2 years.

ECONOMICS OF INCANDESCENT FILAMENT LAMPS

Effect of voltage variation on lamp performance. An important factor which affects the economics of incandescent filament lamps is the fact that a small variation in the supply voltage will cause a considerable varia-

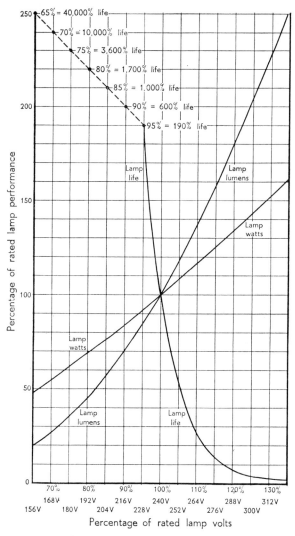

Fig. 30.4   Effect of voltage variation on incandescent filament lamps

tion in lamp life. Fig. 30.4 shows the effect of voltage variation on the life, light output and wattage of incandescent filament lamps. A variation of only 5% from the rated voltage of a filament lamp will cause the life to be either doubled or halved, i.e. a ten-fold inverse variation. On the other hand, a 5% change in voltage will give nearly a four-fold direct variation in lumen output.

Bearing in mind that it is permissible for electricity supply authorities to vary their declared voltage (normally 240 V) by plus or minus 6%, extreme limits of 255 V maximum and 225 V minimum would give very different lives when using a lamp rated for 240 V. It is necessary, therefore, to establish the lamp life that will give the most economic performance.

Assessment of economic lamp operation. Fig. 30.4 shows that an appreciably longer life is obtained by under-running a filament lamp and at first glance it would appear desirable always to use a lamp with a higher voltage rating than the actual supply volts. It will be found, however, that the lamp lumens fall off at a faster rate than the lamp wattage when the lamp is under-run, i.e. lamp efficiency is reduced. It is necessary, therefore, to balance the saving of lamp cost against the value of the reduced light output.

The only fair and accurate method of comparing lamp plus electricity costs is in terms of equal lumen output over equal periods of time and in the case of filament lamps a convenient basis for comparison is cost per thousand lumens per thousand hours' use, i.e. cost per million lumen hours.

For example, if a lamp emits 1200 lm for a life of 1000 hours and the total cost of the lamps plus electricity is 18s. then we obtain 1,200,000 lumen hours for 18s. or 15s. per million lumen hours. If we compare this performance with another lamp which emits 1000 lm for 2000 hours at a cost of 35s. it provides 2,000,000 lumen hours for 35s. or 17s. per million lumen hours. The first lamp is therefore the more economic choice.

Comparison of filament lamp operating costs. Table 30.2 gives an example comparing the cost of operating a 250 V 200 W filament lamp on a 200 V supply with a 200 V 100 W lamp on the same supply, these lamps giving approximately equal lumens. The table shows that the 250 V lamp is under-run by 20% whilst the 200 V lamp is operating at its rated voltage. In each case, separate costs have been calculated for a scheme in which the labour cost of lamp replacement is nil and also where a labour cost of 2s. 8d. per lampway is involved.

By applying the life, lumens and wattage data obtained from Fig. 30.4, it is shown in Table 30.2 that the under-run lamp is dearer than the 200 V lamp for any installation where the replacement labour cost is less than 2s. 8d. It follows that if a lamp is being used in a reasonably accessible location, where the labour cost may be only 1s. or 2s. per lamp, then it would not be economic to use the under-run lamp. If, however, the lamp is being used in an inaccessible location involving a high labour cost of more than 3s., then it would be an economic proposition to use the under-run lamp.

TABLE 30.2

Comparison of Filament Lamp Operating Costs

Comparing the operating costs of a 250 V 200 W filament lamp with a 200 V 100 W lamp on an actual supply voltage of 200 V.

Lamp rating	250 V 200 W	200 V 100 W
Actual supply voltage . . .	200	200
% of rated lamp voltage . .	80%	100%

From Fig. 30.4:

Rated lamp life (hours) . .	1000	1000
% of rated lamp life . . .	1700%	100%
Actual lamp life (hours) . .	17,000	1000
Rated lamp lumens . . .	2880	1230
% of rated lamp lumens . .	45%	100%
Actual lamp lumens . . .	1295	1230
Rated lamp watts . . .	200	100
% of rated lamp watts . .	69%	100%
Actual lamp watts . . .	138	100

Comparison of Costs per 1000 *hours per* 1000 *lumens (one million lumen-hours).*

Nett price per lamp . .	2s. 6d.	2s. 6d.	1s. 6d.	1s. 6d.
Lamp replacement labour cost	Nil	2s. 8d.	Nil	2s. 8d.
Total cost per lamp . .	2s. 6d.	5s. 2d.	1s. 6d.	4s. 2d.
Actual lamp life . . .	17,000	17,000	1000	1000
Lamp and labour cost per 1000 hours' use. . . .	1¾d.	3⅔d.	1s. 6d.	4s. 2d.
Actual lamp lumens . .	1295	1295	1230	1230

Lamp cost per 1000 *hours per* 1000 *lumens*	1⅓d.	2¼d.	1s. 2⅔d.	3s. 4¾d.

Total kilowatt-hours per 1000 hours' use. . . .	138	138	100	100
Electricity cost @ 1½d. per kWh	17s. 3d.	17s. 3d.	12s. 6d.	12s. 6d.
Actual lamp lumens . .	1295	1295	1230	1230

Electricity cost per 1000 *hours per* 1000 *lumens* . . .	13s. 4d.	13s. 4d.	10s. 2d.	10s. 2d.

Total cost per million lumen-hours	13s. 5⅓d.	13s. 6¾d.	11s. 4⅔d.	13s. 6¾d.

CHAPTER 31

Street Lighting

The dense traffic and high speeds which are encountered on modern roads make the driver's visual task more arduous than that of any other road user and nightfall brings added danger due to the decreased range of visibility. Although the modern street-lighting installation is primarily designed to satisfy the needs of the vehicle driver, it is also necessary to safeguard the pedestrian and resident and to ease the task of the police.

It is intended in this chapter to examine the principles upon which current British street-lighting practice is based, and to show the practical steps which must be taken to design an installation.

The driver's visual task. Before any logical decision can be made about a method of lighting it is necessary to study the visual tasks involved. It is therefore important to understand the processes by which the driver receives the required visual information.

When a person is looking at an object the eye is turned so that the image falls on the fovea (page 3). In this area the visual acuity of the eye is at a maximum and the object is seen in the greatest detail. Other objects which lie within the field of view but not on this direct line of sight can be seen, but in less detail. For instance, should the brain require more information about an object 20° from the line of sight, the fixation reflex would turn the eye so that the image would fall on the fovea and details one tenth the size previously perceptible would become apparent. Thus, although the eye examines only one part of the field of view at a time, the whole field is observed and close attention can be given to any particular area that warrants it.

If it were necessary for a driver to study every detail of a road and its surroundings before he made a decision his rate of progress would be poor. Fortunately an experienced driver receives a great deal of information by recognising traffic patterns and only finds it necessary to study those details which differ from normal or which he knows indicate a source of danger. The majority of objects in his field of view are large enough to be recognised without being directly studied but there are some small details, such as the expression on the face of a pedestrian hesitating at the edge of the pavement, which can have a great influence on the driver's actions. During the hours of daylight there is adequate illumination and such small details can be easily seen, but as night approaches the illumination decreases and the size of the smallest perceptible detail increases.

Not only does the ability to see small details decrease at lower illumination levels but so does the ability to detect differences in contrast. A large object which is seen because of its contrast with its background under high-illumination conditions, will be less obvious or even invisible under conditions of low illumination. In order to give the driver similar driving conditions at night to those he meets by day the methods recommended for interior lighting would have to be adopted; and this would be far too expensive. Since it is not economically possible to increase the illumination to a level which would allow the contrast between an object and its background to become more obvious, the only alternative is to increase this contrast by other means. This can best be accomplished by positioning lanterns so that the brightness of the road surface is increased and objects are seen silhouetted against it. This *silhouette principle*, which makes it easier to see large objects, is the basis of the British method of street lighting for main traffic routes.

The effectiveness of this procedure can be assessed from the commonly held opinion that dusk is the most difficult time for driving. Under these conditions of low-level diffuse illumination, it is more difficult to observe objects than at a later time when the illumination is still lower but the street lighting has been switched on. The effect is partially caused by the change in the adaptation of the eye, but is also due to the greater contrast produced by the correct design of artificial lighting.

The optical properties of the road surface. The appearance of the road surface at any point is dependent upon its luminance. This is governed by the illumination at the point, the reflection characteristics of the surface, the direction of the incident light and the position of the observer. In a given installation the illumination distribution remains constant but the road surface appearance changes if the surface conditions change and as the observer moves.

Each lantern produces a patch of light on the road surface. The shape of the patch is in general T-shaped (Fig. 31.1) with the tail of the T pointing towards the observer and the head of the T forming a pool of light under the lantern. The T-shape of the patch is due partly to preferential reflection of the light towards the observer, especially at large angles of incidence. The mechanism of its formation is best understood by considering surfaces representing the extremes; a shiny surface and a matt surface.

A wet road represents the shiniest surface that is likely to be met in practice. If the surface were perfectly smooth, a well-defined image of each lantern would be formed, but owing to the irregularities in the road surface, its roughness and its undulations, the image is spread up and down the road, and to some extent sideways. The result is a series of streaks orientated towards the observer as shown in Fig. 31.2.

When the surface is very rough and matt the preferentially reflected component is greatly reduced or even eliminated, and the reflected light is then

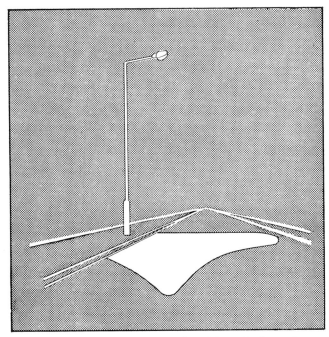

Fig. 31.1　The T-shaped bright patch produced by a single semi-cut-off lantern

Fig. 31.2　The appearance of a shiny or wet road surface

distributed diffusely. If the road surface is light coloured, the head of the T will be large, but if it is dark the head of the T will be reduced in size.

Most surfaces lie somewhere between these extremes. The modern non-skid surface is rough and dark and the tail of the T is barely present.

Consider a surface of this type with a source suspended at a height of 25 ft above it. If the intensity of the source is 100 cd in all directions below the horizontal then the variation of the horizontal illumination along the road is shown by curve A in Fig. 31.3. Curve B shows the luminance along a line

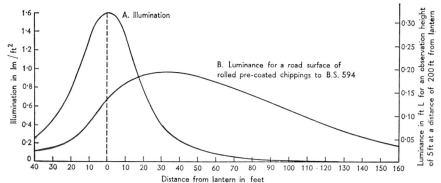

Fig. 31.3 The illumination and luminance from a 1000 cd constant intensity source, at 25 ft mounting height

in the direction of the observer when he is 200 ft along the road. It can be seen that although the illumination falls to one-tenth of its maximum value in less than 50 ft the luminance does not do so in over 160 ft.

If, instead of a uniform source, a practical lantern is considered, then the variation of illumination and luminance will be similar to that shown in Fig. 31.4. This lantern has the same amount of flux in the lower hemisphere

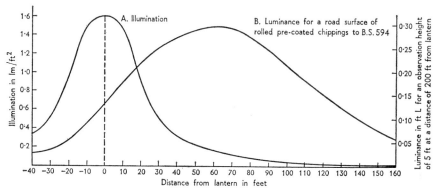

Fig. 31.4 The illumination and luminance from a semi-cut-off lantern at 25 ft mounting height

17+

as the constant intensity source, but a greater proportion is directed on to the road surface and hence the intensity at high angles of elevation has been increased without loss at lower angles. This type of distribution increases the road luminance and spreads the bright patch even further along the road. The improvement occurs not only in the direction of the observer but elsewhere on the road surface as well.

Usually the lighting engineer has no control over the type of road surface, so the design of an installation consists in choosing the type of lanterns best suited to the road and its surface, and then placing lanterns in the correct positions. The types of Group A lanterns to be used for main traffic routes are now specified in BS 1788: 1964 and recommended layouts are given in British Standard Code of Practice CP 1004: 1963.

The light distribution from Group A lanterns. The light distribution from any single lantern should fulfil the following requirements:

(1) Provide a road surface luminance which has the greatest possible uniformity.
(2) Provide sufficient light on the surroundings to reveal objects on the pavement and allow pedestrians to see adequately.
(3) Be free from glare.
(4) Allow a reasonable flexibility in the spacing.

These requirements impose certain limitations on the light distributions and it is necessary to examine the distribution specifications in detail.

From the previous section it can be seen that the road surface luminance is improved if there is a maximum intensity at a fairly high angle of elevation, say between 60° and 80°. This part of the distribution is known as the *beam*. Now although the optics of a lantern are primarily designed to produce the beam it would be incorrect to restrict severely the intensity in the downward direction (say within 30° of the downward vertical), as this would result in a dark patch on the road surface, and underlit pavements. There is, therefore, a limit below which the light in the 0° to 30° zone must not be reduced. An upper limit is also necessary because too much light would result in an unduly bright patch under the lantern and too much direct illumination on some objects, reducing the contrast of the silhouette.

Any light in directions near the horizontal will not contribute to the road surface brightness but will fall directly into the driver's eyes and increase the glare. There is therefore an upper limit to the amount of light in what is known as the *run-back zone*, i.e. immediately above the beam (Fig. 31.5).

It can be seen from Fig. 31.4 that although the main beam illuminates the road at a distance of about 100 ft from the lantern, the area of high luminance which causes the bright patch stretches farther. If the limitation on intensities between the beam and the horizontal were too severe the bright patch would end abruptly at about 120 ft and a dark area on the road surface would result unless the lanterns were positioned at exactly the right spacing. Slight increases in lantern spacing are frequently necessary, so the run-back has to be a compromise which neither produces too much glare nor limits the flexibility of lantern spacing too drastically.

The effect of these basic requirements has been to impose limitations on three main zones of the distribution, the beam, the run back and the downward zone.

The light distribution requirements of BS 1788: 1964 for Group A lanterns. The limits discussed in the previous section have now been given numerical values in BS 1788: 1964. Before discussing the light distributions recognised in the specification it is necessary to define the technical terms used in their description.

Intensities are not expressed directly, but as *intensity ratios* (abbreviation: IR). The IR in any direction is defined as the intensity in that direction divided by the mean intensity in the lower hemisphere of the lantern; the *mean hemispherical intensity* (MHI). The latter is equal to the luminous flux emitted below the horizontal divided by 2π.

Hence,

$$IR = \frac{\text{Intensity}}{\text{MHI}} = \frac{\text{Intensity} \times 2\pi}{\text{Bare lamp flux} \times \text{Light output ratio down}}$$

The reason for expressing intensities as ratios is that the specification controls only the shape of the light distribution. If any individual intensity, such as the peak intensity, had been chosen as the denominator, considerable variation would have resulted. The MHI was chosen because of its constancy from one sample to another of the same model of lantern.

The beam is defined as the cone of light enclosing the peak intensity and all the intensities greater than 90% of the peak value. The *beam centre* is the direction midway between the directions at which the intensity is 90% of the maximum intensity, these intensities being measured at the angle of elevation of maximum intensity.

The *principal vertical polar curve* is the intensity distribution taken in the vertical plane passing through the beam centre, and the angle between this plane and the plane of the street axis is known as the angle of *toe-in*.

There are three zones of control; the 0° to 30° zone in all directions round the lantern, the beam in the principal plane and the run-back above the beam in the plane parallel to the street axis. The beam and the run-back are considered in different planes because, regardless of the angle of toe-in of the beam, the more distant lanterns, which tend to cause glare, are viewed parallel to the road axis.

The requirements in these zones are shown in Fig. 31.5 and can be seen to vary according to whether the distribution is cut-off, semi-cut-off, semi-cut-off with sodium sources or semi-cut-off with low-brightness sources (less than 10 cd/in²) such as fluorescent tubes.

The need for two main types of distribution, cut-off and semi-cut-off, is a result of the compromise (which has already been discussed) between limiting glare and increasing the flexibility of lantern spacing.

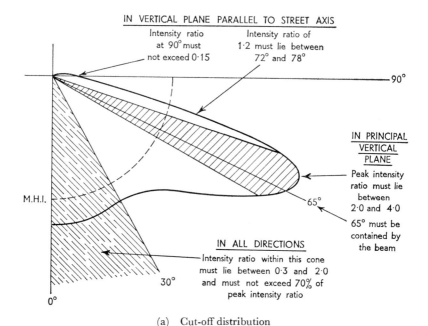

(a)   Cut-off distribution

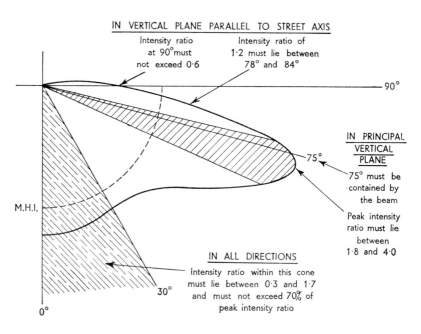

(b)   Semi-cut-off distribution

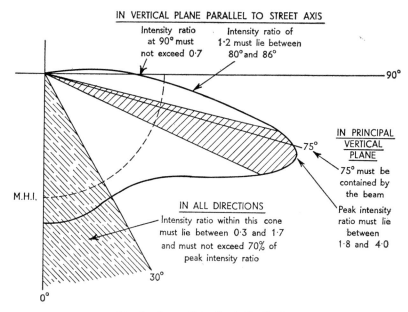

(c)   Semi-cut-off (sodium) distribution

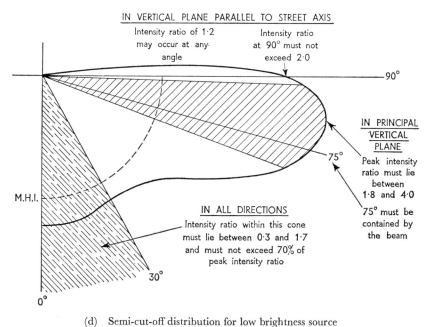

(d)   Semi-cut-off distribution for low brightness source

Fig. 31.5   The light distribution requirements for Group A lanterns

The cut-off distribution (Fig. 31.5(a)) imposes sharp run-back on the intensities above the beam and hence produces less glare. The tail of the T-shaped patch will, of course, be much shorter and the lantern spacing will also need to be short. On a very matt road surface where the tail would necessarily be short there is little disadvantage in using cut-off lanterns even though this demands close spacing.

The semi-cut-off distribution (Fig. 31.5(b)), whilst tending to produce more glare will, when used with a fairly smooth road surface, produce a T-shaped patch with a much longer tail, and the lantern spacing can be longer. The glare from a lantern of this type is not however, unrestricted; the runback is still quite severe.

Lanterns which contain sodium sources or large sources of low brightness, such as fluorescent tubes, are thought to be less glaring than those using other sources. There is therefore some relaxation of the run-back limitations in these cases. The distributions (Fig. 31.5(c) and (d)) are the same as the standard semi-cut-off distribution in all other respects.

There are many types of optical system which can be designed to produce distributions which meet these requirements. Some of these systems are discussed in Chapter 6.

Layout of Group A installations. There are many factors which affect the positioning of lanterns relative to the road and to each other, and these factors must be considered in detail.

It must be realised that the ideal of a uniformly bright road surface is not achieved in practice. There is considerable variation in the appearance of the road surface itself, and some darker patches are inevitable. Most of the objects which the road user requires to see are sufficiently large for at least some part of them to be seen against a bright part of the road. The lanterns must be positioned so that the bright patches merge and the dark patches are reduced to a minimum. Such a procedure would be simple if it were not for financial considerations. The aim is to achieve the best result with the minimum of equipment.

Although the bright patch from a single lantern is T-shaped, it has no definite edge. The luminance decreases from the centre outwards and gradually fades away, and the sharp edge shown in diagrams is purely a convention adopted in order to illustrate the principles involved.

Consider the layout of a typical installation (Fig. 31.6). The lanterns, which have a semi-cut-off distribution, are on the two sides of the road in a staggered arrangement, so that the individual patches of brightness cover the greatest area of road and leave the smallest possible areas of darkness. The effect of altering the various installation parameters can be seen from Figs. 31.7 to 31.11.

Lantern spacing increased (Fig. 31.7). The bright patches no longer merge into each other and the dark areas have increased in size. There is obviously a maximum spacing which can be used without making the road surface unduly patchy.

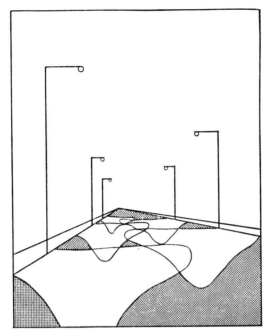

Fig. 31.6   A typical installation (semi-cut-off lanterns
in a staggered arrangement)

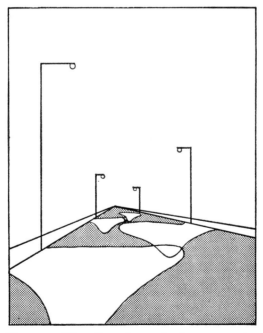

Fig. 31.7   The effect of excessive lantern spacing

Lanterns with cut-off distribution (Fig. 31.8). The lower beam angle and more severe run-back restrictions result in a shorter bright patch. The patches no longer merge and a shorter lantern spacing would be required to maintain the uniformity of road brightness.

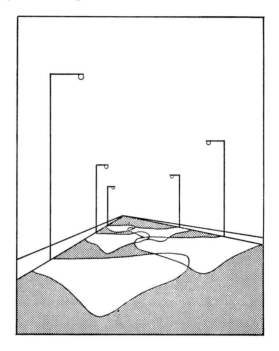

Fig. 31.8   The effect of changing to cut-off lanterns without a reduction in lantern spacing

Greater lantern mounting height (Fig. 31.9). The bright patch from each lantern now covers a larger area. The overall road luminance is of a greater uniformity but is reduced because more light falls on either side of the carriageway. A greater amount of light flux will be required to maintain the road luminance at its original value. The lantern spacing can now be increased without adversely affecting the uniformity of the road luminance but again a greater lantern output will be required if the luminance is not to be decreased.

Wider carriageway (Fig. 31.10). If the original installation is transferred to a road with a wider carriageway the bright patches from lanterns on opposite sides of the road will no longer merge and a dark zig-zag strip will be produced down the centre of the road. There are four possible ways of remedying this shortcoming.

(1) Decrease the lantern spacing. This will only be effective for small increases in road width. The darkness in the centre of the road is reduced because the overall road brightness is increased. At greater road widths the light will still not reach the central areas.

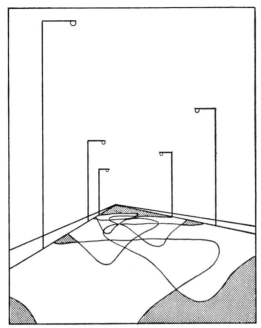

Fig. 31.9   The increase in brightness uniformity
due to increased mounting height

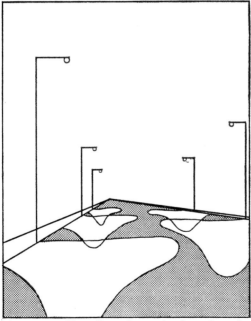

Fig. 31.10   The effect of excessive lateral spacing

(2) Increase the lantern overhang. For mechanical and aesthetic reasons there is a limit to the length of the bracket arm but greater overhang is effective for small increases in road width. By reducing the effective width of the road between the lanterns, the centre of the road is better lit, but the kerbs and pavement become darker.

(3) Increase the lantern mounting height. This is the most effective remedy and could theoretically be applied to roads of any width. Apart from the physical limitations there is one disadvantage; the light is spread into the centre of the road but it is also spread on to the pavement and surroundings and less light falls on to the actual carriageway. An increase in light output from each lantern is therefore required.

(4) Opposite spacings (Fig. 31.11). This is the most commonly used remedy. Although dark areas can still appear in the centre of the road the zig-zag strip is no longer apparent.

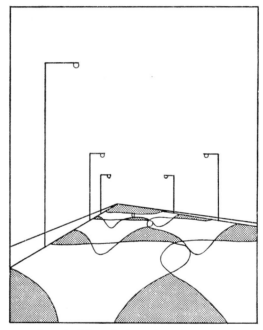

Fig. 31.11   A typical installation of semi-cut-off lanterns in an opposite arrangement

The lighting of bends.   If the staggered or opposite lantern arrangements are applied to a curving road the bright patches will no longer merge to give satisfactory coverage of the road. As can be seen in Fig. 31.12 there will be dark areas on the outside of the bend and a great deal of the light from the lanterns on the inside of the bend will be wasted. The obvious correction is to move some or all of the lanterns from the inside of the bend and reduce the spacing on the outside (Fig. 31.13).

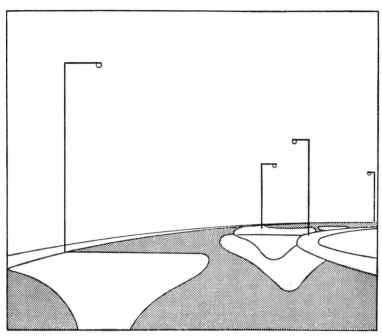

Fig. 31.12 An installation of semi-cut-off lanterns in a staggered arrangement on a bend

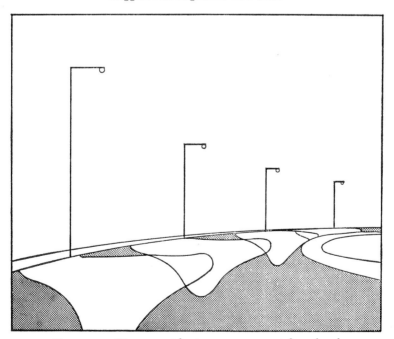

Fig. 31.13 The correct lantern arrangement for a bend

Planning a Group A installation. Having discussed the logic involved in determining the lantern distribution and the layout of lanterns, it is possible to consider more precisely the planning of an installation for Group A roads according to CP 1004: 1963. Eight major decisions need to be made in determining the complete installation. These decisions are concerned with:

Classification of road	Lantern arrangement
Appearance	Spacing and mounting height
Lantern distribution	Selection of lantern
Source	Type of column

Classification of road. The lighting of Group A roads is classified as follows:

Group A1. Lighting for principal traffic routes. Lighting for very important roads which require lighting superior to that of Group A2.

Group A2. Lighting for normal traffic routes. Lighting for the generality of main roads having considerable vehicular and pedestrian traffic.

Group A3. Lighting for minor traffic routes. Lighting for roads such as main rural roads, or minor urban roads carrying traffic not confined to the immediate locality, which do not require lighting up to the standard of Group A2.

Appearance. Not all the aspects of appearance can be considered at this stage, but it is well to have them in mind when the remaining decisions are to be made. No hard and fast rules can be made about appearance, but the Code does lay down some guiding principles. The main requirement is that the equipment should be in harmony with the surroundings.

Columns should not be sited in front of buildings or monuments of architectural interest. It is preferable that the columns are as slender as possible; this usually favours the metal column, but concrete columns may be preferable where there are many modern buildings. The columns and lanterns should be matched to each other and should be of subdued colouring.

Lantern distribution. The relative merits of cut-off and semi-cut-off lighting have already been considered in relation to the road surface, but to some extent they should also be considered in relation to adjacent buildings. These are apt to provide a brighter background with semi-cut-off lighting than with cut-off lighting owing to the greater amount of light flux emerging near the horizontal, and this brighter background helps in reducing the effects of glare from the lanterns. Moreover, the brighter buildings improve the appearance of the scene.

The longer lantern spacing permissible usually makes the semi-cut-off distribution the more economical, and hence the more popular.

Choice of lamp. The lamps most commonly used in Group A installations are sodium vapour, colour corrected mercury vapour and tubular fluorescent. Tungsten and plain mercury vapour lamps are rapidly losing favour, the tungsten being of low efficiency and short life and the mercury vapour having been superseded by the better colour rendering characteristics of the corrected lamp.

The choice of lamp will depend on economic and aesthetic considerations. Where good colour rendering is important, as in shopping centres, the choice will lie between colour corrected mercury vapour and tubular fluorescent. Although the tubular fluorescent has the superior colour rendering, the lantern needed is much bulkier and heavier if it is to contain the number of tubes required to achieve the lighting levels recommended in the Code. If colour rendering is of little importance, advantage can be taken of the very much greater efficiency of sodium vapour lamps.

The final choice, whilst based on these considerations, will also be influenced by local preferences and the necessity for blending with existing installations.

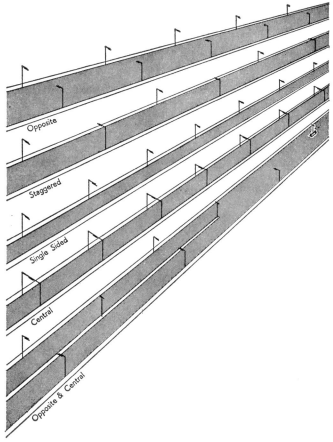

Fig. 31.14   Lantern arrangements

Lantern arrangement. The lantern layout to be used depends largely on the width of the road and whether there is a central reserve. Although no hard and fast rules can be given, the following practice is normally used (Fig. 31.14).

Type of road	*Lantern layout*
Single carriageway (wide)	Opposite
Single carriageway	Staggered
Single carriageway (narrow)	Single sided
Single carriageway (narrow with overhanging trees)	Central suspended
Dual carriageway (narrow central reserve)	Opposite + Central
Dual carriageway (wide central reserve)	Light as separate roads

The columns should be placed as far back from the kerb as practicable in order to minimize the likelihood of vehicles colliding with them.

The overhang, i.e. the horizontal distance of the lantern from the kerb, must not be too great otherwise the pavements will be insufficiently lit, and the illumination on the vertical surfaces of the kerbstones will be unduly increased in comparison to the illumination on the horizontal face. The vertical face will then no longer appear as a distinct dark line indicating the edge of the carriageway.

Spacing and mounting height. Mounting height, spacing and lantern output are inter-related. From the tables given in the Code it is possible to obtain several combinations of these variables that will satisfy the requirements of the installation. The final choice can only be made after comparing the costs of the possibilities. It should be noted, however, that the amounts of light flux recommended in the Code are minima, and it is usual to plan for a higher level to allow for deterioration and to anticipate to some extent the continuing trend towards better standards of lighting.

Selection of lantern. The choice of lantern distribution, and lamp type and wattage will already have been made. The choice of lantern will be determined by considerations such as ease of maintenance and relamping, robustness of construction, and appearance (especially in relation to the column).

Type of column. The factors affecting the choice of material, height and outreach of the column have already been discussed. Where control gear is used, care has to be taken that the control gear compartment is large enough to accommodate the gear and that the door of the compartment is designed to allow installation of the gear. Not only must the column be strong enough to support the weight of the lantern, but it must also be capable of withstanding the wind forces on the lantern. Steel columns must have a rustproof coating. It is preferred that the column is to a design approved by the Council of Industrial Design. Fuller requirements are given in BS 1840: 1960, BS 1308: 1957 and BS 1249: 1951.

It is evident that it is not possible to consider each one of the eight aspects of design in isolation. It may be necessary to consider many of the points in relation to each other and perhaps change the order of their consideration to suit the problems posed by the individual installation. Very often some of the aspects are fixed (perhaps due to local usage), and these may largely govern the decisions taken on the remainder.

A practical example of lantern siting

The actual siting of the lanterns and columns must be planned in detail on a large-scale map and finally confirmed by inspection on site. When inspection is not possible because the site is not yet in existence, models or perspective drawings are advisable to ensure that the installation is not confusing when viewed by the motorist. The following example is given to show the treatment of some of the typical problems which can arise during this stage of the planning.

The road to be lit is an urban shopping street with a 35 ft carriageway width. Group A2 lighting has been decided upon and this is to be provided by semi-cut-off lanterns containing colour-corrected mercury lamps. The road is suitable for the staggered arrangement. With an overhang of 5 ft the effective width from the lantern to the opposite kerb is 30 ft. The appropriate table in the Code of Practice (Fig. 31.15) gives spacings for mounting heights of 25 ft, 30 ft, 35 ft and 40 ft. In this case, heights in excess of 30 ft would be

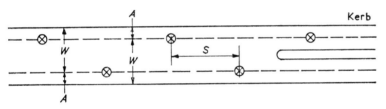

| Group | Mounting height H (ft) | \multicolumn{10}{c}{Effective width W (ft)} | Minimum light flux per lantern in lower hemisphere (lumens) | Maximum overhang A (ft) |
| | | 25 | 30 | 35 | 40 | 45 | 50 | 55 | 60 | 65 | 70 | | |
		\multicolumn{10}{c}{Maximum spacing S (ft)}		
A1	25	100	85	70	60	55						6250	6
	30	120	120	100	90	80	70	65				9000	7·5
	35	140	140	140	125	110	100	90	80	75		12250	8·5
	40	160	160	160	160	140	130	115	105	100	90	16000	9·5
A2	25	110	100	85	75	65						5600	6
	30	130	130	125	110	95	85	80				8100	7·5
	35	155	155	155	150	130	120	110	100	90		11000	8·5
	40	175	175	175	175	170	155	140	130	120	110	14400	9·5
A3	25	120	120	105	90	80						5000	6
	30	145	145	145	130	115	105	95				7200	7·5
	35	170	170	170	170	155	140	130	120	110		9800	8·5
	40	190	190	190	190	190	185	170	155	140	130	12800	9·5

Fig. 31.15   Table 9 from CP 1004, Part 2: 1963

out of proportion with the surrounding buildings and a 30 ft mounting height is therefore chosen. It is appropriate to adopt a 30 ft mounting height and 130 ft spacing, using a lantern with more than 8100 lm emitted below the horizontal. In order to obtain the correct light output a 250 W lamp will not be satisfactory and a 400 W lamp will be necessary. This will give an output well in excess of the 8100 lumens, which is a *minimum* requirement.

At this point the equipment to be used (lantern, lamp, column and control gear) are known. It is now necessary to determine the exact location of each column. For the purpose of this example just three typical sections of the installation will be considered (Fig. 31.16).

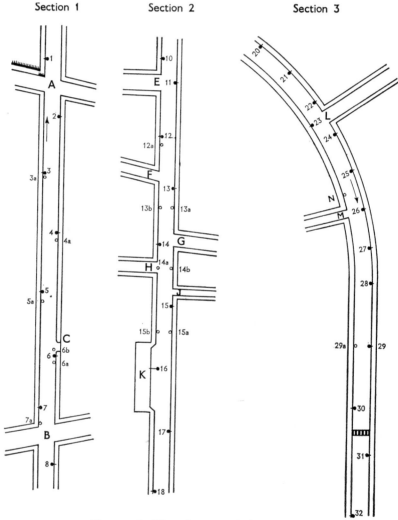

Fig. 31.16 Plans for example installation

Section 1. In this section there are two important cross-roads. These junctions require special treatment because the positioning of the lanterns is quite critical. Not only does the lighting have to show any obstruction, permanent or vehicular, in the junction area, but it also has to make the existence of the junction apparent to the approaching driver. A lantern located at position 1 will fulfil both these requirements for a driver approaching the junction in the direction of the arrow. The bright patch from this lantern will provide a background against which any object in the junction area will be silhouetted. The walls of the buildings and the edge of the kerb in the intersecting road (shown shaded) will be dark, so the break in the building line is clearly seen and the presence of an intersecting road is apparent to the driver. The lantern in position 2 will act in the same way for vehicles travelling in the opposite direction.

The distance of the lanterns from the corners of the intersection should be about one third the normal spacing for the installation. In this installation the distance between lanterns 1 and 2 is slightly less than 130 ft. This closer spacing is an advantage because the junction will now be slightly better lit than the approach roads. Had the intersecting road been so wide that the spacing was greater than the normal spacing it would have been necessary to move the lanterns closer to the corners.

If the road between junctions A and B were lit with lanterns at 130 ft spacing starting from lantern 2 the lanterns would be in positions 3a, 4a, 5a, 6a and 7a. Junction B must be lit in the same way as Junction A and so position 7a is too close to the corner. This lantern has to be moved about 40 ft away from the junction. This results in uneven spacing, so all the lanterns must be moved and the spacing in this section reduced to 122 ft. The new position for lantern 6 will be 6b which is within the limits of a vehicle entrance C and so it will have to be moved by a few feet. It will not be necessary to adjust any of the other positions because the unevenness of spacing is only slight. In practice it will be found that the position of many columns may have to be adjusted to avoid other street furniture, garage accesses and manhole covers.

Section 2. The main feature of this section is a major T-junction at E. Three lanterns are required to light this junction. Lantern 10 acts in the same way as lanterns 1, 2, 7 and 8 in the first section. Lantern 11 warns drivers in the side road that they are approaching a T-junction and creates a bright background against which they can see pedestrians crossing the mouth of the road. Lanterns 11 and 12 will enable drivers travelling in the direction of the arrow to see vehicles turning out of the side road.

This procedure, which provides the best form of lighting for major T-junctions, is not always practicable, e.g. where a complex of T-junctions of minor roads occur as at F, G, H and J. The requirements for each junction would conflict and the result would not only require an excessive number of lanterns but would also produce a disorganised array of columns and lanterns. The only resort is to try several arrangements until one is found which is the best compromise.

As a starting point, consider the effect of a 130 ft spaced staggered arrangement starting from lantern 11. This gives lanterns in positions 12a, 13a, 14a and 15a. It is obvious that the lantern at 14a must be moved. There are two alternatives. By moving it to 14b it will be in the correct position for both junctions H and G. It will now be necessary to move at least lantern 15 to position 15b and probably lantern 13 to 13b otherwise there would be three consecutive lanterns on the same side of the road. The other solution is to move lantern 14 along until it is opposite junction G and reduce the spacing between lanterns 11 and 14 to 110 ft per lantern. Now lantern 12 is in a good position for junctions E and F, lantern 13 is in a good position for junction F, lantern 14 is in a good position for junctions G and H and lantern 15 is in a good position for junction J.

The only other feature of this section is the parking bay at K. It is not necessary to move lantern 16, but it is preferable to increase the outreach of the column so that the lantern is in line with the others on that side of the road.

Section 3. The third section contains a bend with an important T-junction, L. The radius of curvature of the bend is constant at about 600 ft. A table in the Code of Practice (see Table 31.1), recommends lanterns along the outside of the curve at 80 ft spacing. Lantern 23 opposite the junction has to be an extra lantern because it would not be possible to move a lantern from the outside to the inside of the bend at this point without leaving a dark area on the road. These positions have to be checked using the siting gauge described in the Code. This check is most important where the radius of curvature of the

TABLE 31.1

Spacings for Lanterns on the Outside of Regular Curves

Radius of curvature	Spacing	
	Mounting height 25 or 30 ft	Mounting height 35 or 40 ft
ft	ft	ft
500	70	85
600	80	95
700	85	100
800	90	110
900	95	115
1000	100	120
1200	110	130
1400	120	140
1600	125	150
1800	135	160
2000	140	170
2200	—	180
2400	—	185

bend changes. For example, it was originally intended to locate lantern 29, the first lantern after the bend, at position 29a, but a check with the siting gauge showed that this would be unsatisfactory for vehicles approaching in the direction of the arrow.

No special arrangement will be necessary for the minor T-junction M. Lantern 26 is in the correct position and no lantern is necessary at N because lanterns 24 and 25 will provide the necessary background brightness.

The position of the zebra crossing (P) will have been decided by a number of factors, including the lighting system. It is preferable to position it mid-way between lanterns which are at a slightly decreased spacing. The span chosen must, of course, be one in which the near-side lantern is beyond the crossing.

Lighting for Group B roads. Group B lighting is defined as lighting for residential and unclassified roads carrying only local traffic. The Code of Practice (CP 1004, Part 2: 1956) for Group B lighting is in course of revision.

Lighting for special situations. Codes for special cases such as round-abouts and complex junctions, tunnels, city centres, motorways, and bridges are being prepared. At present many different approaches are being used for lighting these, and some typical solutions are given below.

Tunnel lighting. The main problem in lighting tunnels is concerned not so much with conditions during night-time but during daytime. It is econo-mically impossible for the tunnel lighting to give the same level of brightness as that provided by the outside daylight, and the difference in the two levels presents an adaptation problem to the eye.

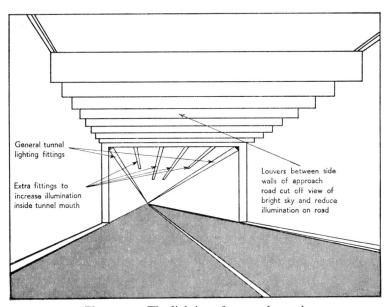

General tunnel
lighting fittings

Extra fittings to
increase illumination
inside tunnel mouth

Louvers between side
walls of approach
road cut off view of
bright sky and reduce
illumination on road

Fig. 31.17   The lighting of a tunnel mouth

As the tunnel is approached, it appears black, owing to the high adaptation level of the eye. This effect can be assuaged by grading the observed brightness so that even at high driving speeds the eye has time to adapt to low levels. There are two stages in the process; reducing the daylight by means of louvers before the entrance to the tunnel; and increasing the brightness level provided by the artificial lighting for a distance inside the mouth (Fig. 31.17).

The problem of providing a means of allowing the eye to adapt gradually also exists at the exit of the tunnel, but it is not so acute because the eye can adapt more quickly from low levels of brightness to high levels, than *vice versa*. Hence, the gradation need only exist for a shorter distance, when the traffic is one way. If it is two way, then both ends must of course be treated as entrances.

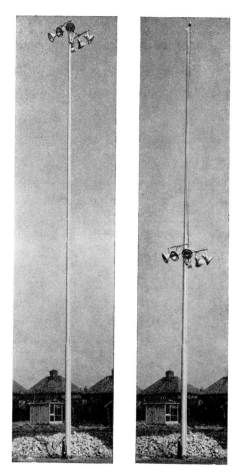

Fig. 31.18   High tower lighting showing the method of lowering for maintenance

Lighting for flyovers, complex junctions and multilevel junctions. If the usual system of lighting roads by means of lanterns spaced at about 150 ft intervals is adopted, these road complexes will appear as a maze of lights and this can mislead the driver in reading the direction of the road. Also, the glare may be excessive when the lanterns are viewed from different levels.

There are two possible ways of overcoming this problem. The complex can be lit from a small number of high towers, the light being directed well away from the driver's line of sight to avoid glare (Fig. 31.18). Alternatively, parapet fittings can be used, but extra care has to be taken to control glare since the fittings will be at the height of the driver's eye. The line of lights should be continuous to eliminate flicker, which can be both annoying and distracting. This system is only effective for narrow carriageways, and is in any case very expensive.

CHAPTER 32

Floodlighting

Floodlighting is the lighting, usually by projection, of the whole of a scene or object to a level considerably greater than that of its surroundings. The term is used by specialists in a number of different contexts, for example in theatre lighting and photographic studios, but to the non-specialist lighting engineer and to the average layman the term implies the lighting of outdoor scenes for spectacle, for advertisement, for sport or for practical utility, as in the lighting of industrial areas.

The floodlighting of buildings was fast growing in popularity in the years prior to 1939 but the equipment used was clumsy and expensive compared with that which is available today. This being the case it is surprising that, in spite of the impetus given to the subject during the festival periods, there has as yet been no great appreciation of the possibilities of floodlighting and no marked increase in the number of floodlit buildings in the country as a whole. Properly engineered schemes of floodlighting can do a great deal to improve the amenities of a town after dark and the cost of equipment and amount of electrical energy required are surprisingly small.

Apart from decorative floodlighting, the use of floodlights for area lighting in industry and for sports is now well established and is fast increasing. Here again the development of new techniques and light sources, in particular the tungsten-halogen lamp, has had a considerable influence on the cost of an installation and on the methods used to achieve the desired results. The use of high towers for the floodlighting of football grounds and railway yards, as compared with the alternative use of a larger number of medium height towers or poles, is a technical problem which is discussed later in this chapter.

The floodlighting of buildings. In designing an installation of flood-lighting for a building, the all-important consideration is the final appearance of the building as a whole as seen by the majority of observers. The object must be to make a picture which will have the right impact on the passer-by.

The subject for floodlighting may be of a purely commercial character or it may be an ancient monument whose beauties it is hoped to reveal by night as well as by day. In either case the type of lighting chosen and the colours, if any, that are used, must be carefully planned to give a designed result. It is seldom that an outstanding effect is achieved by accident.

It is impossible to lay down hard and fast rules which must be followed in order to achieve a satisfying 'picture' but there are certain basic principles which can be applied in the majority of cases and which should be followed unless there is some very good reason to disregard them in a particular instance:

(1) It must be remembered that a picture is made up of contrasts in brightness and in colour and that the areas of shade are just as important as the highlights.

(2) The positions of the floodlights should be chosen to achieve a coherent flow of light (see Fig. 32.1) and the relative position or positions of observers should be established. (It is of interest to note here that if there is a factory building with frontage to a main trunk road, the viewing position is mainly on approaching the building from either direction, because the fast travelling motorist is directly in front of the building for only a short time.)

Fig. 32.1   Canterbury Cathedral, showing the effectiveness of a 'flow of light'

(3) The angle of floodlighting should not be the same as the dominant viewing angle.

(4) The floodlighting should not omit important parts of the building such as the roof line.

(5) A tower or steeple should not be equally illuminated from all directions or it will appear flat and uninteresting.

(6) The fenestration of the building is an important part of its appearance,

and the use of blinds or interior lighting at random is always undesirable.

(7) It is not necessary to achieve even lighting over the building surface
and in fact a gradual fall off of intensity towards the top can increase
the apparent height, if that is the effect required (see Fig. 32.2).

Fig. 32.2 Civic Centre, Plymouth
Architects: Messrs. Jellicoe, Ballantyne & Coleridge
Consulting Engineers: Messrs. Hoare, Lea & Partners

(8) The lighting should not be confined to the frontage only, but the
return ends of the building should have some lighting to ensure a
solid appearance. It is often effective if the lighting of the end of
the building forms a contrast, either in colour or intensity, with that
of the frontage.

(9) The floodlighting equipment should be as inconspicuous as possible
and should not be seen in silhouette against the floodlighted building
or betray its presence by an array of bright patches.

(10) Use should be made of special features, even including nearby trees. These features can be lighted in a contrasting colour or can be used to throw a shadow on to the building (see Fig. 32.3).

Fig. 32.3   Coventry Cathedral
Architect: Sir Basil Spence, R.A., R.D.I., P.P.R.I.B.A.
Lighting Designer: John Reid, A.R.I.B.A.

Illumination values.   Having established the desired appearance of the floodlighted building it is necessary to estimate the amount of light which will be required and the number and type of floodlights which will be needed to give the required result.

The amount of light required will depend on the reflection factor of the building surface and on the 'district' brightness, that is, the amount of other lighting in the immediate vicinity. Table 32.1 gives suggested values of illumination and will serve as a guide, but the function of the building will also have a significant effect on the value to be chosen. A modern commercial building or a new Town Hall might appropriately have much more light than, say, a church or ancient monument.

As has been said already, it is not necessary, or even desirable, that the illumination should be uniform. Accent lighting to emphasise architectural features can be achieved by the use of small floodlights concealed locally to the area to be emphasised, or alternatively these features may be picked out from a distance by means of floodlights having a very narrow beam of high intensity. A low-voltage 150 W lamp with an appropriately designed reflector

can light an area of 5 ft diameter from 100 ft to an intensity of about 50 lm/ft²
(see Fig. 32.4).

Fig. 32.4　Church of Jesus Christ of Latter Day Saints, London, S.W.7
Architects: Messrs. T. P. Bennett & Sons
(Note the lighting of the spire by narrow-angle low-voltage spotlights)

Where colour is used the intensity may be much lower than with white light,
especially if it contrasts with the colour of the district lighting. The important
point to remember is that a small amount of light well directed can produce
far more effective results than a flood of omni-directional lighting of high
intensity.

Colour is nowadays best achieved by the use of coloured fluorescent tubes
or by sodium or mercury discharge lamps, which are all much more effective,
efficient and practicable, than the use of colour filters with incandescent
lamps. Fluorescent floodlights can accommodate one, two or three 5 ft
lamps in a wide range of colours and these are now used for spectacular colour
effects for extensive or limited areas, with dimming included if this is required.

When all the techniques of floodlighting and colour floodlighting with

TABLE 32.1

Recommended Illumination Values for Floodlighting (From Trans. I.E.S. Vol. XV, No. 10, 1950)

Nature of surface	Condition of surface	Reflection factor per cent	Lm/ft² recommended		
			District brightness		
			Low	Medium	High
White glazed brick	Clean	85	1·5	2·5	4·0
	Fairly clean	60	2·0	3·5	6·0
	Fairly dirty	30	4·5	7·5	12·0
Portland stone	Clean	60	2·0	3·5	6·0
	Fairly clean	40	3·5	5·5	9·0
	Fairly dirty	20	6·5	11·0	18·0
Concrete	Clean	45	3·0	5·0	8·0
	Fairly clean	30	4·5	7·5	12·0
	Fairly dirty	15	9·0	15·0	24·0
Middle stone	Clean	40	3·5	5·5	9·0
	Fairly clean	26	5·5	9·0	14·5
	Fairly dirty	13	10·5	17·5	28·0
Dark stone	Clean	30	4·5	7·5	12·0
	Fairly clean	20	6·5	11·0	18·0
	Fairly dirty	10	13·0	22·5	36·0
Yellow brick	Clean	35	4·0	6·5	10·5
	Fairly clean	24	5·5	9·0	14·5
	Fairly dirty	12	10·5	17·5	28·5
Red brick	Clean	25	5·5	9·9	14·5
	Fairly clean	16	8·5	14·0	22·5
	Fairly dirty	8	17·0	28·0	45·0

dimmer control have been integrated with music and the spoken word to form a single production, the result is the form of entertainment now known as *Son et Lumière*. In deciding the visual element the producer has the advantage that the audience is stationary and that all have more or less the same angle of view. Shadow and highlights can be contrived so that they are effective from this particular angle. In the 'Aurama' system (Fig. 32.5) sound is recorded on a tape and to this is added all the necessary lighting cues so that the complete production runs through automatically with split second precision of timing.

Calculating the illumination. The illumination to be expected from the floodlights can be calculated in two ways and it is usual to use both these methods, the first to find the number and wattage of floodlights which will be required and the second to ensure that floodlights of the right distribution are used to give the required evenness of cover. The calculations are firstly a lumen calculation and secondly a candle-power calculation.

Published figures for the floodlight will give the beam flux, the beam angle and the maximum beam candle power and it is necessary to explain these and other terms.

Beam flux is the number of lumens emitted by the floodlight within the limits of the beam angle.

Fig. 32.5   The complete 'Aurama' control equipment for a
Son et Lumière production

Beam spread is the angle subtended at the floodlight by the apparent patch of light on a flat surface at right angles to the axis of the beam (Fig. 32.6). The apparent patch of light is assumed to have a luminance diversity of 10:1.

Note: An asymmetric floodlight will produce an elongated patch of light and it will therefore have two beam angles, vertical and horizontal.

Maximum candle-power.   The maximum intensity, measured in candelas. If this is divided by the square of the distance in ft to the surface, the maximum illumination at that distance is obtained in lm/ft^2.

Maintenance factor.   A factor which is included in lumen calculations to allow for depreciation of the lighting equipment due to dirt and other causes. This factor is normally assumed as 0·8 unless the situation is unusually unfavourable.

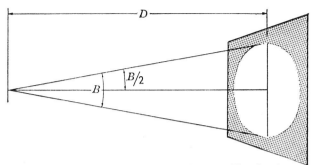

Fig. 32.6 Diagram to illustrate beam angle. The illumination is usually a maximum at the centre of the patch of light. The beam angle is measured from the limits of this apparent patch of light where the illumination has fallen to one-tenth of the maximum value

Waste light factor is a factor which is included in the calculations to allow for the fact that a percentage of the light from the floodlights must necessarily spill beyond the limits of the building or object illuminated. The type of floodlight will be chosen so that there is as little waste light as possible but the amount of waste light will depend on the shape of the area to be lighted (Fig. 32.7). There will be more waste light in the case of a tall chimney than in the floodlighting of a rectangular area such as a building or an advertisement hoarding.

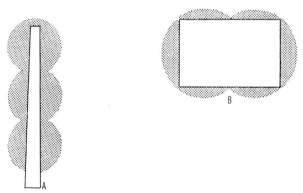

Fig. 32.7 Waste light factor. If the object to be lighted is long and narrow there will be a greater percentage of waste light. The waste light factor is the percentage of the beam lumens which actually reaches the area to be illuminated

Under favourable conditions a waste light factor of 0.9 is assumed. The number of floodlights required will then be as follows:

$$N = \frac{A \times E}{Fb \times W \times M \times P} \qquad (1)$$

where A = area of surface

E = average illumination (lm/ft^2)

Fb = beam flux

W = waste light factor

M = maintenance factor

P = reflection factor of surface.

Candle-power calculation. Having decided, by means of a flux calculation, on the number of floodlights which would be theoretically required to give the desired illumination, it is now necessary to ensure that adequate cover of the area can be provided by this number of floodlights.

The illumination at any point on a surface at right angles to the beam axis is obtained by dividing the candle-power I by the square of the throw distance D

$$E = \frac{I}{D^2} \tag{2}$$

The width of the patch of light produced by the floodlights is a function of distance D and the beam spread B of the floodlight.

$$W = D \times 2 \tan \frac{B}{2} \tag{3}$$

Where the surface to be lighted is not at right angles to the axis of the beam, the illumination will be reduced in proportion to $\cos \theta$, where θ is the angle between the normal to the surface and the axis of the beam. Equation (2) then becomes

$$E = \frac{I}{D^2} \times \cos \theta \tag{4}$$

By use of equations (2) and (3) a floodlight is chosen which will give a patch of light large enough to overlap sufficiently for even coverage and yet not so large that an undue amount of light is wasted beyond the limits of the building or other area to be illuminated.

The patch of light given by a circular floodlight will be a circle when the axis of the beam is normal to the surface illuminated. The circumference of the circle can be taken as a line of constant illumination (an iso-lux curve). When the surface to be illuminated is not normal to the axis of the floodlight beam, the circle becomes geometrically an ellipse. This ellipse no longer represents a line of constant illumination, however, and it is unnecessary and sometimes misleading to calculate its dimensions. The performance of a floodlight when directed obliquely towards a surface should be calculated and plotted by a point by point method such as that described below.

Point-by-point calculations

When the angle θ is not small, that is, when a floodlight is directed obliquely at a surface, the dimensions of the patch of light produced should be calculated by a point-by-point method.

To describe this method we will assume that a floodlight is mounted on a pole of height h above the ground and that the axis of its beam is directed towards a point P on the ground at a distance D from the foot of the pole.

The illumination (E_h) on a horizontal surface at the point P is given by the equation

$$E_h = \frac{I \times \cos^3 \theta}{h^2}$$

The illumination (E_n) at the point P on a plane normal to the floodlight is given by

$$E_n = \frac{I \times \cos^2 \theta}{h^2}$$

The candle-power I in the direction of the point P is obtained from distribution curves for the floodlight.

The point P is often referred to as the 'target point' and it is possible to calculate the illumination at other positions near this target point if the angular displacements of these points are known and the appropriate candle power can be read from the distribution diagrams.

In the case of symmetrical floodlights a complete plot of points can be made in this way but it is usually sufficient to calculate the illumination at a number of selected positions on a line from the base of the pole which continues beyond the target point P and also on a line at right angles also passing through P.

If the floodlight has an asymmetric beam, as in the case of the tungsten halogen floodlight using a linear source, the distribution diagram available usually gives the candelas in two planes and in this case it is not possible to calculate illumination except at positions on the two lines described above.

Fig. 32.8 is an example of a work sheet on which the results of such calculations can be entered. If a number of such diagrams are completed for a particular floodlight and for particular values of h and D, a very useful library of information can be obtained.

The worksheet is used as follows:

(1) Enter the information as to floodlight type, wattage, mounting height, target distance and target elevation angle.
(2) Enter the target elevation angle and target distance in the appropriate boxes immediately below the target point on the plan.
(3) To the left of these boxes enter distances and elevation angles which divide the distance D into, say, eight equal parts.
(4) Enter distances and elevation angles to the right, beyond the target point, as required.
(5) Enter the intensity I in the appropriate boxes.
(6) Calculate the horizontal intensity (E_h) or the normal intensity (E_n) as required from the formulae already given.
(7) On the vertical lines above the boxes, distances may now be marked off

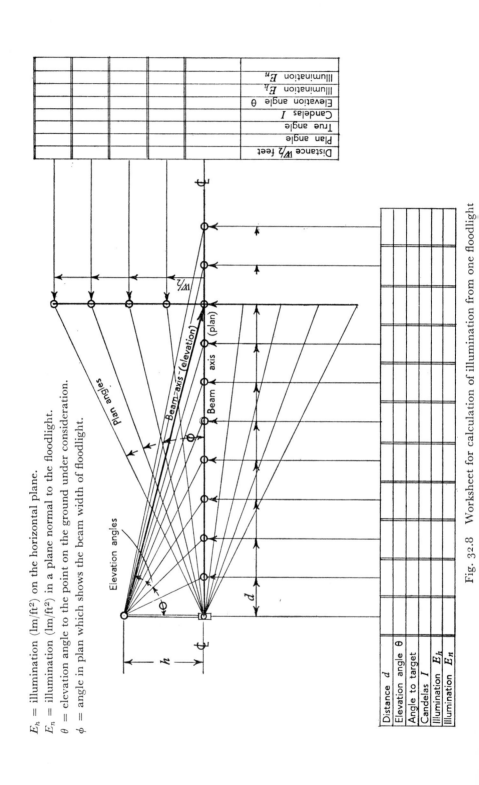

E_h = illumination (lm/ft²) on the horizontal plane.

E_n = illumination (lm/ft²) in a plane normal to the floodlight.

θ = elevation angle to the point on the ground under consideration.

ϕ = angle in plan which shows the beam width of floodlight.

Fig. 32.8 Worksheet for calculation of illumination from one floodlight

representing to scale the illumination values. A smooth curve drawn through these points will give a graphical representation of the variation of illumination.

(*Note:* It will be found in most cases that the maximum illumination is at a point nearer the floodlight than the target point *P*.)

(8) The boxes at the right of the diagram provide, step by step, the information required to calculate the illumination levels at plan positions to one side of the target point (the other side is assumed to be similar). To find the intensity in each direction it is necessary to know the 'true angle' or angle subtended *at the floodlight* by two points on the ground (one of which is the target point). The intensity can then be read from a distribution diagram of the floodlight.

It should be noted that the elevation angle *increases* with increasing angles in plan from the target point and that the true angle is always *smaller* than the plan angle.

(9) Finally, a curve showing the variation of illumination across the beam can be drawn as before, using the lines above the boxes, and setting off on them the illumination values to the same scale as before.

(10) It should be pointed out that this worksheet, when completed, shows the illumination provided by *one* floodlight. Results to be obtained from a group of floodlights must be obtained by summation, the spacing and orientation of the floodlights being so arranged as to achieve the degree of uniformity required.

The work involved in completing the worksheet can be reduced by the use of the graphical method of evaluating angles which is described below. Alternatively, special slide rules are available, and these are valuable when calculations are being made regularly.

Some mention should be made of the introduction of values of normal illumination in addition to horizontal illumination. Horizontal illumination readings at a distance from the floodlight are difficult to measure with accuracy and it is often useful to be able to read the normal illumination as an alternative. Further, visibility is dependent as much on normal, or vertical, illumination as on the horizontal illumination which is frequently specified.

Graphical angle calculation. Floodlight calculations frequently involve the necessity for evaluating angles and slope distances, and the following graphical method may be found useful.

The principle of the graphical method is illustrated in Fig. 32.9. A lighting fitting L is mounted above the horizontal surface ABCD, and it is required to find the angles involved in calculating the illumination at any point X on this surface. The angle in azimuth relative to AB, ABX, is given directly from the angle scale on ABCD. The angle of elevation of XL, XLB, is found by drawing an arc with centre B and radius XB to meet AB at Y, and drawing a vertical line to Z equal in length to the mounting height LB. Because LB is equal to ZY and BX to BY the angle YZB is equal to XLB and may be read from the angle scale on ARSB.

18+

These angles in azimuth and elevation are respectively the angles of longitude and latitude defining the direction LX on an isocandela diagram for the
fitting drawn with the axis of symmetry of the light distribution vertical. The
intensity in direction LX can then be found and the illumination at X
calculated.

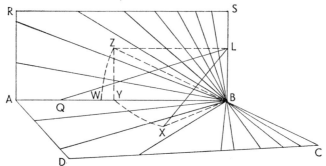

Fig. 32.9   Principle of graphical angle calculation

If the axis of symmetry of the light distribution for the fitting is not directed
vertically towards B but to some other point Q along BA, as would be the
case with a floodlight mounted at L and directed towards Q, then the angle
needed to find the intensity directed towards X is the true angle QLX and
the procedure for finding it is given later.

The actual diagram used in practice is shown in Fig. 32.10 derived by
folding outwards plane ARSB of Fig. 32.9 so that it lies in the same plane as
ABCD. Scales for mounting height and plan distance are then added and the
diagram used as follows.

A plan of the area to be lighted is drawn and the fitting positions marked
on it. A diagram similar to Fig. 32.10 is drawn to the same scale on tracing
paper and placed over the plan with the point B on one of the fitting positions.
The line BA is placed on the line from the fitting position to the aiming point
of the fitting. Taking the left-hand half of the diagram, the angle in azimuth
on the horizontal plane between the aiming point and the point for which the
calculation is to be made can be interpolated, e.g. at point X it is 26°. The
angle of elevation for point X is determined as described for Fig. 32.9 and is
66°.

A little consideration will show that on this diagram other angles and distances are easily found by drawing appropriate triangles or transferring
lengths by means of arcs of circles on to the distance scale. For example, LX,
the slope distance of the fitting to the point, is found by drawing an arc centre
B, radius BZ to meet the distance scale along BA and reading off the required
length at W. In the example illustrated it is 360 ft. Similarly the slope distance
to the aiming point Q can be found by drawing an arc from R to meet the
distance scale BA at S, where RQ is equal to LB, the mounting height of the
fitting.

From the light distribution data of a symmetrical floodlight, the intensity in the direction X when the axis of the beam is directed towards Q can be obtained if the true angle QLX is known. This angle is found as follows:

Continue the arc ZW to a point V such that the distance SV = QX on the plan. The angle SBV (in this case 25°) is the angle QLX we require and can be read on the angle scale. This is so because BS equals the slope distance

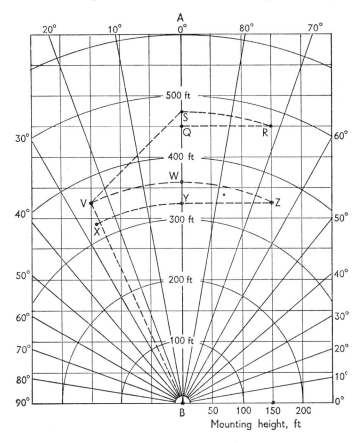

Fig. 32.10   Graphical angle calculation

LQ, BV equals the slope distance LX, and SV, the third side of the triangle, is equal to the true distance QX.

Along the axis line AB the angle QLY or any other similar angle can be obtained more simply by reading on the upper angle scale the angles represented by R and Z and subtracting (since RBZ = QLY). In this case the angle QLY = 72° − 66° = 6°.

On the diagram the line BA is taken as a horizontal reference line. If the area to be lighted is not level the effective mounting height of the fitting will vary for different points on the ground and due allowance can be made on the diagram.

Floodlights at close offset. Where floodlights are to be fixed close to the base of the building to be lighted, it is necessary to use a floodlight with a wide distribution horizontally and a narrow beam vertically. The tungsten-halogen floodlight with its linear lamp is ideal for this purpose and such lamps can be spaced at distances equal to four or five times their offset distance from the building. If they can be placed between the windows at ground-floor level the spacing ratio may be even greater, as an even illumination will be obtained by the time the first floor is reached.

The illustration in Fig. 32.11 shows the effect of tungsten-halogen floodlights mounted very close to the surface illuminated. On the frontage at the right of the picture the floodlights are situated behind the fascia reading 'Midland Bank Ltd.' where the total offset from the building is less than 2 ft. Considerably more offset distance was available on the elevation of the building at the left of the picture but the floodlights were deliberately trained to avoid even lighting from the bottom to the top of the building.

Area floodlighting. In the lighting of areas both for industry and sport there has been a tendency in the past few years to use high towers, especially for railway yard lighting and for first-class football grounds, and it will be

Fig. 32.11　Midland Bank Ltd., Overseas Branch. An example of floodlighting from a close off-set

interesting to discuss the advantages and disadvantages as compared with towers or poles of medium height.

Railway yards sometimes cover very large areas of perhaps 2,000,000 ft^2 and the amount of light required to enable staff to deal safely with shunting and other operations is normally accepted as about 0·5 lm/ft^2.

It is undesirable to install a large number of poles carrying single low-wattage lanterns because they would form a serious and perhaps dangerous obstruction. Shunting yards of this size have been illuminated by towers approximately 150 ft high, of which there are 8 or 10 according to the layout of the yard. Approximately 200 floodlights, each of 1500 W are needed to illuminate such an area to an average level of 0·5 lm/ft^2.

The towers are spaced at distances of up to about 1000 ft and the beams of light are trained along the tracks in both directions. The system gives reasonable visibility but it must be admitted that there is a good deal of glare from the batteries of floodlights. An alternative method is now being considered, using towers of medium height of about 55 ft each carrying two tungsten-halogen floodlights of 1500 W rating.

Each two-light tower can light an area of about 55,000 ft^2 to an average illumination of 0·5 lm/ft^2, and using the same ratio of spacing to mounting height they can be spaced at a maximum distance of 350 ft apart. With this maximum spacing of 350 ft along the track, then the required spacing across the track is:

$$\frac{55,000}{350} = 157 \text{ ft}$$

The total number of poles required for 2,000,000 ft^2 is therefore 36 at 55 ft (as against 8 at 150 ft) and the total wattage is about 108 kW compared with 300 kW for the high tower scheme. The following table makes the comparison more clear and assumes a total area of 2,000,000 ft^2 and an average illumination of 0·5 lm/ft^2.

TABLE 32.2

	No. of towers	Height (ft)	Max. spacing (ft)	S/H ratio	No. of floods	Cross spacing	Area per tower (sq. ft)
High towers 150 ft.	8	150	1000	6·5	200	250	250,000
Medium towers 55 ft.	36	55	350	6·5	72	157	55,000

Football grounds. For first class grounds the system using four towers (Figs. 32.12 and 32.13) has now become accepted practice. This system gives minimum glare to spectators and also to the players, because there is no glare source within the area bounded by the two goal lines. For instance, a corner kick or throw-in can be taken without fear of a player being dazzled as the ball passes between him and the lights. The only disadvantage of the system is the high first cost.

Fig. 32.12   One of the four flood-lighting towers at Portsmouth Football Ground

Fig. 32.13   A four-tower floodlighting system in use at Portsmouth

Side-lighting systems of lower cost are becoming popular for the smaller grounds, the most usual system employing towers of 40 ft to 55 ft arranged on both sides of the ground, each carrying a number of floodlights with line filament lamps (Fig. 32.14). A number of these installations use tungsten-halogen 1500 W floodlights with a total of 6, or sometimes 8, floodlights on each tower. The quality of light is good, in that the distribution of light is sufficient to carry across the field and ensures that distant play can be seen clearly from any position on the ground. This was not so with early side-lighting installations where the floodlights illuminated mainly the near side of the field, and players in the distance were seen only in silhouette.

Fig. 32.14   Enfield Football Ground, showing the four lightweight towers on one side of the pitch

Building sites.   The provision of safety and working light for building sites is another application of floodlighting which needs special consideration. The equipment must be robust in order to withstand the risk of damage inseparable from the conditions of use, and must also be easily portable. Conventional floodlights are rather too bulky to be ideal for the purpose. Tungsten-halogen floodlights are small for the amount of light produced and, in the case of building sites, have the added advantage that the support socket is made to fit the standard scaffold tubing used so universally. The recommended level of illumination for loading and unloading, transport by crane or other means, or for areas where work of any kind is carried on, is 1 lm/ft². Floodlights should be mounted as high as practicable and a convenient structure such as a crane tower or scaffold can frequently be used. It should be noted that there are always a large number of obstructions at a building site and if unwanted and dangerous areas of shadow are to be avoided there should be multi-directional lighting wherever possible.

It is required that the voltage used on building sites should be limited for safety reasons to 120 V, and tungsten-halogen lamps for this voltage are made in both 500 W and 1000 W ratings especially for the building trade.

Security floodlighting.   A specialised use of floodlights which is, perhaps unfortunately, becoming more important in the modern world is known as security floodlighting.

Basically such lighting is arranged to cause as much glare as possible to persons approaching the prohibited area. The defenders behind the lights can then see without being seen. There is usually an 8 ft wire mesh fence all round the area and asymmetric floodlights are mounted about 8 ft above the ground and some distance inside the fence. It is important that the fence itself should have a black finish to prevent too much light being reflected from it towards the defenders. It is not very satisfactory to mount the fittings on the fence itself because this means that there will be comparatively dark areas at mid-span between the lights, unless the spacing between them is kept unduly small.

APPENDIX 1. LAMP CHARACTERISTICS

1. General Lighting Service, Incandescent Filament Lamps

Rating Watts	Cap	Class	Bulb finish	Dimensions Overall length mm	Bulb diam. mm	Neck diam. mm	Light centre length mm	Nominal initial lumens at 240 V	Lighting design lumens	Lamp cap temp. rise max. av. degrees C
40	B22/25 x 26	Coiled-coil	Internally frosted	As single coil see below				410	390	As single coil
60								700	665	
100								1330	1260	
25		Single coil		105	60	33	75	219	200	—
40				105	60	33	75	340	325	125
60				105	60	33	75	610	575	125
100				{105 125}	68	37	{75 90}	1230	1160	135
150				160	80	39	120	2060	1960	135
200	E27/27		Clear	161·5	80	39	121·5	2880	2720	130
300				233	110	50	178	4550	4300	130
500				233	110	50	178	8200	7700	—
750	E40/45			300	150	55	225	13,100	12,400	—
1000				300	150	55	225	18,400	17,300	
1500				335	170	60	250	29,300	27,500	—

Minimum average life—1000 hours   Fittings free space—Refer BS 161

18*

2. *High-Pressure Mercury (Colour-Corrected) Discharge Lamps*

Rating Watts	Cap	Dimensions		Lighting design lumens	Lamp operating voltage	Lamp operating current amps	Starting current amps
		Overall length mm	Bulb diam. mm				
80	B22/25 × 26 3 pin	148	70	2720	105/135	0·8	1·5-1·0
125	B22/25 × 26 3 pin	168	75	4900	110/140	1·15	2·0-1·5
250	E40/45	220	90	11,000	115/145	2·15	4·0-3·0
400	E40/45	280	120	19,200	120/150	3·25	7·0-5·0
700	E40/45	320	140	34,500	125/155	5·6	10·0-7·0
1000	E40/45	400	165	49,000	130/160	7·5	15·0-8·0

Quoted life—5000 hours   Fitting free space—Refer BS 3677   Control gear—Refer BS 3707

3. *Tubular Fluorescent Discharge Lamps—General Characteristics*

Nominal rating	Cap	Nominal dimensions		Starting voltage at 25 °C volts	Operating voltage at 25 °C volts	Operating current at 25 °C amps	Average life
watts		Overall length inches	Bulb diam. inches				hours
20 T.8	G13 (medium bi-pin)	24	1½	170	57	0·37	5000
30 T.8		36	1	210	96	0·36	5000
30 T.12		36	1½	205	81	0·405	5000
40		48	1½	205	103	0·43	7500
65		60	1½	220	110	0·67	7500
80		60	1½	220	99	0·87	7500
125		96	1½	330	149	0·94	7500
4	G5 (miniature bi-pin)	6	5/8	—	32	0·135	5000
6		9	5/8	—	46·5	0·147	5000
8		12	5/8	—	56	0·170	5000
13		21	5/8	—	95	0·167	5000
15 T.8	G13 (medium bi-pin)	18	1	90	47/65	0·31	5000
15 T.12		18	1½	90	38/55	0·36	5000
40 2ft		24	1½	95	40/54	0·88	5000
50		60	1	210	150/180	0·40	5000
85		96	1½	320	163/193	0·55	5000
		Maximum circle diameter					
22 ⎫ Circular	4 pin	8·50		95	55/69	0·40	5000
32 ⎬		12·25		145	72/92	0·45	5000
40 ⎭		16·25		180	100/120	0·42	5000

Method of start — — Starterless

Low-temperature operation — — Dependent on circuitry, operation is generally satisfactory down to 0 °C for switch-start and +5 °C for the starterless condition.

Colour specification — — Refer BS 1853

Control gear — — Refer BS 2818, Part I

4. *Tubular Fluorescent Discharge Lamps—Colour Designation and Lumens*

Nominal rating (watts)	White		Warm White		Daylight		Natural		Colour-matching or Northlight	
	Initial 100 hours	Lighting design	Initial 100 hours	Lighting design	Initial 100 hours	Lighting design	Initial 100 hours	Lighting design	Initial 100 hours	Lighting design
20	1150	1050	1150	1050	1100	1000	850	750	750	650
30 T.8	2000	1750	2000	1750	1950	1700	1600	1400	1300	1100
30 T.12	1900	1650	1900	1650	1800	1600	1500	1300	1200	1000
40	2800	2600	2800	2600	2700	2500	2200	2000	1800	1600
65	4900	4500	4800	4400	4600	4200	3600	3100	2950	2600
80	5400	4900	5300	4800	5100	4600	4100	3500	3300	2800
125	9000	8400	8800	8200	8500	7900	6800	6200	5500	5000
4	160	135	160	135	150	125	120	100	—	—
6	290	240	290	240	275	230	230	190	—	—
8	425	360	425	360	400	340	325	270	—	—
13	750	650	750	650	—	—	590	500	—	—
15 T.8	750	625	750	625	700	600	575	500	500	400
15 T.12	750	650	750	650	700	625	575	525	500	425
40 2ft	1800	1500	1800	1500	1700	1400	1400	1150	1200	950
50	3500	3100	3500	3100	—	—	2700	2300	—	—
85	7100	6600	6900	6400	6600	6000	5400	4800	4400	3800
22 Circular	—	—	1050	850	1100	980	—	—	750	650
32 Circular	—	—	1800	1500	1850	1645	—	—	1300	1130
40 Circular	—	—	2520	2150	2520	2310	—	—	1750	1555

5. *Low-Pressure Sodium Discharge Lamps*

Rating	Type	Cap	Dimension (max.)		Type of start	Lighting design lumens	Starting voltage	Starting current	Operating current	Operating voltage
			Overall length mm	Bulb diam. mm			volts	amps	amps	volts
watts										
40	SOX	BY.22.d.	311	53	Starterless	4200	400	Less than operating current	0·6	75
60	,,	,,	424	53	,,	7050	400		0·6	115
100	,,	,,	525	67	,,	11,900	410		0·9	125
150	,,	,,	775	67	,,	20,000	600		0·9	185
200	,,	,,	1120	67	,,	28,500	600		0·9	265
60	SLI	G.13	419	39·5	Switch	5700	200	1·3	0·8	82
200	,,	,,	902	39·5	Switch	20,000	290	2·0	1·6	140
200	,,	,,	902	39·5	Switch and starterless	25,000	410	1·6	1·6	145

Average life—6000 hours   Operating position—Horizontal ±20°   Control gear—Refer BS 3768

APPENDIX 2. CONVERSION TABLES

1. *Multiplication Factors for the Mutual Conversion of Units of Illumination*

Unit to be converted		Lumens per square foot	Lux	Phots	Milliphots
1 lumen per square foot (formerly foot-candle)	=	1	$1\cdot076 \times 10$	$1\cdot076 \times 10^{-3}$	$1\cdot076$
1 lux (or 1 lumen per square metre)	=	$9\cdot29 \times 10^{-2}$	1	10^{-4}	10^{-1}
1 phot (or 1 lumen per square cm)	=	$9\cdot29 \times 10^{2}$	10^{4}	1	10^{3}
1 milliphot (or 10^{-3} lumens per square cm)	=	$9\cdot29 \times 10^{-1}$	10	10^{-3}	1

2. *Multiplication Factors for the Mutual Conversion of Units of Luminance*

Units to be converted		Foot-lamberts	Lamberts	Millilamberts	Apostilbs	Candelas per square inch	Candelas per square foot	Nits	Stilbs
1 foot-lambert	=	1	$1\cdot076 \times 10^{-3}$	$1\cdot076$	$1\cdot076 \times 10$	$2\cdot21 \times 10^{-3}$	$3\cdot18 \times 10^{-1}$	$3\cdot42$	$3\cdot42 \times 10^{-4}$
1 lambert	=	$9\cdot29 \times 10^{2}$	1	10^{3}	10^{4}	$2\cdot05$	$2\cdot96 \times 10^{2}$	$3\cdot18 \times 10^{3}$	$3\cdot18 \times 10^{-1}$
1 millilambert	=	$9\cdot29 \times 10^{-1}$	10^{-3}	1	10	$2\cdot05 \times 10^{-3}$	$2\cdot96 \times 10^{-1}$	$3\cdot18$	$3\cdot18 \times 10^{-4}$
1 apostilb	=	$9\cdot29 \times 10^{-2}$	10^{-4}	10^{-1}	1	$2\cdot05 \times 10^{-4}$	$2\cdot96 \times 10^{-2}$	$3\cdot18 \times 10^{-1}$	$3\cdot18 \times 10^{-5}$
1 candela per square inch	=	$4\cdot52 \times 10^{2}$	$4\cdot87 \times 10^{-1}$	$4\cdot87 \times 10^{2}$	$4\cdot87 \times 10^{3}$	1	$1\cdot44 \times 10^{2}$	$1\cdot55 \times 10^{3}$	$1\cdot55 \times 10^{-1}$
1 candela per square foot	=	$3\cdot14$	$3\cdot38 \times 10^{-3}$	$3\cdot38$	$3\cdot38 \times 10$	$6\cdot94 \times 10^{-3}$	1	$1\cdot076 \times 10$	$1\cdot076 \times 10^{-3}$
1 nit (or 1 candela per square metre)	=	$2\cdot92 \times 10^{-1}$	$3\cdot14 \times 10^{-4}$	$3\cdot14 \times 10^{-1}$	$3\cdot14$	$5\cdot45 \times 10^{-4}$	$9\cdot29 \times 10^{-2}$	1	10^{-4}
1 stilb (or 10^{4} candelas per square metre)	=	$2\cdot92 \times 10^{3}$	$3\cdot14$	$3\cdot14 \times 10^{3}$	$3\cdot14 \times 10^{4}$	$6\cdot45$	$9\cdot29 \times 10^{2}$	10^{4}	1

Glossary

ABSORPTION FACTOR—The ratio of the luminous flux absorbed by a body to the flux it receives.

ACCOMMODATION—The (generally) spontaneous adjustment of the eye made for the purpose of looking at an object situated at a given distance.

ANODE—The positive electrode in a discharge tube. An anode collects electrons from the ionised gas.

ADAPTATION—1. The process taking place when the eye becomes accustomed to the luminance or the colour of the field of view.

2. The final state of the process. In particular the terms light adaptation and dark adaptation are used, according to whether the luminance is of the order of at least several cd/m² or less than some hundredths of a cd/m².

BALLAST—Equipment used with discharge lamps for starting and stabilising the discharge. *Note:* A stabiliser may be resistive, inductive or capacitive or a combination of these.

BLACK BODY—*See* FULL RADIATOR.

BLIND SPOT—The area of the retina at which the fibres of the optic nerve leave the eye; it contains no light-receptors and the nerve fibres themselves are insensitive to light.

BRIGHTNESS—A term commonly used colloquially to mean either luminance or luminosity, but used technically for the latter only.

CANDELA—The unit of luminous intensity. The magnitude of the candela is such that the luminance of a full radiator at the temperature of solidification of platinum is 60 cd/cm².

CATHODE—A negative electrode in a discharge tube. A cathode receives positive ions from the ionised gas and emits electrons.

CATHODE FALL (of potential)—That part of the arc voltage of a discharge lamp which is associated with the cathode and through which positive ions are accelerated, thereby acquiring sufficient energy to eject electrons.

CHOKE—A circuit element consisting largely of inductance.

CHROMATICITY—The colour quality of a light definable by its chromaticity co-ordinates, or by its dominant (or complementary) wavelength and its purity taken together.

CILIARY MUSCLE—A ring of muscular tissue attached to the inside of the eye-ball and—by means of suspensory ligaments—to the membraneous capsule containing the lens of the eye. It is constantly at work changing or maintaining the focus of the eye.

COLOUR RENDERING—The effect which the spectral characteristics of a light have on the appearance of coloured objects illuminated by it. Colour rendering may be represented with the aid of the spectral distribution of energy or luminous flux in the C.I.E. spectral bands.

COLOUR TEMPERATURE—The absolute temperature of the full radiator for which the ordinates of the spectral distribution curve of emission are proportional (or approximately so), in the visible region, to those of the distribution curve of the radiation considered, so that both radiations have the same chromaticity.

By extension, in certain countries, the colour temperature defines the temperature of the full radiator which appears to the colorimetric standard observer to have closely the same colour appearance as certain selective radiators, e.g. discharge and fluorescent lamps.

CONE—Special retinal receptor elements, or their cone-shaped light-sensitive extremities, which are primarily concerned with perception of light and colour by the light-adapted eye (i.e. for photopic vision).

CONTRAST—The subjective assessment of the difference in appearance of two parts of a field of view seen simultaneously or successively. (Hence: luminosity contrast, lightness contrast, colour contrast, simultaneous contrast, successive contrast.)

CONTROL GEAR—A term used for all the electrical equipment in a lighting fitting required to start and operate the lamp. This may include ballast, capacitors and starting device.

CONVERGENCE—Adjustment of the visual axes (by means of the extra-ocular muscles) in binocular vision so that they are directed to a common point of regard.

CORNEA—The transparent 'window' of the eye that admits and refracts the incident light.

DAYLIGHT FACTOR—The daylight factor is a measure of the daylight illumination at a point on a given plane expressed as a ratio of the illumination on the given plane at that point and the simultaneous exterior illumination on a horizontal plane from the whole of an unobstructed sky of assumed or known luminance distribution. Direct sunlight is excluded from both interior and exterior values of illumination.

DIFFUSE REFLECTION—Diffusion by reflection in which, on the macroscopic scale, there is no direct reflection, i.e. whatever the angle of the incident ray a diffusely reflecting surface will appear equally bright when viewed from any angle.

DIFFUSER—A device used to alter the spatial distribution of the luminous flux from a source and depending essentially on the phenomenon of diffusion.

DIPLOPIA—Double vision: it occurs if the visual axes of the two eyes do not converge to a common point of regard, as may happen in fatigue.

DIRECT LIGHTING—A system of lighting in which most of the luminous flux is emitted from the light sources directly towards the principal area to be lighted, e.g. the 'working area'.

DIRECTIONAL INTENSITY RATIO—The ratio of the maximum luminous intensity from a street lighting lantern to the average emitted below the horizontal. The average intensity in the lower hemisphere is equal to

$$\frac{\text{Total flux in lower hemisphere}}{2\pi}$$

Nowadays the abbreviation 'intensity ratio' is often used.

DIRECTIONAL LIGHTING—Lighting designed to illuminate the working plane, or an object, predominantly from a preferred direction.

DISCHARGE LAMP—A lamp which depends on an electric discharge through a gas or a metal vapour or a mixture of several gases or vapours.

EFFICACY—The effectiveness with which radiant power produces a specific function, e.g. luminous efficacy, erythemal efficacy.

ELECTROLUMINESCENCE—Light production in a phosphor by the direct conversion of electrical power.

FIXATION REFLEX—The physiological mechanism whereby the gaze involuntarily tends to be directed to particularly bright, or moving, objects in the general field of view.

FLUORESCENCE—Luminescence that persists for less than about 10^{-8} seconds after excitation.

FOCUS—The position of the light source in a lighting fitting or lighting device which gives the normal correct distribution of luminous flux. When light from a projector is concentrated at a point, this point is sometimes referred to as the secondary focus.

FOOT-LAMBERT (ft-L)—A unit of luminance; the luminance of a uniform diffuser emitting a luminous flux of one lumen per square foot.

FOVEA—A slightly indented area of the retina to which the line of sight is directed. Although extremely small (about one thousandth of an inch in diameter) it contains a large number of cone receptors and gives the most acute vision. It corresponds to a region of the external field $1°$ to $2°$ in diameter.

FULL RADIATOR—The thermal radiator which has the maximum spectral concentration of radiant emittance at a given temperature. A theoretical example is a perfectly black body, so called because it absorbs all radiation falling upon it.

GENERAL LIGHTING—Lighting designed to illuminate an area without provision for special local requirements.

GLARE—Excessive luminance—usually localised—having regard to the prevailing state of adaptation of the eyes; it may be direct or due to reflections; exposure to it excites some degree of dissatisfaction and/or loss of visual sensitivity.

GLOW DISCHARGE—A self-maintained discharge characterised by a secondary emission from the cathode which is much greater than the thermionic emission, by a considerable voltage drop and by low current density at the cathode.

HETEROPHORIA—A term used to denote a tendency to imperfect team-work by the various muscles which move the two eyes so as to maintain binocular single vision.

ILLUMINATION—The quotient of the flux incident on an element of surface by the area of that element. Units of illumination are given in Appendix 2, Table 1.

INCANDESCENCE—The self-emission of radiant power in the visible spectrum due to the thermal excitation of atoms or molecules.

ION—An atom having an unbalanced set of electric charges. Positive ions are atoms with one or more electrons missing, and hence carry an uncompensated positive charge on the nucleus. Negative ions are atoms with extra electrons.

IONISATION—The production of positive or negative ions.

INDIRECT LIGHTING—A system of lighting in which most of the luminous flux is emitted by the light sources away from the principal area to be lighted so that this area is illuminated almost entirely by reflected light.

INERT GAS—A gas with no chemical reactivity. Five such gases are available; in order of increasing density they are: helium, neon, argon, krypton and xenon.

INFRARED RADIATION—The invisible radiation beyond the red end of the spectrum, involving wavelengths between about 780 nm and 105 nm. It is divided, for convenience, into:

> IRA, near infrared, 780 nm to 1400 nm
> IRB, medium infrared, 1400 nm to 3000 nm
> IRC, long wavelength, > 3000 nm

IRIS—The coloured, contractile, and centrally perforated disc in front of the eye lens. It controls the aperture of the eye's optical system.

IRRADIANCE—The radiant power incident on unit area of a surface.

LENS—Of the eye. A bi-convex, normally clear, 'elastic' refracting body which, subject to muscular control, can change its curvature—and therefore its power—so as to focus the eye for seeing sharply at different distances.

LIGHT-OUTPUT RATIO OF A FITTING—The ratio of the total flux emitted from the fitting to that emitted by the light source alone operating in free air. It is usually expressed as a percentage.

LIGHTING DESIGN LUMENS—The value of light flux from a lamp recommended for lighting calculations. It is closely the average-through-life value, but for long life lamps is measured at 2000 hours.

LOCAL LIGHTING—Lighting designed to increase the illumination at certain specified positions; for instance, those at which work is carried on.

LUMEN—The luminous flux emitted within unit solid angle (one steradian) by a point source having a uniform intensity of one candela.

LUMINANCE—Objective or photometric brightness: the luminous intensity per unit area of any surface from any particular direction. Units of luminance are given in Appendix 2, Table 2.

LUMINESCENCE—The process whereby radiation is emitted for certain wavebands in excess of that which would be expected from a full radiator at the temperature of the emitter. Particular aspects of luminescence are referred to as fluorescence and phosphorescence.

LUMINOSITY—The technical term for the sensation of brightness, i.e. the attribute of visual sensation according to which an area appears to emit more or less light.

LUMINOUS EFFICACY OF A LIGHT SOURCE—The quotient of the total luminous flux emitted by the total power consumed. For an electric lamp it is expressed in lumens per watt and its theoretical maximum value is 680 lm/W.

LUMINOUS FLUX—The rate of flow of radiant energy according to its capacity to produce visual sensation. The unit of luminous flux is the lumen.

LUMINOUS INTENSITY—The degree of concentration of luminous flux emanating in a cone from a point source of light. The conception of intensity can be applied to surface sources since they can be regarded as being made up of an infinite number of point sources. It is measured in flux per unit solid angle, the unit being the candela (cd).

MAINTENANCE FACTOR—CLEANING—The ratio of the illumination provided by an installation in the average condition of dirtiness expected in service, to the illumination from the same installation when clean.

MIXED REFLECTIONS—The simultaneous occurrence of specular and diffuse reflection.

MULTILAYER INTERFERENCE REFLECTORS OR FILTERS (DICHROIC)—Efficient colour reflectors or filters produced by the vacuum deposition of many very thin layers of two or more materials of different refractive indices. Required bands in the ultraviolet, visible or infrared regions can be reflected, other bands being transmitted or vice versa.

NANOMETRE—A unit of length employed in specifying the wavelength of light. It is equal to 10^{-9} metres.

OPALESCENT—A material is said to be opalescent if it diffuses light to such an extent that the material itself becomes effectively the source of light, e.g. an opal glass.

OPAQUE—A material is said to be opaque if it does not transmit light.

PERFECT DIFFUSER—A surface which reflects diffusely all incident light and whose luminance is the same in all directions. The luminance of such a surface in foot-lamberts is numerically equal to its illumination in lumens per square foot.

PANORAMA—The view all round; the general or total visual field; the visible environment.

PARAFOVEA—The part of the retina surrounding the fovea, i.e. concentric with the small area of acuity.

PHOTO-ELECTRIC EMISSION—The emission of electrons from a surface under the influence of light, ultraviolet or infrared radiation.

PHOSPHOR—A solid material that exhibits the property of luminescence. Phosphors used in lamps are hard crystalline substances, processed in high temperature furnaces.

PHOTOPIC VISION—Vision almost entirely by cones, in daylight and artificial lighting at a level of luminance above about 1 cd/m^2. Vision normally characterised by the ability to appreciate colours.

PREFOCUS—Usually applied to a specific type of projector lamp base which is fixed to the lamp in an exact spatial relationship to the filament, therefore obviating the necessity for lampholder adjustment when replacing a lamp.

PRESBYOPIA—A term generally applied to the state of the eyes when the power of accommodation has diminished so far with age that the shortest distance at which objects can be focused sharply is inconveniently long.

PURKINJE EFFECT—The displacement of the spectral sensitivity of the light-adapted eye towards the blue end of the spectrum during the transition from light adaptation to dark adaptation.

QUANTUM—The unit of energy involved in absorption or emission of radiation (ultraviolet, visible or infrared). Its value is proportional to the frequency of the radiation in question.

QUICK-START TRANSFORMER—A starting device for enabling a fluorescent lamp to start within one or two seconds by providing quick cathode preheating.

RADIO INTERFERENCE SUPPRESSOR—A small capacitor, usually 0·006 μF, connected across opposite ends of a fluorescent lamp to reduce radio interference.

REFLECTION FACTOR—The ratio of the reflected luminous flux to the incident luminous flux. It is usually expressed as a percentage.

RETINA—An outgrowth of the brain forming a thin lining to the hind part of the eyeball and containing the light-sensitive rods and cones which are the peripheral end organs of the optic nerve.

ROD—Special retinal receptor elements or their rod-shaped light-sensitive extremities which are primarily concerned with perception of light by the dark-adapted eye, i.e. for scotopic vision. The rods probably play no part in colour discrimination.

SCOTOPIC VISION—Vision when the eyes are adapted to very dim light; nocturnal vision. Its sensory organs are the rods; it is achromatic and of low-contrast sensitivity; the sense of focus is poor.

SERIES CAPACITOR—A capacitor placed in series with an inductance to form part of the ballast for a lamp.

SHUNT CAPACITOR—A capacitor placed across the supply mains to improve the power factor of inductively ballasted lamp circuits.

SKY FACTOR (at a given point inside a building)—The ratio of the illumination on a horizontal plane at the point due to the light received directly from the sky, to the illumination due to an unobstructed hemisphere of sky of assumed or known luminance.

SPACING/HEIGHT RATIO—The ratio of the spacing between adjacent fittings to the height of the fittings above the working plane.

SPECULAR REFLECTION—Reflection in accordance with the laws of optical reflection, as in a mirror.

SOLID ANGLE—The solid angle, in steradians, of a surface seen from a point is numerically equal to its projected area on a sphere, centred at that point, divided by the square of the radius of the sphere. A sphere subtends 4π steradians at its centre.

STARTER SWITCH—An automatic switch, usually fitting into a small meta canister, employed in the starting of discharge lamps, e.g. fluorescent lamps.

STEREOPSIS—Stereoscopic vision; the capacity for three dimensional seeing: it is a function of the two eyes acting in unison, but each receiving slightly different views of solid objects.

TASK ANALYSIS—As applied to visual tasks: the critical 'dissection' of a job for the purpose of assessing its demands in respect of visual capacities and conditions of lighting.

THERMIONIC EMISSION—The escape of electrons from the surface of a conductor owing to its temperature. A number of materials, usually containing barium, are capable of giving substantial emissions at relatively low temperature and are used as thermionic emitters in discharge lamps.

TRANSISTOR—A semi-conducting crystal device containing three electrodes and capable of switching or amplifying electric currents.

TRANSLUCENT—Incompletely diffusing material, through which objects are not seen distinctly.

TRANSMISSION FACTOR—The ratio of luminous flux transmitted by a body to that which it receives.

TRANSPARENT—A material is said to be transparent when it transmits light without diffusion, so that bodies beyond can be seen distinctly.

TRICHROMATIC THEORY—The theory that assumes the perception of colours to result from the integration of three primary sensations, each due to the stimulation of a differently 'tuned' type of retinal receptor.

TUNGSTEN-HALOGEN LAMP (tungsten-iodine: quartz-iodine)—An incandescent tungsten lamp containing a small quantity of a halogen. The lamp is so designed that, at the wall temperature, the halogen will combine with evaporated tungsten and this compound will dissociate at the filament temperature redepositing the tungsten on the filament.

ULTRAVIOLET RADIATION—The radiation beyond the violet end of the visible spectrum, with wavelengths less than 400 nm. It is divided, for convenience, into:

UVA, transmitted by glass, 400 nm to 320 nm.
UVB, sunburning region of sunlight, 320 nm to 280 nm.
UVC, transmitted by quartz, < 280 nm.

UTILISATION FACTOR—The ratio of the flux reaching a given plane to that emitted from the lamps. Unless otherwise stated the plane is taken to be the working plane.

VISIBLE SPECTRUM—The range of electromagnetic waves giving the sensation of light. In order of decreasing wavelength the colour of the light passes from deep red, through orange, yellow, green and blue to violet. (The term spectrum means the entire range of electromagnetic wavelengths.)

VISUAL ACUITY—Capacity for discerning detail. Acuteness of vision is much greater at the fovea than at other parts of the retina.

VISUAL AXIS—Or fixation line: the line joining any point of regard to the centre of the fovea of the observing eye: it is not quite coincident with the optical axis of the eye.

VISUAL CORTEX—The part of each hemisphere of the brain which receives the nerve impulses originated in the retina and integrates them so that visual perceptions are formed.

VISUAL SKILL—Acquired expertise in visual discrimination, as distinguished from in-born visual functional capacity.

WORKING PLANE—The plane (imaginary or real) at which work is usually done and at which, therefore, the illumination is specified and measured. Unless otherwise indicated, this plane is assumed to be horizontal and 0·85 metre (2ft 9in.) above the floor.

BIBLIOGRAPHY

Suggestions for Further Reading

FUNDAMENTALS

Sight, light and work. H. C. Weston. Lewis, London, 1962.
'Temperature radiation of solids.' G. A. W. Rutgers. Article in *Handbuch der Physik*, vol. 26. Springer, Berlin, 1958.
Luminescent materials. G. F. J. Garlick. Oxford, 1949.
'Ionisation in gases.' A. von Engel. Article in *Handbuch der Physik*, vol. 21. Springer, Berlin, 1956.
'Radiation from low pressure discharges.' R. G. Fowler. Article in *Handbuch der Physik*, vol. 22. Springer, Berlin, 1956.
The measurement of colour. W. D. Wright. Hilger, London, 1964.
Electroluminescence. H. K. Henisch. Pergamon, Oxford, 1962.
Anodic oxidation of aluminium and its alloys. Information Bulletin No. 14 of The Aluminium Development Association, 33 Grosvenor Street, London, W.1.

MEASUREMENTS AND CALCULATIONS

Photometry. J. W. T. Walsh. Constable, London, 1958.
Light calculations and measurements. H. A. E. Keitz. Philips Technical Library, Eindhoven, 1955.
The scientific basis of illuminating engineering. P. Moon. Dover, New York (London, Constable), 1961.
Illumination engineering. W. B. Boast. McGraw-Hill, New York, 1953.
Radiometric standards and measurements. E. J. Gillham. National Physical Laboratory, 1961.
Photometric units and the unit of light. J. S. Preston. National Physical Laboratory, 1961.
Physical Photometry. B. H. Crawford. National Physical Laboratory, 1962.
Infra-red spectroscopy and molecular structure. Mansel Davies (Ed.). Elsevier, 1963.
'Characteristics and applications of photo-electric cells.' F. A. Benson. *Trans. Illum. Engng Soc.*, 23 March 1938.

LIGHT SOURCES

Electronic flash photography. R. L. Aspden. Temple Press, London, 1959.
A new power stroboscope for high speed photography.' W. D. Chesterman, D. R. Clegg and A. J. Meadowcroft. *Proc. Instn. Civ. Engrs*, vol. 98, pt. II, Oct. 1951.
The collected works of Irving Langmuir, vol. 2. Pergamon, Oxford, 1960.
'Concerning Langmuir's theory on the loss in the gas of incandescent lamps' (translated title). Marc-la-Toison. Paris, *Lux*, June 1964.
'Iodine incandescent lamps.' J. W. van Tijen. *Philips Technical Review*, vol. 23, 1959.

'Quartz iodine lamps.' J. M. Moore and C. M. Jolly. *G.E.C. Journal of Science and Technology*, 1962.

Gas discharge lamps. J. Funke and P. J. Oranje. Philips Technical Library, Eindhoven, 1951.

EQUIPMENT AND APPLICATIONS

Light and plant growth. R. van der Veen and G. Meijer. Philips Technical Library, Eindhoven, 1962.

Applications of germicidal, erythemal and infrared energy. M. Luckiesh. van Nostrand, New York, 1946.

Hospital lighting. R. G. Hopkinson (Ed.). Heinemann, London, 1964.

Architectural physics: lighting. R. G. Hopkinson. H.M.S.O., London, 1951.

Principles of lighting. W. R. Stevens. Constable, London, 1951.

B.S.I. PUBLICATIONS

CP 1004: 1963	Parts 1 and 2. Street lighting.
BS 52: 1963	Bayonet lamp-caps, lampholders and B.C. adaptors (lampholder plugs).
BS 89: 1954	Electrical indicating instruments.
BS 98: 1962	Dimensions of screw lamp-caps and lampholders (Ediswan type).
BS 161: 1956	Tungsten filament general service electric lamps (200–250 V).
BS 229: 1957	Flameproof enclosure of electrical apparatus.
BS 232: 1952	Vitreous-enamelled steel reflectors for use with tungsten filament lamps.
BS 233: 1953	Glossary of terms used in illumination and photometry.
BS 354: 1961	Recommendations for photometric integrators.
BS 398: 1948	Classification of symmetrical light distribution from lighting fittings.
BS 469: 1960	Electric lamps for railway signalling.
BS 495: 1960	Lamp-caps and lampholders for double-capped tubular lamps.
BS 555: 1962	Tungsten filament miscellaneous electric lamps.
BS 677: 1945	Photoelectric type portable photometers.
BS 841: 1939	Lamp-caps and lampholders for architectural lamps.
BS 867: 1939	Traction lamps (series burning).
BS 873: 1959	The construction of road traffic signs and internally illuminated bollards.
BS 889: 1947	Flameproof electric lighting fittings (bulkhead and well-glass types).
BS 941: 1958	Automobile filament lamps.
BS 950: 1941	Artificial daylight fittings for colour matching.
BS 1164: 1952	Dimensions of prefocus lamp-caps and lampholders.
BS 1249: 1951	Cast iron columns for street lighting.
BS 1259: 1958	Intrinsically safe electrical apparatus and circuits for use in explosive atmospheres.
BS 1270: 1960	Schedule for electric discharge lamps for general purposes.
BS 1298: 1946	Dimensions of festoon lamp-caps for voltages not exceeding 50.
BS 1308: 1957	Concrete street lighting columns.
BS 1376: 1953	Colours of light signals.
BS 1546: 1963	Electric lamps for lighthouses.
BS 1615: 1961	Anodic oxidation coatings on aluminium.

BS 1788: 1964	Street lighting lanterns for use with electric lamps.
BS 1840: 1960	Steel columns for street lighting.
BS 1853: 1960	Tubular fluorescent lamps for general lighting service.
BS 1871: 1952	Minimum requirements for silvering for glass reflectors for lighting purposes.
BS 1875: 1952	Bi-pin lamp-caps and lampholders for tubular fluorescent lamps.
BS 1950: 1953	Vitreous-enamelled steel reflectors for use with mercury electric discharge lamps (types MB/V and MA/V).
BS 2516: 1954	Tail lights for vehicles, including cycles.
BS 2660: 1955	Colours for building and decorative paints.
BS 2818: Part I: 1962	Auxiliaries for operation of fluorescent lamps on a.c. 50 c/s supplies. Ballasts.
BS 3143: 1959	Road danger lamps.
BS 3205: 1960	Photographic electronic flash equipment.
BS 3648: 1963	Cycle rear lamps.
BS 3677: 1963	Schedule of fluorescent mercury discharge lamps.
BS 3707: 1964	Ballasts for high-pressure mercury vapour discharge lamps operating on a.c. 50 c/s supplies.
BS 3767: 1964	Schedule of sodium discharge lamps.
BS 3768: 1964	Ballasts for sodium vapour discharge lamps operating on a.c 50 c/s supplies.
BS 3772: 1964	Starters for use with fluorescent lamps operating on a.c. 50 c/s supplies.
BS 3820: 1964	Electric lighting fittings.
BS AU40: 1963	Motor vehicle lighting and signalling equipment.
BS G181	Electric lamps for aircraft.
BS G191	Lighting for aircraft indicators using integral filament lamps.
BS 2G100	General requirements for electrical equipment and indicating instruments for aircraft.
BS 4017: 1966	Capacitors for use in tubular fluorescent, mercury and sodium discharge lamp circuits.
Not yet issued	Sealed-beam headlamps for motor vehicles.
Not yet issued	Recommended practice for the use of lighting and signalling equipment on cars and commercial vehicles.
Not yet issued	Lighting fittings for civil land aerodromes.

LIGHTING REGULATIONS

Offices, Shops and Railway Premises Act 1963.
Factories (Standards of Lighting) Regulations, 1941. S.R. & O. No. 94.
The Standards for School Premises Regulations, 1959. S.I. No. 890.
The Traffic Signs Regulations and General Directions, 1957. S.I. No. 13.

RECOMMENDATIONS AND TECHNICAL REPORTS

The I.E.S. Code. Recommendations for good interior lighting 1961.

I.E.S. Technical Reports

No. 1   Lighting in corrosive, flammable and explosive situations.
No. 2   The calculation of coefficients of utilisation—The British Zonal method.

No. 3   The lighting of building sites and works of engineering construction.
No. 4   Lighting during daylight hours.
No. 5   Lecture theatres and their lighting.
No. 6   The floodlighting of buildings.
No. 7   Lighting for sport.

I.E.S. Monographs

No. 1   Inter-reflections and flux distribution in lighted interiors, by J. A. Lynes.
No. 2   Average illumination on the vertical and calculation of zonal multipliers for continuous distributions, by R. Croft.
No. 3   The new approach to inter-reflections, by R. O. Philips and S. J. Prokhovnik.
No. 4   The concept 'Road Surface Luminance' and its application to public lighting, by J. B. de Boer.
No. 5   Factors governing the light output ratio of lighting fittings, by R. H. Simons.
No. 6   Measurements of the luminance distribution of the sky near Sydney, Australia, by D. Paix; Exact determination of the daylight (sky component) from rectangular sloping window apertures with a 'CIE overcast sky', by R. Kittler and S. Ondrejicka.
No. 7   Flux distribution within a sector solid and total flux from a linear source, by A. R. Bean.
No. 8   Graphical and tabulated data for routine illumination calculations, by A. R. Bean.
No. 9   A theoretical study of the problem presented by depreciation of the luminous flux in interior lighting installations, by E. Wittig, R. Krossawa and D. Matanovic; Transmission and reflection characteristics of diffusing louvers, by A. R. Bean and R. H. Simons.

Final Report of the Advisory Committee on Traffic Signs for Motorways (Anderson Report). H.M.S.O., 1962.
Report of the Committee on Traffic Signs for All-Purpose Roads (Worboys Report). H.M.S.O., 1963.
A.P.L.E. Technical Report No. 1. The lighting of traffic signs.
The British Lighting Council. Interior lighting design.
The British Lighting Council Certified Scheme for Office Lighting.

Index